THE DYNAMIC STABILITY OF ELASTIC SYSTEMS

HOLDEN-DAY SERIES IN MATHEMATICAL PHYSICS

Julius J. Brandstatter, Editor

V. V. Bolotin, *Dynamic Stability of Elastic Systems*

S. G. Lekhnitskii, *Theory of Elasticity of an Anisotropic Elastic Body*

D. A. Pogorelov, *Fundamentals of Orbital Mechanics*

A. N. Tychonov and A. A. Samarski, *Partial Differential Equations of Mathematical Physics*

M. M. Vainberg, *Variational Methods for the Study of Nonlinear Operators*

V. V. Bolotin

THE DYNAMIC STABILITY OF ELASTIC SYSTEMS

Translated by V. I. Weingarten, L. B. Greszczuk,
K. N. Trirogoff and K. D. Gallegos

HOLDEN-DAY, INC.
San Francisco, London, Amsterdam
1964

Library of Congress Catalog Card Number: 64-16573
Printed in the United States of America

TRANSLATORS' PREFACE

Within the past few years, interest in the dynamic stability of elastic systems has increased. This interest is reflected in the appearance of a large number of papers on this subject. Unfortunately, few of the papers are in English, the majority being written in either Russian or German. In addition, there is available no English text which presents the mathematical theory of the subject with its applications. To fill this need in American scientific literature, it was decided to undertake the translation of *Dynamic Stability of Elastic System* (Gostekhizdat, Moscow, 1956) by V. V. Bolotin, which, together with its German translation (VEB Deutscher Verlag Der Wissenschaften, Berlin, 1961) is the only comprehensive work on the subject of dynamic stability.

At the time the translation was initiated, the German edition was not yet available, and the book was translated from the Russian. With the appearance of the German edition, the translation was checked and all changes in the German edition were incorporated into the English translation. Footnotes in the Russian edition were eliminated and the German referencing system was adapted.

The translators would like to thank R. M. Cooper, J. H. Cunningham, E. Fitzgerald, P. Seide, J. E. Taylor, N. Xerikos, and J. C. Yao for their assistance in this translation. Further acknowledgements are due to the Aerospace Corporation and Douglas Aircraft, Inc., for their aid and cooperation in the preparation of the manuscript.

Los Angeles, 1964 V. I. W., L. B. G., K. N. T., K. D. G.

PREFACE TO THE GERMAN EDITION

Four years have passed since the appearance of the Russian edition of the present book. During this time a series of works on dynamic stability were published, containing interesting results. In addition, the general theory was applied to a new class of problems whose analysis appeared to be of a mathematical nature which fell within the narrow limits of the theory of dynamic stability. All of the above are considered in the German edition of the book. References are included of some works published through 1956, which were unknown to me when the book was first published.

G. Schmidt, from the Institute for Applied Mathematics and Mechanics, German Academy of Sciences, Berlin, preparated the excellent translation and contributed corrections in some places. The translation was also reviewed at the Institute for Vibration Technology, Karlsruhe Technical University; F. Weidenhammer and G. Benz especially gave worthwhile advice. C. W. Mishenkov, from the Moscow Power Institute, assisted me with the preparation of complete references. To all these people, I would like to express my deep thanks.

Moscow, December 1960 V. V. Bolotin

PREFACE TO THE RUSSIAN EDITION

This book is an attempt to present systematically the general theory of dynamic stability of elastic systems and its numerous applications. Investigations of the author are used as the basis for the book, part of which was published previously in the form of separate articles. The author's method of presentation is retained where the problems treated have been analyzed by other authors.

The book is devoted to the solution of engineering problems. As in every other engineering (or physics) investigation, the presentation consists of first choosing an initial scheme or pattern, and then using the approximate mathematical methods to obtain readily understood results. This intent, and the desire to make the book easily understood by a large number of readers, is reflected in the arrangement and structure of the book.

The book consists of three parts. PART I is concerned with the simplest problems of dynamic stability which do not require complicated mathematical methods for their solutions. By using these problems, the author wishes to acquaint the reader with previously investigated problems. At the same time, certain peculiarities of the phenomena of instability, which previously have been only sketchily mentioned, are clarified. PART I also contains methods of solution of the general problem.

PART II begins with two chapters containing the minimum necessary mathematical information; a conversant reader can disregard these chapters. The properties of the general equations of dynamic stability are then examined; methods are presented for the determination of the boundaries of the regions of instability and the amplitudes of parametrically excited vibrations for the general case.

PART III is concerned with applications. Various problems of the dynamic instability of straight rods, arches, beams, statically indeterminate rod systems, plates, and shells are examined. The choice of examples was dictated by the desire to illustrate the general methods and present solutions to practical problems. The number of examples was limited by the size of the book.

I would like to take this opportunity to express my sincere thanks to A. S. Vol'mir for having read the manuscript and for having given valuable advice.

Moscow, January 1956 V. V. Bolotin

CONTENTS

Part III. Applications of the General Theory

INTRODUCTION

● **1.** In recent years a new branch of the applied theory of elasticity has evolved, the *theory of the dynamic stability of elastic systems*. The problems which are examined in this branch of elasticity are related to those in the theory of vibrations and the stability of elastic systems. As in many other areas of learning that lie on the borderline of two fields, the theory of dynamic stability is now going through a period of intensive development.

The theory of dynamic stability is easily illustrated by examples.

(a) If a straight rod is subjected to a periodic longitudinal load (Fig. 1a)

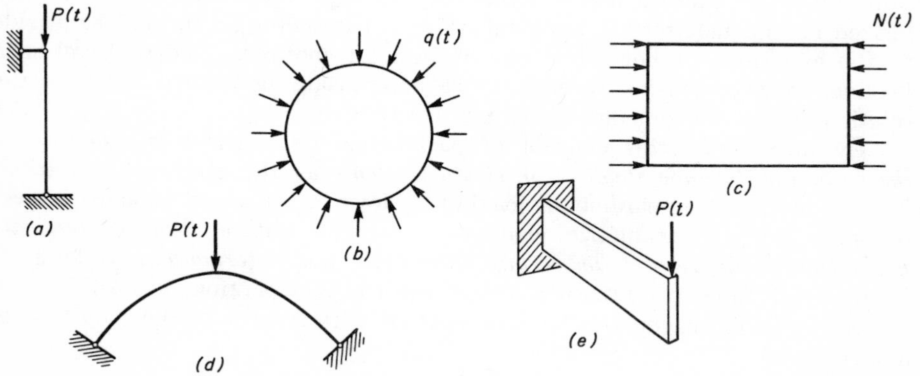

FIG. 1.

and if the amplitude of the load is less than that of the static buckling value, then, in general, the rod experiences only longitudinal vibrations. However, it can be shown that for certain relationships between the disturbing frequency θ and the natural frequency of transverse vibration ω, a straight rod becomes dynamically unstable and transverse vibrations occur; the amplitude of these vibrations rapidly increases to large values. The relationship of the frequencies at which it approaches such a resonance (so-called *parametric resonance*) differs from the frequency relationship for the ordinary forced vibration resonance. For sufficiently small values of the longitudinal force,[1] this relationship is $\theta = 2\omega$.

[1] The phenomenon of parametric resonance in a stretched string, of which one end is attached to an oscillating tuning fork, was discovered by Melde (1859). The first theoretical explanation of this phenomenon was given by Rayleigh (1883–1887). See, for example, his *Theory of Sound* [1]. A survey of early works on parametric resonance can be found in *Zhurn. Tekhn. Fiz.* 4 (1934).

(b) A circular ring compressed by a uniformly distributed radial loading (Fig. 1b) generally undergoes only axial deformation. However, for certain relationships between the frequency of the load and the natural frequency of the bending vibrations of the ring, the initial form of the ring becomes dynamically unstable and develops intense bending vibrations.

(c) Periodic forces acting in the middle plane of a plate (Fig. 1c) can excite intense transverse vibrations under certain conditions.

(d) A periodic loading applied symmetrically with respect to the arch (Fig. 1d) generally causes only symmetrical vibrations, but can excite asymmetrical vibrations of very large amplitude under certain conditions.

(e) Periodic forces acting on a beam of narrow cross section in the plane of its greatest rigidity (Fig. 1e) can excite bending-torsional vibrations from this plane under certain conditions.

The number of examples can be increased. Whenever static loading of a particular kind causes a loss of static stability, vibrational loading of the same kind will cause a loss of dynamic stability. Such a loading is characterized by the fact that it is contained as a parameter on the left-hand side of the equations of perturbed equilibrium (of motion). We will call such loading *parametric*; this term is more appropriate because it indicates the relation to the phenomenon of parametric resonance.[2]

By introducing this concept of parametric loading, we can define the *theory of the dynamic stability of elastic systems* as the study of vibrations induced by pulsating parametric loading.[3] However, it would be more correct to speak not of parametric loading in general, but of *loadings that are parametric with respect to certain forms of the deformations.* Thus, a longitudinal force compressing a straight rod is a parametric loading with respect to the transverse deflections but not with respect to the longitudinal deformations.

● **2.** A detailed review of the literature on the theory of dynamic stability, complete through 1951, can be found in an article by E.A. Beilin and G. U. Dzhanelidze [1]; here however, we will focus on certain fundamental stages of the development of the theory.

An article by N. M. Beliaev [1], published in 1924, can be considered to be the first work on this problem. In the article, the problem of dynamic stability of a straight rod hinged on both ends was examined, and boundaries of the principal region of instability were determined. In 1935, Krylov and Bogoliubov [2] returned to the problem and examined the case of arbitrary support conditions. Applying the Galerkin variational method, the authors reduced the general problem to the same equation as already examined by Beliaev except that the coefficients of the equation are approximate parameters (in the sense of the Galerkin method). A year earlier, Kochin [1]

[2] In recent years the term has become more generally used. (Rzhanitsyn [1]).

[3] Sometimes the theory of dynamic stability is interpreted in a broader sense to include problems concerning the vibrations of elastic systems under the effects of certain parametric impact loading. This definition will not be used here.

examined the mathematically related problem of the vibrations of a crankshaft. Another related problem was investigated in connection with the vibrations of the driving system of an electric locomotive (see Timoshenko [1] and Bondarenko [1]).

We note that the first non-Russian works on the *dynamic stability* of rods appeared in the late' thirties and early' forties (Mettler [1], Utida and Sezawa [1], Lubkin and Stoker [1]).

The dynamic stability of plates loaded by compressive periodic longitudinal forces was investigated by Bodner [1], Khalilov [1], Einaudi [1], and Ambartsumian and Khachatrian [1]. The problem of the dynamic stability of a circular ring subjected to radial pulsating loading was solved by Dzhanelidze and Radtsig [1]. A number of particular problems were investigated in a pamphlet by Chelomei [1]. The problem of the dynamic stability of symmetric arches loaded by compression and bending was investigated by Bolotin [4], [7]. Markov [1], Oniashvili [1], Bolotin [18], Federhofer [1], Yao [1]; Bublik and Merkulov [1] investigated particular problems on the dynamic stability of shells.

The question of the influence of damping on the boundaries of the regions of instability was discussed by Mettler [2] and Naumov [1]. Note that the corresponding problem in a more general form was solved in 1927 by Andronov and Leontovich [1]. The case of variable loading represented by piecewise constant segments was investigated by Smirnov [1], and Makushin [1].

The above works have a common characteristic in that the problem of dynamic stability is reduced (exactly or approximately) to one second-order differential equation with periodic coefficients (Mathieu-Hill equation). Meanwhile, Chelomei [1] had already shown that the problem of dynamic stability in the general case reduces to systems of differential equations with periodic coefficients. Brachkovskii [1], (using the Galerkin method) and Bolotin [5], (using integral equations) established a class of problems that can be reduced exactly to one second-order equation. A generalization of these results for the case of dissipative systems was given by Dzhanelidze [1]. Although the properties of the equations obtained by the Galerkin method have now been well studied, the number of publications based on this approximation continues to grow (Malkina [1]).

In certain papers,[4] the problem of the stability of plane bending, requiring an examination of systems of differential equations, is reduced to one Mathieu-Hill equation.

Gol'denblat [1] investigated the problem of the stability of a compressed, thin-walled rod symmetrical about one axis. The problem was reduced to a system of two differential equations. Using the results of Artem'ev [1], Gol'denblat presented a method for constructing the regions of instability by means of expanding with respect to the powers of the small parameter. A similar method, devoid however of rigorous substantiation, was applied

[4] V.Yu. Salion [1], [2], [3].

by Mettler [4] to the problem of the dynamic stability of the plane bending of a beam. Weidenhammer [1], using the same method, investigated the problem of the stability of a rod clamped on the ends. Another version of the method is given by Kucharski [1], who applied it to the special problem of the dynamic stability of plates, and by Reckling [1], [2], [3], who applied his version to the special problem of the dynamic stability of plane bending. Still another variation of this method was applied by Yakubovich [1], [2], [3].

Another method, where the small parameter is not assumed, is given in an article by Bolotin [5]. This article also investigates the structure of the general equations of dynamic stability. Bolotin [5] and Piszczek [2], [3], [4], [5] also investigated the general problem of the dynamic stability of plane bending; Bolotin [12] investigated the problem of the dynamic stability of plates. In the present book, this method is extended to dissipation systems and is applied systematically to problems involving the stability of rods, arches, beams, frames, plates and shells.

The works enumerated above examined the regions in which a given form of motion becomes dynamically unstable. The idea of the inadequacy of the linear treatment for determining the amplitudes in the resonance regions was first clearly formulated by Gol'denblat [2], who indicated the relationship of this problem with those problems involving the parametric excitation of electrical oscillations (see Mandel'shtam and Papaleksi [1]). The presentation of nonlinear theory applicable to the problem of the dynamic stability of a compressed rod was given by Bolotin [2]. An analogous problem was examined almost simultaneously by Weidenhammer [2]; see also Bolotin [13] and Mettler and Weidenhammer [1]. In a paper by Bolotin [6], the nonlinear theory is extended to the secondary regions of instability and also to the case of a rod having initial curvature. Other nonlinear problems were investigated by Bolotin [14], [21] and Ivovich [1], [2], [3], [4]. In another article (Bolotin [11]), the solution of the related problem of the vibrations of a rotating shaft having different principal bending stiffnesses is given. Certain nonlinear problems on the dynamic stability of plates and shells were investigated by Bolotin [9], [18], which included the stretching of the middle surface. The present book gives the solution of a number of new nonlinear problems, particularly for arches, beams, and statically indeterminate rod systems.

To date there are very few experimental data available on this subject, although these data represent a field of definite interest. Experiments of parametrically excited transverse vibrations of compressed rods are described by Bolotin [2]. These experiments determine the amplitudes of steady-state vibrations and investigate damping, the beat phenomenon and the process of establishing the vibrations. This paper also gives a comparison of the experimental results with theoretical results. The parametrically excited vibrations of compressed curved arches are described in previous papers by Bolotin [4], [8]. Experiments on the dynamic stability of plane bending of beams were conducted by Burnashev [1] and Sobolev [1].

● **3.** The theory of dynamic stability has already opened the way for direct engineering applications. Parametrically excited vibrations are similar in appearance to the accompanying forced vibrations and can therefore qualify as ordinary resonance vibrations, by practical engineering standards. In a number of cases, however, in the presence of periodic vibrations the usual methods of damping and vibration isolation may break down and even bring about the opposite results. Although the vibrations may not threaten the structure or its normal operation, they can bring about fatigue failure if they continue to act. Therefore, the study of the formation of parametric vibrations and the methods for the prevention of their occurrence is necessary in the various areas of mechanics, transportation, and industrial construction.

The theory of dynamic stability is one of the newest branches of the mechanics of deformable solids. Although during the last decade much has already been done to clarify many problems that were only recently still completely obscure, a large and rewarding field for investigations remains.

PART I

ELEMENTARY PROBLEMS OF DYNAMIC INSTABILITY

One

DETERMINATION OF REGIONS OF DYNAMIC INSTABILITY

§ 1. Differential Equation of the Problem

● **1.** Consider the problem of the transverse vibrations of a straight rod loaded by a periodic longitudinal force (Fig. 2). The rod is assumed to be simply supported and of uniform cross section along its length. We will make the usual assumptions in the field of strength of materials, i.e., that Hooke's law holds and plane sections remain plane. The case of nonlinear elasticity will be examined in Chapter Three and subsequent chapters of the book.

This problem is one of the simplest problems of dynamic stability. It was first formulated in this manner by Beliaev [1].

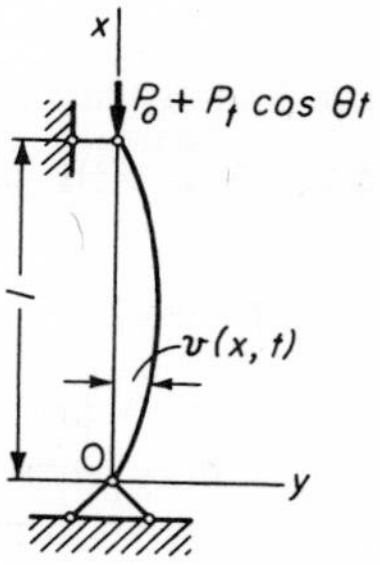

FIG. 2.

We will proceed from the well-known equation of the static bending of a rod

$$EJ\frac{d^2v}{dx^2} + Pv = 0 ,$$

where $v(x)$ is the deflection of the rod, EJ is its bending stiffness, and P is the longitudinal force. After two differentiations, the equation takes the form

$$EJ\frac{d^4v}{dx^4} + P\frac{d^2v}{dx^2} = 0 ; \tag{1.1}$$

this gives the condition that the sum of the y components of all the forces per unit length acting on the rod is equal to zero.

To arrive at the equation for the transverse vibrations of a rod loaded by the periodic longitudinal force

$$P(t) = P_0 + P_t \cos \theta t ,$$

it is necessary to introduce additional terms into Eq. (1.1) that take into account the inertia forces (Mettler [1]).

As in the case of the applied theory of vibrations, we will not include the inertia forces associated with the rotation of the cross sections of the rod with respect to its own principal axes. The influence of longitudinal inertia forces will be considered in later chapters. In the meantime, note that longitudinal inertia forces can substantially influence the dynamic stability of a rod only in the case where the frequency of the external force is near the longitudinal natural frequencies of the rod, i.e., when the longitudinal vibrations have a resonance character. In the following discussion, we will consider that the system is not close to the resonance of the longitudinal vibrations.

With these limiting assumptions, the inertia forces acting on the rod can be reduced to a distributed loading whose magnitude is

$$-m\frac{\partial^2 v}{\partial t^2},$$

where m is the mass per unit length of the rod. Thus, we arrive at the differential equation

$$EJ\frac{\partial^4 v}{\partial x^4} + (P_0 + P_t \cos \theta t)\frac{\partial^2 v}{\partial x^2} + m\frac{\partial^2 v}{\partial t^2} = 0 \tag{1.2}$$

for the dynamic deflections $v(x, t)$ of the rod at any arbitrary instant of time.

● **2.** We will seek the solution of Eq. (1.2) in the form

$$v(x, t) = f_k(t) \sin \frac{k\pi x}{l}, \qquad (k = 1, 2, 3, \cdots), \tag{1.3}$$

where $f_k(t)$ are unknown functions of time and l is the length of the rod. One easily sees that expression (1.3) satisfies the boundary conditions of the problem, requiring in the given case that the deflection, together with its second derivative, vanish at the ends of the rod. We remind the reader that the "coordinate functions"

$$\varphi_k(x) = \sin \frac{k\pi x}{l}$$

are of the same form as that of the free vibrations and the buckling of a simply supported rod.

Substitution of expression (1.3) into Eq. (1.2) gives

$$\left[m\frac{d^2 f_k}{dt^2} + EJ\frac{k^4\pi^4 f_k}{l^4} - (P_0 + P_t \cos \theta t)\frac{k^2\pi^2 f_k}{l^2}\right] \sin \frac{k\pi x}{l} = 0\,.$$

For expression (1.3) to really satisfy Eq. (1.2), it is necessary and sufficient that the quantity in brackets should vanish at any t. In other words, the functions $f_k(t)$ must satisfy the differential equation

$$\frac{d^2 f_k}{dt^2} + \omega_k^2\left(1 - \frac{P_0 + P_t \cos \theta t}{P_{*k}}\right) f_k = 0, \qquad (k = 1, 2, 3, \cdots), \tag{1.4}$$

where

$$\omega_k = \frac{k^2\pi^2}{l^2}\sqrt{\frac{EJ}{m}} \tag{1.5}$$

is the kth frequency of the free vibrations of an unloaded rod, and

$$P_{*k} = \frac{k^2\pi^2 EJ}{l^2} \tag{1.6}$$

is the kth Euler buckling load (the asterisk denotes this quantity in future problems).

For convenience, we represent Eq. (1.4) in the form

$$\frac{d^2 f_k}{dt^2} + \Omega_k^2 (1 - 2\mu_k \cos \theta t) f_k = 0 , \qquad (k = 1, 2, 3, \cdots) , \tag{1.7}$$

where Ω_k is the frequency of the free vibrations of the rod loaded by a constant longitudinal force P_0,

$$\Omega_k = \omega_k \sqrt{1 - \frac{P_0}{P_{*k}}} , \tag{1.8}$$

and μ_k is a quantity we will call the *excitation parameter*

$$\mu_k = \frac{P_t}{2(P_{*k} - P_0)} . \tag{1.9}$$

Since Eq. (1.7) is identical for all the forms of vibrations, i.e., it is identical for all k, we will in the future omit the indices of Ω_k and μ_k and write this equation in the form

$$f'' + \Omega^2(1 - 2\mu \cos \theta t) f = 0 . \tag{1.10}$$

The prime denotes differentiation with respect to time.

● **3.** Equation (1.10) is the well-known Mathieu equation. For the more general case of the longitudinal force given by

$$P(t) = P_0 + P_t \Phi(t) ,$$

where $\Phi(t)$ is a periodic function with a period T,

$$\Phi(t + T) = \Phi(t) ,$$

we obtain the equation

$$f'' + \Omega^2[1 - 2\mu\Phi(t)] f = 0 .$$

Such an equation, more general than the Mathieu equation, is usually called the *Hill* equation.

Mathieu-Hill equations are encountered in various areas of physics and engineering. Certain problems in theoretical physics lead to similar equations, particularly the problem of the propagation of electromagnetic waves in a medium with a periodic structure. In the quantum theory of metals, the problem of the motion of electrons in a crystal lattice reduces to the Mathieu-Hill equation. The Mathieu-Hill equation is also encountered in the investigations of the stability of the oscillatory processes in nonlinear systems, in the theory of the parametric excitation of electrical oscillations, and other branches of the theory of oscillations. Certain problems of celestial mechanics and cosmogony also lead to the Hill equation, particularly the theory of the motion of the moon.

A vast amount of literature is devoted to the investigation of the Mathieu-Hill equation (for example, see Strutt [1], McLachlan [1], Meixner and Schäfke [1]). One of the most interesting characteristics of this equation is that, for certain relationships between its coefficients, it has solutions which are unbounded. The values of the coefficients cover certain regions in the plane of the two parameters μ and Ω, i.e., the regions that correspond to the regions of dynamic instability in the physical problem under consideration.

For example, Figure 3 shows the distribution of the regions of instability for the Mathieu equation

$$\frac{d^2f}{dx^2} + (\lambda - h^2 \cos 2x)f = 0 .$$

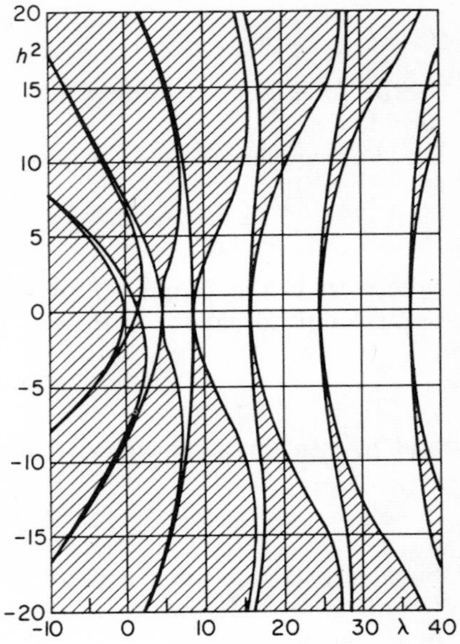

FIG. 3.

In such a form, the coefficients of the equation depend on the two parameters λ and h^2, which are plotted as coordinates. The regions in which the solutions of the equation are unbounded are crosshatched. As evident from the figure, the regions of instability occupy a considerable part of the plane of the parameters.

Therefore, to answer the question as to whether or not the rod is stable, it is necessary to find the point corresponding to the given ratio of parameters on the λ, h^2 plane. If a point occurs in the noncrosshatched region, it means that the initial straight form of the rod is dynamically stable. However, if the same point is found in the crosshatched region, then any initial deviation from the straight form of the rod will increase unboundedly with time, i.e., the straight form of the rod will be dynamically unstable.

The determination of the regions of dynamic instability constitutes one of the main problems of the theory.

§ 2. Some Properties of the Mathieu-Hill Equation

● 1. Consider the differential equation

$$f'' + \Omega^2[1 - 2\mu\Phi(t)]f = 0 , \tag{1.11}$$

where $\Phi(t)$ is a periodic function with a period

$$T = \frac{2\pi}{\theta} . \tag{1.12}$$

We will assume that this function can be represented in the form of the converging Fourier series

$$\Phi(t) = \sum_{k=1}^{\infty} (\mu_k \cos k\theta t + \nu_k \sin k\theta t) . \tag{1.13}$$

First of all, note that Eq. (1.11) does not change its form on addition of the period to t. This follows from the fact that

$$\Phi(t + T) = \Phi(t) .$$

Therefore, if $f(t)$ is a solution of Eq. (1.11), then $f(t + T)$ is also its solution.

Let $f_1(t)$ and $f_2(t)$ be any two linearly independent solutions of Eq. (1.11). Then, on the basis of the previous discussion, $f_1(t + T)$ and $f_2(t + T)$ are also its solution, and consequently can be represented in the form of a linear combination of the primary functions,

$$\begin{aligned} f_1(t + T) &= a_{11} f_1(t) + a_{12} f_2(t) \\ f_2(t + T) &= a_{21} f_1(t) + a_{22} f_2(t) \end{aligned} \tag{1.14}$$

where a_{ik} are constants.

Thus, the addition of the period to t results in a linear transformation of the initial system of solutions. If we take some other linearly independent solution instead of the initially chosen solutions $f_{1,2}(t)$, then the coefficients of transformation (1.14) generally will change. In particular, one can try to choose solutions $f^*_{1,2}(t)$ such that the secondary coefficients in (1.14) vanish:

$$a_{11} = a_{21} = 0 .$$

The transformation in this case will take its simplest form and will be reduced to the simple multiplication of functions by certain constants[5]

$$\begin{aligned} f_1^*(t + T) &= \rho_1 f_1^*(t) , \\ f_2^*(t + T) &= \rho_2 f_2^*(t) . \end{aligned} \tag{1.15}$$

In contrast to (1.14), we introduced here the notation

$$a_{11} = \rho_1 , \qquad a_{22} = \rho_2 .$$

From the theory of linear transformations, it is known (for example, see Chapter Ten) that any transformation of the type in (1.14) can be reduced to the simplest or, as is more commonly referred to, the diagonal form, where the numbers $\rho_{1,2}$ are determined from the *characteristic equation*[6]

$$\begin{vmatrix} a_{11} - \rho & a_{12} \\ a_{21} & a_{22} - \rho \end{vmatrix} = 0 . \tag{1.16}$$

● 2. The characteristic equation plays an important role in the theory of the Mathieu-Hill equation since it defines the character of solution of the Mathieu-Hill equation in many respects, as we will see below. We will now show how this equation is formed.

Let $f_1(t)$ and $f_2(t)$ be two linearly independent solutions of Eq. (1.11) satisfying the initial conditions

[5] These solutions are the well-known *Floquet solutions.*

[6] For the sake of simplicity, we have omitted here one detail which will be explained later: the case where the characteristic equation has multiple roots of nonlinear elementary divisors.

$$\begin{aligned} f_1(0) &= 1\,, \qquad f_1'(0) = 0\,, \\ f_2(0) &= 0\,, \qquad f_2'(0) = 1\,. \end{aligned} \tag{1.17}$$

Then, setting $t = 0$ in (1.14), we obtain

$$\begin{aligned} a_{11} &= f_1(T)\,, \\ a_{21} &= f_2(T)\,. \end{aligned}$$

Differentating (1.14) termwise and letting $t = 0$, we have

$$\begin{aligned} a_{12} &= f_1'(T)\,, \\ a_{22} &= f_2'(T)\,. \end{aligned}$$

Thus, the characteristic equation takes the form

$$\begin{vmatrix} f_1(T) - \rho & f_1'(T) \\ f_2(T) & f_2'(T) - \rho \end{vmatrix} = 0$$

or, expanding the determinant

$$\rho^2 - 2A\rho + B = 0\,. \tag{1.18}$$

In Eq. (1.18) A and B are

$$\begin{aligned} A &= \tfrac{1}{2}[f_1(T) + f_2'(T)] \\ B &= f_1(T)f_2'(T) - f_2(T)f_1'(T)\,. \end{aligned}$$

By their very meaning, the roots of the characteristic equation (and consequently its coefficients) do not depend on the choice of the solutions $f_{1,2}(t)$. One can show, for example, that the term B of the characteristic equation is always equal to unity. Because the functions $f_{1,2}(t)$ are solutions of Eq. (1.11), then

$$\begin{aligned} f_1'' + \Omega^2[1 - 2\mu\Phi(t)]f_1 &= 0\,, \\ f_2'' + \Omega^2[1 - 2\mu\Phi(t)]f_2 &= 0\,. \end{aligned}$$

Multiplying the first of these identities by $f_2(t)$, the second by $f_1(t)$, and subtracting one from the other, we obtain

$$f_1(t)f_2''(t) - f_2(t)f_1''(t) = 0\,.$$

On integrating we obtain

$$f_1(t)f_2'(t) - f_2(t)f_1'(t) = \text{const.}$$

The quantity on the left-hand side coincides with the B term in Eq. (1.18) for $t = T$. For the determination of the constant on the right-hand side, we set $t = 0$. Then, making use of the initial conditions, we find

$$f_1(T)f_2'(T) - f_2(T)f_1'(T) = 1\,,$$

Thus, the characteristic equation takes the form

$$\rho^2 - 2A\rho + 1 = 0\,; \tag{1.19}$$

its roots obviously are related by

$$\rho_1 \cdot \rho_2 = 1. \tag{1.20}$$

● **3.** It was shown in ●1 that among the particular solutions of Eq. (1.1) two linearly independent solutions $f_{1,2}^*(t)$ exist that satisfy Eq. (1.15),

$$f_k^*(t+T) = \rho_k f_k^*(t), \qquad (k = 1, 2).$$

These solutions, which acquire a constant multiplier by the addition of the period to t, can be represented in the form

$$f_k^*(t) = \chi_k(t)e^{(t/T)\ln\rho_k}, \qquad (k = 1, 2). \tag{1.21}$$

where $\chi_{1,2}(t)$ are certain periodic functions of period T. Indeed,

$$f_k^*(t+T) = \chi_k(t)e^{((t/T)+1)\ln\rho_k} = \rho_k f_k^*(t).$$

It follows from Eq. (1.21) that the behavior of the solutions as $t \to \infty$ depends on the value of the characteristic roots (more precisely, on the value of its moduli). In fact, taking into account that

$$\ln\rho = \ln|\rho| + i\arg\rho,$$

we can rewrite Eq. (1.21) in the following form:

$$f_k^*(t) = \varphi_k(t)e^{(t/T)\ln|\rho_k|}, \qquad (k = 1, 2). \tag{1.22}$$

where $\varphi_k(t)$ is the bounded (almost periodic) function

$$\varphi_k(t) = \chi_k(t)e^{(it/T)\arg\rho}.$$

If the characteristic number ρ_k is greater than unity, then the corresponding solution (1.22) will have an unbounded exponential multiplier. If the same characteristic number is less than unity, then the corresponding solution is damped as t increases. Finally, if the characteristic number is equal to unity, then the solution is periodic (or almost periodic), i.e., it will be bounded in time.

Let

$$|A| = \tfrac{1}{2}|f_1(T) + f_2'(T)| > 1.$$

Then, as can be seen from Eq. (1.19), the characteristic roots will be real, and one of them will be greater than unity. In this case the general integral of Eq. (1.11) will unboundedly increase with time,

$$f(t) = C_1\chi_1(t)e^{(t/T)\ln\rho_1} + C_2\chi_2(t)e^{(t/T)\ln\rho_2}.$$

However, if

$$\tfrac{1}{2}|f_1(T) + f_2'(T)| < 1,$$

the characteristic equation has conjugate complex roots, and since their product must be equal to unity, their modulus will be equal to unity. The case of complex characteristic roots corresponds to the region of bounded solutions. On the boundaries separating the regions of the bounded solutions from the regions where the general integral unboundedly increases with time, the following condition must be satisfied:

$$|f_1(T) + f_2'(T)| = 2. \tag{1.23}$$

Eq. (1.23) can be used to determine the boundaries of the regions of dynamic instability. However, for its use, it is necessary to know the particular solutions of the problem, at least during the first period of vibration. This calculation, however, leads to serious computational difficulties. Only in certain special cases it is possible to integrate the differential equation of the type (1.11) in terms of elementary functions. One of these cases will be considered in the following section.

§ 3. Construction of the Regions of Dynamic Instability for a Particular Case

Let the longitudinal force vary according to the piecewise constant law, i.e., during the first period

$$P(t) = P_0 + P_t \quad \text{if} \quad 0 < t \le t_0 ,$$
$$P(t) = P_0 - P_t \quad \text{if} \quad t_0 < t \le T .$$

Such a law of varying load occurs rarely in practice. However, in the case where $t_0 = T/2$, we have a variation which for small P_t can be considered to be a first, crude approximation to the harmonic regime

$$P(t) = P_0 + P_t \sin \theta t .$$

This is the case we will consider in the following.

It is now possible to write the vibration equation in the form

$$f'' + \Omega^2[1 - 2\mu\Phi(t)]f = 0 ,$$

where

$$\Phi(t) = 1 \quad \text{if} \quad 0 < t \le T/2 ,$$
$$\Phi(t) = -1 \quad \text{if} \quad T/2 \le t < T ,$$

and the excitation parameter, as before, is equal to

$$\mu = \frac{P_t}{2(P_* - P_0)} .$$

During the first half-period, the vibrations are described by a differential equation with constant coefficients,

$$f'' + \Omega^2(1 - 2\mu)f = 0 .$$

Its general solution is

$$f(t) = C_1 \sin p_1 t + D_1 \cos p_1 t ,$$

where, for the sake of brevity,

$$p_1 = \Omega\sqrt{1 - 2\mu} .$$

The particular solution that satisfies the initial conditions $f_1(0) = 1$ and $f_1'(0) = 0$ is

$$f_1(t) = \cos p_1 t .$$

The second solution that satisfies the initial conditions $f_2(0) = 0$, $f_2'(0) = 1$ obviously will be

$$f_2(t) = \frac{1}{p_1} \sin p_1 t \ .$$

These two solutions must be extended to the second time interval, $T/2 < t \leq T$, during which the vibrations are described by

$$f'' + \Omega^2(1 + 2\mu) f = 0 \ .$$

The general solution of this equation is

$$f(t) = C_2 \sin p_2 t + D_2 \cos p_2 t \ ,$$

where similarly to the previous case, $p_2 = \Omega\sqrt{1 + 2\mu}$. The constants C_2 and D_2 must be found from the condition that on the boundary of the two half-periods (at $t = T/2$), the functions $f_{1,2}(t)$ and their first derivatives be continuous:

$$\left.\begin{aligned} f_{1,2}\left(\frac{T}{2} - \varepsilon\right) &= f_{1,2}\left(\frac{T}{2} + \varepsilon\right) \\ f'_{1,2}\left(\frac{T}{2} - \varepsilon\right) &= f'_{1,2}\left(\frac{T}{2} + \varepsilon\right) \end{aligned}\right\} \quad (\varepsilon \to 0) \ .$$

Substitution gives

$$\cos \frac{p_1 T}{2} = C_2 \sin \frac{p_2 T}{2} + D_2 \cos \frac{p_2 T}{2} \ ,$$

$$- p_1 \sin \frac{p_1 T}{2} = p_2 C_2 \cos \frac{p_2 T}{2} - p_2 D_2 \sin \frac{p_2 T}{2}$$

for the continuation of the function $f_1(t)$. Solving these equations for the constants C_2 and D_2 and inserting $T = 2\pi/\theta$, we find

$$C_2 = \cos \frac{\pi p_1}{\theta} \sin \frac{\pi p_2}{\theta} - \frac{p_1}{p_2} \sin \frac{\pi p_1}{\theta} \cos \frac{\pi p_2}{\theta} \ ,$$

$$D_2 = \cos \frac{\pi p_1}{\theta} \cos \frac{\pi p_2}{\theta} + \frac{p_1}{p_2} \sin \frac{\pi p_1}{\theta} \sin \frac{\pi p_2}{\theta} \ .$$

Similarly, for the function $f_2(t)$, we find

$$C_2 = \frac{1}{p_1} \sin \frac{\pi p_1}{\theta} \sin \frac{\pi p_2}{\theta} + \frac{1}{p_2} \cos \frac{\pi p_1}{\theta} \cos \frac{\pi p_2}{\theta} \ ,$$

$$D_2 = \frac{1}{p_1} \sin \frac{\pi p_1}{\theta} \cos \frac{\pi p_2}{\theta} - \frac{1}{p_2} \cos \frac{\pi p_1}{\theta} \sin \frac{\pi p_2}{\theta} \ .$$

Substituting the values of coefficients C_2 and D_2 in the expressions for $f_2(t)$, we can calculate

$$A = \tfrac{1}{2}[f_1(T) + f_2'(T)] \ .$$

After a number of cumbersome transformations, we obtain

$$A = \cos \frac{\pi p_1}{\theta} \cos \frac{\pi p_2}{\theta} - \frac{p_1^2 + p_2^2}{2 p_1 p_2} \sin \frac{\pi p_1}{\theta} \sin \frac{\pi p_2}{\theta} \ . \tag{1.24}$$

Using the results of the preceding paragraph, we can conclude that for

$$\left| \cos \frac{\pi p_1}{\theta} \cos \frac{\pi p_2}{\theta} - \frac{p_1^2 + p_2^2}{2p_1 p_2} \sin \frac{\pi p_1}{\theta} \sin \frac{\pi p_2}{\theta} \right| < 1$$

the equation of the problem under consideration does not have unbounded increasing solutions—the initial straight form of the rod is dynamically stable. For

$$\left| \cos \frac{\pi p_1}{\theta} \cos \frac{\pi p_2}{\theta} - \frac{p_1^2 + p_2^2}{2p_1 p_2} \sin \frac{\pi p_1}{\theta} \sin \frac{\pi p_2}{\theta} \right| > 1 ,$$

the amplitudes of the transverse vibrations will unboundedly increase with time. The equation

$$\left| \cos \frac{\pi p_1}{\theta} \cos \frac{\pi p_2}{\theta} - \frac{p_1^2 + p_2^2}{2p_1 p_2} \sin \frac{\pi p_1}{\theta} \sin \frac{\pi p_2}{\theta} \right| = 1 \tag{1.25}$$

permits one to determine the boundaries of the regions of dynamic instability. This equation can be found in many references. (See, for example, Den-Hartog [1])

Detailed calculations are carried out in the work by V. M. Makushin [1]. One of the diagrams from this work is shown in Figure 4. The regions of instability are cross hatched.

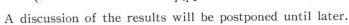

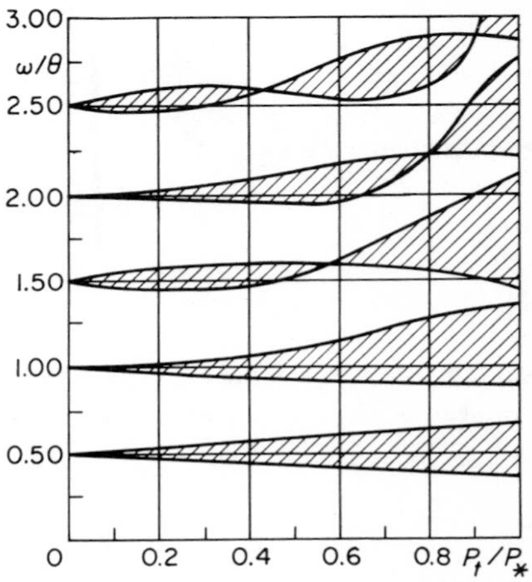

FIG. 4.

Equation (1.25) can be generalized for the case when the longitudinal force changes according to an arbitrary piecewise constant law. The corresponding equation has the form

$$\left| \left(2 \cos p_1 t_0 \sin p_2 t_0 - \frac{p_1^2 + p_2^2}{p_1 p_2} \sin p_1 t_0 \cos p_2 t_0\right) \sin p_2 T + \left(2 \cos p_1 t_0 \cos p_2 t_0 + \frac{p_1^2 + p_2^2}{p_1 p_2} \sin p_1 t_0 \sin p_2 t_0\right) \cos p_2 T \right| = 1 .$$

A discussion of the results will be postponed until later.

§ 4. Derivation of the Boundary Frequency Equation

● **1.** A method of determining the boundaries of the regions of instability is presented below for the case of an arbitrary periodic function given in (1.13).

It was shown in § 2 that the region of real characteristic numbers coincides with the region of unboundedly increasing solutions of the differential equation (1.11). On the other hand, the region of complex characteristic roots corresponds to the bounded (almost periodic) solutions.

Multiple roots occur on the boundaries dividing the regions of real and complex roots; moreover, as follows from (1.20), such roots can be either $\rho_1 = \rho_2 = 1$ or $\rho_1 = \rho_2 = -1$.

In the first case, as seen from Eq. (1.15), the solution of the differential equation will be periodic with a periodic $T = 2\pi/\theta$; in the second case,[7] we will have the period $2T$.

Therefore, the regions of unboundedly increasing solutions are separated from the regions of stability by the periodic solutions with periods T and $2T$. More exactly, two solutions of identical periods bound the region of instability, two solutions of different periods bound the region of stability.

The last property is easily obtained from the following considerations. Assume that the region of real roots (the region of instability) lies in the interval between $\rho = 1$ and $\rho = -1$. Because of the continuous dependence of the characteristic roots on the coefficients of the differential equation, the root $\rho = 0$ must then be among them, and consequently, also $\rho = \infty$, which is impossible. Thus, the roots $\rho = 1$ and $\rho = -1$ bound the region of the complex roots, i.e., the region of stability.[8]

● **2.** It follows from the preceding discussion that the determination of the boundaries of the regions of instability is reduced to finding the conditions under which the given differential equation has periodic solutions with periods T and $2T$. From the viewpoint of the physical problem considered here, such results seem completely natural. Indeed, the periodic motion is essentially the boundary case of vibrations with unboundedly increasing amplitudes.

To find conditions for the existence of periodic solutions, we can often proceed in the following manner (for example, see Timoshenko [1]). Having introduced the "small parameter" μ (the excitation parameter, for example, can be accepted as such a parameter), one seeks the solution to

$$f'' + \Omega^2[1 - 2\mu\Phi(t)]f = 0$$

in the form of a power series of μ

$$f = f_0 + \mu f_1 + \mu^2 f_2 + \cdots .$$

Here f_k are unknown functions of time. Substituting this expression into the differential equation and comparing the coefficients of μ^k, one obtains a system of differential equations with constant coefficients which can be solved by the method of successive approximations. The solutions found in this manner have limitations imposed on them since terms going to infinity must be absent, i.e., we must require the periodicity of solutions.

However, the conditions for the existence of periodic solutions can be obtained in a different manner, i.e., without using the "method of the small parameter" borrowed from nonlinear mechanics. The fact that the periodic solutions do exist and that they can be expanded into Fourier series is known.

[7] A more detailed analysis shows that only one of the particular solutions will be periodic. The second solution will have the form $f(t) = \chi_1(t) + t\chi_2(t)$, where $\chi_1(t)$ and $\chi_2(t)$ are periodic functions of time.

[8] A rigorous proof of this theorem can be found in the book by Strutt [1].

This permits one to seek the periodic solutions of Eq. (1.11) directly in the form of a trigonometric series. As an example, we will apply this method to the Mathieu differential equation

$$f'' + \Omega^2(1 - 2\mu \cos \theta t)f = 0\,. \tag{1.26}$$

We seek the periodic solution with a period $2T$ in the form

$$f(t) = \sum_{k=1,3,5}^{\infty}\left(a_k \sin \frac{k\theta t}{2} + b_k \cos \frac{k\theta t}{2}\right). \tag{1.27}$$

Substituting the series (1.27) into Eq. (1.26) and equating the coefficients of identical $\sin (k\theta t)/2$ and $\cos (k\theta t)/2$ leads to the following system of linear homogeneous algebraic equations in terms of a_k and b_k:

$$\left(1 + \mu - \frac{\theta^2}{4\Omega^2}\right)a_1 - \mu a_3 = 0\,,$$

$$\left(1 - \frac{k^2\theta^2}{4\Omega^2}\right)a_k - \mu(a_{k-2} + a_{k+2}) = 0 \qquad (k = 3, 5, 7, \cdots)\,,$$

$$\left(1 - \mu - \frac{\theta^2}{4\Omega^2}\right)b_1 - \mu b_3 = 0\,,$$

$$\left(1 - \frac{k^2\theta^2}{4\Omega^2}\right)b_k - \mu(b_{k-2} + b_{k+2}) = 0 \qquad (k = 3, 5, 7, \cdots)\,.$$

Note that the first system contains only a_k coefficients, the second contains only b_k coefficients.

● 3. As is known, the system of linear homogeneous equations has solutions different from zero only in the case where the determinant composed of the coefficients of this system is equal to zero. This also holds in the case where the system contains an infinite number of unknowns. Thus, the necessary condition for the existence of the periodic solution of Eq. (1.26) is that the obtained determinants of the homogeneous systems be equal to zero. Combining the two conditions under the $\pm$ sign, we obtain

$$\begin{vmatrix} 1 \pm \mu - \dfrac{\theta^2}{4\Omega^2} & -\mu & 0 & \cdots \\ -\mu & 1 - \dfrac{9\theta^2}{4\Omega^2} & -\mu & \cdots \\ 0 & -\mu & 1 - \dfrac{25\theta^2}{4\Omega^2} & \cdots \\ \cdots & \cdots & \cdots & \cdots \end{vmatrix} = 0\,.$$

This equation relating the frequencies of the external loading with the natural frequency of the rod and the magnitude of the external force will be called *the equation of boundary frequencies*, where *boundary frequencies* are understood to be the frequencies of the external loading θ, corresponding to the boundaries of the regions of instability. Equation (1.28) makes it possible to find regions of instability that are bounded by the periodic solutions with a period $2T$. To determine the regions of instability bounded by the periodic solutions with a period T, we proceed in an analogous manner. Substituting the series

$$f(t) = b_0 + \sum_{k=2,4,6}^{\infty}\left(a_k \sin\frac{k\theta t}{2} + b_k \cos\frac{k\theta t}{2}\right)$$

into Eq. (1.26), we obtain the following systems of algebraic equations:

$$\left(1-\frac{\theta^2}{\Omega^2}\right)a_2 - \mu a_4 = 0\,,$$

$$\left(1-\frac{k^2\theta^2}{4\Omega^2}\right)a_k - \mu(a_{k-2}+a_{k+2}) = 0\,, \qquad (k = 4, 6, \cdots)\,,$$

$$b_0 - \mu b_2 = 0\,,$$

$$\left(1-\frac{\theta^2}{\Omega^2}\right)b_2 - \mu(2b_0+b_4) = 0\,,$$

$$\left(1-\frac{k^2\theta^2}{4\Omega^2}\right)b_k - \mu(b_{k-2}+b_{k+2}) = 0\,, \qquad (k = 4, 6, \cdots)\,.$$

Equating the determinants of the homogeneous system to zero, we arrive at the following equations for the boundary frequencies

$$\begin{vmatrix} 1-\dfrac{\theta^2}{\Omega^2} & -\mu & 0 & \cdots \\ -\mu & 1-\dfrac{4\theta^2}{\Omega^2} & -\mu & \cdots \\ 0 & -\mu & 1-\dfrac{16\theta^2}{\Omega^2} & \cdots \\ \cdots & \cdots & \cdots & \cdots \end{vmatrix} = 0 \qquad (1.29)$$

and

$$\begin{vmatrix} 1 & -\mu & 0 & 0 & \cdots \\ -2\mu & 1-\dfrac{\theta^2}{\Omega^2} & -\mu & 0 & \cdots \\ 0 & -\mu & 1-\dfrac{4\theta^2}{\Omega^2} & -\mu & \cdots \\ 0 & 0 & -\mu & 1-\dfrac{16\theta^2}{\Omega^2} & \cdots \\ \cdots & \cdots & \cdots & \cdots & \cdots \end{vmatrix} = 0\,, \qquad (1.30)$$

respectively.

● **4.** The determinants obtained in ● 3 are infinite, and therefore the question of their convergence must be considered.[9]

One can show that these determinants belong to a known class of converging determinants, i.e., to normal determinants. The determinant

$$\Delta = \begin{vmatrix} 1+c_{11} & c_{12} & c_{13} & \cdots \\ c_{21} & 1+c_{22} & c_{23} & \cdots \\ c_{31} & c_{32} & 1+c_{33} & \cdots \\ \cdots & \cdots & \cdots & \cdots \end{vmatrix} \qquad (1.31)$$

[9] See Whittaker and Watson [1]. Infinite determinants were investigated for the first time in connection with the integration of the Hill equation (Lunar Theory, 1877).

is called *normal* if the double series

$$\sum_{i=1}^{\infty}\sum_{k=1}^{\infty} c_{ik}$$

is absolutely convergent.

We can examine, for example, the determinant (1.28). Multiplying the kth row $(k = 1, 2, 3, \cdots)$ by $-4\Omega^2/[(2k-1)^2\theta^2]$, we can reduce it to the same form as Eq. (1.31), where

$$c_{kk} = \begin{cases} -\dfrac{4\Omega^2}{\theta^2}(1 \pm \mu) & (k = 1)\,, \\[2ex] -\dfrac{4\Omega^2}{(2k-1)^2\theta^2} & (k \neq 1)\,, \end{cases}$$

$$\underset{(i \neq k)}{c_{ik}} = \begin{cases} -\dfrac{4\Omega^2}{(2k-1)^2\theta^2} - \mu & (i = k \pm 1)\,, \\[2ex] 0 & (i \neq k \pm 1)\,. \end{cases}$$

Constructing the double series

$$\sum_{i=1}^{\infty}\sum_{k=1}^{\infty} c_{ik}\,,$$

we can prove that it converges absolutely. Actually we have the inequality

$$\sum_{i=1}^{n}\sum_{k=1}^{n} |\,c_{ik}\,| < \frac{4\Omega^2}{\theta^2}(1 + 2\mu)\sum_{k=1}^{n}\frac{1}{(2k-1)^2}\,,$$

where the series on the right-hand side is convergent.

Similarly, one can prove the convergence of the remaining determinants.

§ 5. Determination of the Regions of Dynamic Instability

● 1. For the clarification of the distribution of the regions of instability, we will examine the case of a very small periodic component of the longitudinal force. Letting $\mu \to 0$ in Eqs. (1.28), (1.29), and (1.30), we find that the solutions with a period $2T$ lie in pairs near the frequencies

$$\theta_* = \frac{2\Omega}{k}\,, \qquad (k = 1, 3, 5, \cdots)\,,$$

for very small values of μ, and with a period T near the frequencies

$$\theta_* = \frac{2\Omega}{k}\,, \qquad (k = 2, 4, 6, \cdots)\,.$$

Both cases can be combined in one formula:

$$\theta_* = \frac{2\Omega}{k}\,, \qquad (k = 1, 2, 3, \cdots)\,. \tag{1.32}$$

Equation (1.32) gives the relationship between the frequency of the external force and the frequencies of the free vibrations of the rod, near which the formation of unboundedly increasing vibrations is possible; namely, these relationships define the regions of the dynamic instability of a rod.

We shall distinguish the first, second, third, etc. regions of dynamic instability according to the number k contained in Eq. (1.32). The region of instability situated near $\theta_* = 2\Omega$ is, as will be shown later, the most dangerous and has therefore the greatest practical importance. We will call this region the *principal region of dynamic instability.*

The origin of the resonance at $\theta = 2\Omega$ is easily seen from the following argument. Imagine that the rod (Fig. 2) vibrates in the transverse direction with the natural frequency Ω. During this vibration, the longitudinal displacement of the moving end also will be a periodic function of time, having, however, the frequency 2Ω. Indeed, for every period of transverse vibration, two periods of vibration of the moving support occur. To sustain the resonant vibrations so that the external force applied at the moving end has a frequency 2Ω, it is necessary that $\theta = 2\Omega$.

Before going on to further calculations, let us discuss the characteristics of the *parametric resonance.* If the ordinary resonance of forced vibrations occurs when the natural and exciting frequencies are equal, then parametric resonance occurs when the exciting frequency is equal to double the frequency of the free vibrations. Another essential difference of parametric resonance lies in the possibility of exciting vibrations with frequencies smaller than the frequency of the principal resonance. Finally, qualitatively new in parametric resonance is the existence of continuous regions of excitation (regions of dynamic instability), which we will now calculate.

● **2.** Since we are considering infinite determinants, the calculations can best be performed by systematically investigating the first, second, third, and higher order determinants. The difference between two successive approximations serves as a practical estimation of the accuracy of the calculations.

For numerical calculations, it is possible to represent the infinite determinants of the type (1.28) in the form of chain fractions. We will show this on an example for the determinant

$$\begin{vmatrix} a_1 & 1 & 0 & 0 & \cdots \\ 1 & a_2 & 1 & 0 & \cdots \\ 0 & 1 & a_3 & 1 & \cdots \\ \cdot & \cdot & \cdot & \cdot & \cdot \end{vmatrix} = 0 .$$

(Any of our determinants can be reduced to such a form.)

We will systematically expand the first, second and higher order determinants. The equation of the first approximation obviously will be $a_1 = 0$. In the second approximation, we obtain

$$a_1 - \frac{1}{a_2} = 0 .$$

The equation of the third approximation is

$$\begin{vmatrix} a_1 & 1 & 0 \\ 1 & a_2 & 1 \\ 0 & 1 & a_3 \end{vmatrix} = 0$$

which can be reduced to the form

$$a_1 - \frac{1}{a_2 - (1/a_3)} = 0\,,$$

and, generally,

$$a_1 - \cfrac{1}{a_2 - \cfrac{1}{a_3 - \cfrac{1}{a_4 - \cdots}}} = 0\,. \tag{1.33}$$

Consider the determinant (1.28), for which

$$a_1 = -\frac{1}{\mu}\left(1 \pm \mu - \frac{\theta^2}{4\Omega^2}\right),$$

$$a_k = -\frac{1}{\mu}\left[1 - \frac{(2k-1)^2\theta^2}{4\Omega^2}\right], \qquad (k \geq 2)\,;$$

Eq. (1.33) has the form

$$1 \pm \mu - \frac{\theta^2}{4\Omega^2} - \cfrac{\mu^2}{1 - \cfrac{9\theta^2}{4\Omega^2} - \cfrac{\mu^2}{1 - (25\theta^2/4\Omega^2) - \cdots}} = 0$$

or

$$\frac{\theta^2}{4\Omega^2} = 1 \pm \mu - \cfrac{\mu^2}{1 - \cfrac{9\theta^2}{4\Omega^2} - \cfrac{\mu^2}{1 - (25\theta^2/4\Omega^2) - \cdots}}\,.$$

The formula obtained is especially convenient when using the method of successive approximations. Substituting an approximate value for the boundary frequency into the right-hand side of this formula, we obtain a more exact value each time.[10]

● **3.** The advantage of the above method is that it makes it possible to calculate the boundaries of the regions of instability with the desired accuracy. At this point, however, we will not perform any numerical calculations but will instead try to develop somewhat different formulas for the boundaries of the regions of instability.

Let us examine (1.28) to determine the boundaries of the principal region of instability. Retaining the upper diagonal element, i.e., the "first-order determinant," and equating it to zero:

$$1 \pm \mu - \frac{\theta^2}{4\Omega^2} = 0\,,$$

we obtain the approximate formula for the boundaries of the principal region,

$$\theta_* = 2\Omega\sqrt{1 \pm \mu}\,. \tag{1.34}$$

As is known, Beliaev derived the equation

[10] In this manner Beliaev [1] calculated the boundaries of the principal region of instability.

$$\theta_* = 2\omega\sqrt{1 - \frac{P_0}{P_*}}\left[1 \pm \frac{P_t}{4(P_* - P_0)}\right],$$

which in our notation takes the form

$$\theta_* = 2\Omega\left(1 \pm \frac{\mu}{2}\right).$$

This formula was obtained by interpolating the results of separate numerical calculations of the Hill determinant, and it can be considered sufficiently accurate. It is not difficult to see that both equations give practically identical results[11] up to the value $\mu = 0.5$.

To increase the accuracy of Eq. (1.34), we will consider the second approximation:

$$\begin{vmatrix} 1 \pm \mu - \frac{\theta^2}{4\Omega^2} & -\mu \\ -\mu & 1 - \frac{9\theta^2}{4\Omega^2} \end{vmatrix} = 0. \tag{1.35}$$

Substituting the approximate value of the boundary frequencies (1.34) into the lower diagonal element in (1.35), which only slightly affects the final results, and solving the equation with respect to θ, we obtain

$$\theta_* = 2\Omega\sqrt{1 \pm \mu + \frac{\mu^2}{8 \pm 9\mu}},$$

where the last term under the radical takes into account the correction for the second approximation. This correction increases as μ increases, but even at $\mu = 0.3$ it does not exceed one percent. Thus, the accuracy of the very simple equation (1.34) is shown to be sufficient for practical purposes.

The result obtained is best understood if one remembers that the "first-order determinant" (1.28) corresponds to taking into account the effect of the first terms of Eq. (1.27), i.e.,

$$f(t) = a \sin\frac{\theta t}{2} + b \cos\frac{\theta t}{2}.$$

The first approximation gives good results, signifying that the periodic solutions on the boundaries of the principal regions of instability are close to harmonic vibrations. We will subsequently return to this deduction.

Let us discuss one interpretation of Eq. (1.34). Rewriting this equation in the form

$$\theta_* = 2\omega\sqrt{1 - \frac{P_0}{P_*} \pm \frac{P_t}{2P_*}}$$

we can compare it with Eq. (1.8), which determines the natural frequency of a rod loaded by a constant axial force:

$$\Omega = \omega\sqrt{1 - \frac{P_0}{P_*}}.$$

[11] This value, which follows from Eq. (1.9), corresponds to the case seldom encountered in practical problems: $P_0 + P_t = P_*$.

Comparing these equations, we arrive at the conclusion that the frequencies corresponding to the boundaries of the principal region of dynamic instability can be determined for the first approximation as the doubled frequency of the free vibrations of the rod loaded with the constant longitudinal forces $P_0 + \frac{1}{2}P_t$ and $P_0 - \frac{1}{2}P_t$, respectively.

To determine the boundaries of the second region of instability, it is necessary to consider Eqs. (1.29) and (1.30). By restricting ourselves to second-order determinants

$$\begin{vmatrix} 1 - \dfrac{\theta^2}{\Omega^2} & -\mu \\ -\mu & 1 - \dfrac{4\theta^2}{\Omega^2} \end{vmatrix} = 0 ,$$

$$\begin{vmatrix} 1 & -\mu \\ -2\mu & 1 - \dfrac{\theta^2}{\Omega^2} \end{vmatrix} = 0 ,$$

we obtain the following approximate formulas for the boundary frequencies:

$$\theta_* = \Omega\sqrt{1 + \tfrac{1}{3}\mu^2} , \qquad \theta_* = \Omega\sqrt{1 - 2\mu^2} . \tag{1.36}$$

These equations can be made more accurate if one considers higher-order determinants.[12]

To calculate the third region of instability, one must refer to (1.28), and proceeding from the second-order determinant (1.35) obtain

$$\theta_* = \tfrac{2}{3}\Omega\sqrt{1 - \frac{9\mu^2}{8 \pm 9\mu}} . \tag{1.37}$$

Comparing Eqs. (1.34), (1.36), and (1.37), we see that the width of the regions of dynamic instability rapidly decreases as the number of the region increases

$$\frac{\Delta\theta}{\Omega} \sim \mu, \mu^2, \mu^3, \cdots . \tag{1.38}$$

The principal region of instability has the greatest width.

The distribution of the first three regions of instability on the plane $(\mu, \theta/2\Omega)$ is shown in Figure 5 (the regions of instability are crosshatched). In contrast to Figure 3, here the values of $\lambda^{-1/2}$ are plotted on the vertical axis and the values of $h^2/2$ on the horizontal axis. In addition to this, Figure 5 considers only that part of the plane which is of practical interest. This part of the plane is surrounded by a frame in Figure 3.

[12] In the literature (see for example Chelomei [1]), one can find the assertion that the second and, generally, the even regions of instability degenerate into curves. This assertion is incorrect; the source of the error is in the poor choice of the zero approximation in the "method of the small parameter."

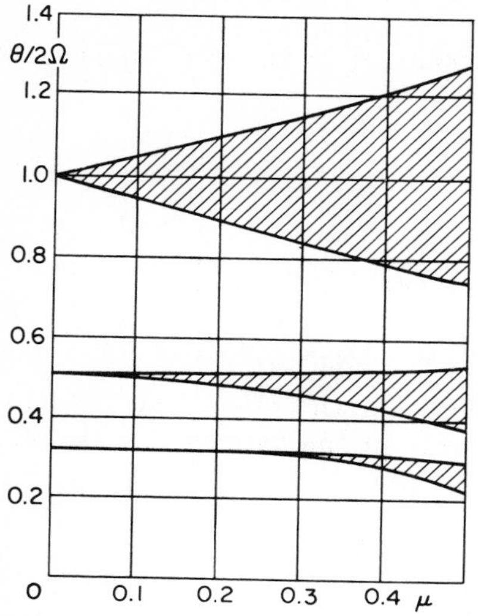

FIG. 5.

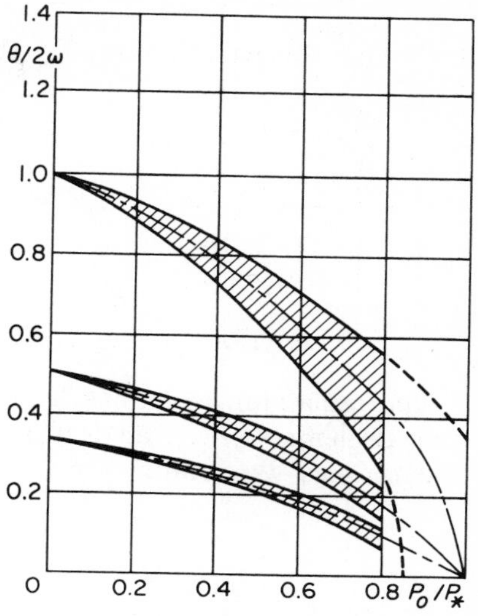

FIG. 6.

The regions of instability on the plane $(P_0/P_*,\ \theta/2\Omega)$ appear in Figure 6. The ratio P_t/P_0 is assumed to be constant and is equal to 0.3. As $P_t \to 0$, the regions of instability degenerate into the backbone curves given by

$$\frac{\theta}{2\omega} = \frac{1}{k}\sqrt{1 - \frac{P_0}{P_*}}\,, \qquad (k = 1, 2, 3, \cdots)\,.$$

The boundaries of the regions cannot be obtained from Eqs. (1.34), (1.36), and the other equations when P_0/P_* is large. Here one must use the Mathieu diagram (Fig. 3) or tables of the eigenvalues of the Mathieu equation.[13]

● 4. We shall briefly discuss the use of the above method in the more general case of the Hill equation. Let the longitudinal force be of the form

$$P(t) = P_0 + \sum_{k=1}^{\infty} P_{tk} \cos k\theta t\,.$$

The corresponding equation will be

$$f'' + \Omega^2\Big(1 - \sum_{k=1}^{\infty} 2\mu_k \cos k\theta t\Big) f = 0\,, \tag{1.39}$$

where

$$\mu_k = \frac{P_{tk}}{2(P_* - P_0)}\,.$$

Again we seek the periodic solution in the form of a series

[13] See Strutt [1]. The construction of the regions of instability for the case of large coefficients of excitation was done by Lubkin and Stoker [1].

$$f(t) = \sum_{k=1,3,5}^{\infty} \left(a_k \sin \frac{k\theta t}{2} + b_k \cos \frac{k\theta t}{2} \right);$$

substituting this equation into Eq. (1.39) we obtain for the boundary frequencies

$$\begin{vmatrix} 1 \pm \mu_1 - \frac{\theta^2}{4\Omega^2} & -(\mu_1 \pm \mu_2) & -(\mu_2 \pm \mu_3) & \cdots \\ -(\mu_1 \pm \mu_2) & 1 \pm \mu_3 - \frac{9\theta^2}{4\Omega^2} & -(\mu_1 \pm \mu_4) & \cdots \\ -(\mu_2 \pm \mu_3) & -(\mu_1 \pm \mu_4) & 1 \pm \mu_5 - \frac{25\theta^2}{4\Omega^2} & \cdots \\ \cdots & \cdots & \cdots & \cdots \end{vmatrix} = 0 . \qquad (1.40)$$

The remaining equations have an analogous form. Retaining only the diagonal elements, i.e., neglecting the influence of the harmonics in the final computations, we obtain

$$\theta_* \approx \frac{2\Omega}{k}\sqrt{1 \pm \mu_k}, \qquad (k = 1, 2, 3, \cdots). \qquad (1.41)$$

Comparing this equation with Eq. (1.34), which corresponds to the case of a harmonically changing longitudinal force, we see that in the first approximation each region of instability depends only on the corresponding harmonic in the expansion of the longitudinal force. This was already observed by Krylov and Bogoliubov [2]. The influence of the ith harmonic on the width of the kth region of instability is of the order $(\mu_k \pm \mu_i)^2$, as seen from the equation of the boundary frequencies.

We will apply the results obtained to the case where the longitudinal force changes according to a piecewise constant law (§ 3). Displacing the initial instant of time by T/4 and expanding the longitudinal force in Fourier series, we have

$$P(t) = P_0 + \frac{4P_t}{\pi} \sum_{k=1,3}^{\infty} \frac{1}{k} \cos k\theta t ,$$

which converges uniformly everywhere with the exception of the points at which the magnitude of the longitudinal force changes. We obtain

$$\mu_k = \frac{4}{\pi k}\mu ,$$

where

$$\mu = \frac{P_t}{2(P_* - P_0)} .$$

For this case Eq. (1.41) gives

$$\theta_* = \frac{2\Omega}{k}\sqrt{1 \pm \frac{4}{\pi k}\mu}, \qquad (k = 1, 3, 5, \cdots). \qquad (1.42)$$

Comparing Eq. (1.34) with the equation obtained for $k = 1$, we see that the principal region of instability is approximately $4/\pi$ times wider than that described by the Mathieu equation in the case of a piecewise constant variation of longitudinal force.

The harmonic longitudinal force is sometimes replaced by a force changing according to the piecewise constant law, its amplitude being determined from some other prior consideration. This replacement can be justified when discussing the principal region of instability. Qualitatively incorrect results are obtained if the secondary regions are determined according to a piecewise constant law of changing longitudinal force. Thus, the third, fifth, and, generally, the odd regions of instability for the case of a harmonic longitudinal force have a width of the order of $\Delta\theta/\Omega \sim \mu^k$, but in the case of piecewise constant law the width is of the other of $\Delta\theta/\Omega \sim \mu/k$.

§ 6. Some Experimental Results

The experimental verification of the theoretical results presented above can easily be carried out in the laboratory (Bolotin [2]). One of the possible designs of the experimental setup is shown in Figure 7.

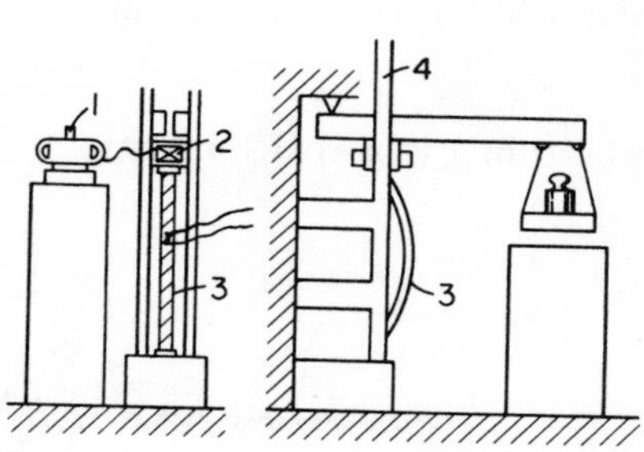

FIG. 7.

The test fixture is assembled on the base of the vertical ram. The specimen (3 on diagram), made of flat-bar steel, is placed between the guides of the ram (4), while the stationary support of the specimen is fixed on the lower plate, and the moving support slides in the guide. This test set up provides free vertical translation of the moving end of the rod; free rotation of the support cross sections is provided by means of ball bearings. All this allows the conditions of the test to approach the theoretical conditions.

In the author's experiments, strain-gages connected to an oscillograph recorded the vibrations. To eliminate the deformations due to axial compression, two gages were used, one of which was placed on the tension side and another on the compression side. The gages were connected in parallel to the circuit of a measuring bridge, i.e., in the two adjacent arms, so that the influence of the deformation of the opposite sign is doubled and the compression deformation is eliminated.

The gages had a sensitivity factor of $s = 2.1$ and a resistance of 200Ω. An a.c. amplifier was used, with a carrier frequency of 8000 cps. A type B-4 galvanometer was used, whose characteristics were: sensitivity 1 mm/ma, natural frequency of the system in air 3500 cps, resistance 1Ω, and maximum current 100 ma.

The vibrator (2) produced the periodic component of the longitudinal force. The frequency of the load was determined by a sliding contact on the shaft of the vibrator, periodically closing a circuit connected in the system. This simple device made it possible to determine not only the phase time but also the phase angle between the external force and the excited vibrations.

The experiments confirmed the theory concerning the existence of a continuous region of dynamic instability. Generally, the periodic longitudinal force induces transverse vibrations at any frequency. The amplitude of these vibrations is negligible, and the vibrations take place with the frequency of the external force. These vibrations are obviously dependent on the initial curvature and eccentricity of the longitudinal force. However, in a certain range of frequencies lying in the vicinity of $\theta = 2\Omega$, strong transverse vibrations develop with amplitudes increasing to high values.

Characteristically this growth, at least initially, follows the exponential law (Fig. 8). This is in complete agreement with the theory, according to which the solutions of the Mathieu equations on the boundaries of the regions of instability have the form

$$f(t) = \chi(t)e^{(t/T)\ln\rho},$$

where $\ln\rho$ is a real quantity.

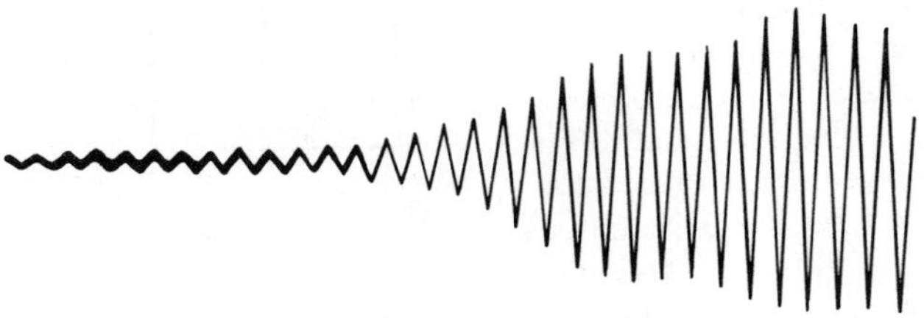

FIG. 8.

At this point, it is worth mentioning the experiments on the parametric excitation of electrical oscillations conducted under the guidance of Mandel'shtam and Papaleksi [2]. Figure 9 shows an oscillogram of the growth of the current in an oscillatory contour whose inductance periodically changes with time by means of an external mechanical force (Lazarev [1]). This oscillogram is a perfect analog to the oscillograms obtained from the rod experiment. In particular, in both cases the amplitude growth follows an exponential law. Further growth of amplitude is slowed down and finally stops, which in both cases is caused by the effect of nonlinear factors. This question will be examined in detail later.

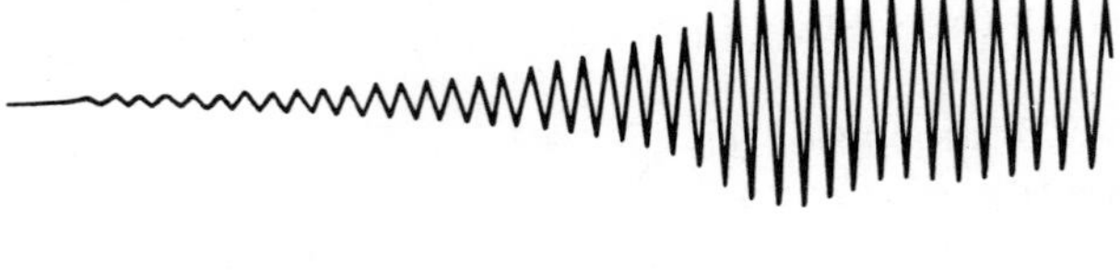

FIG. 9.

The experiment confirms not only the qualitative but also the quantitative results, and in particular, Eq. (1.34). In using this formula, however, one must take into account that the force developed in the vibrator increases in proportion to the square of the frequency. It is possible to write down that

$$P_t = \frac{\theta^2}{4\Omega^2} \bar{P}_t ,$$

where $\bar{P}_t$ is the amplitude of the longitudinal force which the vibrator develops at the frequency 2Ω. By considering this relation, and from Eq. (1.34), we obtain

$$\theta_* = \frac{2\Omega}{\sqrt{1 \pm \dfrac{\bar{P}_t}{2(P_* - P_0)}}}$$

or the shorter form

$$\theta_* = \frac{2\Omega}{\sqrt{1 \pm \bar{\mu}}} . \qquad (1.43)$$

The principal region of instability whose boundaries are determined from Eq. (1.43) is shown in Figure 10. On the same curve are plotted the experimental results which obviously agree well with the theory. The boundaries of the principal region of instability can be determined very accurately at the appearance of vibrations occurring with a frequency less than half that of the external forces. Outside the region of instability, as already mentioned, the steady-state vibrations occur at the frequency of the external load (Fig. 11).

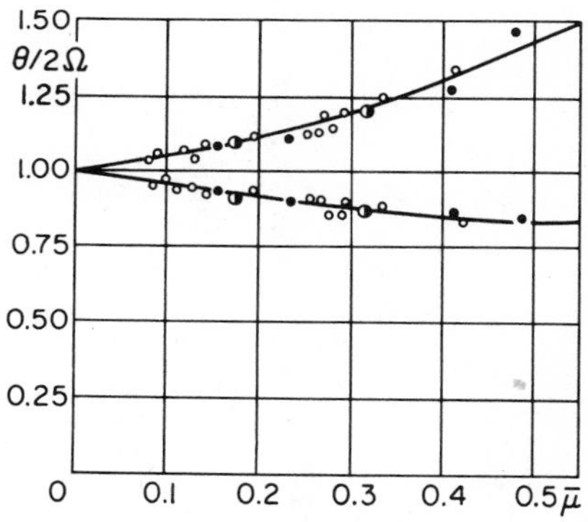

FIG. 10.

The above results are related to the principal region of instability. No correlation could be found experimentally regarding the second, third, and higher regions—at least for a small amplitude of longitudinal force.[14] It is true that in approaching the synchronism $\theta = \Omega$, the intensity of vibrations

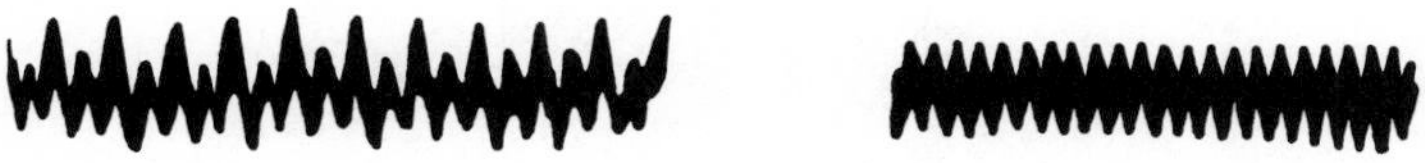

(a) (b)

FIG. 11.

[14] Translator's note: These secondary regions were found experimentally by Utida and Sezawa [1] and Weingarten [1].

occurring with a given external force amplitude increases somewhat. However, the region of increase in vibration amplitude is not bounded by some narrow band of frequencies, but spreads far beyond the limits of the boundaries predicted from theory. The result gives a basis for supposing that similar vibrations are produced by the influence of additional factors such as eccentricity and initial curvature. As we will see in later sections, this lack of agreement between theory and experiment for the secondary regions of instability can be removed by considering the problem with damping.

Two

THE INFLUENCE OF DAMPING ON THE REGIONS OF DYNAMIC INSTABILITY

§ 7. Investigation of Differential Equations

●1. For reasons which will be understood by the reader later (§ 11), we will restrict ourselves here to consideration of the effect of linear damping. More precisely, we will consider resistance forces which introduce into the differential equation an additional term containing a first derivative of the displacement with respect to time:

$$f'' + 2\varepsilon f' + \Omega^2(1 - 2\mu \cos \theta t) f = 0 . \tag{2.1}$$

The coefficient of damping ε will be determined experimentally for each case.

Let us write the solution of the differential equation (2.1) in the form

$$f(t) = u(t) \cdot v(t) ,$$

where $u(t)$ and $v(t)$ are at present unknown functions of time. Substituting this equation into Eq. (2.1), we have

$$u''v + 2u'(v' + \varepsilon v) + \Omega^2(1 - 2\mu \cos \theta t)\, uv + uv'' + 2\varepsilon uv' = 0 .$$

We will require the coefficient of u' to vanish in the above expression. In this way we obtain the following two differential equations:

$$u''v + \Omega^2(1 - 2\mu \cos \theta t)\, uv + uv'' + 2\varepsilon uv' = 0 ,$$
$$v' + \varepsilon v = 0 .$$

The second equation gives $v = Ce^{-\varepsilon t}$; after substituting this value back into the first equation and dividing by $Ce^{-\varepsilon t}$, we obtain

$$u'' + \Omega^2\left(1 - \frac{\varepsilon^2}{\Omega^2} - 2\mu \cos \theta t\right)u = 0 . \tag{2.2}$$

The Mathieu-Hill equation thus obtained differs from the equation of the conservative problem (1.10) by the presence of an additional damping term, which represents a correction to the frequency:

$$\Omega_\varepsilon = \Omega \sqrt{1 - \frac{\varepsilon^2}{\Omega^2}} . \tag{2.3}$$

As already shown in Eq. (1.21), the two linear independent solutions of the Mathieu-Hill equation have the form

$$u_1(t) = \chi_1(t)e^{(t/T)\ \ln \rho_1},$$
$$u_2(t) = \chi_2(t)e^{(t/T)\ \ln \rho_2},$$

where $\chi_{1,2}(t)$ are periodic functions of period T, and $\rho_{1,2}$ are the roots of the characteristic equation. These roots are related by (1.20)

$$\rho_1 \cdot \rho_2 = 1 .$$

Returning to Eq. (2.1), we can represent its solution in the form

$$f_1(t) = \chi_1(t) \exp\left(\frac{t}{T} \ln \rho_1 - \varepsilon t\right),$$

$$f_2(t) = \chi_2(t) \exp\left(\frac{t}{T} \ln \rho_2 - \varepsilon t\right),$$

or, separating the real part of ln ρ, in the form

$$f_1(t) = \varphi_1(t) \exp\left(\frac{t}{T} \ln |\rho_1| - \varepsilon t\right),$$
$$f_2(t) = \varphi_2(t) \exp\left(\frac{t}{T} \ln |\rho_2| - \varepsilon t\right). \tag{2.4}$$

Here, as before, $\varphi_{1,2}(t)$ are bounded (almost periodic) functions

$$\varphi_1(t) = \chi_1(t)e^{(it/T)\ \arg \rho_1},$$
$$\varphi_2(t) = \chi_2(t)e^{(it/T)\ \arg \rho_2}.$$

●**2.** One easily sees that the behavior of the solutions of Eq. (2.1) depends on the relationship between the coefficient of damping ε and the real part of ln ρ. This means that the solutions will unboundedly increase when

$$\varepsilon < \frac{\ln |\rho|}{T},$$

and will be damped when

$$\varepsilon > \frac{\ln |\rho|}{T}.$$

In examining this question in more detail, let the characteristic numbers $\rho_{1,2}$ be complex conjugates; then,

$$\ln |\rho| = 0,$$

and both solutions lead to vibrations which are damped at the same rate as the corresponding free vibrations:

$$f_1(t) = \varphi_1(t)e^{-\varepsilon t},$$
$$f_2(t) = \varphi_2(t)e^{-\varepsilon t}.$$

We will now investigate the cases of real roots; moreover, we will assume

$$|\rho_1| < 1, \quad |\rho_2| > 1 .$$

Then the first solution will also be damped with time. For the second solution,

$$f_2(t) = \varphi_2(t) \exp\left(\frac{t}{T} \ln \rho_2 - \varepsilon t\right),$$

two cases must be investigated. If

$$\varepsilon > \frac{\ln |\rho_2|}{T},$$

then the second solution will be bounded. However, if

$$\varepsilon < \frac{\ln |\rho_2|}{T}$$

holds, then the second solution, and consequently the general integral, will increase unboundedly with time.

We will investigate the boundary case

$$\varepsilon = \frac{\ln |\rho_2|}{T}.$$

It is of special importance to us that the second solution be periodic, namely, at $\rho > 0$ a period T will occur; at $\rho < 0$, a period $2T$.

Thus, the problem of finding the regions of instability for Eq. (2.1) is reduced to the determination of the conditions under which it has periodic solutions with periods T and $2T$. Here also, two solutions of an identical period bound the region of increasing solutions and two solutions of different periods bound the region of damped solutions.

Note that the regions of instability for Eq. (2.1) lie inside the regions of instability for Eq. (2.2). The latter describes, by the way, the vibrations of a conservative system with a frequency of free vibrations calculated with corrections for damping.

§ 8. Derivation of the Equation of Boundary Frequencies Including the Consideration of Damping

Further calculations are not difficult. For determining the conditions under which Eq. (2.1) has periodic solutions with a period $2T$, we substitute into this equation the series[15]

$$f(t) = \sum_{k=1,3,5}^{\infty} \left(a_k \sin\frac{k\theta t}{2} + b_k \cos\frac{k\theta t}{2}\right),$$

carry out the trigonometric transformations, and then equate the coefficients of the same sin $(k\theta t)/2$ and cos $(k\theta t)/2$. As a result, we obtain the system of linear algebraic equations

$$\begin{aligned}
\left(1 + \mu - \frac{\theta^2}{4\Omega^2}\right)a_1 - \mu a_3 - \frac{\Delta}{\pi}\frac{\theta}{2\Omega} b_1 &= 0, \\
\left(1 - \mu - \frac{\theta^2}{4\Omega^2}\right)b_1 - \mu b_3 + \frac{\Delta}{\pi}\frac{\theta}{2\Omega} a_1 &= 0, \\
\left(1 - \frac{k^2\theta^2}{4\Omega^2}\right)a_k - \mu(a_{k-2} + a_{k+2}) - \frac{\Delta}{\pi}\frac{k\theta}{2\Omega} b_k &= 0, \\
\left(1 - \frac{k^2\theta^2}{4\Omega^2}\right)b_k - \mu(b_{k-2} + b_{k+2}) + \frac{\Delta}{\pi}\frac{k\theta}{2\Omega} a_k &= 0 \qquad (k = 3, 5, \cdots),
\end{aligned} \tag{2.5}$$

[15] This method was applied by Rayleigh [1], for investigating the conditions necessary for "sustaining motion." See also Andronov and Leontovich [1].

where Δ denotes the decrement of damping of the free vibrations of a rod loaded by a constant component of the longitudinal force,

$$\Delta = \frac{2\pi\varepsilon}{\omega\sqrt{1-(P_0/P_*)}} . \tag{2.6}$$

Equating the determinant of the homogeneous system (2.5) to zero, we obtain an equation for the boundary frequencies:

$$\begin{vmatrix} \cdots & \cdots & \cdots & \cdots \\ 1-\dfrac{9\theta^2}{4\Omega^2} & -\mu & 0 & -\dfrac{\Delta}{\pi}\dfrac{3\theta}{2\Omega} \\ -\mu & 1+\mu-\dfrac{\theta^2}{4\Omega^2} & -\dfrac{\Delta}{\pi}\dfrac{\theta}{2\Omega} & 0 \\ 0 & \dfrac{\Delta}{\pi}\dfrac{\theta}{2\Omega} & 1-\mu-\dfrac{\theta^2}{4\Omega^2} & -\mu \\ \dfrac{\Delta}{\pi}\dfrac{3\theta}{2\Omega} & 0 & -\mu & 1-\dfrac{9\theta^2}{4\Omega^2} \\ \cdots & \cdots & \cdots & \cdots \end{vmatrix} = 0 . \tag{2.7}$$

This equation makes it possible to calculate the boundaries of the regions of instability which lie near the frequency

$$\theta_* = \frac{2\Omega}{k}, \quad (k = 1, 3, 5, \cdots) .$$

The second equation is obtained by taking a solution in the form of the series

$$f(t) = b_0 + \sum_{k=2,4,6}^{\infty}\left(a_k \sin\frac{k\theta t}{2} + b_k \cos\frac{k\theta t}{2}\right) .$$

A substitution of this series leads to a system of equations:

$$\begin{gathered} b_0 - \mu b_2 = 0 , \\ \left(1-\frac{\theta^2}{\Omega^2}\right)a_2 - \mu a_4 - \frac{\Delta}{\pi}\frac{\theta}{\Omega}b_2 = 0 , \\ \left(1-\frac{\theta^2}{\Omega^2}\right)b_2 - \mu(2b_0 + b_4) + \frac{\Delta}{\pi}\frac{\theta}{\Omega}a_2 = 0 , \\ \left(1-\frac{k^2\theta^2}{4\Omega^2}\right)a_k - \mu(a_{k-2} + a_{k+2}) - \frac{\Delta}{\pi}\frac{k\theta}{2\Omega}b_k = 0 , \\ \left(1-\frac{k^2\theta^2}{4\Omega^2}\right)b_k - \mu(b_{k-2} + b_{k+2}) + \frac{\Delta}{\pi}\frac{k\theta}{2\Omega}a_k = 0 \\ (k = 4, 6, \cdots) . \end{gathered} \tag{2.8}$$

The equation of the boundary frequencies

$$\begin{vmatrix} \cdots & \cdots & \cdots & \cdots & \cdots \\ 1-\frac{4\theta^2}{\Omega^2} & -\mu & 0 & 0 & -\frac{\Delta}{\pi}\frac{2\theta}{\Omega} \\ -\mu & 1-\frac{\theta^2}{\Omega^2} & 0 & -\frac{\Delta}{\pi}\frac{\theta}{\Omega} & 0 \\ 0 & 0 & 1 & -\mu & 0 \\ 0 & \frac{\Delta}{\pi}\frac{\theta}{\Omega} & -2\mu & 1-\frac{\theta^2}{\Omega^2} & -\mu \\ \frac{\Delta}{\pi}\frac{2\theta}{\Omega} & 0 & 0 & -\mu & 1-\frac{4\theta^2}{\Omega^2} \\ \cdots & \cdots & \cdots & \cdots & \cdots \end{vmatrix} = 0 \qquad (2.9)$$

makes it possible to find the regions of instability which lie near

$$\theta_* = \frac{2\Omega}{k}, \quad (k = 2, 4, 6, \cdots).$$

It is easy to see that, at $\Delta = 0$, the equations obtained coincide with the equations of the conservative problem, (1.28), (1.29) and (1.30).

Furthermore, let us consider the case where $\mu \to 0$, corresponding to an infinitely small amplitude of the longitudinal force. For this case, the determinant (2.7) takes the form

$$\Delta(\theta) = \Delta_1(\theta) \cdot \Delta_3(\theta) \cdots \Delta_k(\theta) \cdots, \qquad (2.10)$$

where

$$\Delta_k(\theta) = \begin{vmatrix} 1-\frac{k^2\theta^2}{4\Omega^2} & -\frac{\Delta}{\pi}\frac{k\theta}{2\Omega} \\ \frac{\Delta}{\pi}\frac{k\theta}{2\Omega} & 1-\frac{k^2\theta^2}{4\Omega^2} \end{vmatrix}.$$

One can write the determinant (2.9) in an analogous form

$$\Delta(\theta) = \Delta_2(\theta) \cdot \Delta_4(\theta) \cdots \Delta_k(\theta) \cdots, \qquad (2.11)$$

where $\Delta_k(\theta)$ is denoted as before.

Since all $\Delta_k(\theta) > 0$, the determinants (2.10) and (2.11) cannot take on zero values. Owing to the uniformity of the determinant, the determinants on the left-hand side of Eq. (2.7) and, respectively, Eq. (2.9), are not equal to zero for a sufficiently small value of the exciting parameter. In other words, in the presence of damping, the loss of dynamic stability of the straight form of the rod can occur only at values of the amplitude of the longitudinal force greater than a certain minimum value.

The determinantion of these values (which we will subsequently call *critical*) is of general practical interest.

§ 9. Determination of the Critical Values of the Excitation Parameter

•1. We will begin with the principal region of instability, for which purpose we retain the central elements in the determinant (2.7)

$$\begin{vmatrix} 1+\mu-\dfrac{\theta^2}{4\Omega^2} & -\dfrac{\Delta}{\pi}\dfrac{\theta}{2\Omega} \\ \dfrac{\Delta}{\pi}\dfrac{\theta}{2\Omega} & 1-\mu-\dfrac{\theta^2}{4\Omega^2} \end{vmatrix} = 0\,. \tag{2.12}$$

Solving Eq. (2.12) with respect to the exciting frequency, we obtain

$$\theta_* = 2\Omega\sqrt{1-\tfrac{1}{2}\left(\frac{\Delta}{\pi}\right)^2 \pm \sqrt{\left(\mu^2-\left(\frac{\Delta}{\pi}\right)^2+\tfrac{1}{4}\left(\frac{\Delta}{\pi}\right)^4\right.}}\,.$$

Since the decrement of damping Δ is usually very small compared to unity ($\Delta = 0.01 - 0.05$), we can simplify this formula by neglecting the terms containing higher powers of Δ/π:

$$\theta_* = 2\Omega\sqrt{1 \pm \sqrt{\mu^2-\left(\frac{\Delta}{\pi}\right)^2}}\,. \tag{2.13}$$

Let us investigate Eq. (2.13). As long as the expression under the inner radical is positive for the boundary frequency, this formula gives two real values which correspond to two boundaries of the principal region of instability. The limiting case (Fig. 12)

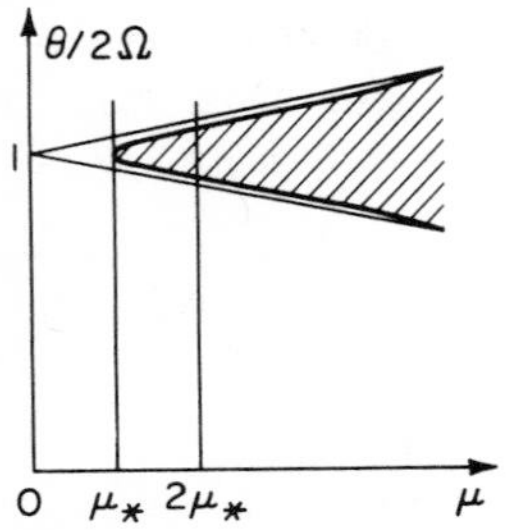

FIG. 12.

$$\mu^2-\left(\frac{\Delta}{\pi}\right)^2 = 0$$

defines the minimum value of the excitation parameter for which the occurrence of undamped vibrations is still possible. Thus, the critical value of the excitation parameter is

$$\mu_{*1} = \frac{\Delta}{\pi}\,. \tag{2.14}$$

Equation (2.14) shows that the greater the damping, the greater the amplitude of longitudinal force required to cause dynamic instability of the rod. Note that the influence of damping is significant only for small excitation parameters. Therefore, the boundaries of the regions of instability determined by Eqs. (1.34) and (2.13) practically coincide for $\mu > 2\mu_*$.

●2. We will now determine the boundaries of the second region of instability. Equating the determinant composed of the central elements of the determinant (2.9) to zero, we have

$$\begin{vmatrix} 1-\dfrac{\theta^2}{\Omega^2} & 0 & -\dfrac{\Delta}{\pi}\dfrac{\theta}{\Omega} \\ 0 & 1 & -\mu \\ \dfrac{\Delta}{\pi}\dfrac{\theta}{\Omega} & -2\mu & 1-\dfrac{\theta^2}{\Omega^2} \end{vmatrix} = 0\,.$$

The solution of this equation gives:

$$\theta_* = \Omega\sqrt{1-\mu^2 \pm \sqrt{\mu^4-\left(\frac{\Delta}{\pi}\right)^2(1-\mu^2)}}\,. \tag{2.15}$$

The minimum value of μ for which Eq. (2.15) gives two real values for the frequency is found from the condition

$$\mu^4 - \left(\frac{\Delta}{\pi}\right)^2 (1 - \mu^2) = 0 .$$

Solving this equation we find, approximately,

$$\mu_{*2} = \sqrt{\frac{\Delta}{\pi}} . \tag{2.16}$$

For determining the boundaries of the third region of instability, we return to Eq. (2.7), retaining in it all the elements written out. It is difficult to obtain an exact solution of such an equation. Therefore, we will substitute the approximate value of the boundary frequency $\theta_* = 2\Omega/3$ in all the elements. This only slightly influences the final result in all but the upper and lower diagonal elements. Equation (2.7) can be re-written then in the form

$$\begin{vmatrix} \xi & -\mu & 0 & -\Delta/\pi \\ 0 & (8/9 + \mu) & -\Delta/3\pi & 0 \\ 0 & \Delta/3\pi & (8/9 - \mu) & -\mu \\ \Delta/\pi & 0 & -\mu & \xi \end{vmatrix} = 0 ,$$

where for simplification we let

$$\xi = 1 - \frac{9\theta^2}{4\Omega^2} .$$

Resolving the determinant and neglecting quantities of the order of $(\Delta/\pi)^4$, $(\Delta/\pi)^6$, etc., we obtain

$$\xi = \frac{8/9\,\mu^2 \pm \sqrt{\mu^6 - (\Delta/\pi)^2[(64/81) - (2/3)\,\mu^2]}}{(64/81) - \mu^2} . \tag{2.17}$$

The boundary frequency is calculated by

$$\theta_* = \frac{2\Omega}{3}\sqrt{1 - \xi} \tag{2.18}$$

where ξ is determined from Eq. (2.17). One can see from Eqs. (2.17) and (2.18) that the third resonance occurs only when

$$\frac{\Delta}{\pi} < \frac{\mu^3}{(64/81) - (2/3)\mu^2}$$

which gives, approximately,

$$\mu_{*3} = \sqrt[3]{\frac{\Delta}{\pi}} . \tag{2.19}$$

Combining Eqs. (2.14), (2.16) and (2.19), we conclude that for the excitation of vibrations at the critical frequency of the kth order

$$\theta_* = \frac{2\Omega}{k} , \quad (k = 1, 2, 3, \cdots) ,$$

it is necessary that the coefficient of excitation exceed the critical value

$$\mu_{*k} = \sqrt[k]{\frac{\Delta}{\pi}}, \quad (k = 1, 2, 3, \cdots). \tag{2.20}$$

● **3.** Now we can finally say why the principal region of instability is the most critical.

A graph of the distribution of the regions of instability including damping is presented in Figure 13. The graph differs from the corresponding graph for the conservation problem (Fig. 5). The presence of damping cuts off that part of the regions of instability which borders on the axis of the ordinate, and makes impossible the onset of resonance for sufficiently small coefficients of excitation. It is interesting to note that the effect of damping, which is not essential for determining the principal region of instability, becomes particularly noticeable with respect to the secondary regions. This is seen not only from Figure 13 but from Figure 14 as well, where the dependence of the critical excitation parameter of the damped rod is shown.

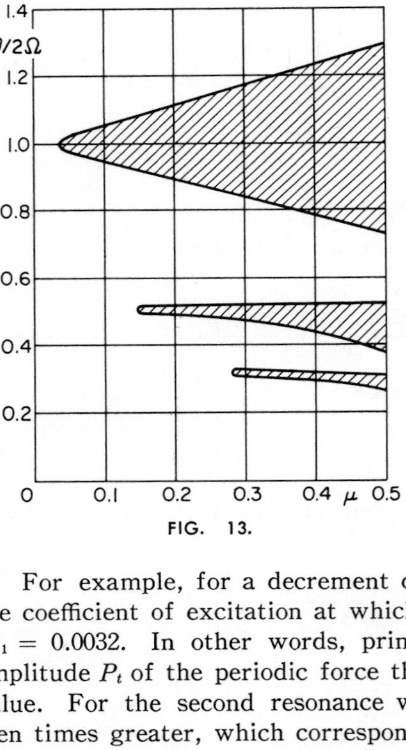

FIG. 13.

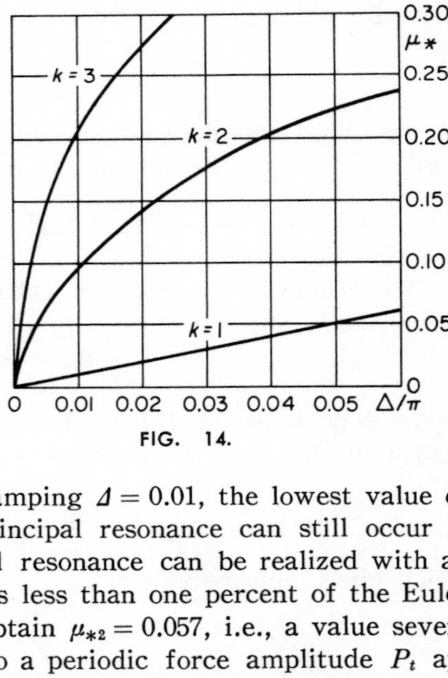

FIG. 14.

For example, for a decrement of damping $\Delta = 0.01$, the lowest value of the coefficient of excitation at which principal resonance can still occur is $\mu_{*1} = 0.0032$. In other words, principal resonance can be realized with an amplitude P_t of the periodic force that is less than one percent of the Euler value. For the second resonance we obtain $\mu_{*2} = 0.057$, i.e., a value seventeen times greater, which corresponds to a periodic force amplitude P_t approximately 12 percent of the Euler value. Still larger longitudinal forces are required in order to excite the third, fourth, and higher orders of resonances. Such values of the excitation parameter are seldom encountered in engineering practice.

The considerations mentioned above show the important role damping plays in problems of dynamic stability of elastic systems. Unfortunately a systematic study of the damping of engineering structures is not available. More studies have been made on that part of damping that is related to the dissipation of energy in the material of vibrating structures. But even in machine elements where the character of the work tends to reduce the external loss of energy to a minimum, the internal dissipation of energy comprises only a small part of the general losses. In structures, the role of the external loss (the loss in the supports and couplings, and the loss in the environment) is undoubtedly much greater. Therefore, it is possible only to indicate approximately the limits of the variation of the decrements of damping (for steel constructions $\varDelta = 0.005$–0.05).

In any case, the above analysis shows that the principal region of instability is the most critical; the second and, even more so, the third regions of instability can occur only with sufficiently large amplitudes of the longitudinalforce.

§ 10. The General Case of An Arbitrary Periodic Load

Above we considered in detail the case of a harmonically varying longitudinal force. For the more general case of periodic loading, we shall confine ourselves to a brief discussion.

It is evident that all the arguments mentioned in § 7 are also valid for the case where the loading is given in the form of the series

$$P(t) = P_0 + \sum_{k=1}^{\infty} P_{tk} \cos k\theta t \,.$$

The differential equation of the problem will be

$$f'' + 2\varepsilon f' + \Omega^2\Big(1 - \sum_{k=1}^{\infty} 2\mu_k \cos k\theta t\Big) f = 0\,, \tag{2.21}$$

where

$$\mu_k = \frac{P_{tk}}{2(P_* - P_0)}\,.$$

The periodic solutions of Eq. (2.21) correspond, as before, to the boundaries of the regions of dynamic instability. Letting

$$f(t) = \sum_{k=1,3,5}^{\infty} \left(a_k \sin\frac{k\theta t}{2} + b_k \cos\frac{k\theta t}{2}\right),$$

we arrive at the equation of the critical frequencies:

$$\begin{vmatrix} \cdots & \cdots & \cdots & \cdots \\ 1+\mu_3-\dfrac{9\theta^2}{4\Omega^2} & -(\mu_1+\mu_2) & 0 & -\dfrac{\varDelta}{\pi}\dfrac{3\theta}{2\Omega} \\ -(\mu_1+\mu_2) & 1+\mu_1-\dfrac{\theta^2}{4\Omega^2} & -\dfrac{\varDelta}{\pi}\dfrac{\theta}{2\Omega} & 0 \\ 0 & \dfrac{\varDelta}{\pi}\dfrac{\theta}{2\Omega} & 1-\mu_1-\dfrac{\theta^2}{4\Omega^2} & -(\mu_1-\mu_2) \\ \dfrac{\varDelta}{\pi}\dfrac{3\theta}{2\Omega} & 0 & -(\mu_1-\mu_2) & 1-\mu_3-\dfrac{9\theta^2}{4\Omega^2} \\ \cdots & \cdots & \cdots & \cdots \end{vmatrix} = 0\,. \tag{2.22}$$

This equation makes it possible to calculate the boundaries of all the odd regions of instability. For the even regions of instability, we obtain

$$\begin{vmatrix} \cdots & \cdots & \cdots & \cdots & \cdots \\ 1+\mu_4-\frac{4\theta^2}{\Omega^2} & -(\mu_1+\mu_3) & 0 & 0 & -\frac{\Delta}{\pi}\frac{2\theta}{\Omega} \\ -(\mu_1+\mu_3) & 1+\mu_2-\frac{\theta^2}{\Omega^2} & 0 & -\frac{\Delta}{\pi}\frac{\theta}{\Omega} & 0 \\ 0 & 0 & 1 & -\mu_1 & 0 \\ 0 & \frac{\Delta}{\pi}\frac{\theta}{\Omega} & -2\mu_1 & 1-\mu_2-\frac{\theta^2}{\Omega^2} & -(\mu_1-\mu_3) \\ \frac{\Delta}{\pi}\frac{2\theta}{\Omega} & 0 & 0 & -(\mu_1-\mu_3) & 1-\mu_4-\frac{4\theta^2}{\Omega^2} \\ \cdots & \cdots & \cdots & \cdots & \cdots \end{vmatrix} = 0\,. \quad (2.23)$$

In the first approximation we will neglect the mutual effect of separate harmonics in the expansion of the longitudinal force. The determinants (2.22) and (2.23) break down into separate equations:

$$\begin{vmatrix} 1+\mu_k-\frac{k^2\theta^2}{4\Omega^2} & -\frac{\Delta}{\pi}\frac{k\theta}{\Omega} \\ \frac{\Delta}{\pi}\frac{k\theta}{\Omega} & 1-\mu_k-\frac{k^2\theta^2}{4\Omega^2} \end{vmatrix} = 0\,, \qquad (k=1,2,3,\cdots)\,. \quad (2.24)$$

From Eq. (2.24) we can find a relationship between the parameters that must be satisfied in order to excite the first, second, and higher resonances:

$$\mu_k > \frac{\Delta}{\pi}\,, \qquad (k=1,3,5,\cdots)\,. \quad (2.25)$$

According to this formula, the formation of the kth resonance depends solely on the kth harmonic of the longitudinal force. To take into account the influence of the remaining harmonics, one must retain the additional elements in the determinants (2.22) and (2.23).

As an example, we shall investigate the case of the piecewise constant law of variation of the longitudinal force (§ 5, ● 4). In this case

$$\mu_k = \frac{4\mu}{\pi k}\,, \qquad (k=1,3,5,\cdots)$$

and Eq. (2.25) gives

$$\mu > \frac{k\Delta}{4}\,, \qquad (k=1,3,5,\cdots)\,.$$

It is easily seen that in the case of piecewise constant longitudinal force, the danger of secondary resonances is somewhat greater. Thus at a decrement of damping $\Delta = 0.01$, the third resonance can occur with an excitation parameter of

$$\mu = \frac{3(0.01)}{4} = 0.0075$$

(instead of $\mu = 0.253$, as in the case of a harmonic longitudinal force).

In the example investigated, the boundaries of the regions of instability can be determined with the same accuracy by application of the criteria mentioned in § 7, ●2. In fact, the characteristic roots in this case can be found directly from Eq. (1.19), where A is determined according to Eq. (1.24). The equation for the computation of the boundaries of the regions of instability has the form

$$\varepsilon T = \ln |\bar{A} \pm \sqrt{\bar{A}^2 - 1}|,$$

where $$\bar{A} = \left| \cos \frac{p\pi_1}{\theta} \cos \frac{\pi p_2}{\theta} - \frac{p_1^2 + p_2^2}{2p_1 p_2} \sin \frac{\pi p_1}{\theta} \sin \frac{\pi p_2}{\theta} \right| .$$

Three

DETERMINATION OF NONLINEAR TERMS

§ 11. Preliminary Remarks

According to linear theory, one expects the vibration amplitudes in the regions of dynamic instability to increase unboundedly with time and indeed very rapidly, i.e., to increase exponentially. However, this conclusion contradicts experimental results that show that vibrations with steady-state amplitudes exist in the instability regions. The first portion of the oscillogram in Figure 8 shows that the amplitude of the vibrations increases approximately exponentially. As the amplitudes increase, the character of the vibrations changes; the speed of the growth gradually decreases until vibrations of constant (or almost constant) amplitude are finally established.

The forces acting upon a rod can be considered to be linear functions of displacements, velocities, and accelerations only for sufficiently small deflections. With increasing amplitudes, the influence of nonlinear factors becomes more and more apparent, i.e., these factors limit the infinite increase of amplitudes predicted by linear theory. Therefore, we cannot determine according to linear theory either the magnitude of the steady-state amplitudes or whether or not the vibrations become stationary. Consideration of the preceding questions is possible only on the basis of nonlinear differential equations.

The question arises of whether or not the presence of nonlinear factors introduces some changes in the distribution of regions of instability given by linear theory. This is not the case. The boundaries of the regions of dynamic instability can be given accurately by the linear differential equations.

Although rigorous investigation of this question will be postponed until Chapter 16, in the meantime let us refer to its analogy with the problems of static stability, for example, to the problem of the buckling of a straight rod subjected to a static longitudinal force. If one linearizes the equations of the problem, it is known that one obtains the correct magnitude of the critical force (Euler buckling force); however, the deflections of the rod in the critical and post-critical regions cannot be determined. For the determination of these deflections, one must take an exact (nonlinear) expression of the curvature.

The idea that the linear approximation is sufficient for determining the dynamic stability of a rod was first clearly formulated by Gol'denblat [2].

However, contrary assertions can frequently be found; Beliaev [1] assumed that the consideration of the nonlinear curvature must in some manner influence the regions of dynamic instability.

For a more precise determination of the boundaries of the regions of instability at large values of P_t, Beliaev proposed to make use of "differential equations for a slightly curved rod". Analogous assumptions have been repeatedly made.

An investigation of the relationship between linear and nonlinear theory is of basic importance to the problems under consideration. We will return to this question in the second part of the book, where we will relate it to the results of the Liapunov theory of the stability of motion.

§ 12. Buckling in the Postcritical Region

In the present chapter, we will analyze the nonlinearities on which the amplitudes of parametrically excited vibrations depend. We will begin with the simplest problem of strength of materials in which it is necessary to consider the effect of a nonlinearity, i.e., we will begin with the problem of the bending of a straight rod by a longitudinal force that exceeds the Euler buckling value (Fig. 15). The equation for the buckling (elastic line) has the form

$$\frac{1}{\rho} + \frac{Pv}{EJ} = 0 , \qquad (3.1)$$

where $1/\rho$ is the exact expression for the curvature. The distance measured along the arc of the deformed rod is taken as an independent variable. If the axial deformation along the rod axis is disregarded, then the arc length coincides with the x-coordinate for the undeformed rod.

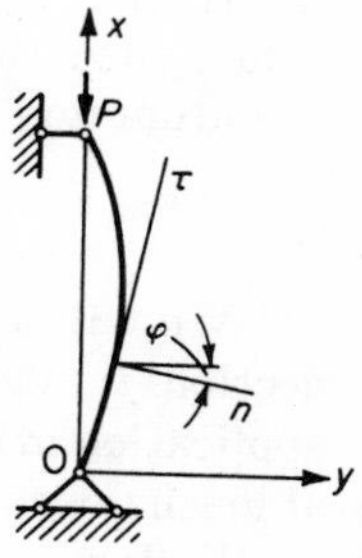

Let s be the arc length and φ the angle between the ox-axis and the tangent of the elastic line (Fig. 15). Considering that $\sin \varphi = dv/ds$ and differentiating this expression along the arc length s, we obtain

$$\frac{d^2v}{ds^2} = \cos \varphi \cdot \frac{d\varphi}{ds} ,$$

which gives

$$\frac{1}{\rho} = \frac{d\varphi}{ds} = \frac{d^2v}{ds^2} \cdot \frac{1}{\cos \varphi} .$$

Since

$$\cos \varphi = \sqrt{1 - \sin^2 \varphi} = \sqrt{1 - \left(\frac{dv}{ds}\right)^2},$$

we obtain the following expression for the curvature:

FIG. 15.

$$\frac{dv}{dx} = \tan\varphi \qquad \frac{dv}{ds} = \sin\varphi , \quad \frac{dx}{ds} = \cos\varphi$$

$$\frac{1}{\rho} = \frac{\frac{d^2v}{dx^2}}{\left[1 + \left(\frac{dv}{dx}\right)^2\right]^{3/2}} = \frac{\frac{d^2v}{dx^2}}{\left[1 + \tan^2\varphi\right]^{3/2}}$$

$$\frac{1}{\rho} = \cos^3\varphi \, \frac{d^2v}{dx^2} \qquad \frac{dv}{dx} = \tan\varphi$$

$$\frac{1}{\rho} = \cos^3\varphi \, \frac{d\varphi}{dx} \qquad \frac{d^2v}{dx^2} = \sec^2\varphi \, \frac{d\varphi}{dx}$$

$$\frac{1}{\rho} = \frac{d\varphi}{ds} \qquad \frac{d^2v}{dx} = \sec^2\varphi \cdot \frac{d\varphi}{ds} \cdot \frac{ds}{dx}$$

$$= \sec^2\varphi \cdot \frac{d\varphi}{ds} \cdot \frac{1}{\cos\varphi}$$

$$= \sec^3\varphi \, \frac{d\varphi}{ds}$$

$$\frac{1}{\rho} = \frac{\dfrac{d^2v}{ds^2}}{\sqrt{1-\left(\dfrac{dv}{ds}\right)^2}} .$$

Equation (3.1) for the buckling of a rod takes the form

$$\frac{\dfrac{d^2v}{ds^2}}{\sqrt{1-\left(\dfrac{dv}{ds}\right)^2}} + \frac{Pv}{EJ} = 0 . \tag{3.2}$$

This nonlinear differential equation can be reduced to a form more conveniently solved. Expanding the radical by the binomial formula

$$\left[1-\left(\frac{dv}{ds}\right)^2\right]^{-1/2} = 1 + \frac{1}{2}\left(\frac{dv}{ds}\right)^2 + \frac{3}{8}\left(\frac{dv}{ds}\right)^4 + \cdots , \tag{3.3}$$

we rewrite Eq. (3.2) in the following form:

$$\frac{d^2v}{ds^2}\left[1 + \frac{1}{2}\left(\frac{dv}{ds}\right)^2 + \frac{3}{8}\left(\frac{dv}{ds}\right)^4 + \cdots\right] + \frac{Pv}{EJ} = 0 . \tag{3.4}$$

The first term in Eq. (3.3) corresponds to the usual linear approximation in strength of materials. We obtain the first nonlinear approximation by retaining two terms in Eq. (3.3); such an approximation will be suitable for deflections that are not large.

If the longitudinal force does not greatly exceed the Euler buckling value, then the elastic curve differs only slightly from the form of the first eigenfunction of the linear problem:

$$v(s) = f \sin \frac{\pi s}{l} . \tag{3.5}$$

We will use the Galerkin variational method for finding the unknown deflection f. Variational methods recently have found greater and more effective application in different divisions of the applied theory of elasticity and structural mechanics; we assume that the reader is familiar with these methods.[16]

Following the Galerkin method, we substitute Eq. (3.5) into the left-hand side of differential equation (3.4) and require the resulting equation to be orthogonal to the selected function $\sin \pi s/l$:

$$\int_0^l \left\{\frac{d^2v}{ds^2}\left[1 + \frac{1}{2}\left(\frac{dv}{ds}\right)^2 + \frac{3}{8}\left(\frac{dv}{ds}\right)^4 + \cdots\right] + \frac{Pv}{EJ}\right\} \sin \frac{\pi s}{l} ds = 0 .$$

On integration,

$$\int_0^l \sin \frac{\pi s}{l} ds = \frac{l}{2} , \qquad \int_0^l \cos^2 \frac{\pi s}{l} \sin^2 \frac{\pi s}{l} ds = \frac{l}{8} ,$$

$$\int_0^l \cos^4 \frac{\pi s}{l} \sin^2 \frac{\pi s}{l} ds = \frac{l}{16} ,$$

16 See Pratusevich [1] for a preliminary discussion. See Lanczos [1] and Wang [1] for readings in English.

and we obtain

$$\left(1 + \frac{\pi^2 f^2}{8l^2} + \frac{3}{32}\frac{\pi^4 f^4}{l^4} + \cdots\right) f - \frac{P}{P_*} f = 0 \tag{3.6}$$

for the determination of f. Here, as before,

$$P_* = \frac{\pi^2 EJ}{l^2}.$$

One possible solution of Eq. (3.6) is $f = 0$; this solution obviously corresponds to the initial (uncurved) shape of the rod. The nonzero solutions can be found from the condition

$$1 + \frac{\pi^2 f^2}{8l^2} + \frac{3}{32}\frac{\pi^4 f^4}{l^4} + \cdots - \frac{P}{P_*} = 0. \tag{3.7}$$

If higher powers of f are neglected in Eq. (3.7), we obtain the well-known approximate equation[17]

$$f = \frac{2\sqrt{2}}{\pi} l \sqrt{\frac{P}{P_*} - 1}. \tag{3.8}$$

A comparison with the exact solution of the same problem, using elliptical integrals, shows that Eq. (3.8) gives good results for $f < 0.2l$; consequently, $P < 1.045\, P_*$. In order to obtain the second approximation, one should retain the f^4 terms, and so on.

Note that this equation and also the equations for the higher approximations can be obtained as a special case from the results of Euler [1]. In some later works a correction to the second approximation was calculated incorrectly, as indicated by Nikolai [1].

§ 13. Nonlinear Elasticity

● 1. Let us return to the problem of the dynamic stability of a simply supported straight rod that is compressed by a periodic longitudinal force. We proceed from the equation

extra additional Term

$$f'' + 2\varepsilon f' + \Omega^2(1 - 2\mu \cos \theta t) f + \varphi(f, f', f'') = 0 \tag{3.9}$$

which differs from Eq. (2.1) only by a certain nonlinear function $\varphi(f, f', f'')$ of displacements, velocities, and accelerations. The determination of this function is our next problem.

Among the terms entering into the nonlinear function $\varphi(f, f', f'')$, it is always possible to single out terms that do not contain derivatives of displacements with respect to time. Formally these nonlinear terms characterize the nonlinear elasticity of the system. Taking this into account, we will group all the static nonlinear factors under the general designation of *nonlinear elasticity*, regardless of whether they are of a geometrical or physical origin.

Nonlinear elasticity is the only nonlinear factor in the problem of the

[17] See, for example, Biezeno and Grammel [1], Vol. I.

bending of a rod by a force exceeding the Euler buckling load. The corresponding equation can be obtained from Eq. (3.9) if we assume $f = \text{const.}$ and eliminate terms explicitly dependent on time. As a result, we obtain

$$\Omega^2 f + \phi(f) = 0$$

or

$$\left(1 - \frac{P}{P_*}\right)f + \frac{1}{\omega^2}\phi(f) = 0 \, .$$

$$\Omega_k = \omega_k \sqrt{1 - \frac{P_0}{P_{*k}}}$$

$$P_{*k} = \frac{k^2\pi^2 EJ}{l^2}$$

$$J = I \qquad (3.10)$$

Comparing Eq. (3.10) with Eq. (3.6) we conclude that the nonlinear function corresponding to the complete expression for the curvature has the form

$$\phi(f) = \omega^2 f\left(\frac{\pi^2 f^2}{8l^2} + \frac{3}{32}\frac{\pi^4 f^4}{l^4} + \cdots\right).$$

This means that the function $\phi(t)$, which takes into account the influence of the nonlinear curvature, can be represented in the form of a series containing odd powers of the deflection:

$$\phi(f) = \sum_{k=1}^{\infty} \gamma_k f^{2k+1}; \qquad (3.11)$$

where

$$\gamma_1 = \frac{\pi^2\omega^2}{8l^2}, \qquad \gamma_2 = \frac{3}{32}\frac{\pi^4\omega^4}{l^4}, \cdots .$$

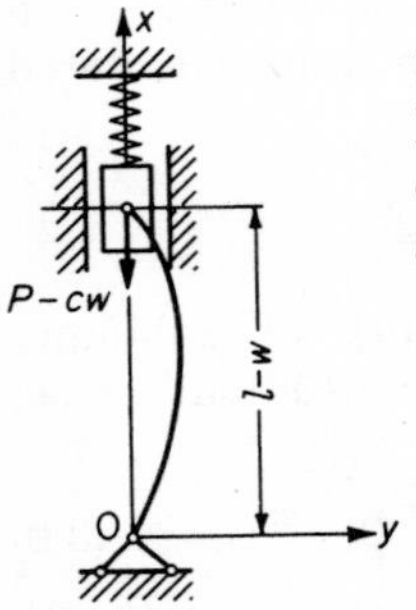

FIG. 16.

It can be shown that consideration of certain other nonlinearities also leads to nonlinear functions of the type (3.11). For example, let us examine a rod with a longitudinal elastic coupling (Fig. 16). During vibration, an additional force arises from the reaction of the spring:

$$\Delta P = -cw \, . \qquad (3.12)$$

The displacement of the moving end of the rod is denoted by w, the stiffness of the spring is denoted by c, and the axial deformation of the rod is not considered.

It is essential that the longitudinal displacement w be nonlinearly related to the transverse deflection of the rod.

The longitudinal displacement of the moving end can be found as the difference between the initial length l and the projection of its deformed center line:

$$w = l - \int_0^l \cos\varphi \, ds = l - \int_0^l \sqrt{1 - \left(\frac{dv}{ds}\right)^2} \, ds \, .$$

Expansion of the radical in a series:

$$\sqrt{1 - \left(\frac{dv}{ds}\right)^2} = 1 - \frac{1}{2}\left(\frac{dv}{ds}\right)^2 - \frac{1}{8}\left(\frac{dv}{ds}\right)^4 + \cdots$$

and termwise integration gives

$$w = \frac{1}{2}\int_0^l \left(\frac{dv}{ds}\right)^2 ds + \frac{1}{8}\int_0^l \left(\frac{dv}{ds}\right)^4 ds + \cdots . \tag{3.13}$$

The first term of this series appears frequently as an expression for the deflection of the moving end of a rod.

If we substitute the expression

$$v(s, t) = f(t) \sin \frac{\pi s}{l}$$

into Eq. (3.13) and use the definite integrals

$$\int_0^l \cos^2 \frac{\pi s}{l} ds = \frac{l}{2}, \qquad \int_0^l \cos^4 \frac{\pi s}{l} ds = \frac{3}{8} l, \cdots ,$$

we find

$$w = \frac{\pi^2 f^2}{4l} + \frac{3}{64}\frac{\pi^4 f^4}{l^3} + \cdots . \tag{3.14}$$

Taking into account the additional longitudinal force (3.12), the equation of the vibrations of a rod (2.1) takes the form

$$f'' + 2\varepsilon f' + \omega^2\left(1 - \frac{P_0 + P_t \cos \theta t + \Delta P}{P_*}\right) f = 0$$

[compare with Eq. (1.4)]. After substituting Eq. (3.14), we obtain

$$f'' + 2\varepsilon f' + \omega^2\left(1 - \frac{P_0 + P_t \cos \theta t}{P_*}\right) f + \psi(f) = 0 ,$$

where

$$\psi(f) = \frac{\pi^2 \omega^2 c}{4lP_*} f^3 + \frac{3}{64}\frac{\pi^4 \omega^2 c}{l^3 P_*} f^5 + \cdots ;$$

Thus, a consideration of a longitudinal elastic spring also results in a nonlinear function of the type (3.11). In further considerations, we will limit ourselves to nonlinear terms not exceeding third order and will write the nonlinear function in the form

$$\psi(f) = \gamma f^3 . \tag{3.15}$$

The *coefficient of nonlinear elasticity*[18] is

$$\gamma = \frac{\pi^2 \omega^2}{8l^2}\left(\frac{2cl}{P_*} + 1\right), \tag{3.16}$$

where the second term accounts for the effect of nonlinear curvature. It is seen from this formula that, with accuracy to within quantities of third order, the influence of the nonlinear curvature is equivalent to the influence of a longitudinal elastic coupling with a spring stiffness

$$c = \frac{\pi^2 EJ}{2l^3} .$$

[18] More exactly, it is the coefficient of the cubic term in the developed series.

●**2.** Nonlinearities of the above type often arise in applications, for example in rods of statically indeterminate systems which remain geometrically unchanged after the rods are unloaded (so-called redundant rods).

In fact, during the bending of such rods their ends approach one another, causing additional elastic forces to appear in the remaining part of the system which tends to hinder the approach of the ends. Since the approach of the ends described by Eq. (3.14) is nonlinearly related to the deflections of the rod, the elastic forces also have a nonlinear character.

Nonlinear elastic forces can arise also in systems that are usually treated as statically determinate. For example, riveted or welded girders are statically determinate when they are assumed to be pin jointed and statically indeterminate if the resistance of the joints is considered. Still more complicated relations arise in three-dimensional constructions, e.g., in the frames of metal bridges. In determining the nonlinear characteristics of any rod entering into the make-up of a frame structure, the total influence of the three-dimensional construction must be considered.

The presence of nonlinear elasticity influences the carrying capacity of the compressed rods, which lose their stability in the elastic range. It is known that even an insignificant increase of critical force results in dangerous deformations for single rods in which the nonlinear elasticity is dependent on the nonlinear curvature. Therefore, the critical load for such rods can be considered in practice to be equal to the limit load.[19] If a rod is a part of a statically indeterminate system, its deflection in the postcritical stage can be considerably smaller. Let us illustrate this concept with a simple example (Fig. 17).

It is possible for element AB to become unstable when subjected to external loading. To determine the coefficient of resistance for the remaining part of the construction, we compute the approach of endpoints A and B subjected to unit forces (Fig. 17). According to the well-known equation of structural mechanics,

$$\delta_{11} = \sum \frac{\bar{N}_1^2 s}{EF}.$$

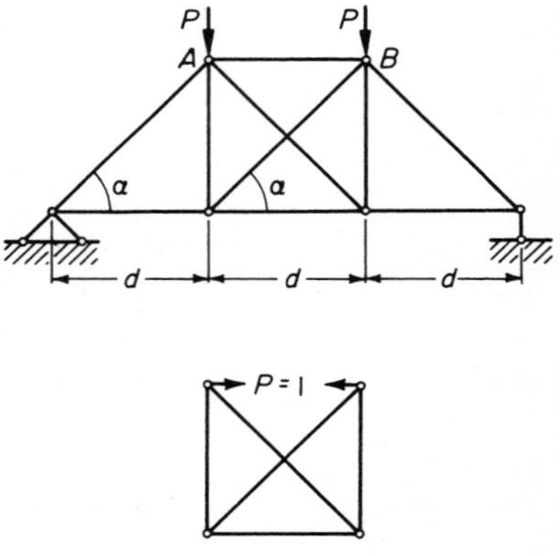

FIG. 17

For simplicity, the areas of all the rods will be assumed to be equal. Computations give

$$\delta_{11} = \frac{d}{EF}\left(1 + 2\tan^3\alpha + \frac{2}{\cos^3\alpha}\right);$$

hence, the coefficient of resistance is

[19] The case of very flexible rods where large deflections occur without yielding and where creep of the material is possible will not be considered.

$$c = \frac{1}{\delta_{11}} = \frac{EF}{d\left(1 + 2\tan^3\alpha + \dfrac{2}{\cos^3\alpha}\right)}.$$

In accordance with Eq. (3.16), the coefficient of nonlinear elasticity is

$$\gamma = \frac{\pi^2\omega^2}{8d^2}\left(\frac{2cd}{P_*} + 1\right).$$

The expression in parentheses can be written in the form

$$\frac{2cd}{P_*} + 1 = \frac{2\lambda^2}{\pi^2\left(1 + 2\tan^3\alpha + \dfrac{2}{\cos^3\alpha}\right)} + 1,$$

where λ is the slenderness ratio of the rod. Following from Eqs. (3.10) and (3.15), the deflection of the middle of the rod is determined from the equation

$$f = \frac{\omega}{\sqrt{\gamma}}\sqrt{\frac{N}{N_*} - 1}$$

or

$$f = \frac{2d\sqrt{2}}{\pi k(\alpha, \lambda)}\sqrt{\frac{N}{N_*} - 1}$$

where N is the longitudinal force in the rod, N_* is its critical value, and k is the nondimensional coefficient

$$k(\alpha, \lambda) = \sqrt{\frac{2\lambda^2}{\pi^2\left(1 + 2\tan^3\alpha + \dfrac{2}{\cos^3\alpha}\right)} + 1}.$$

Since $k(\alpha, \lambda)$ is of the order of magnitude of the slenderness ratio λ (at $\alpha = 45°$ we have $k \approx 0.15\lambda$), the deflection of rod AB can be a tenth the displacement of a single rod.

Further consideration of problems dealing with frame constructions in the postcritical state falls outside the framework of the present book.

●3. We have previously restricted our treatment to the case of an elastic material with linear properties. Nonlinear elastic properties of a material can also be considered with the aid of Eq. (3.11). Since the stress σ and the strain e satisfy the inequality $(d^2\sigma)/(de^2) \leq 0$ for the majority of known materials (Fig. 18), nonlinearity of this kind generally will be "soft" in contrast to "hard" nonlinearity of cases considered earlier.[20]

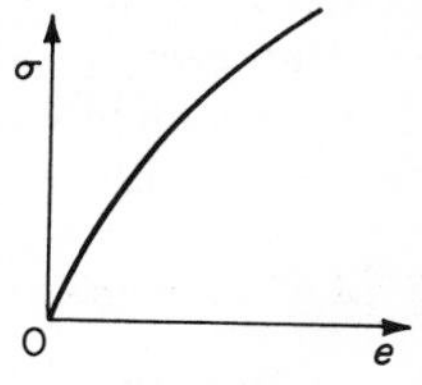

FIG. 18.

For example let the properties of the material be described by the relation

[20] The nonlinearity is called "soft" if the quasi-elastic coefficient decreases with displacement and "hard" if the quasi-elastic coefficient increases with displacement.

$$\sigma = E(e - \beta e^3),$$

where β is a constant. Since plane sections remain plane, we can assume that

$$e = y\frac{d^2v}{dx^2},$$

and we find

$$M = \int_F \sigma y dF = EJ\frac{d^2v}{dx^2} - B\left(\frac{d^2v}{dx^2}\right)^3$$

for the bending moment in the beam cross section, where B is a new constant. After substitution in the ordinary differential equation, the last term on the right-hand side yields a nonlinear function of the form in (3.15) for $\lambda < 0$.

The question arises whether or not the nonlinear function (3.11) can include all the possible cases of nonlinear elasticity. Even in the case where the magnitude of elastic forces depends on the sign of the deflections, we must introduce into (3.11) terms containing even powers of the deflection (nonsymmetrical power characteristic). Furthermore, nonlinear elastic forces exist whose dependence on the deflections cannot be represented in the form of converging power series. The simplest example of this type is the rod with deflection restrictors which are springs (Fig. 19).

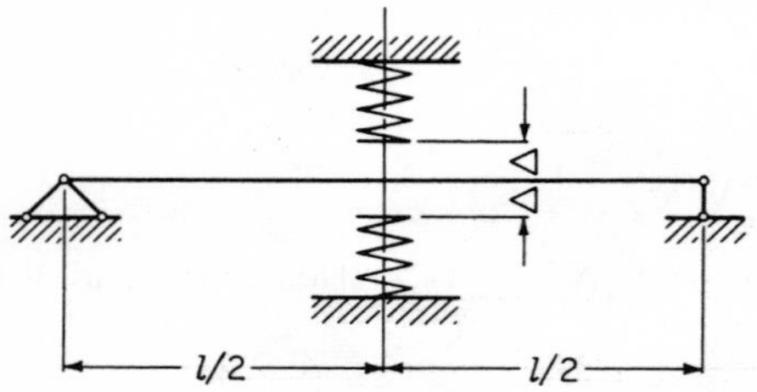

FIG. 19.

Assume that the stiffness of the restrictors is sufficiently small that one can neglect the influence of the additional support on the form of an elastic curve (only in this case can the nonlinearity be considered small). The nonlinear function then takes the form

$$\psi(f) = \begin{cases} 0 & \text{for } |f| \leq \Delta, \\ \dfrac{cl}{2m}f & \text{for } |f| > \Delta, \end{cases}$$

where c is the spring constant of the restrictor. An expression of this kind obviously cannot be represented in the form of a power series.

However, problems of this type are seldom encountered, while functions (3.11) encompass the majority of problems. In all following considerations, we will confine ourselves to the function (3.11).

§ 14. Nonlinear Inertia[21]

● 1. Previously we have considered nonlinear factors of static origin. In

[21] This designates the nonlinear (more exactly, cubic) part of the expression for the inertia effect that enters mechanical problems through the choice of variables. In Lagrangian mechanics, on the other hand, one speaks only generally of inertia forces even if these are described by a nonlinear expression relating the chosen generalized coordinates.

dynamic problems one must also consider nonlinear inertia forces and nonlinear damping.

As an example of *nonlinear inertia*, we will investigate a simple problem by assuming that the mass M_L is concentrated on the moving end of the rod (Fig. 20). In this case the additional longitudinal force

$$\Delta P = -M_L w''$$

arises during vibrations of the rod. As before, $w(t)$ denotes the longitudinal displacement of the moving end,

$$w = \frac{\pi^2}{4l} f^2 + \frac{3}{64}\frac{\pi^4}{l^3} f^4 + \cdots .$$

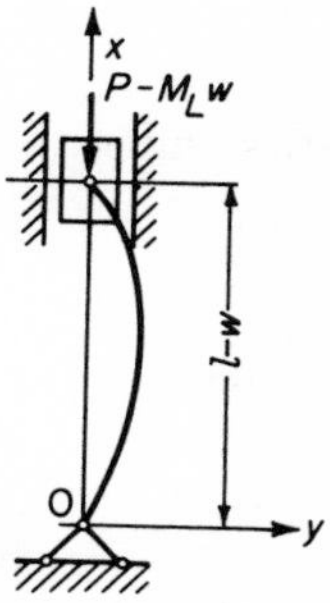

FIG. 20.

By considering this longitudinal force, the differential equation of the transverse vibrations takes the form

$$f'' + 2\varepsilon f' + \omega^2\left(1 - \frac{P_0 + P_t \cos\theta t - M_L w''}{P_*}\right) f = 0 ,$$

where

$$w'' = \frac{\pi^2}{2l}[ff'' + (f')^2] + \frac{3}{16}\frac{\pi^4}{l^3} f^2 [ff'' + 3(f')^2] + \cdots .$$

If we substitute the frequency Ω of the free vibrations of a loaded rod and the excitation parameter μ, we obtain

$$f'' + 2\varepsilon f' + \Omega^2(1 - 2\mu\cos\theta t) f + 2\kappa f[ff'' + (f')^2] = 0 .$$

Terms which are higher than third order have been neglected. The influence of the nonlinear inertia forces is considered in the function

$$\psi(f, f', f'') = 2\kappa f[ff'' + (f')^2] . \tag{3.17}$$

The coefficient

$$\kappa = \frac{\pi^4 M_L}{4ml^3} \tag{3.18}$$

will be called the *coefficient of nonlinear inertia.*

●2. A nonlinear expression of the type of (3.17) was first found in an article by Krylov and Bogoliubov [2] in connection with the investigation of the free vibrations of struts. The necessity to account for this nonlinearity in the case of parametric resonance was indicated in an article by Gol'denblat [2].

The presence of a concentrated mass on the moving end is not the only condition which gives rise to nonlinear inertia forces. During transverse vibrations, every section of the rod undergoes some longitudinal displacement. This displacement is of second order in comparison to the transverse deflection

$$w(x) \approx \frac{1}{2}\int_0^x \left(\frac{\partial v}{\partial \xi}\right)^2 d\xi .$$

Therefore a distributed loading due to the inertia forces,

$$n(x, t) = -m\frac{\partial^2 w}{\partial t^2},$$

acts on the rod. Assume that this longitudinal loading only slightly influences the shape of vibrations, and again take

$$v(x, t) = f(t) \sin \frac{\pi x}{l}. \tag{3.19}$$

After substitution and integration, we find

$$n(x, t) = -\frac{\pi^2 m}{2l^2}\left(x + \frac{l}{2\pi} \sin \frac{2\pi x}{l}\right)[ff'' + (f')^2].$$

Obviously, the additional longitudinal force in each cross section is

$$\Delta N(x, t) = \int_l^{l-x} n(\xi, t)d\xi$$

or, after integration,

$$\Delta N(x, t) = -\frac{\pi^2 m}{4}\left(1 - \frac{x^2}{l^2} - \frac{1}{\pi^2} \sin^2 \frac{\pi x}{l}\right)[ff'' + (f')^2].$$

We will now construct the differential equation of the vibrations of a rod. In contrast to Eq. (1.2), it must contain an additional term that considers the influence of the longitudinal force $\Delta N(x, t)$ as a function of x. By neglecting damping, the equation will have the form

$$EJ\frac{\partial^4 v}{\partial x^4} + (P_0 + P_t \cos \theta t)\frac{\partial^2 v}{\partial x^2} + \frac{\partial}{\partial x}\left(\Delta N\frac{\partial v}{\partial x}\right) + m\frac{\partial^2 v}{\partial t^2} = 0.$$

With the aid of the Galerkin variational method, this can be reduced to an ordinary differential equation. In fact, if we substitute Eq. (3.19), multiply by $\sin \pi x/l$, and integrate, we obtain

$$f'' + \omega^2\left(1 - \frac{P_0 + P_t \cos \theta t}{P_*}\right)f + 2\kappa f[ff'' + (f')^2] = 0,$$

where

$$\kappa = -\frac{\pi^2}{4l^2}\int_0^l \sin \frac{\pi x}{l}\frac{d}{dx}\left[\left(1 - \frac{x^2}{l^2} - \frac{1}{\pi^2} \sin^2 \frac{\pi x}{l}\right) \cos \frac{\pi x}{l}\right]dx.$$

The calculation of this integral gives

$$\kappa = \frac{\pi^4}{4l^2}\left(\frac{1}{3} - \frac{3}{8\pi^2}\right). \tag{3.20}$$

The coefficient κ, determined by Eq. (3.20), takes into account the influence of the inertia forces of the rod itself. Comparing Eqs. (3.18) and (3.20), we see that the inertia forces of the rod have the same influence as an equivalent mass

$$M_L = \left(\frac{1}{3} - \frac{3}{8\pi^2}\right)ml$$

concentrated on the moving end.

●**3.** We shall show how to estimate the magnitude of the coefficient of nonlinear inertia for elements of complicated rod systems. Consider, for example, element AB of the upper boom of a multiple span truss (Fig. 21). Periodic stresses arise in the rods of the truss subjected to external loading:

$$q = q_0 + q_t \cos \theta t \; .$$

The magnitude of these stresses can be calculated by ordinary structural dynamics methods. The truss experinces the usual forced vibrations; additional vibrations of second order amplitudes are superimposed if one of the rods becomes unstable.

If rod AB becomes dynamically unstable, its vibrations will be accompanied by vibrations of the entire truss due to the approach of the ends (expressed by a quantity w). Assuming that the truss is statically determinate (ideal hinges), we obtain the vibration form shown in Figure 21b. The amplitudes obviously are quantities of second order in comparison to the deflection of rod AB. It is important to emphasize that we are concerned with the *additional* deformation of the truss arising only from the approach of the ends of element AB.

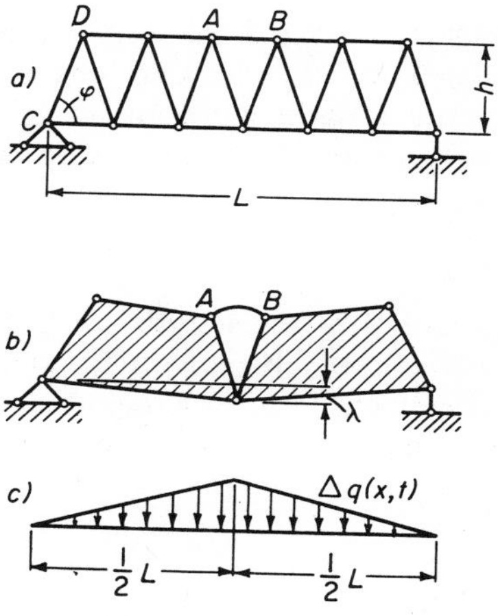

FIG. 21.

We will now calculate the coefficients of nonlinear elasticity. The deflection of the middle of a span can be found from simple geometric considerations and is

$$\lambda = \frac{wL}{4h} \, ,$$

where L is the span of the truss and h is its height. Additional inertia loading on the truss, as seen from Figure 21 c, is

$$\Delta q(x, t) = \begin{cases} -\dfrac{m_q x}{2h} \dfrac{d^2 w}{dt^2} & \text{for} \quad x \leq \dfrac{L}{2} \, , \\ -\dfrac{m_q(L - x)}{2h} \dfrac{d^2 w}{dt^2} & \text{for} \quad x > \dfrac{L}{2} \, , \end{cases}$$

where m_q denotes the sum of the mass of the truss per unit length and the mass of the given distributed load. Hence, one easily finds the additional stress[22] in rod AB:

[22] Our calculation is only approximate; we actually referred all of the mass of the truss and the loading to the lower boom. This type of procedure is often used in "linear" structural dynamics. It appears that this approximate method is sufficiently accurate for practical purposes (see Bernstein [1]).

$$\Delta N = -\frac{m_q L^3}{48h^2}\frac{d^2w}{dt^2}\,. \tag{3.21}$$

As seen from Eq. (3.21), the influence of the inertia forces of the truss on the magnitude of the longitudinal force in the rod is equivalent to the influence of the concentrated mass

$$M_L = \frac{m_q L^3}{48h^2}$$

placed on the moving end of the rod. The coefficient of nonlinear inertia of the rod AB is

$$\kappa \approx \frac{m_q n^3}{2mh^2}\,, \tag{3.22}$$

where m is the mass per unit length of the rod and n is the number of panels of the bottom girder. The coefficient of the nonlinear inertia for other rods is determined in a similar manner. Thus, for the supporting cross strut CD (Fig. 21), we obtain

$$\kappa = \frac{\pi^4(n-1)^2}{6ns^2\cos\varphi}\frac{m_q}{m} \tag{3.23}$$

where s is the length of the strut and φ is the angle it makes with the horizontal. In general, if one considers only the vertical inertia forces, the coefficient κ can be computed by the following approximate formula for beam elements (statically determinate and statically indeterminate) of the truss:

$$\kappa = \frac{\pi^4}{4\mathrm{m}l^3}\int_L m_q(s)\psi^2(s)ds\,. \tag{3.24}$$

In (3.24), $\psi(s)$ are the ordinates of the influence line of a force which results from a unit vertical force in the corresponding element. To derive this formula, we must assume that all of the mass of the rod system can be referred to a definite line, e.g., to the line of action. Then the additional inertia forces can be determined by the formula

$$\Delta q(s,t) = -m_q(s)\psi(s)\frac{d^2w}{dt^2}\,,$$

from which, according to the loading of the influence line, we find

$$\Delta N(t) = -\frac{d^2w}{dt^2}\int_0^L m_q(s)\psi^2(s)ds$$

for the force in the rod. The equivalent mass obviously is

$$M_L = \int_0^L m_q(s)\psi^2(s)ds\,,$$

from which Eq. (3.24) follows. Eqs. (3.22) and (3.23) are its special cases.

Eq. (3.24) can also be easily extended to any rod system; for this purpose the concept of the "influence line" must be interpreted in a broader sense. Other examples for determining the coefficient of nonlinear inertia will be encountered.

§ 15. Nonlinear Damping

●1. The damping of free and forced vibrations has not yet been fully considered. Up to this point, the complex and diverse processes accompanying energy dissipation during vibrations and the influence of a large number of factors that are difficult to take into account by theoretical means, have resulted in the reduction of the effect of damping to the addition of certain "suitable" terms in the equation of the conservative problem. These terms are selected so that the theoretical results are in satisfactory agreement with experimental data. A large number of "hypotheses" of every kind, which do not agree with the experimental data, are characteristic of the present state of the art on damping (see Davidenkov [1] and Panovko [1]).

We will investigate the equation of damped vibrations

$$f'' + \omega^2 f = R(f, f'), \tag{3.25}$$

where $R(f, f')$ is an additional term which considers the resistance forces. The simplest and most widely used expression for the calculation of damping

$$R(f') = -2\varepsilon f' \tag{3.26}$$

(where ε is a constant) leads to the results briefly summarized as follows.

The amplitudes of free vibrations decrease geometrically so that the logarithmic decrement of damping

$$\ln \frac{f(t)}{f(t+T)} = \varepsilon T = \delta \tag{3.27}$$

is independent of the amplitude. The period of the free vibrations is denoted by T:

$$T = \frac{2\pi}{\sqrt{\omega^2 - \varepsilon^2}} \approx \frac{2\pi}{\omega}.$$

The dissipation of energy for one period,

$$\Delta W = -\int_T R(f')df \tag{3.28}$$

is proportional to the square of the amplitude, and the relative dissipation

$$\psi = \frac{\Delta W}{W} \tag{3.29}$$

is independent of the amplitude.[23]

Numerous experiments show, however, that energy loss during vibrations is only slightly dependent on the velocity. (For example, the area of loop of elastic hysteresis is practically independent of the duration of the vibration cycle, i.e., practically independent of the speed of deformation.) At the same

[23] Computations give $\psi = 2\delta$.

time, according to Eq. (3.26), it would seem that the resistance forces are greatly dependent on the velocity. Lately, the "hypothesis of viscous resistance" has often been criticized from this viewpoint.[24] It is proposed to consider instead that the forces of resistance are proportional to the amplitude and oriented in the direction opposite to that of the velocity:

$$R(f, f') = -\psi |f| \operatorname{sign} f', \tag{3.30}$$

where we write

$$\operatorname{sign} f' = \begin{cases} 1 & \text{for } f' > 0, \\ -1 & \text{for } f' < 0 \end{cases}$$

or make use of the "complex modulus," borrowed from acoustics and electrical engineering, etc.

Equation (3.26) does not answer the question of what quantities the resistance forces depend on. It is simply an indirect method of considering damping. Furthermore, there is no basis for interpreting the damping coefficient as a material constant. On the contrary, it is more logical (this is confirmed by experimental data) to consider the corresponding energy dissipation as a material constant or (almost the same thing) the logarithmic decrement of damping. In this case, the "hypothesis of viscous resistance," and also the methods that have been proposed instead, give analogous, and for suitably selected constants, the same results.

We will call the damping *linear* if the relative dissipation energy ψ is independent of the amplitude. One can easily see that this definition is somewhat broader than the one generally used. For example, it also includes the damping described by Eq. (3.30) which is, strictly speaking, nonlinear. For the explicit calculation, we are especially interested not in the change of the damping during the period but in its over-all effect during a period. Its measure is described by the relative dissipation of energy. From this viewpoint, the expressions for the resistance forces given by Eqs. (3.26) and (3.30) are equivalent.

The most detailed investigations on nonlinear damping consider effects of the internal damping in the material. As is known, the energy losses due to internal friction form the most significant part of the general energy dissipation. At the same time, this part lends itself to theoretical considerations.[25]

Among the expressions for the consideration of internal damping, we will indicate only a generalization of the "classical" damping expression (3.26) by

$$R(f') = -h |f'|^k \operatorname{sign} f'.$$

For a determination of constants h and k numerous experiments have been carried out on bending and torsional vibrations. Thus, according to the data of Lunts [1], $k = 2.17$ for steel; according to other data, the index k takes

[24] For a survey of the literature, see Panovko [1].

[25] The physical aspect of the problem of internal friction is discussed, for example, by Kolsky [1].

on values from 2 to 3.

Davidenkov [1] related the magnitude of internal friction to the phenomenon of elastic hysteresis. In order to describe the upper and lower branches of the hysteresis curve $\sigma = \sigma(e)$, he proposed the equation

$$\sigma = E\left\{e \mp \frac{\eta}{n}\left[(e_0 \pm e)^n - 2^{n-1}e_0^n\right]\right\} \tag{3.31}$$

where n and η are material constants and e_0 is the deformation amplitude (Fig. 22). On the basis of Eq. (3.31), a series of special problems were investigated by Pisarenko [1].

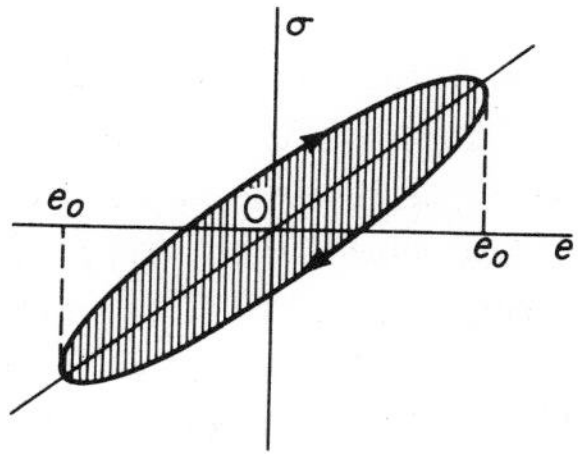

FIG. 22.

● 2. As seen from the above, the usual methods for considering damping can hardly be used for the solution of the stated problem. In particular, resulting nonlinear "hypotheses" are inadequate for two reasons. First, even if one assumes that they are correct, the hypotheses take into account only a comparatively small part of the total dissipation of energy. We have already indicated this (§ 9). Second, the application of these "hypotheses" creates serious mathematical difficulties and they have not been overcome even in the simplest problems of free and forced vibrations. All this stimulates the search for new methods which are more suitable and adaptable to the calculation of damping.

It would appear to be more logical to consider the coefficient of damping in Eq. (3.26) not as a constant but as a function of displacement. Considering that this function must be even, and approximating it by a power series, we obtain the following expression:

$$R(f, f') = -2(\varepsilon + \varepsilon_1 f^2 + \varepsilon_2 f^4 + \cdots)f' \tag{3.32}$$

(here $\varepsilon, \varepsilon_1, \varepsilon_2, \cdots$, are constants to be determined from experiments).

The expression of the type (3.32) is encountered in radio engineering in the theory of vacuum-tube generators. It corresponds to the so-called "soft" condition of the generators when the series of this expression contains the first two terms, and to the "hard" condition (see Teodorchik [1]) when it contains three terms. It is known that problems with nonlinearities of the type (3.32) are readily adaptable to mathematical treatment. An investigation of free vibrations leads to an amplitude-dependent decrement.

In this connection we will consider a recent proposal of Panovko [1]. We will not go into the basic theory of this proposal (the elliptic form of the hysteresis loop and the independence of its area on the frequency), but note only that it corresponds to the expression for the resistance force

$$R(f, f') = -bA^n\sqrt{1 - \frac{f^2}{A^2}}\,\operatorname{sign} f',$$

where A is the amplitude of the vibrations and b and n are constants. Let

$$f = A\cos(\omega t + \lambda),$$

where A is a constant for the forced vibration problem and is a "slowly changing" function of time in the free vibration problem with damping. Then,

$$R(f, f') = -bA^n \sin(\omega t + \lambda)$$

or

$$R(f, f') = -\frac{b}{\omega} A^{n-1} f' . \tag{3.33}$$

For damped vibrations the last equation is approximate.

In a certain sense, Eqs. (3.32) and (3.33) are equivalent. If the damping coefficient is a function of the instantaneous value of displacement in Eq. (3.32), then it is dependent on the amplitude. Eq. (3.33) is simpler, but it is "quasi-linear." It becomes unsuitable, for example, for vibrations with two different frequencies. Independently of this, we are inclined to favor Eq. (3.32) since it can be reduced to the following mechanical considerations.

Let us return to our model (Fig. 16). Together with the usual resistance force, we will consider a friction force that arises from the guidance of the moving support. We will assume that it is proportional to the velocity of the movement of the support:

$$\Delta P = -k_L w' .$$

The equation for the free vibrations of a damped rod takes the form

$$f'' + 2\varepsilon f' + \omega^2\left(1 + \frac{k_L w'}{P}\right) f = 0 \tag{3.34}$$

(compare with § 13 and § 14). By a termwise differentiation of Eq. (3.14), we find

$$w' = \frac{\pi^2}{2l} f f' + \frac{3}{16} \frac{\pi^4}{l^3} f^3 f' + \cdots .$$

Substitution into Eq. (3.34) yields

$$f'' + 2\varepsilon f' + \omega^2 f + \frac{\pi^2 k_L \omega^2}{2lP_*} f^2 f' + \frac{3}{16} \frac{\pi^4 k_L \omega^2}{l^3 P_*} f^4 f' + \cdots = 0 ,$$

which reduces to a nonlinear function of the type (3.32).

If the displacements are small, then the nonlinear function can be confined to terms not higher than third order. This function assumes the form

$$\psi(f, f') = 2\varepsilon_L f^2 f' \tag{3.35}$$

where ε_L is the *coefficient of nonlinear damping*:

$$\varepsilon_L = \frac{\pi^4 k_L}{4ml^3} . \tag{3.36}$$

We will show that if a rod is part of a rod system, the nonlinearity of the damping can be explained by the energy dissipation in the remaining part of the system. This follows from considerations similar to those expressed in § 14.

As long as the amplitudes of the vibrations of the rod are sufficiently small, the energy dissipation actually occurs in the rod itself. Because of the approach of the ends of the rod, additional displacements of the entire truss, which are nonlinearly related to the displacements of the rod, arise for larger amplitudes. It is the energy loss due to these displacements that produces damping that is nonlinear. Under certain additonal assumptions, the coefficient of nonlinear damping for this case can be determined by analytical means.

Let us investigate the truss shown in Figure 21. As is often done, we will represent the resistance forces directed opposite to the motion in the form of a distributed loading that is proportional to the velocity of the motion at every point. Considering that

$$\lambda = \frac{wL}{4h},$$

we obtain

$$\Delta q(x, t) = \begin{cases} -\dfrac{k_q x}{2h} w' & \text{for } x \leq L/2, \\ -\dfrac{k_q (L-x)}{2h} w' & \text{for } x > L/2, \end{cases}$$

where k_q is the resistance coefficient for the truss. An additional longitudinal force

$$\Delta P = -\frac{k_q L^3}{48h^2} w'$$

is formed in the element AB. Thus, the damping in a truss is equivalent to the damping caused by the resistance developed in the moving support that has the coefficient

$$k_L = \frac{k_q L^3}{48h^2}.$$

The coefficient of nonlinear damping will be

$$\varepsilon_L = \frac{\pi^4 k_q L^3}{192 m h^2 l^3}$$

or, approximately,

$$\varepsilon_L = \frac{k_q n^3}{2mh^2}, \tag{3.37}$$

where n is the number of panels of the lower girder. It is seen from Eq. (3.37) that the nonlinear part of the damping increases rapidly as the number of panels of the truss increases.

●**3.** The nonlinear resistances described so far are characterized by the fact that, depending upon the amplitude, their work in a period increases faster than the work of viscous (velocity proportional) *friction.* Somewhat apart from this, we have so-called *dry friction,* which usually is considered constant in magnitude with its direction opposite to that of the velocity:

$$R(f') = -k_0 \operatorname{sign} f'.$$

It is readily seen that the work of dry friction during a period,

$$\Delta W = \int_T k_0 (\operatorname{sign} f')\, df$$

is proportional to the first power of the amplitude, i.e., it increases more slowly than the work of linear viscous friction. Therefore, dry friction, taken separately, cannot explain the presence of steady-state vibrations at parametric resonance.

Dry friction can arise in support attachments where it acts with viscous resistance (combined friction). It is interesting that the presence of dry friction in the moving support produces damping of the *transverse* vibrations of the rod according to a law that is characteristic for a linear resistance. In other words, dry friction in a moving support and viscous resistance of transverse vibration are in a certain sense equivalent. In fact, the frictional force in the moving support is

$$\Delta P = -k_0 \operatorname{sign} w'$$

or[26]

$$\Delta P = -k_0 \operatorname{sign} (ff').$$

A substitution in the equation of free vibration yields

$$f'' + \omega^2 \left[1 + \frac{k_0 \operatorname{sign} (ff')}{P_*}\right] f = 0.$$

But since

$$f \operatorname{sign} (ff') = |f| \operatorname{sign} f',$$

this equation takes the form

$$f'' + \omega^2 f + \frac{k_0 \omega^2}{P_*} |f| \operatorname{sign} f' = 0.$$

Thus, the presence of dry friction in the moving support is considered in the equation of transverse vibrations by the term of the type (3.30), i.e., by a resistance equivalent to the viscous resistance.

26 Terms of higher order obviously do not influence the sign of w'.

Four

FREE AND FORCED VIBRATIONS OF A NONLINEAR SYSTEM

§ 16. Method of Slowly Changing Amplitudes

●1. The modern methods for the investigation of nonlinear vibrations are based on the well-known works of Liapunov [1] and Poincaré [1]; see also Malkin [1].

A rigorous investigation of nonlinear differential equations in the general case leads to serious mathematical difficulties. However, a broad class of differential equations exists which can be solved by effective approximate methods. In particular, the equations describing the vibrations of systems with small nonlinearities belong to this class of equations.

Let us consider the nonlinear differential equation

$$f'' + 2\varepsilon f' + \omega^2 f + \psi(f, f', f'') = 0 . \tag{4.1}$$

By introducing a nondimensional time and a nondimensional displacement, we can write this equation in the form

$$\eta'' + \frac{2\varepsilon}{\omega}\eta' + \eta + \psi(\eta, \eta', \eta'') = 0 .$$

The prime denotes differentiations with respect to the nondimensional time. We will call the nonlinearity small if the condition

$$\left|\frac{\psi(\eta, \eta', \eta'')}{\eta}\right| \ll 1 \tag{4.2}$$

is fulfilled. In addition, we will assume that the damping is small:

$$\frac{2\varepsilon}{\omega} = \frac{\delta}{\pi} \ll 1 . \tag{4.3}$$

As we will see, the problem under consideration will satisfy these conditions.

●2. One of the simplest methods for the solution of differential equations with small nonlinearities is the *method of slowly changing amplitudes* (van der Pol method). Although it is not sufficiently rigorous, it possesses physical clearness. This method is widely applied in radio engineering where it has helped to yield a whole series of important results (Teodorchik [1]).

The basic idea of the method of slowly changing amplitudes is as follows.

If the nonlinearity and the damping of a system are sufficiently small, the solution of the nonlinear equation (4.1), at least during a period, differs only slightly from the solution of the linear differential equation

$$f'' + \omega^2 f = 0 ,$$

i.e., from the harmonic vibration

$$f(t) = a \sin \omega t.$$

It is said, for such a case, that the solution of the differential equation (4.1) is of an almost periodic character. Accordingly, we will seek an approximate solution of Eq. (4.1) in the form

$$f(t) = a(t) \sin \bar{\omega} t ; \tag{4.4}$$

where $\bar{\omega}$ is a frequency that generally differs from the "linear frequency" ω, and $a(t)$ is the "slowly changing amplitude." The expression "slowly changing amplitude" means that the increase in amplitude for the period is small in comparison to its mean value, i.e.,

$$\begin{aligned} \left|\frac{a'}{a}\right| \frac{2\pi}{\omega} &\ll 1 , \\ \left|\frac{a''}{a'}\right| \frac{2\pi}{\omega} &\ll 1 . \end{aligned} \tag{4.5}$$

Since the initial instant of time is arbitrary, we will consider the initial phase angle equal to zero.

We now substitute Eq. (4.4) into the nonlinear function $\psi(f, f', f'')$ and expand it in a Fourier series,

$$\psi(f, f', f'') = \Phi(a, \bar{\omega}) \sin \bar{\omega} t + \psi(a, \bar{\omega}) \cos \bar{\omega} t + \cdots. \tag{4.6}$$

Terms containing the higher harmonics are not written out. In determining the coefficients

$$\Phi(a, \bar{\omega}) = \frac{\bar{\omega}}{\pi} \int_0^{2\pi/\bar{\omega}} \psi(f, f', f'') \sin \bar{\omega} t \, dt,$$

$$\Psi(a, \bar{\omega}) = \frac{\bar{\omega}}{\pi} \int_0^{2\pi/\bar{\omega}} \psi(f, f', f'') \cos \bar{\omega} t \, dt$$

we make use of the inequality (4.5) which is approximately written as

$$\begin{aligned} f' &= a\bar{\omega} \cos \bar{\omega} t + a' \sin \bar{\omega} t \approx a\bar{\omega} \cos \bar{\omega} t, \\ f'' &= - a\bar{\omega}^2 \sin \bar{\omega} t + 2a'\bar{\omega} \cos \bar{\omega} t + a'' \sin \bar{\omega} t \approx - a\bar{\omega}^2 \sin \bar{\omega} t \end{aligned} \tag{4.7}$$

A substitution of Eqs. (4.4) and (4.6) into Eq. (4.1) yields

$$\begin{aligned} - a\bar{\omega}^2 \sin \bar{\omega} t + 2a'\bar{\omega} \cos \bar{\omega} t &\underline{+ a'' \sin \bar{\omega} t + 2\varepsilon a' \sin \bar{\omega} t} + 2\varepsilon a\bar{\omega} \cos \bar{\omega} t \\ &+ \omega^2 a \sin \bar{\omega} t + \Phi(a, \bar{\omega}) \sin \bar{\omega} t + \Psi(a, \bar{\omega}) \cos \bar{\omega} t + \cdots = 0 . \end{aligned}$$

On the basis of Eqs. (4.3) and (4.5), the underlined terms can be neglected. By equating the coefficients of $\sin \bar{\omega} t$ and $\cos \bar{\omega} t$ to zero, we obtain the equations

$$(\omega^2 - \bar{\omega}^2)\, a + \Phi(a, \bar{\omega}) = 0,$$
$$\frac{da}{dt} = -\varepsilon a - \frac{1}{2\bar{\omega}} \Psi(a, \bar{\omega}) . \tag{4.8}$$

The first equation of (4.8) establishes the dependence of frequency on the vibration amplitude; the second equation defines the amplitude change with respect to time. In particular, for the linear system with damping, we obtain:[27]

$$\bar{\omega} = \omega = \text{const}, \quad a = a_0 e^{-\varepsilon t} .$$

●**3.** Another basis for this method given by K. F. Teodorchik [1] will now be discussed. The differential equation (4.1) will be written in the form

$$f'' + \bar{\omega}^2 f = (\bar{\omega}^2 - \omega^2) f - 2\varepsilon f' - \psi(f, f', f'') . \tag{4.9}$$

The vibrations of this nonlinear system will be considered as forced vibrations of a linear conservative system with a frequency $\bar{\omega}$ subjected to the external force

$$\Sigma F = (\bar{\omega}^2 - \omega^2) f - 2\varepsilon f' - \psi(f, f', f'') .$$

Expanding the right-hand side of this expression in a Fourier series and using Eq. (4.7) gives

$$\Sigma F = F(a, \bar{\omega}) \sin \bar{\omega} t + G(a, \bar{\omega}) \cos \bar{\omega} t ,$$

where

$$F(a, \bar{\omega}) = (\bar{\omega}^2 - \omega^2) a - \Phi(a, \bar{\omega}),$$
$$G(a, \bar{\omega}) = -2\varepsilon\bar{\omega} a - \Psi(a, \bar{\omega}) .$$

From the beginning we have assumed that the solution does not contain a cosine expression, and, therefore,

$$F(a, \bar{\omega}) = 0 .$$

This equation is identical to the first equation of (4.8). Furthermore, we will consider the differential equation

$$f'' + \bar{\omega}^2 f = G(a, \bar{\omega}) \cos \bar{\omega} t . \tag{4.10}$$

If $G(a, \bar{\omega})$ is a slowly changing function, then

$$f(t) = a(t) \sin \bar{\omega} t$$

is an approximate (asymptotic) solution of Eq. (4.10), where

$$a(t) = \frac{1}{2\bar{\omega}} \int_0^t G(\tau)\, d\tau .$$

Differentiation leads to the second equation of (4.8):

[27] This solution differs from the exact solution only by the addition of the damping correction, Eq. (2.3), to the frequencies.

$$\frac{da}{dt} = \frac{1}{2\bar{\omega}} G(a, \bar{\omega}) .$$

In spite of all their physical clarity, both the above justifications are not mathematically rigorous. The rigorous proof of the method of slowly changing amplitudes was given by Mandel'shtam and Papaleksi [1]. Applying the method of the small parameter, they showed that the first approximations are the same in both methods. The first approximation according to the method of Krylov and Bogoliubov [1] (see also Bogoliubov and Mitropol'skii [1]) and to the method of Andronov and Khaikin [1] leads also to analogous results.

It would be erroneous to assume that the accuracy of the slowly changing amplitude method is limited. If higher harmonics are introduced,

$$f(t) = a_1(t) \sin \bar{\omega}t + a_2(t) \sin 2\bar{\omega}t + a_3(t) \sin 3\bar{\omega}t + \cdots,$$

we can increase the accuracy of the results. The smaller the nonlinearity, the greater the accuracy given by the first harmonic approximation.

● **4.** The method of slowly changing amplitudes can also be applied to the problem of forced vibrations. For example, let us consider the differential equation

$$f'' + 2\varepsilon f' + \omega^2 f + \Psi(f, f', f'') = S \sin \theta t . \tag{4.11}$$

We will seek its solution in the form

$$f(t) = a(t) \sin \theta t + b(t) \cos \theta t , \tag{4.12}$$

where $a(t)$ and $b(t)$ are slowly changing amplitudes. Writing Eq. (4.11) in the form

$$f'' + \theta^2 f = S \sin \theta t + (\theta^2 - \omega^2) f - 2\varepsilon f' - \psi(f, f', f'') , \tag{4.13}$$

substituting Eq. (4.12) into the right-hand side of Eq. (4.13) and separating out the sin θt and cos θt terms, we obtain

$$f'' + \theta^2 f = F(a, b) \sin \theta t + G(a, b) \cos \theta t + \cdots . \tag{4.14}$$

This yields

$$F(a, b) = S + (\theta^2 - \omega^2)\, a - 2\varepsilon\theta b - \Phi(a, b) ,$$
$$G(a, b) = -\,(\theta^2 - \omega^2)\, b - 2\varepsilon\theta a - \Psi(a, b) ,$$

where

$$\Phi(a, b) = \frac{\theta}{\pi}\int_0^{2\pi/\theta} \psi(f, f', f'') \sin \theta t \, dt ,$$

$$\Psi(a, b) = \frac{\theta}{\pi}\int_0^{2\pi/\theta} \psi(f, f', f'') \cos \theta t \, dt .$$

An approximate solution of the differential equation (4.14) is

$$a(t) = \frac{1}{2\theta}\int_0^t G(\tau)\, dt , \quad b(t) = \frac{1}{2\theta}\int_0^t F(\tau)\, dt .$$

By differentiating, we obtain the van der Pol equations

$$\frac{da}{dt} = \frac{1}{2\theta}G(a, b)\,, \qquad \frac{db}{dt} = \frac{1}{2\theta}F(a, b)\,,$$

or, more explicity,

$$\frac{da}{dt} = \frac{1}{2\theta}[-(\theta^2 - \omega^2)b - 2\varepsilon\theta a - \Psi(a, b)]\,,$$

$$\frac{db}{dt} = \frac{1}{2\theta}[S + (\theta^2 - \omega^2)a - 2\varepsilon\theta b - \Phi(a, b)]\,.$$

Thus, instead of a second-order differential equation (4.11), we obtain a simpler system of two first-order differential equations that are not explicitly dependent on time. In the case of steady-state vibrations.

$$\frac{da}{dt} = \frac{db}{dt} = 0\,,$$

and for determining the steady-state amplitudes, we obtain the following system of algebraic equations:

$$\begin{aligned} -(\theta^2 - \omega^2)\,b - 2\varepsilon\theta a - \Psi(a, b) &= 0\,, \\ S + (\theta^2 - \omega^2)\,a - 2\varepsilon\theta b - \Phi(a, b) &= 0\,. \end{aligned} \tag{4.15}$$

This equation system can also be derived by other means. For example, one can substitute Eq. (4.12) directly into Eq. (4.11), which will be written in the form $L(f, f', f'') = 0$. One then requires that the result of the substitution (in accordance with the Galerkin variational method) be orthogonal to the coordinate functions $\sin\theta t$ and $\cos\theta t$:

$$\int_0^{2\pi/\theta} L(f, f', f'')\sin\theta t\,dt = 0\,, \qquad \int_0^{2\pi/\theta} L(f, f', f'')\cos\theta t\,dt = 0\,.$$

This method leads directly to equations (4.15).

§ 17. Free Vibrations of a Nonlinear System

●1. Let us consider the problem of the free vibrations of a rod, taking into account the nonlinear terms introduced in the previous chapter.[28] The differential equation of this problem is

$$f'' + 2\varepsilon f' + \omega^2 f + \psi(f, f', f'') = 0\,, \tag{4.16}$$

where $\psi(f, f', f'')$ is a nonlinear function of displacements, velocities, and accelerations. Limited to quantities not higher than third order, the nonlinear function can be represented in the form

$$\psi(f, f', f'') = \gamma f^3 + 2\varepsilon_L f^2 f' + 2\kappa f[ff'' + (f')^2] \tag{4.17}$$

The first term considers the influence of nonlinear terms of static origin, the second term considers the nonlinear character of damping, and finally,

[28] A comprehensive theoretical and experimental investigation of the free vibrations and forced vibrations of a nonlinear system can be found in Ivovich [1], [2], [3], [4].

the third term considers the influence of the inertia forces that arise from longitudinal displacements. We will subsequently discuss nonlinear elasticity, nonlinear damping, and nonlinear inertia.

It is easy to show that the differential equation of the problem belongs to a class of differential equations with small nonlinearities. This characteristic follows from the problem itself. It is known that the linear treatment of problems on the free vibrations of rods gives results that agree well with experimental data. The additional nonlinear terms in differential equation (4.16) serve as corrections which make the linear approximation more precise.

To obtain a quantitative estimate, one must reduce Eq. (4.16) to a nondimensional form and apply the condition (4.2). The calculation will be left to the reader. During stable equilibrium the influence of nonlinearities depends upon the amplitude of the vibrations (its growth is proportional to the square of the amplitude). This means that the vibration amplitudes must be sufficiently small. In all practical problems this condition is assumed to be satisfied.

●**2.** We will now consider calculations. Substituting the expression $f = a \sin \bar{\omega} t$ into Eq. (4.17) and introducing

$$\begin{aligned} \sin^3 \bar{\omega} t &= \tfrac{1}{4}(3 \sin \bar{\omega} t - \sin 3\bar{\omega} t)\,, \\ \sin \bar{\omega} t \cos^2 \bar{\omega} t &= \tfrac{1}{4}(\sin \bar{\omega} t + \sin 3\bar{\omega} t)\,, \\ \sin^2 \bar{\omega} t \cos \bar{\omega} t &= \tfrac{1}{4}(\cos \bar{\omega} t - \cos 3\bar{\omega} t)\,, \end{aligned}$$

we obtain

$$\psi(f, f', f'') = (\tfrac{3}{4}\gamma - \kappa\bar{\omega}^2) a^3 \sin \bar{\omega} t + \frac{\varepsilon_L \bar{\omega}}{4} a^3 \cos \bar{\omega} t + \cdots . \tag{4.18}$$

In accordance with the method of slowly changing amplitudes, the derivatives a' and a'', and also terms containing higher harmonics, are neglected. From Eq. (4.18) it follows that

$$\begin{aligned} \Phi(a, \bar{\omega}) &= (\tfrac{3}{4}\gamma - \kappa\bar{\omega}^2) a^3, \\ \Psi(a, \bar{\omega}) &= \frac{\varepsilon_L \bar{\omega}}{4} a^3, \end{aligned}$$

so that Eq. (4.8) for our case takes the form

$$\omega^2 - \bar{\omega}^2 + (\tfrac{3}{4}\gamma - \kappa\bar{\omega}^2) a^2 = 0 \tag{4.19}$$

and

$$\frac{da}{dt} = -\left(\varepsilon + \frac{\varepsilon_L}{4} a^2\right) a\,. \tag{4.20}$$

Equation (4.19) permits one to determine the frequency of the free vibrations of the nonlinear system,

$$\bar{\omega} = \omega \sqrt{\frac{1 + \frac{3}{4} \frac{\gamma}{\omega^2} a^2}{1 + \kappa a^2}}\,. \tag{4.21}$$

As one can see from Ex. (4.21), the natural frequency of the nonlinear system depends upon the vibration amplitude. Therefore, the existence of nonlinear elasticity leads to an increase of the frequency with amplitude; conversely, nonlinear inertia causes a decrease of the natural frequency. Considering the nonlinearity to be small, we can write Eq. (4.21) in the form

$$\bar{\omega} \approx \omega\left[1 + \frac{a^2}{2}\left(\frac{3}{4}\frac{\gamma}{\omega^2} - \kappa\right)\right] \tag{4.22}$$

For $\kappa < \frac{3}{4}\gamma/\omega^2$ the frequency of free vibrations will increase with a growth of amplitude; for $\kappa > \frac{3}{4}\gamma/\omega^2$ the frequency will decrease with an increase of amplitude. For

$$\kappa = \frac{3}{4}\frac{\gamma}{\omega^2} \tag{4.23}$$

the effect of nonlinear elasticity and nonlinear inertia are the same; the free vibrations remain isochronous. In this sense a nonlinear inertia with a coefficient κ and a nonlinear elasticity with a cofficient $\gamma = \frac{4}{3}\kappa\omega^2$ are equivalent. We remind the reader that an analogous relationship exists for the linear system: the influence of transverse forces of inertia is equivalent to the influence of a continuous elastic foundation with a resistance coefficient of $k = -m\omega^2$. The factor $\frac{4}{3}$ in our case can be explained by the nonlinear character of the system.

Let us consider the case where the longitudinal elastic coupling is absent. We will show that the nonlinear inertia term always turns out to be dominant in this case. The coefficient of nonlinear elasticity according to Eq. (3.16) is

$$\gamma = \frac{\pi^2\omega^2}{8l^2} . \tag{4.24}$$

Since the imperfect elasticity of the material usually gives a "soft" nonlinearity, one must consider Eq. (4.24) as the maximum value of the coefficient of nonlinear elasticity in the absence of nonlinear couplings. On the other hand, the smallest value of the coefficient κ given in Eq. (3.20) is

$$\kappa = \frac{\pi^4}{4l^2}\left(\frac{1}{3} - \frac{3}{8\pi^2}\right) .$$

If we consider that for this value

$$\frac{4}{3}\frac{\kappa\omega^2}{\gamma} = \frac{8\pi^2}{3}\left(\frac{1}{3} - \frac{3}{8\pi^2}\right) \approx 8 ,$$

we arrive at a conclusion which is important for all future considerations: *In the absence of nonlinear couplings, the predominant nonlinear factor is nonlinear inertia.* This conclusion is valid for all rods which constitute statically determinate systems and also for those rods of statically indeterminate systems, for which $\kappa > \frac{3}{4}\gamma/\omega^2$.

Let us now estimate the order of magnitude of the nonlinear correction to the frequency. If we substitute the values of the coefficients γ and κ into Eq. (4.22), we can write this equation in the form

$$\bar{\omega} = \omega\left(1 - k\frac{a^2}{l^2}\right),$$

where

$$k \approx 3.2 + 12\frac{M_L}{ml}.$$

M_L denotes the "longitudinal mass" which is concentrated on the moving end of the rod. The mass of the rod is not considered during computations (it is accounted for by the term 3.2).

Let $M_L = 0$. In this case the change in the free vibration does not exceed 3 percent even at such a large amplitude as $a/l = 0.1$. If the rod is part of a rod system, the influence of the nonlinear terms can then increase by ten or one hundred times. This is evident from § 14.

Figure 23 shows an oscillogram of the vibrations of a rod with a large inertia nonlinearity. The change of period of the free vibration can easily be seen.

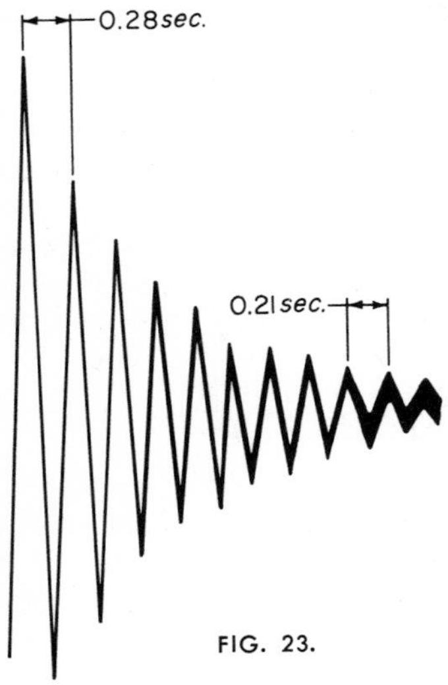

FIG. 23.

●3. For an explanation of the law of damping one must return to Eq. (4.20). If we write it in the form

$$\varepsilon\, dt = -\frac{da}{a + \frac{\varepsilon_L}{4\varepsilon}a^3},$$

we obtain, on integration:

$$-\varepsilon t = \ln a - \frac{1}{2}\ln\left(\frac{4\varepsilon}{\varepsilon_L} + a^2\right) + \ln C$$

or

$$\frac{Ca}{\sqrt{\frac{4\varepsilon}{\varepsilon_L} + a^2}} = e^{-\varepsilon t}$$

The constant of integration is

$$C = \frac{\sqrt{\frac{4\varepsilon}{\varepsilon_L} + a_0^2}}{a_0}$$

where a_0 is the initial amplitude. Therefore

$$\frac{a_0}{a}\sqrt{\frac{\frac{4\varepsilon}{\varepsilon_L} + a_0^2}{\frac{4\varepsilon}{\varepsilon_L} + a^2}} = e^{-\varepsilon t}.$$

Solving this equation with respect to the amplitude a, we finally obtain

$$a = \frac{a_0 e^{-\varepsilon t}}{\sqrt{1 + (1 - e^{-2\varepsilon t})\frac{\varepsilon_L}{4\varepsilon} a_0^2}} . \tag{4.25}$$

For the special case of linear damping,

$$a = a_0 e^{-\varepsilon t} . \tag{4.26}$$

As expected, nonlinear damping gives a more rapid decrease of the amplitudes.

For practical purposes the following interpretation of Eq. (4.20) might be useful. If one divides the whole damping period into sufficiently small intervals of time, one can average the nonlinear part of the damping by assuming it is constant during every interval:

$$\bar{\varepsilon} = \varepsilon + \frac{\varepsilon_L}{4} \bar{a}^2 . \tag{4.27}$$

Here $\bar{a}$ is an average value of the amplitude in the given time interval. For every interval, Eq. (4.20) takes the form

$$\frac{da}{dt} = - \bar{\varepsilon} a$$

from which

$$a = a_0 e^{-\bar{\varepsilon} t} .$$

Thus Eq. (4.20) describes damped vibrations occurring with a variable damping coefficient. Such a "quasi-linear" treatment is all the more suitable since essentially it gives the basis for a generally accepted method of reducing experimental diagrams of damped vibrations. As is known, the experimental damping coefficient is determined from the condition

$$\bar{\varepsilon} = \frac{1}{\Delta t} \ln \frac{a(t)}{a(t + \Delta t)} \tag{4.28}$$

whether it is constant during the entire process of damping or changes with amplitude. In the last case the damping is nonlinear, or more precisely, it does not follow the exponential law of Eq. (4.26). The application of Eq. (4.28) assumes that the damping is "linearized" within the "limits" of each time interval Δt.

§ 18. Forced Vibrations of a Nonlinear System

● 1. We will discuss briefly the problem of forced vibrations of a nonlinear system.[29] The steady-state amplitudes of these vibrations can be determined from Eq. (4.15). The amplitude of the "generalized force", denoted by S, for example is

$$S = \frac{2P}{ml}$$

[29] See footnote 28.

for the case of a rod loaded at the center (Fig. 24).

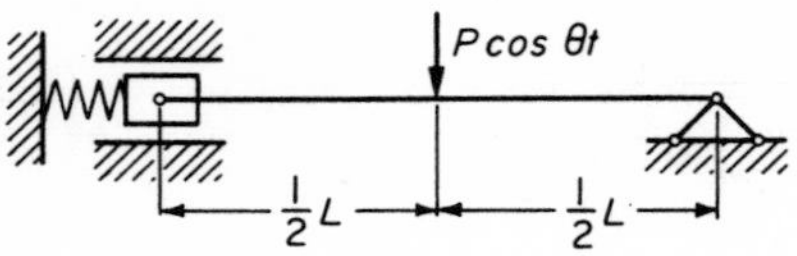

FIG. 24.

Substituting the approximate solution

$$f(t) = a \sin \theta t - b \cos \theta t$$

into the expression for the nonlinear function, Eq. (4.17), and performing the operations indicated in the preceding paragraph, we obtain

$$\Phi(a, b) = A^2[(\tfrac{3}{4}\gamma - \kappa\theta^2)a + \tfrac{1}{4}\varepsilon_L\theta b] ,$$
$$\Psi(a, b) = A^2[-(\tfrac{3}{4}\gamma - \kappa\theta^2)b + \tfrac{1}{4}\varepsilon_L\theta a] .$$

Here A is the amplitude of the vibrations, i.e., $A^2 = a^2 + b^2$. Therefore Eqs. (4.15) take the form

$$\begin{aligned} -(\theta^2 - \omega^2)\, b - 2\varepsilon\theta a - A^2[-(\tfrac{3}{4}\gamma - \kappa\theta^2)\, b + \tfrac{1}{4}\varepsilon_L\theta a] &= 0 , \\ S + (\theta^2 - \omega^2)\, a - 2\varepsilon\theta b - A^2[(\tfrac{3}{4}\gamma - \kappa\theta^2)\, a + \tfrac{1}{4}\varepsilon_L\theta b] &= 0 . \end{aligned} \tag{4.29}$$

The system of equations (4.29) is unsolvable in the general form; therefore we restrict ourselves to the case where the damping, either linear or nonlinear, can be neglected. The system of equations for this case is simplified to

$$\begin{aligned} -(\theta^2 - \omega^2)\, b + A^2 b\, (\tfrac{3}{4}\gamma - \kappa\theta^2) &= 0 , \\ S + (\theta^2 - \omega^2)\, a - A^2 a(\tfrac{3}{4}\gamma - \kappa\theta^2) &= 0 , \end{aligned}$$

and obviously can be satisfied by $b = 0$, $A = a$. The amplitude of the steady-state vibrations is determined from the cubic equation.

$$S + (\theta^2 - \omega^2)\, A - A^3(\tfrac{3}{4}\gamma - \kappa\theta^2) = 0 . \tag{4.30}$$

●**2.** The roots of Eq. (4.30) can be graphically determined as the coordinates of the intersection points of a straight line

$$y = \frac{S + (\theta^2 - \omega^2)A}{\tfrac{3}{4}\gamma - \kappa\theta^2} \tag{4.31}$$

with the cubic parabola $y = A^3$. Figure 25 corresponds to the case where the nonlinear elasticity is dominant, i.e., $\tfrac{3}{4}\gamma - \kappa\omega^2 > 0$.

As the exciting frequency changes from zero to infiinity, the straight line (4.31) rotates clockwise from the initial position MN to the end position M_1N_1. As long as the frequency is sufficiently small (at least for $\theta < \omega$), the straight line intersects the cubic parabola once, i.e., Eq. (4.30) has one real root. For larger frequencies, three real roots occur and, consequently, three possible amplitude values also occur. At

$$\theta = \frac{\sqrt{3}}{2}\sqrt{\frac{\gamma}{\kappa}} \tag{4.32}$$

the straight line takes a horizontal position so that Eq. (4.30), in addition to having the one finite root, has also the roots $A = \pm\infty$.

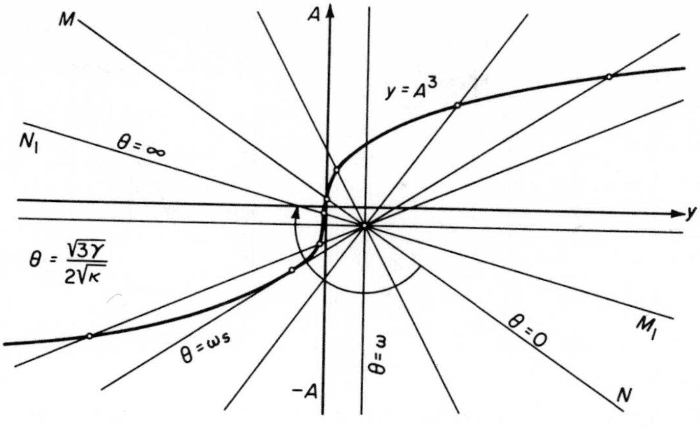

FIG. 25.

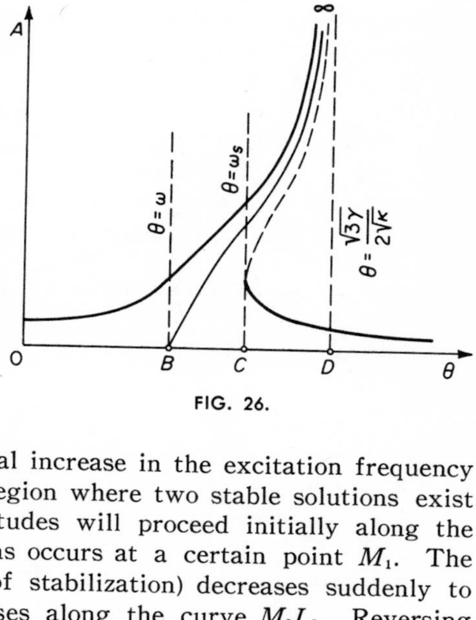

FIG. 26.

The resonance curve is shown in Figure 26. It is different not only from the resonance curve of the linear problem but also from the resonance curve for the case where only nonlinear elasticity is present.[30] As in the much investigated case of nonlinear elasticity, from the three correct solutions which exist in the region CD, only two will be stable. The unstable, i.e., the physically impossible solution is denoted by a dotted line.

The existence of two stable solutions leads to a phenomenon which is called the "overhang." By a gradual increase in the excitation frequency we can bring the system into the region where two stable solutions exist (Fig. 27a). The growth of the amplitudes will proceed initially along the curve K_1M_1, until a jump of vibrations occurs at a certain point M_1. The amplitude (not considering the time of stabilization) decreases suddenly to the magnitude MM_2, and then decreases along the curve M_2L_2. Reversing this frequency process, the amplitude of the vibrations will initially increase smoothly along the curve L_2N_2 (Fig. 27b). The sudden jump now occurs at the point N_2, after which the amplitudes follow the curve N_1K_1. This shows that the amplitude of the forced vibrations depends not only on the

[30] This last case examined in many textbooks on the theory of vibrations (for example, Stoker [1]) can be obtained from our equations, if in them one sets $\kappa = 0$. The values of the amplitude increase for increasing frequencies.

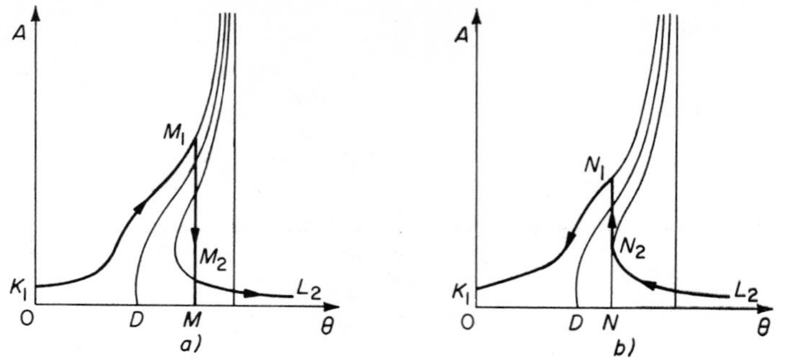

FIG. 27.

excitation frequency at the considered instant of time but also on the "history" of the nonlinear system.

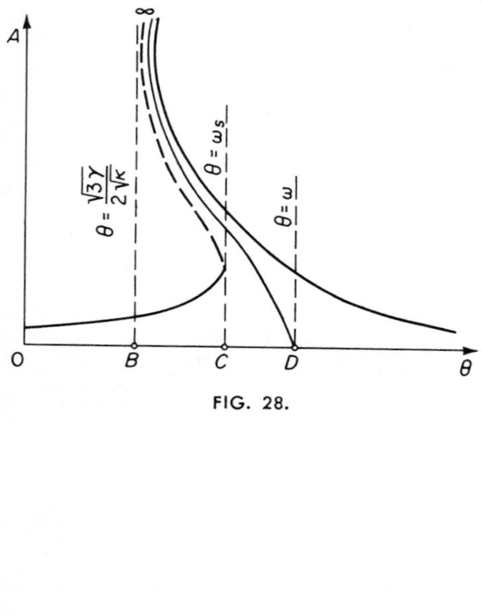

FIG. 28.

The question of the "overhang" will be examined in connection with parametrically excited vibrations (§ 23).

We have examined the case where the nonlinearities are due essentially to elasticity. If the influence of nonlinear inertia is predominant, the resonance curve bends toward the decreasing frequencies; the "overhang" of the resonance curve also bends toward the decreasing frequencies (Fig. 28).

Five

AMPLITUDES OF VIBRATIONS AT THE PRINCIPAL PARAMETRIC RESONANCE

§ 19. Basic Equations

● 1. Let us investigate the differential equation

$$f'' + 2\varepsilon f' + \Omega^2(1 - 2\mu \cos \theta t) f + \psi(f, f', f'') = 0 . \tag{5.1}$$

which describes parametrically excited vibrations including the effects of nonlinear factors, and let us formulate the problem of finding the solutions that correspond to steady-state vibrations.

It was established in § 8 that the solutions of the linear problem have the form

$$f(t) = \sum_{k=1,3,5,\ldots}^{\infty} \left(a_k \sin \frac{k\theta t}{2} + b_k \cos \frac{k\theta t}{2} \right) \tag{5.2}$$

on the boundaries of the first, third and, generally, the odd regions of dynamic instability, where a_k and b_k are constant coefficients. It would be natural to seek the solutions of the nonlinear problem that are valid within the limits of the odd regions of instability in the same form. The following considerations lead to this form of solution.

For a specific choice of its coefficients, Eq. (5.2) can satisfy Eq. (5.1). In fact, the result of the substitution of the series into Eq. (5.1) will not contain other periodic terms except $\sin k\theta t/2$ and $\cos k\theta t/2$ for odd values of k. However, this applies only if the nonlinear function $\psi(f, f', f'')$ does not contain terms of even powers. The function

$$\psi(f, f', f'') = \gamma f^3 + 2\varepsilon_L f^2 f' + 2\kappa f[f f'' + (f')^2] \tag{5.3}$$

satisfies this requirement.

Experimental results are the third and decisive reason for the use of Eq. (5.2); they indicate that the steady-state vibrations within the limits of the odd regions of instability have exactly such a form. We will postpone a discussion of the experimental data until § 22.

● 2. Let us seek the solution of Eq. (5.1) in the form of Eq. (5.2). Substitution gives

$$\sum_{k=1,3,5}^{\infty}\left(\Omega^2-\frac{k^2\theta^2}{4}\right)\left(a_k\sin\frac{k\theta t}{2}+b_k\cos\frac{k\theta t}{2}\right)$$
$$+\varepsilon\theta\sum_{k=1,3,5}^{\infty}k\left(a_k\cos\frac{k\theta t}{2}-b_k\sin\frac{k\theta t}{2}\right)$$
$$-\Omega^2\mu\sum_{k=1,3,5}^{\infty}a_k\left[\sin(k+2)\frac{\theta t}{2}+\sin(k-2)\frac{\theta t}{2}\right]$$
$$-\Omega^2\mu\sum_{k=1,3,5}^{\infty}b_k\left[\cos(k+2)\frac{\theta t}{2}+\cos(k-2)\frac{\theta t}{2}\right]+\psi^*(f,f',f'')=0\,. \quad (5.4)$$

The nonlinear function in Eq. (5.4) is expanded in a Fourier series

$$\psi^*(f,f',f'')=\sum_{k=1,3,5}^{\infty}\left(\Phi_k\sin\frac{k\theta t}{2}+\Psi_k\cos\frac{k\theta t}{2}\right); \quad (5.5)$$

its coefficients

$$\begin{aligned}\Phi_k(a_1,a_3,\ldots,b_1,b_3,\ldots)&=\frac{\theta}{2\pi}\int_0^{4\pi/\theta}\psi^*(f,f',f'')\sin\frac{k\theta t}{2}\,dt\,,\\ \Psi_k(a_1,a_3,\ldots,b_1,b_3,\ldots)&=\frac{\theta}{2\pi}\int_0^{4\pi/\theta}\psi^*(f,f',f'')\cos\frac{k\theta t}{2}\,dt\,,\end{aligned} \quad (5.6)$$

are obviously nonlinear functions of the coefficients of Eq. (5.2), and in the case of Eq. (5.3) are homogeneous functions of third order. Substituting Eq. (5.5) into Eq. (5.4) and equating the coefficients of $\sin k\theta t/2$ and $\cos k\theta t/2$, we obtain the following system of equations:

$$\begin{aligned}\left[\Omega^2(1+\mu)-\frac{\theta^2}{4}\right]a_1-\varepsilon\theta b_1-\Omega^2\mu a_3+\Phi_1(a_i,b_i)&=0\,,\\ \left[\Omega^2(1-\mu)-\frac{\theta^2}{4}\right]b_1+\varepsilon\theta a_1-\Omega^2\mu b_3+\Psi_1(a_i,b_i)&=0\,,\\ \left(\Omega^2-\frac{k^2\theta^2}{4}\right)a_k-k\varepsilon\theta b_k-\Omega^2\mu(a_{k-2}+a_{k+2})+\Phi_k(a_i,b_i)&=0\,,\\ \left(\Omega^2-\frac{k^2\theta^2}{4}\right)b_k+k\varepsilon\theta a_k-\Omega^2\mu(b_{k-2}+b_{k+2})+\Psi_k(a_i,b_i)&=0\,,\\ (k=3,5,\ldots)\,,\end{aligned} \quad (5.7)$$

where for brevity we denote

$$\begin{aligned}\Phi_k(a_1,a_3,\ldots,b_1,b_3,\ldots)&=\Phi_k(a_i,b_i)\,,\\ \Psi_k(a_1,a_3,\ldots,b_1,b_3,\ldots)&=\Psi_k(a_i,b_i)\,.\end{aligned}$$

●3. In order to determine the amplitudes of the steady-state vibrations within the limits of the even regions of excitation, we will seek solutions in the form

$$f(t)=b_0+\sum_{k=2,4,6}^{\infty}\left(a_k\sin\frac{k\theta t}{2}+b_k\cos\frac{k\theta t}{2}\right). \quad (5.8)$$

This form is suggested by considerations analogous to those stated in ●1.

Substituting Eq. (5.8) into Eq. (5.1) and expanding the nonlinear function in the series

$$\psi^*(f, f', f'') = \Psi_0 + \sum_{k=2,4,6}^{\infty} \left(\Phi_k \sin \frac{k\theta t}{2} + \Psi_k \cos \frac{k\theta t}{2} \right),$$

we obtain the following system of equations:

$$\begin{aligned} \Omega^2(b_0 - \mu b_2) + \Psi_0(a_i, b_i) &= 0, \\ (\Omega^2 - \theta^2)a_2 - \mu\Omega^2 a_4 - 2\varepsilon\theta b_2 + \Phi_2(a_i, b_i) &= 0, \\ (\Omega^2 - \theta^2)b_2 - \mu\Omega^2(2b_0 + b_4) + 2\varepsilon\theta a_2 + \Psi_2(a_i, b_i) &= 0, \\ \left(\Omega^2 - \frac{k^2\theta^2}{4}\right)a_k - \mu\Omega^2(a_{k-2} + a_{k+2}) - k\varepsilon\theta b_k + \Phi_k(a_i, b_i) &= 0. \\ \left(\Omega^2 - \frac{k^2\theta^2}{4}\right)b_k - \mu\Omega^2(b_{k-2} + b_{k+2}) + k\varepsilon\theta a_k + \Psi_k(a_i, b_i) &= 0, \\ (k = 4, 6, \ldots). & \end{aligned} \tag{5.9}$$

Coefficients Φ_k and Ψ_k for $k \geq 2$ are calculated according to Eq. (5.6), and the coefficient Ψ_0 according to the formula

$$\Psi_0(a_2, a_4, \ldots, b_0, b_2, b_4, \ldots) = \frac{\theta}{4\pi} \int_0^{4\pi/\theta} \psi^*(f, f', f'')dt.$$

In conclusion, note that Eqs. (5.7) and (5.9) could be obtained differently, i.e., by means of the Galerkin variational method. For example, if we substitute series (5.2) into Eq. (5.1), we can require that the corresponding expression of $L(f, f', f'')$ be orthogonal to each of the coordinate functions $\sin k\theta t/2$ and $\cos k\theta t/2$:

$$\int_0^{4\pi/\theta} L(f, f', f'') \sin \frac{k\theta t}{2} dt = 0, \qquad \int_0^{4\pi/\theta} L(f, f', f'') \cos \frac{k\theta t}{2} dt = 0,$$
$$(k = 1, 3, 5, \ldots).$$

These expressions reduce to Eq. (5.7).

§ 20. Determination of Steady-State Amplitudes[31]

●1. If we investigate the vibrations for the principal resonance $\theta \approx 2\Omega$, we can neglect the influence of higher harmonics in the expansion of Eq. (5.2) and can assume

$$f(t) = a \sin \frac{\theta t}{2} + b \cos \frac{\theta t}{2} \tag{5.10}$$

as an approximation.[32] Therefore, Eqs. (5.7) are essentially simplified, and a system of two equations for the coefficients a and b remains:

[31] See Bolotin [2]

[32] The method of the slowly changing amplitude also leads to this approximation.

$$\left[\Omega^2(1+\mu) - \frac{\theta^2}{4}\right]a - \varepsilon\theta b + \Phi(a, b) = 0 ,$$
$$\left[\Omega^2(1-\mu) - \frac{\theta^2}{4}\right]b + \varepsilon\theta a + \Psi(a, b) = 0 . \tag{5.11}$$

For the determination of the quantities $\Phi(a, b)$ and $\Psi(a, b)$, we substitute Eq. (5.10) into Eq. (5.3). Computations give

$$\psi^*(f, f', f'') = \frac{A^2}{4}(3\gamma a - \varepsilon_L\theta b - \kappa\theta^2 a) \sin\frac{\theta t}{2} + \frac{A^2}{4}(3\gamma b + \varepsilon_L\theta a - \kappa\theta^2 b) \cos\frac{\theta t}{2} + \cdots .$$

Terms containing higher harmonics are not written out; the amplitude of steady-state vibrations is denoted by A:

$$A^2 = a^2 + b^2 .$$

Thus, the first coefficients of the expansion of the function $\psi^*(f, f', f'')$ in a Fourier series are

$$\Phi(a, b) = \frac{A^2}{4}(3\gamma a - \varepsilon_L\theta b - \kappa\theta^2 a) ,$$
$$\Psi(a, b) = \frac{A^2}{4}(3\gamma b + \varepsilon_L\theta a - \kappa\theta^2 b) . \tag{5.12}$$

●**2.** For further investigation, we write the system of equations (5.11) in the following form:

$$(1+\mu-n^2)a - \frac{n\Delta}{\pi}b + A^2\left(\frac{3\gamma}{4\Omega^2}a - \frac{n\Delta_L}{\pi}b - \kappa n^2 a\right) = 0 ,$$
$$(1-\mu-n^2)b + \frac{n\Delta}{\pi}a + A^2\left(\frac{3\gamma}{4\Omega^2}b + \frac{n\Delta_L}{\pi}a - \kappa n^2 b\right) = 0 , \tag{5.13}$$

where

$$n = \frac{\theta}{2\Omega} , \qquad \Delta = \frac{2\pi\varepsilon}{\Omega} , \qquad \Delta_L = \frac{\pi\varepsilon_L}{2\Omega} . \tag{5.14}$$

It is obvious that Eqs. (5.13) will be satisfied for $a = b = A = 0$. This solution corresponds to the case where transverse vibrations of the rod are absent.

One can find the non-zero solutions in the following manner. We will consider Eq. (5.13) as a system of homogeneous linear equations with respect to a and b. This system has solutions that differ from zero only in the case where the determinant composed of the coefficients disappears:

$$\begin{vmatrix} 1+\mu-n^2 - A^2\left(\kappa n^2 - \frac{3\gamma}{4\Omega^2}\right) & -\frac{n}{\pi}(\Delta + \Delta_L A^2) \\ \frac{n}{\pi}(\Delta + \Delta_L A^2) & 1-\mu-n^2 - A^2\left(\kappa n^2 - \frac{3\gamma}{4\Omega^2}\right) \end{vmatrix} = 0 . \tag{5.15}$$

Expanding the determinant and solving the resulting equation with respect to the amplitude A of the steady-state vibrations, we find

$$A = \sqrt{\frac{p(1-n^2) - \frac{n^2}{\pi^2}\Delta\Delta_L \pm \sqrt{\mu^2\left(p^2 + \frac{n^2}{\pi^2}\Delta_L^2\right) - \frac{n^2}{\pi^2}[p\Delta + \Delta_L(1-n^2)]^2}}{p^2 + \frac{n^2}{\pi^2}\Delta_L^2}} \tag{5.16}$$

where

$$p = \kappa n^2 - \frac{3\gamma}{4\Omega^2}. \tag{5.17}$$

● **3.** Equation (5.16) is too cumbersome for further investigation. Therefore we shall first clarify how the character of the resonance curves depends upon the form of the nonlinear function. For the case $\psi(f) = \gamma f^3$ (the case of nonlinear elasticity), Eq. (5.16) gives

$$A = \frac{2\Omega}{\sqrt{3\gamma}}\sqrt{n^2 - 1 \pm \sqrt{\mu^2 - \frac{n^2\Delta^2}{\pi^2}}} \tag{5.18}$$

A diagram of the dependence of the amplitude on the frequency is shown in Figure 29a, where the two solutions plotted correspond to the two signs in Eq. (5.18). One solution (represented by the dotted line) is obviously unstable. It is characteristic for the case of nonlinear elasticity that resonance curves are bent toward the increasing exciting frequencies. We have already encountered analogous properties during the investigation of forced vibrations (§ 18).

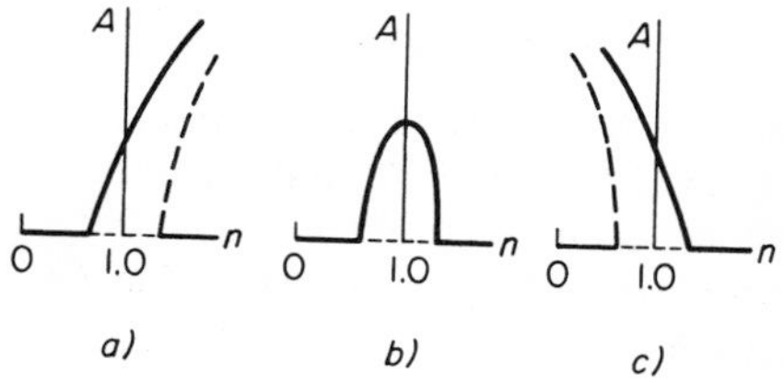

FIG. 29.

Let us consider the case of nonlinear damping

$$\psi(f, f') = 2\varepsilon_L f^2 f'.$$

Equation (5.16) assumes the form

$$A = \frac{\sqrt{\pi}}{\sqrt{n\Delta_L}}\sqrt{\sqrt{\mu^2 - (1-n^2)^2} - \frac{n\Delta}{\pi}}.$$

The corresponding resonance curve is represented in Figure 29b. As seen from the figure, the resonance curve in this case is approximately symmetric about the maximum.

Finally, for the case of the nonlinear inertia,

$$\psi(f, f', f'') = 2\kappa f[f f'' + (f')^2],$$

we obtain the amplitude equation

$$A = \frac{1}{n\sqrt{\kappa}}\sqrt{1 - n^2 \pm \sqrt{\mu^2 - \frac{n^2\Delta^2}{\pi^2}}} . \tag{5.19}$$

Here we also have two solutions, one of which is unstable (Fig. 29c). Contrary to the case of nonlinear elasticity, the resonance curves are bent toward the decreasing exciting frequencies.

We note that the base of the resonance curves in all three cases (as in the general case) does not depend on the magnitude and the character of the nonlinearity but coincides with the interval of the instability determined by the methods of linear theory. In fact, if we set $A = 0$ in Eq. (5.15), we obtain

$$\begin{vmatrix} 1 + \mu - n^2 & -\frac{n\Delta}{\pi} \\ \frac{n\Delta}{\pi} & 1 - \mu - n^2 \end{vmatrix} = 0 ,$$

which coincides with the equation of the critical frequencies, Eq. (2.12).

It is evident that in the case of nonlinear elasticity or nonlinear inertia, it is possible to have an "overhang" of the resonance curve beyond the limits of the region of excitation (compare with § 18). In the first case, the "overhang" will occur toward the increasing frequencies; in the second case, it will occur toward the decreasing frequencies. This phenomenon will be investigated in detail in § 23.

●**4.** The form of the resonance curves for each of the three fundamental cases is so typical that, according to the character of the curves, it is possible to judge which nonlinear factors predominate in each case. It can be seen from Eq. (5.16) that the manner in which the resonance curve is bent depends on the sign of the quantity

$$p = \kappa n^2 - \frac{3\gamma}{4\Omega^2} .$$

For

$$\frac{4}{3}\frac{\kappa\Omega^2}{\gamma} > 1 , \qquad (n \approx 1) ,$$

the resonance curves bend toward the decreasing frequencies, i.e., the amplitudes will increase as the exciting frequencies decrease. If, however,

$$\frac{4}{3}\frac{\kappa\Omega^2}{\gamma} < 1 , \qquad (n \approx 1) ,$$

the resonance curves will then bend toward the increasing frequencies.

As in the case of free vibrations (§ 17), it can be shown that if the rod does not have longitudinal elastic springs, then the nonlinear inertia is the decisive nonlinear factor. From the relation derived in § 17

$$\frac{4}{3}\frac{\kappa\omega^3}{\gamma} \geqq \frac{8\pi^2}{3}\left(\frac{1}{3} - \frac{3}{8\pi^2}\right) ,$$

it follows that

$$\frac{4}{3}\frac{\kappa n^2\Omega^2}{\gamma} \geqq \frac{8\pi^2}{3}\left(\frac{1}{3} - \frac{3}{8\pi^2}\right)\frac{\theta^2}{4\omega^2}.$$

However, for the principal region of instability,

$$\frac{8\pi^2}{3}\left(\frac{1}{3} - \frac{3}{8\pi^2}\right)\frac{\theta^2}{4\omega^2} > 1$$

only if the longitudinal force is not near the Euler value.

The dominating influence of nonlinear inertia is confirmed by experimental data. An oscillogram of parametrically excited vibrations taken near the principal resonance $\theta = 2\Omega$ is shown in Figure 30. This oscillogram shows

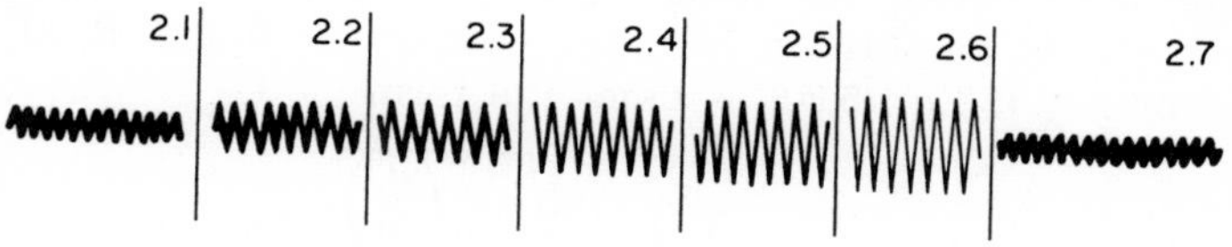

FIG. 30.

the vibrations for an exciting frequency decreasing by steps. The first frame corresponds to the upper boundary of the region of parametric excitation ($\theta = 42.0$ cps). Figure 11a is an enlargement of this frame. Along with the parametrically excited vibrations, forced vibrations also occur with a doubled frequency (i.e., with the frequency of the external force). Subsequent frames correspond to a stepwise decrease of the exciting frequency. It is characteristic that the accompanying vibrational amplitude increases. The sixth frame corresponds to an "overhang" of the resonance curve ($\theta = 36.5$ cps), after which the "break" of the amplitude occurs. Only forced vibrations having a frequency of the external force remain.

The dependence of the amplitude on the frequency can be seen also in Figure 31. In contrast to the oscillogram in Figure 30, this oscillogram shows a continuous record. A decrease of the exciting frequency by 20 percent, which takes the system beyond the limits of the region of instability along the "overhang," increases the amplitudes by a factor greater than 3.

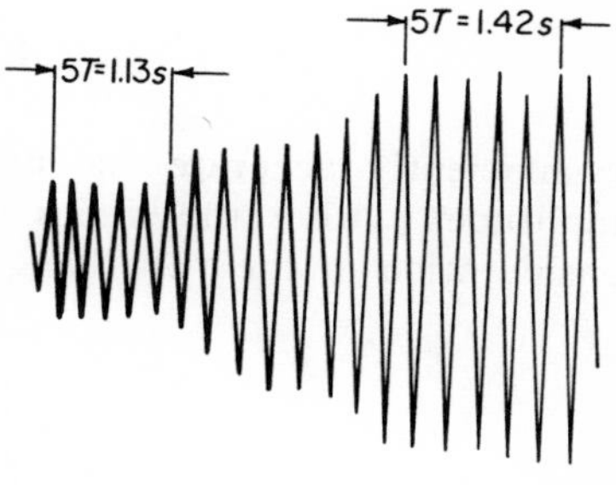

FIG. 31.

§ 21. Investigation of the Equation for Steady-State Amplitudes

● **1.** We will first clarify the influence of linear damping on the magnitude of the steady-state amplitudes. For this purpose, we neglect in Eq. (5.16) the terms that take into account the nonlinear portion of the damping, and represent A in the form

$$A = \frac{1}{\sqrt{p}} \sqrt{1 - n^2 \pm \sqrt{\mu^2 - \frac{n^2 \Delta^2}{\pi^2}}}\,, \tag{5.20}$$

where as before,

$$p = \kappa n^2 - \frac{3\gamma}{4\Omega^2}\,,$$

Equation (5.20) gives real values for the amplitude as long as $n\Delta/\pi < \mu$, or since $n \approx 1$, as long as $\Delta/\pi < \mu$. If however $\Delta/\pi > \mu$, then steady-state vibrations do not arise. This result is found to be in complete agreement with the results of linear theory.

On the other hand, the influence of sufficiently small damping on the magnitude of the amplitudes is imperceptible for practical purposes. For example, for $n = 1$, Eq. (5.20) assumes the form

$$A = \sqrt{\frac{\mu}{|p|}} \cdot \sqrt[4]{1 - \left(\frac{\mu_*}{\mu}\right)^2}$$

where μ_* is the critical value of the excitation parameter (§ 9). Even at $\mu_* = \frac{1}{2}\mu$, the influence of damping comprises a magnitude of 6 percent. With a further decrease of damping, the approximate values computed for the conservative case are even more exact. This is seen, for example, from Figure 32, which represents the dependence of the dimensionless amplitude on the ratio of the excitation parameters. Generally, at

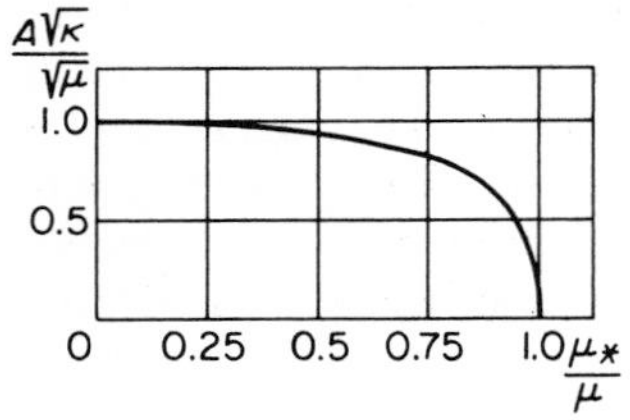

FIG. 32.

$$\mu > 3\mu_* \tag{5.21}$$

the simple formula of the conservative problem

$$A = \sqrt{\frac{1 - n^2 \pm \mu}{p}} \tag{5.22}$$

is sufficiently accurate for practical purposes. In particular, the largest amplitudes within the limits of the region of instability (i.e., without the consideration of the "overhang") can be determined according to the formula

$$A = \sqrt{\frac{2\mu}{|p|}}\,. \tag{5.23}$$

In the case of predominant nonlinear inertia ($p > 0$), the greatest amplitudes are attained on the lower boundary of the resonance region; in the case of predominant nonlinear elasticity ($p < 0$), the greatest amplitudes are attained on its upper boundaries. Equation (5.22) can also be written in the form

$$A^2 = \frac{1}{p}\left(\frac{\theta_*^2}{\theta^2} - 1\right). \tag{5.24}$$

Here the upper or lower critical frequency is taken for θ_*, depending on the sign of p. For the proof, let us investigate Eq. (5.15) with $\Delta = \Delta_L = 0$:

$$\begin{vmatrix} 1+\mu-n^2-A^2p & 0 \\ 0 & 1-\mu-n^2-A^2p \end{vmatrix} = 0 .$$

If we compare it with Eq. (2.12) for the boundary frequencies, we see that it is satisfied for $n^2 + A^2p = n_*^2$. Consequently,

$$A^2 = \frac{1}{p}(n_*^2 - n^2) , \qquad \left(n_* = \frac{\theta_*}{2\Omega}\right) ,$$

from which Eq. (5.24) follows.

In what follows, unless otherwise stipulated, we will assume that the condition in Eq. (5.21) is fulfilled, and we will make use of Eqs. (5.22), (5.23) and (5.24).

●**2.** We will now turn to the question concerning the influence of the magnitude of external loading on the steady-state amplitudes.

As seen from Eq. (5.23), the amplitude of the vibrations grows in proportion to the square root of the excitation parameter,

$$A = \sqrt{\frac{2\mu}{|p|}} , \tag{5.25}$$

i.e., in proportion to the square root of the amplitude of the periodic force. A nonlinear dependence between the loading and the vibration amplitude is usually characteristic for problems described by nonlinear differential equations. However, the amplitude of the longitudinal displacements at the point of application of the force grows also in proportion to the excitation parameter.

It is clear that the constant component of the longitudinal force P_0 must increase the amplitudes of the vibrations. Actually an increase of the force P_0 leads also to an increase of the excitation parameter:

$$\mu = \frac{P_t}{2(P_* - P_0)} .$$

This dependence is more complicated, however. The force P_0 is usually of gravitational origin, i.e., related in one way or another to the weight, and therefore its increase usually causes an increase in the nonlinear inertia of the system. This also can bring about a decrease of the amplitudes. We will illustrate this by a simple example (See Fig. 20).

Let the simply supported rod be loaded by the force $P_0 + P_t \cos \theta t$, where the force P_0 is associated with the rod mass P_0/g. Neglecting the influence of nonlinear elasticity and linear and nonlinear damping, we obtain

$$\kappa = \frac{\pi^4(P_0+kG)}{4Gl^2} ,$$

where $G = mgl$ is the free weight of the rod itself and k is the coefficient in (3.20) designated by κ. Equation (5.22) at $\theta = 2\Omega$ gives $A^2 = \mu/\kappa$, or

$$A^2 = \frac{2l^2}{\pi^4} \frac{P_t G}{(P_0 + kG)(P_* - P_0)} . \tag{5.26}$$

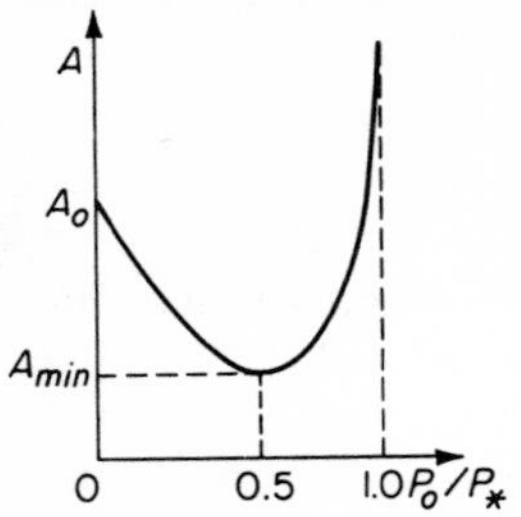

FIG. 33.

The dependence of the amplitude on the constant component P_0 is shown in Figure 33. For $P_0 = 0$, the vibration amplitude is relatively large:

$$A_0^2 = \frac{2l^2 P_t}{\pi^4 k P_*} .$$

An increase of the force P_0 decreases the amplitude until a minimum is reached at $P_0 = \frac{1}{2}(P + kG) \approx \frac{1}{2}P_*$. Subsequently, the amplitude again increases.

●3. In the presence of two factors, i.e., the nonlinear elasticity and the nonlinear inertia, the resonance curves assume the form shown in Figure 34. Figure 34a corresponds to the case $p > 0$ (predominant nonlinear inertia).

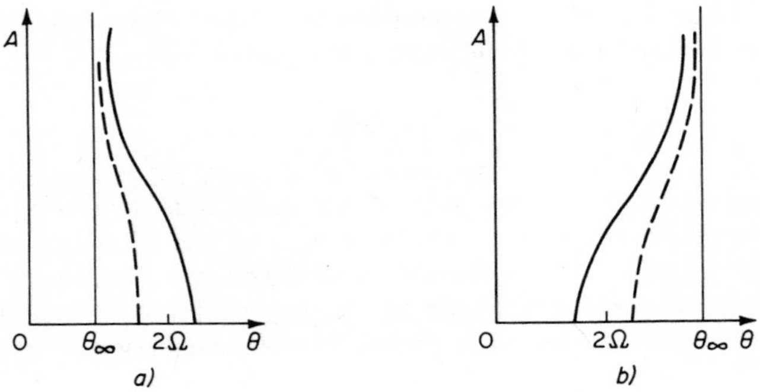

FIG. 34

As seen from the diagrams, the "overhang" in this case is bounded by the frequency θ_∞. This frequency is determined by equating the expression for p to zero:

$$\pi n^2 - \frac{3\gamma}{4\Omega^2} = 0 .$$

Hence,

$$\theta_\infty = 2n_\infty \Omega = \sqrt{\frac{3\gamma}{\kappa}} \tag{5.27}$$

The quantity $\omega_L = \sqrt{\gamma/\kappa}$ is none other than the linearized frequency of the "longitudinal system" (the nonlinear elasticity plus the nonlinear inertia). Thus in the case of an end mass M_L and a connection with a spring constant c, we have

$$\kappa = \frac{\pi^4 M_L}{4ml^3} , \qquad \gamma = \frac{\pi^4 c}{4ml^3}$$

which gives $\omega_L^2 = c/M_L$. Equation (5.27) can be interpreted as the condition for the occurrence of resonance in the "longitudinal" system although it differs from the condition of synchronization by the factor of $\sqrt{3}$ for the natural frequency.

If the nonlinear elasticity and the nonlinear inertia compensate one another, then the frequency θ_∞ lies in the region of dynamic instability. This is the most unfavorable case from the point of view of the amplitudes of the vibrations: the parametric resonance and the resonance in the "longitudinal system" are superimposed on one another (Fig. 35). The amplitudes are limited by nonlinear damping and by terms of higher order (in the expression for the nonlinear function).

The factor $\sqrt{3}$ in the resonance condition stems from the nonlinearities of the "longitudinal system." In fact, the linear coefficient which replaces the elasticity of this system is very large during small displacements (infinitely large during displacements tending to zero, if the rod is considered incompressible) and approaches a constant value c when the deflections are increasing. This process is shown in Figure 36, where the reaction of the system to the longitudinal displacement is plotted along the vertical axis.

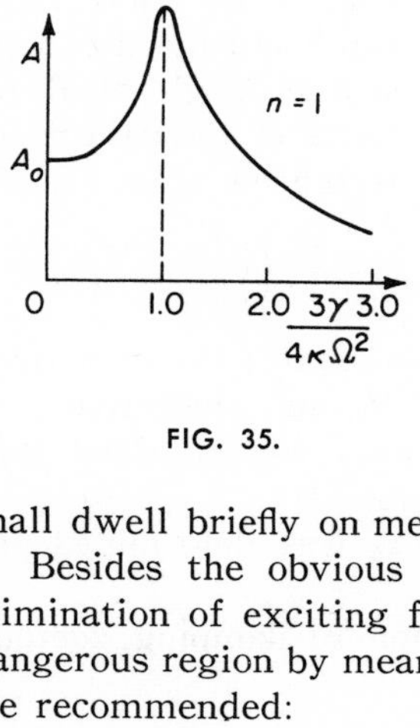

FIG. 35.

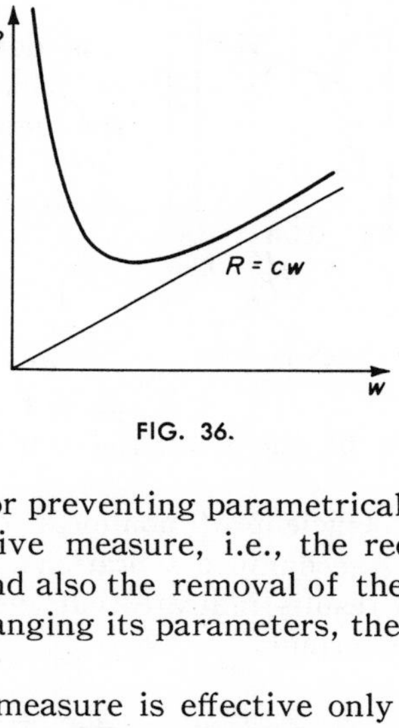

FIG. 36.

● **4.** We shall dwell briefly on methods for preventing parametrically excited vibrations. Besides the obvious preventive measure, i.e., the reduction or the total elimination of exciting forces and also the removal of the structure from the dangerous region by means of changing its parameters, the following methods are recommended:

(1) *Linear damping.* This preventive measure is effective only when the damping is so large that $\mu_* \approx \mu$. For $\mu_* > \mu$ parametric resonance is impossible. For a choice of suitable damping characteristics one should use the equation in § 9.

(2) *Nonlinear damping.* The introduction of a "longitudinal damper" reduces the amplitudes of the parametric vibrations approximately inversely proportional to $\sqrt{\Delta_L}$. This method should be considered only as a supplementary measure.

(3) *The introduction of nonlinearities by springs and inertia members.* If the features of the construction allow its use, such a method may prove

useful. One must remember, however, that the influence of the indicated nonlinearities is opposite, and that there exist combinations which are unfavorable to the decrease of vibrations. Consequently, the increase of a nonlinear elasticity of the system does not always reduce the amplitudes. The same is true for nonlinear inertia. This method does not permit the total elimination of the vibrations.

§ 22. Experimental Verification of the Theory

● **1.** In the experimental setup described in § 6, a series of rods were investigated and the amplitudes of steady-state vibrations determined. The experimental data were compared with theoretical results. Some of these data, along with a description of methods for the determination of the nonlinear characteristics, are cited below.

The coefficient of nonlinear elasticity γ was determined experimentally; the rod was loaded with a longitudinal force exceeding the critical value. In § 13, the formula

$$f = \frac{\omega}{\sqrt{\gamma}} \sqrt{\frac{P}{P_*} - 1} \tag{5.28}$$

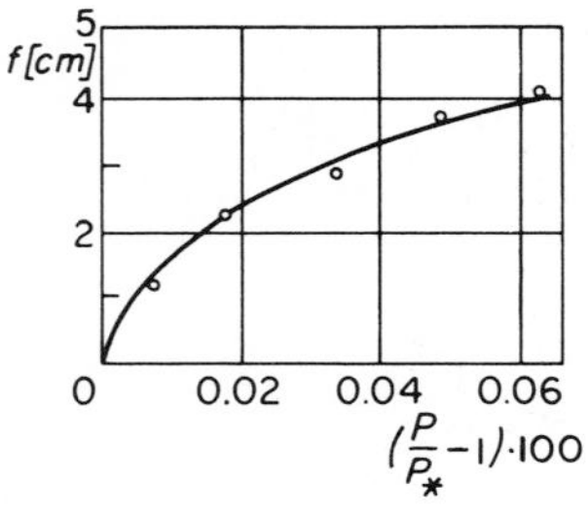

FIG. 37.

was derived. Experiments show that Eq. (5.28) describes quite satisfactorily the dependence of the deflections on the longitudinal force if the latter is slightly greater than the Euler buckling force (Fig. 37). It follows from Eq. (5.28) that

$$\gamma = \frac{\omega^2}{f^2}\left(\frac{P}{P_*} - 1\right).$$

For a longitudinal force P within the limits $P_* \leqq P \leqq 1.00065\, P_*$ and deflections measured in the middle of the span, $\gamma/\omega^2 = 0.42 \times 10^{-4}\,\text{cm}^{-2}$ was obtained for one of the specimens.

The coefficient of nonlinear damping ε_L was determined from oscillograms of free damped vibrations.

These results indicate that the decrement of damping, computed according to the formula

$$\Delta = \frac{1}{T} \ln \frac{A(t)}{A(t+T)},$$

increases with amplitude. Experimental values for the above-mentioned specimen are plotted in Figure 38. The increase of the decrement is satisfactorily given by the parabola $\varepsilon = 0.10 + 0.02\, A^2$, from which it follows that $\varepsilon_L = 0.08\,\text{cm}^{-2}\text{sec}^{-1}$.

The coefficient of nonlinear inertia was calculated from the formula

$$\kappa = \frac{\pi^4 M_L}{4ml^3},$$

where reduced mass M_L is found from elementary considerations (Fig. 39).

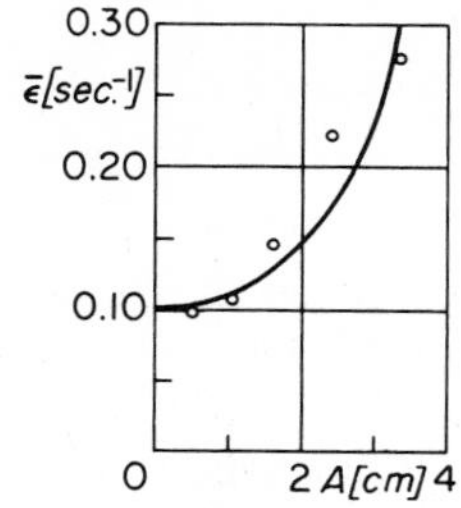

FIG. 38.

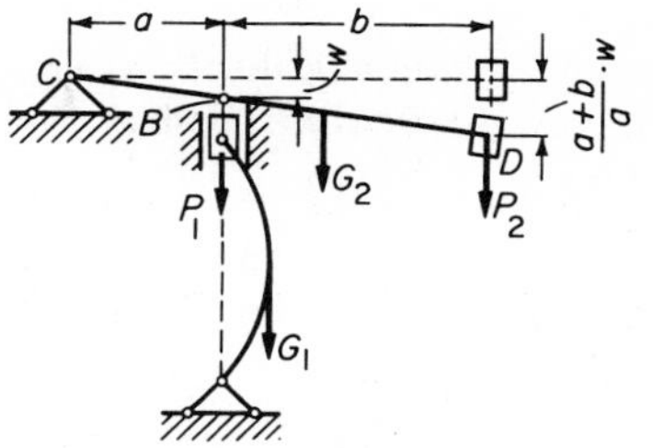

FIG. 39.

We introduce the following notation: let G_1 be the weight of the specimen, G_2 be the weight of loading arm CD producing the constant component of axial force, P_1 be the weight of the moving support of the vibrator and other hardware, and P_2 be the weight of the additional loading on the end of the lever. If w is the vertical displacement of point B, then the displacement of the end of the lever arm is $w(a+b)/a$. The axial inertia force in the rod is then

$$\Delta N = \left(P_1 + kG_1 + \frac{(a+b)^2}{a^2}(P_2 + \tfrac{1}{3}G_2)\right)\frac{w''}{g},$$

from which

$$M_L = \frac{1}{g}\left(P_1 + kG_1 + \frac{(a+b)^2}{a^2}(P_2 + \tfrac{1}{3}G_2)\right).$$

For the case where $G_1 = 6.0\,\text{kg}$, $G_2 = 31.0\,\text{kg}$, $P_1 = 30.0\,\text{kg}$, $P_2 = 12.0\,\text{kg}$, $a = 40\,\text{cm}$, $b = 130\,\text{cm}$, $l = 170\,\text{cm}$, we obtain $M_L g = 429.0\,\text{kg}$. Consequently,

$$\kappa = \frac{(3.14^4)(429)}{(4)(6.0)(170^2)} = 0.061\,\text{cm}^{-2}.$$

The coefficient of nonlinear inertia (more accurately, the characteristic magnitude)

$$p = \kappa n^2 - \frac{3\gamma}{4\Omega^2},$$

can also be determined from experiments on the damping of free vibrations. According to the approximate formula (4.22), the frequency of the nonlinear system is

$$\bar{\Omega} = \Omega\left[1 + \tfrac{1}{2}a^2\left(\frac{3\gamma}{4\Omega^2} - \kappa\right)\right].$$

Near the principal resonance, $n \approx 1$ and the formula is

$$\bar{\Omega} = \Omega(1 - \tfrac{1}{2}a^2 p).$$

If the natural frequencies are determined for various amplitudes, we can compute the coefficient

$$p = \frac{2}{a^2}\left(\frac{\Omega}{\overline{\Omega}} - 1\right).$$

This method is unreliable, however; it can be recommended only for systems with pronounced nonlinearities.

●**2.** The resonance curves were determined in such a manner that at least five-sixths of the experimental points were within the limits of the principal instability region (of the linear approximation). The recording was made stepwise for increasing and decreasing frequencies; this permitted the determination of "overhanging" vibrations.

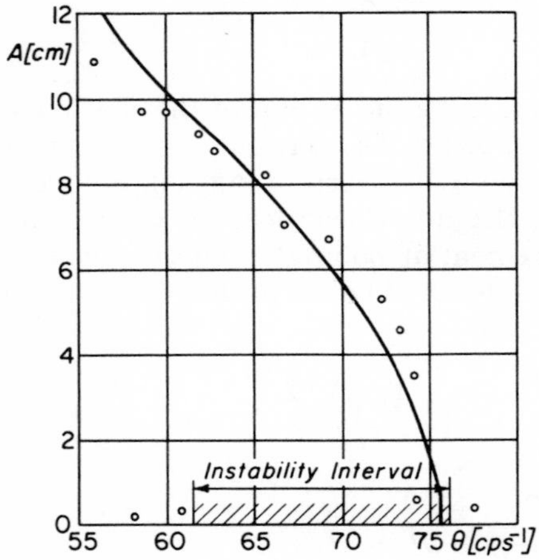

FIG. 40.

The resonance curve for one of the specimens is given in Figure 40. If we apply the equations derived from theory, we must consider that the amplitude of a periodic force produced by the vibrator grows proportionally to the square of the exciting frequency. The value of the excitation parameter for $n = 1$ is denoted by $\bar{\mu}$. Then,

$$\mu = \bar{\mu} n^2 . \tag{5.29}$$

This expression for μ should be substituted in all previously derived theoretical formulas. The results of calculations for the case corresponding to Figure 40 are:

Frequency of free vibrations	$\Omega = 33.8$ cps
Euler buckling force	$P_* = 183$ kg
Constant component of the axial force	$P_0 = 55$ kg
Amplitude of the variable component (at $n = 1$)	$\overline{P}_t = 54.2$ kg
Excitation parameter	$\bar{\mu} = \dfrac{\overline{P}_t}{2(P_* - P_0)} = \dfrac{54.2}{2(183 - 55)} = 0.212$
Reduced longitudinal mass	$M_L g = 316$ kg
Coefficient of nonlinear inertia	$\kappa = \dfrac{(3.14^4)(316)}{(4)(6.0)(170)^2} = 0.044\ \text{cm}^{-2}$

The nonlinearities of the elasticity and also the linear and nonlinear damping are so small that they can be neglected in the calculation of amplitudes. The experimentally determined coefficient of linear damping, for example, is $\varepsilon = 0.08\ \text{sec}^{-1}$; therefore, the critical excitation parameter is

$$\mu_* = \frac{\Delta}{\pi} = \frac{2\varepsilon}{\Omega} = 0.0047 \ll \bar{\mu} .$$

The coefficient of nonlinear elasticity γ is small compared to $\kappa\Omega^2$, and therefore the influence of nonlinear elasticity can also be neglected.

The boundaries of the principal region of instability are determined from Eq. (1.43):

$$\theta_* = \frac{2\Omega}{\sqrt{1 \mp \bar{\mu}}} .$$

Substitution gives 61.3 cps and 75.9 cps for the lower and upper boundaries respectively. Experimental results give 60.8 cps and 74.2 cps (Fig. 40). The deviation is within the limits of the accuracy of the experimental recording of the oscillogram.

The vibration amplitudes are determined according to Eq. (5.22) in conjunction with Eq. (5.29):

$$A^2 = \frac{1 - n^2(1 - \bar{\mu})}{\kappa n^2} .$$

On the lower boundary of the region of instability, $n_*^2 = 1/(1 + \bar{\mu})$, from which $A^2 = 2\bar{\mu}/\kappa$ follows. The theoretical results are plotted in Figure 40 as a solid line. The somewhat higher values for the experimental amplitudes near the upper boundaries of the region of instability may be explained by the fact that the vibrations are always accompanied by more or less intensive beats. However, in the figure the maximum amplitudes are given without any correction for the error caused by the beats.

Analogous experiments were conducted with a number of other specimens, where the constant and periodic components of the axial force were varied for each of them. All the results agreed satisfactorily with the theory. The experimental data are shown in Figures 41 and 42.

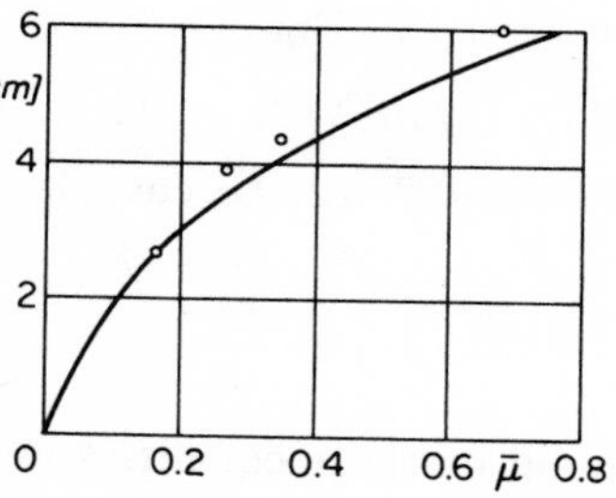

FIG. 41.

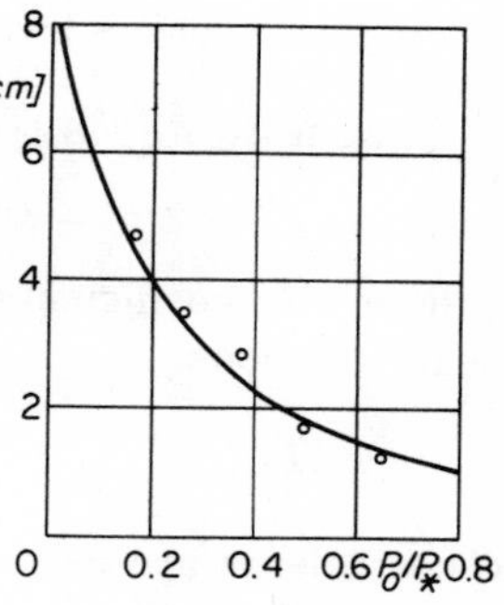

FIG. 42.

Figure 42 shows the variation of the vibration amplitudes at $\theta = 2\Omega$ for a changing P_0. In the case of increasing P_0, the natural frequency Ω decreases and the variable loading P_t drops accordingly.

Six

NONSTEADY-STATE VIBRATIONS

§ 23. Derivation of Differential Equations for Buildup of Vibrations. Stability of Vibrations

●1. We will now derive the differential equations for the buildup of vibrations for frequencies in the neighborhood of the principal resonance. For this purpose, we can use Eq. (5.10), treating a and b not as constant quantities but as slowly changing functions of time:

$$f(t) = a(t) \sin \frac{\theta t}{2} + b(t) \cos \frac{\theta t}{2} . \tag{6.1}$$

Let us recall that we have agreed to mean by the expression *slowly changing functions* that the increase of such a function during a period is small as compared to the average value for this period; i.e., the following inequalities are valid:

$$\begin{aligned} &\left|\frac{a'}{a}\right| \frac{4\pi}{\theta} \ll 1 , \qquad \left|\frac{b'}{b}\right| \frac{4\pi}{\theta} \ll 1 , \\ &\left|\frac{a''}{a'}\right| \frac{4\pi}{\theta} \ll 1 , \qquad \left|\frac{b''}{b'}\right| \frac{4\pi}{\theta} \ll 1 . \end{aligned} \tag{6.2}$$

We substitute Eq. (6.1) into the differential equation

$$f'' + 2\varepsilon f' + \Omega^2(1 - 2\mu \cos \theta t) f + \psi(f, f', f'') = 0 ,$$

where only the coefficients of $\sin \theta t/2$ and $\cos \theta t/2$ will be considered in the nonlinear functions:

$$\psi^*(f, f', f'') = \Phi(a, b) \sin \frac{\theta t}{2} + \Psi(a, b) \cos \frac{\theta t}{2} + \cdots .$$

These coefficients are calculated with the aid of the inequalities (6.2).

If the coefficients of $\sin \theta t/2$ and $\cos \theta t/2$ are set equal to zero, we then obtain the system of differential equations

$$\underline{a'' + 2\varepsilon a'} - \theta b' + \left(\Omega^2(1 + \mu) - \frac{\theta^2}{4}\right)a - \varepsilon\theta b + \Phi(a, b) = 0 ,$$

$$\underline{b'' + 2\varepsilon b'} + \theta a' + \left(\Omega^2(1 - \mu) - \frac{\theta^2}{4}\right)b + \varepsilon\theta a + \Psi(a, b) = 0 .$$

This system can be simplified if one considers the inequalities (6.2) and relatively small damping, $2\varepsilon/\Omega \ll 1$. As a result we obtain the system of differential equations

$$\begin{aligned} \theta\frac{db}{dt} &= \left(\Omega^2(1+\mu) - \frac{\theta^2}{4}\right)a - \varepsilon\theta b + \Phi(a, b)\,, \\ \theta\frac{da}{dt} &= -\left(\Omega^2(1-\mu) - \frac{\theta^2}{4}\right)b - \varepsilon\theta a - \Psi(a, b) \end{aligned} \tag{6.3}$$

for the buildup of transient vibrations.

The above system contains two first-order differential equations whose coefficients do not explicitly contain time. The investigation of these equations will present a simpler problem than the investigation of Eq. (5.1).

● **2.** The equations for steady-state amplitudes can be obtained from Eqs. (6.3) if one assumes that

$$\frac{da}{dt} = \frac{db}{dt} = 0\,.$$

These equations are obviously identical to Eqs. (5.11).

Let $a = a_0$, $b = b_0$ be one of the steady-state solutions which satisfy Eq. (5.11). Let us investigate the stability of these equations and consider the behavior of the system for a small disturbance of the amplitude values:

$$\begin{aligned} a &= a_0 + \xi\,, \\ b &= b_0 + \eta\,. \end{aligned} \tag{6.4}$$

If we substitute Eqs. (6.4) into Eqs. (6.3), we obtain the equations for the disturbed motion:

$$\begin{aligned} \theta\frac{d\eta}{dt} &= \left(\Omega^2(1+\mu) - \frac{\theta^2}{4}\right)(a_0+\xi) - \varepsilon\theta(b_0+\eta) + \Phi(a_0+\xi,\, b_0+\eta)\,, \\ \theta\frac{d\xi}{dt} &= -\left(\Omega^2(1-\mu) - \frac{\theta^2}{4}\right)(b_0+\eta) - \varepsilon\theta(a_0+\xi) + \Psi(a_0+\xi\,,\, b_0+\eta)\,. \end{aligned} \tag{6.5}$$

The perturbation functions $\Phi(a, b)$ and $\Psi(a, b)$ are expanded in the power series

$$\begin{aligned} \Phi(a, b) &= \Phi(a_0\,, b_0) + \left[\frac{\partial\Phi}{\partial a}\right]_0 \xi + \left[\frac{\partial\Phi}{\partial b}\right]_0 \eta + \cdots\,, \\ \Psi(a, b) &= \Psi(a_0\,, b_0) + \left[\frac{\partial\Psi}{\partial a}\right]_0 \xi + \left[\frac{\partial\Psi}{\partial b}\right]_0 \eta + \cdots\,. \end{aligned}$$

Further, we introduce the notation

$$\left[\frac{\partial\Phi}{\partial a}\right]_0 = \left[\frac{\partial\Phi}{\partial a}\right]_{\substack{a=a_0\\ b=b_0}}\,,$$

$$\left[\frac{\partial\Phi}{\partial b}\right]_0 = \left[\frac{\partial\Phi}{\partial b}\right]_{\substack{a=a_0\\ b=b_0}}$$

and so forth, and substituting these expressions into Eqs. (6.5) obtain

$$\theta \frac{d\eta}{dt} = \left(\Omega^2(1+\mu) - \frac{\theta^2}{4}\right)\xi - \varepsilon\theta\eta + \left[\frac{\partial\Phi}{\partial a}\right]_0 \xi + \left[\frac{\partial\Phi}{\partial b}\right]_0 \eta + \cdots,$$

$$\theta \frac{\partial\xi}{\partial t} = -\left(\Omega^2(1-\mu) - \frac{\theta^2}{4}\right)\eta - \varepsilon\theta\xi - \left[\frac{\partial\Psi}{\partial a}\right]_0 \xi - \left[\frac{\partial\Psi}{\partial b}\right]_0 \eta + \cdots.$$

For sufficiently small disturbances, the behavior of the system is determined by a linear approximation. The corresponding differential equations are the *variational equations.* These equations have the form

$$\begin{aligned} \theta \frac{d\xi}{dt} &= a_{11}\xi + a_{12}\eta, \\ \theta \frac{d\eta}{dt} &= a_{21}\xi + a_{22}\eta \end{aligned} \tag{6.6}$$

where

$$a_{11} = -\left[\frac{\partial\Psi}{\partial a}\right]_0 - \varepsilon\theta,$$

$$a_{12} = -\left[\Omega^2(1-\mu) - \frac{\theta^2}{4}\right] - \left[\frac{\partial\Psi}{\partial b}\right]_0,$$

$$a_{22} = \left[\frac{\partial\Phi}{\partial b}\right]_0 - \varepsilon\theta,$$

$$a_{21} = \left[\Omega^2(1+\mu) - \frac{\theta^2}{4}\right] + \left[\frac{\partial\Phi}{\partial a}\right]_0.$$

The expressions

$$\xi = \xi_0 e^{(\lambda/\theta)t}, \qquad \eta = \eta_0 e^{(\lambda/\theta)t}$$

satisfy the variational equations. The characteristic equation has the form

$$\begin{vmatrix} a_{11} - \lambda & a_{12} \\ a_{21} & a_{22} - \lambda \end{vmatrix} = 0. \tag{6.7}$$

The disturbances ξ and η decay with time only if both roots of λ have negative real parts. Obviously this condition is fulfilled for

$$a_{11} + a_{22} < 0, \tag{6.8}$$

and

$$\begin{vmatrix} a_{11} & a_{12} \\ a_{21} & a_{22} \end{vmatrix} > 0. \tag{6.9}$$

● 3. Let us first investigate the stability of the initial form of equilibrium, $a_0 = b_0 = 0$.

Since the functions $\Phi(a, b)$ and $\Psi(a, b)$ are homogeneous third-order polynomials, then obviously

$$\left[\frac{\partial\Phi}{\partial a}\right]_0 = \left[\frac{\partial\Phi}{\partial b}\right]_0 = \left[\frac{\partial\Psi}{\partial a}\right]_0 = \left[\frac{\partial\Psi}{\partial b}\right]_0 = 0.$$

The inequality (6.8) for this case gives $\varepsilon > 0$ (the damping must therefore be different from zero). This condition is fulfilled for all practical problems. The inequalities (6.9) take the following form after a rearrangement of rows and columns:

$$\begin{vmatrix} \Omega^2(1+\mu) - \dfrac{\theta^2}{4} & -\varepsilon\theta \\ \varepsilon\theta & \Omega^2(1-\mu) - \dfrac{\theta^2}{4} \end{vmatrix} > 0 .$$

If this condition is written with an equals sign, it is identical to Eq. (2.12) for the boundary frequencies in the harmonic approximation. The condition is therefore fulfilled everywhere except in the principal resonance region.

Let us now investigate the stability of the non-zero solutions. We will confine ourselves to the case which includes only nonlinear inertia in the nonlinear expression:

$$\begin{aligned} \frac{\partial\Phi}{\partial a} &= -\frac{\kappa\theta^2}{4}(3a^2+b^2) , \\ \frac{\partial\Phi}{\partial b} &= \frac{\partial\Psi}{\partial a} = -\frac{\kappa\theta^2}{2}ab , \\ \frac{\partial\Psi}{\partial b} &= -\frac{\kappa\theta^2}{4}(a^2+3b^2) . \end{aligned} \tag{6.10}$$

The application of the criterion (6.8) gives $\varepsilon > 0$ (the damping must differ from zero). To simplify the calculations, we will assume the damping is so small that it can be neglected.

The first solution of the problem as given by Eq. (5.13) is

$$a_0 = \frac{1}{n\sqrt{\kappa}}\sqrt{1-n^2+\mu}, \qquad b_0 = 0 .$$

By substitution into Eqs. (6.10), we obtain

$$\begin{aligned} \left[\frac{\partial\Phi}{\partial a}\right]_0 &= -3\Omega^2(1+\mu) + \frac{3\theta^2}{4} , \\ \left[\frac{\partial\Phi}{\partial b}\right]_0 &= \left[\frac{\partial\Psi}{\partial a}\right]_0 = 0 , \\ \left[\frac{\partial\Psi}{\partial b}\right]_0 &= -\Omega^2(1+\mu) + \frac{\theta^2}{4} , \end{aligned}$$

and therefore,

$$\begin{aligned} a_{11} &= a_{22} = 0 , \\ a_{12} &= 2\mu\Omega^2 , \\ a_{21} &= -2\left(\Omega^2(1+\mu) + \frac{\theta^2}{4}\right) . \end{aligned}$$

One easily sees that for $\theta < 2\Omega\sqrt{1+\mu}$, i.e., in the entire region where the first solution exists (Fig. 29c), the inequality

$$\begin{vmatrix} a_{11} & a_{12} \\ a_{21} & a_{22} \end{vmatrix} > 0$$

is satisfied and, of course, $a_{11} + a_{22} \equiv 0$. In the damped-free case both characteristic roots are purely imaginary, i.e., the perturbations do not decay asymptotically although they remain bounded with respect to time. According to Liapunov, this is one of the cases in which the first approximation cannot determine whether the solutions are stable or unstable. This result is due to the simplifications of the problem. It is sufficient to assume the presence of an arbitrarily small damping in order to obtain $a_{11} + a_{22} < 0$, by which the so-called "asymptotic" stable solutions are guaranteed.

It can be shown in an analogous manner that the second solution,

$$a_0 = 0\,, \qquad b_0 = \frac{1}{n\sqrt{\kappa}}\sqrt{1 - n^2 - \mu}\,,$$

is unstable. The calculation is left to the reader.

●4. So far we have investigated the stability with respect to small perturbations, or more briefly, *stability in the small*. The stability with respect to perturbations of finite magnitude is of great practical importance; one denotes this *stability in the large*. This will be illustrated by an example (Fig. 43).

Let us assume that the exciting frequency of the system is found outside of the resonance region; it is smaller than the lowest boundary frequency ($OM < OC$). In this case, the zero solution is stable and transverse vibrations will not occur. However, at the same frequency still another stable solution is possible, corresponding to steady-state transverse vibrations with the amplitude MN. These vibrations can be realized by selecting a value from the resonance region CD for the frequency of the system, and through this attaining "overhanging" vibrations by a stepwise decrease of the exciting frequency. These same vibrations can be developed differently; if one imparts a sufficiently strong perturbation to the system, this disturbance "grows" on the stable branch ND of the amplitude curve. For example, a transverse impulse or an initial deflection of the rod can be such a perturbation. In the following, we will have the case of "amplitude" perturbation in mind.

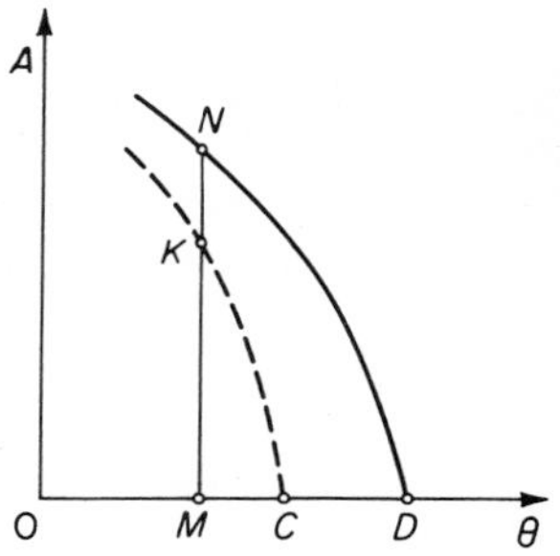

FIG. 43.

The unstable branch KC plays an important role in determining if the rise of steady-state vibrations depends upon the magnitude of the disturbance. This branch plays the role of a "divide," separating the region of "attraction" of the zero solution from the region of "attraction" of the solutions which correspond to the points on ND. As long as the disturbance is smaller than KM, the system returns to the original state of equilibrium. If the disturbance is larger than KM, steady-state vibrations arise with an amplitude MN (Benz [1])**[33].

The limiting depth of the "overhang" is determined by the "stability

[33] References followed by a double asterisk were added in the German translation.

in the large." If one uses the theory of small perturbations, one finds that the steady-state solution corresponding to the branch ND is stable in all regions of its existence. However, experiments show that frequencies lying only slightly below the resonance region CD cause a "break" of the vibrations. The depth of the "overhang" is influenced by the disturbances that are not eliminated in practice; steady-state vibrations are stable until the system is transferred to the unstable branch KC by the disturbances.

The magnitude of the disturbances for which steady-state vibrations can still be maintained decreases as the frequency moves away from the resonance region (see Fig. 43). The smaller the disturbances, the farther the frequency of the system can be removed from the region of parametric excitation. Under laboratory conditions it is possible to obtain "overhanging" vibrations whose amplitude is more than twice as great as the amplitude of the vibrations on the lower boundary of the excitation region. An oscillogram of such a form has already been shown in Figure 31.

Moreover, the limiting depth of the "overhang" is fundamentally bounded. Thus, in the damped-free case, the "overhang" can progress only up to the frequency

$$\theta_\infty = \sqrt{\frac{3\gamma}{\kappa}} .$$

This is clearly shown in Figure 34. The limiting depth of the "overhang" is also influenced by linear and nonlinear damping (Fig. 44).

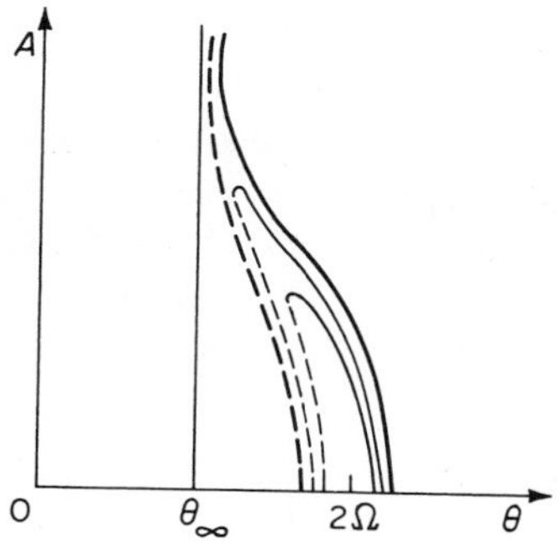

FIG. 44.

It should be noted that only one of the possible disturbances was considered, i.e., the amplitude disturbance. In real problems, variations of the exciting frequency, the loading amplitude, etc., can be considered as disturbances. A comprehensive investigation can be obtained by the use of qualitative methods in the theory of differential equations.

§ 24. The Buildup of Vibrations[34]

●1. We obtained the system of equations (6.3) for the calculation of non-steady-state vibrations in the neighborhood of the principal resonance. With the notation given in (5.14), we can write this system in the form

$$\begin{aligned} \frac{4n^2}{\theta}\frac{db}{dt} &= (1 + \mu - n^2)a - \frac{n\Delta}{\pi}b + \Phi(a, b) , \\ \frac{4n^2}{\theta}\frac{da}{dt} &= -(1 - \mu - n^2)b - \frac{n\Delta}{\pi}a - \Psi(a, b) . \end{aligned} \tag{6.11}$$

One can obtain a complete solution of the system (6.11) for only a few special cases. If one assumes the amplitudes sufficiently small, one can

[34] See the investigation of the building-up of vibrations performed by F. Weidenhammer [7]**.

neglect nonlinear terms and obtain the system of equations

$$\frac{4n^2}{\theta}\frac{db}{dt} = (1+\mu-n^2)a - \frac{n\Delta}{\pi}b\,,$$
$$\frac{4n^2}{\theta}\frac{da}{dt} = -(1-\mu-n^2)b - \frac{n\Delta}{\pi}a\,.$$

A substitution of $a = a_0e^{ht}$ and $b = b_0e^{ht}$ leads to the characteristic equation

$$\begin{vmatrix} 1+\mu-n^2 & -\frac{n\Delta}{\pi}-\frac{4n^2h}{\theta} \\ -\frac{n\Delta}{\pi}-\frac{4n^2h}{\theta} & -(1-\mu-n^2) \end{vmatrix} = 0\,.$$

The solution of this equation gives

$$h = \pm\frac{\Omega}{2n}\sqrt{\mu^2-(1-n^2)^2} - \varepsilon\,. \tag{6.12}$$

The maximum value of the characteristic exponent is obtained near $\theta = 2\Omega$ where

$$h_{\max} \approx \frac{\mu\Omega}{2} - \varepsilon\,.$$

In a general case it is necessary to use numerical integration, which is sufficiently simple. If we take the half-period, $\Delta t = \pi/\theta$, of the exciting force as the time interval, then according to the "tangent method" we obtain

$$a_{k+1} = a_k + \Delta a_k\,,$$
$$b_{k+1} = b_k + \Delta b_k\,;$$

where

$$\Delta a_k = \frac{\pi}{4n^2}\left[-(1-\mu-n^2)b_k - \frac{n\Delta}{\pi}a_k - \Psi(a_k, b_k)\right],$$
$$\Delta b_k = \frac{\pi}{4n^2}\left[(1+\mu-n^2)a_k - \frac{n\Delta}{\pi}b_k + \Phi(a_k, b_k)\right].$$

The result of the numerical integration for one of the examples is given in Figure 45. In addition, a dashed curve corresponding to the exponential growth of the amplitudes with the exponent given in Eq. (6.12) and the

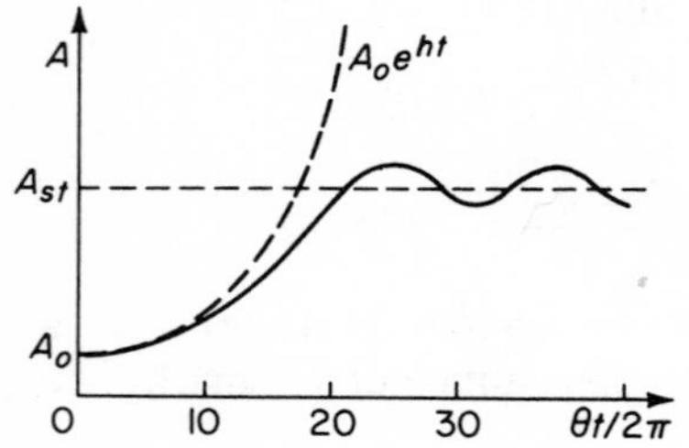

FIG. 45.

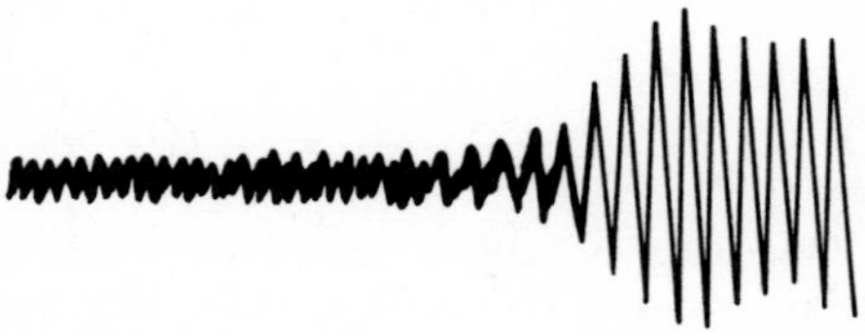

FIG. 46.

horizontal line $A = A_{st}$ corresponding to steady-state amplitude are also given. It is seen from the figure that while the amplitudes are not very large, the growth of the amplitudes is described with great accuracy by the exponential law. The results of the integration show that other solutions corresponding to beating arise along with the steady-state solutions of the system (6.11).

●**2.** We now discuss the experimental results. All oscillograms of the build-up of the vibrations have an initial section showing an exponential increase (Fig. 8). From the oscillogram one can obtain a characteristic exponent that agrees rather well with theoretical values given in Eq. (6.12).

The following data correspond to the oscillogram shown in Figure 8:

$$\Omega = 40.5 \text{ cps}, \quad n = 0.97,$$
$$\mu = 0.123, \quad \varepsilon = 0.12 \text{ sec}^{-1}.$$

The substitution of these values into Eq. (6.12) gives $h = 2.24 \text{ sec}^{-1}$ whereas the experimental values determined by the formula

$$h = \frac{1}{\Delta t} \ln \frac{\Delta_{k+1}}{A_k}$$

vary within the limits $h = 2.15$–2.07 sec^{-1}.

Characteristic diagrams of the build-up of these vibrations are given in Figures 46 and 47. It can be seen from Figure 46 that the forced vibrations occuring with the frequency of the longitudinal force are gradually forced out by parametrically excited vibrations occurring with half the frequency. The oscillogram shown in Figure 47 corresponds to a substantial excitation parameter ($\mu = 0.27$). The amplitudes increase in a typical nonlinear manner, accompanied by beats.

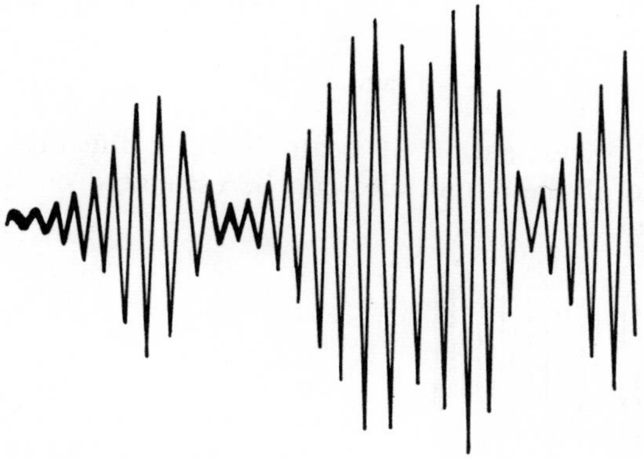

FIG. 47.

§ 25. Condition of Beats

●**1.** Experiments indicate that beats can also occur in addition to steady-state vibrations of constant amplitude. Some oscillograms of beats are shown in Figures 48–52.

In the first case, the envelope of the beats is described with sufficient accuracy by the harmonic law; in the second, it contains a large number of harmonics. In general, one notices that the intensity of the beats (in the case where the nonlinear inertia is predominant) decreases appreciably as the lower boundary of the region of excitation is approached. This is seen from the oscillograms in Figures 48–50 obtained for three successively decreasing values of the exciting frequency.

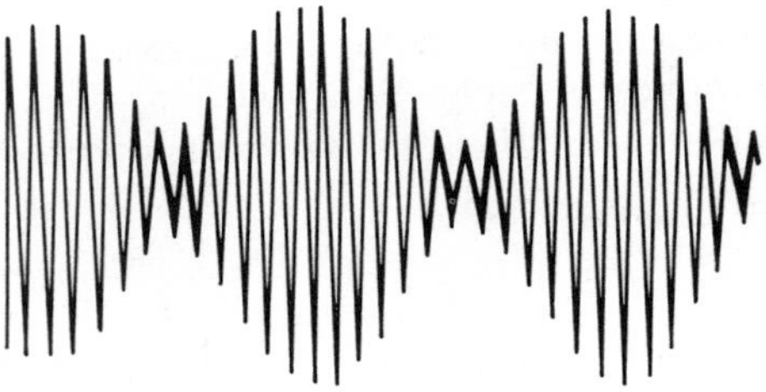

FIG. 48.

For small excitation parameters, the beats do not appear at all. The vibrations are steady-state (Fig. 51). Conversely, for very large excitation parameters, the vibrations are essentially nonlinear: the amplitudes increase quickly until disruptions of the vibrations occur (Fig. 52).

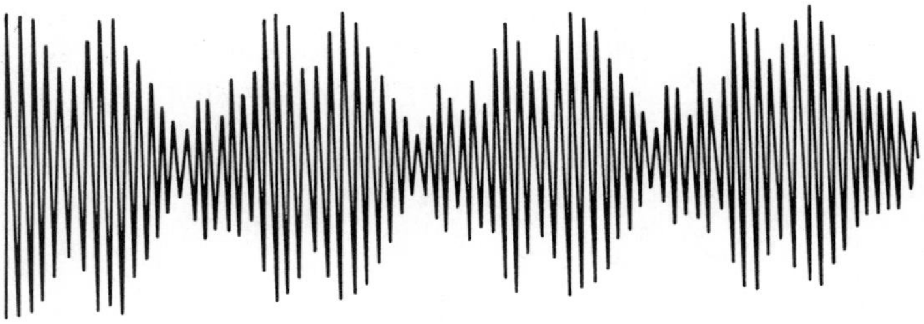

FIG. 49.

●2. An analytical investigation of beats is very difficult. However, the order of magnitude of the amplitudes can be estimated on the basis of the following considerations.

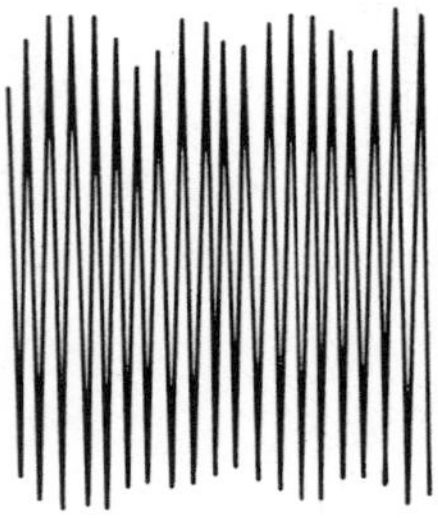

FIG. 50.

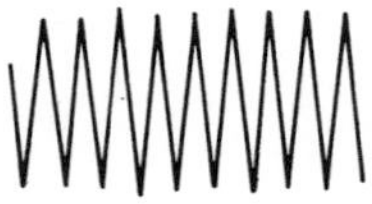

FIG. 51.

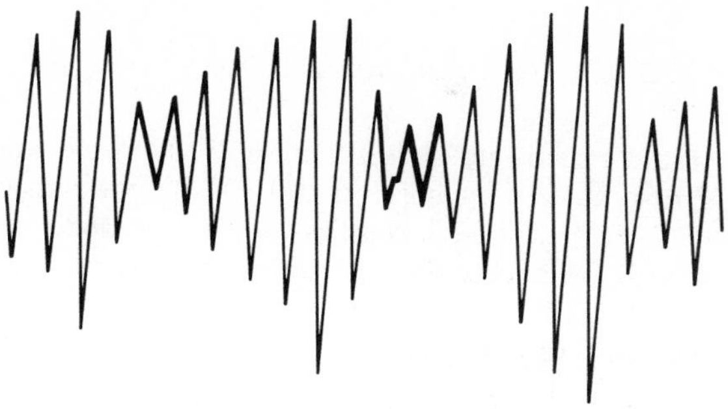

FIG. 52.

Let us try to satisfy the differential equations (6.11), using the expressions

$$a = a_0 \cos \alpha t\,, \qquad b = b_0 \sin \alpha t \tag{6.13}$$

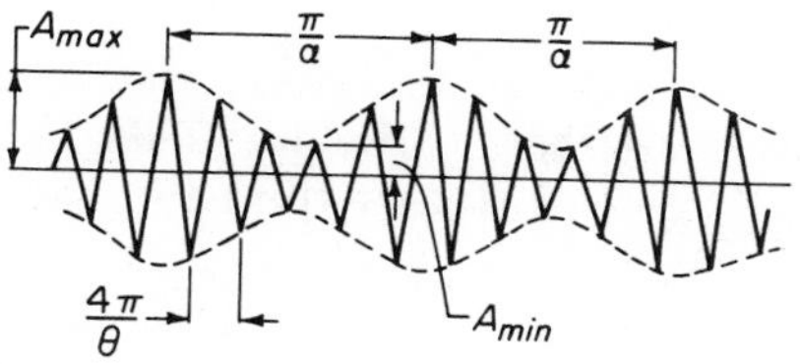

FIG. 53.

where a_0 and b_0 are constant coefficients; the beat frequency α is assumed to be sufficiently small compared to the exciting frequency θ (Fig. 53). Only under this condition can the expressions (6.13) be considered as slowly changing functions of time.

The vibration amplitude is

$$A = \sqrt{a^2 + b^2}$$

or

$$A = \sqrt{\frac{a_0^2 + b_0^2}{2} + \frac{a_0^2 - b_0^2}{2} \cos 2\alpha t}\,.$$

Let $|a_0| > |b_0|$. In this case it is obvious that

$$A_{\max} = |a_0|\,,$$
$$A_{\min} = |b_0|\,.$$

Confining ourselves to the case of nonlinear inertia, we find

$$\Phi(a, b) = -\kappa n^2 a A^2 = -\frac{\kappa n^2 a_0}{4}(3a_0^2 + b_0^2) \cos \alpha t + \cdots\,,$$

$$\Psi(a, b) = -\kappa n^2 b A^2 = -\frac{\kappa n^2 b_0}{4}(a_0^2 + 3b_0^2) \sin \alpha t + \cdots\,.$$

These values and also Eq. (6.13) are substituted into Eq. (6.11). If damping is not taken into account, we obtain

$$\frac{2n\alpha}{\Omega}b_0 = (1+\mu-n^2)a_0 - \frac{\kappa n^2 a_0}{4}(3a_0{}^2 + b_0{}^2)\,,$$
$$\frac{2n\alpha}{\Omega}a_0 = (1-\mu-n^2)b_0 - \frac{\kappa n^2 b_0}{4}(a_0{}^2 + 3b_0{}^2)\,. \tag{6.14}$$

Equation (6.14) contains three unknowns, namely, the beat amplitudes a_0 and b_0 and the beat frequency α. By solving Eq. (6.14), we can express two unknowns in terms of the third, which remains undetermined. For the solution of the problem, it will be necessary to make use of some additional physical considerations.

Eliminating the beat frequency α from Eq. (6.14), we obtain

$$(1+\mu-\mathrm{n}^2)\alpha_0^2 - \frac{3\kappa n^2}{4}(a_0{}^4 - b_0{}^4) - (1-\mu-n^2)b_0{}^2 = 0\,.$$

Since
$$\frac{1+\mu-n^2}{\kappa n^2} = A_0{}^2,$$

where A_0 is the amplitude of steady-state vibrations, the equation previously obtained takes the form

$$\frac{3}{4}a_0^4 - A_0^2 a_0^2 + \frac{1-\mu-n^2}{1+\mu-n^2}A_0{}^2 b_0{}^2 - \frac{3}{4}b_0{}^4 = 0\,. \tag{6.15}$$

Equation (6.15) contains the minimum amplitude of the beats, b_0, in addition to the basic unknown a_0. Experiments show that $b_0^2/a_0^2 \ll 1$. This is seen, for example, from Figure 48. Eliminating the b_0 terms from Eq. (6.15) on this basis, we obtain

$$A_{\max} \approx \frac{2}{\sqrt{3}}A_0\,. \tag{6.16}$$

Thus, the maximum amplitude for the beats exceeds the steady-state amplitude by approximately 15 percent.

In a more rigorous examination, one must consider also the initial conditions, since they define the character of the vibrations in many respects.

Seven

SECONDARY RESONANCES

§ 26. Parametrically Excited Vibrations for Second-Order Resonances[35]

●1. The amplitudes of steady-state vibrations occurring near the second-order resonance can be determined from Eq. (5.9).

We confine ourselves to the harmonic approximation

$$f(t) = b_0 + a_2 \sin \theta t + b_2 \cos \theta t \,, \tag{7.1}$$

which leads to the system of equations

$$\begin{aligned} \Omega^2(b_0 - \mu b_2) + \Psi_0(a_2, b_0, b_2) &= 0 \,, \\ (\Omega^2 - \theta^2)a_2 - 2\varepsilon\theta b_2 + \Phi_2(a_2, b_0, b_2) &= 0 \,, \\ (\Omega^2 - \theta^2)b_2 - 2\mu\Omega^2 b_0 + 2\varepsilon\theta a_2 + \Psi_2(a_2, b_0, b_2) &= 0 \,, \end{aligned} \tag{7.2}$$

considering only one nonlinear inertia term:

$$\psi(f, f', f'') = 2\kappa f[f f'' + (f')^2] \,.$$

Substituting Eq. (7.1) and carrying out the necessary transformations, we obtain

$$\begin{aligned} \psi^*(f, f', f'') = &- \kappa\theta^2 b_0(a_2{}^2 + b_2{}^2) - \kappa\theta^2[a_2(a_2{}^2 + b_2{}^2) + 2b_0{}^2 a_2] \sin \theta t \\ &- \kappa\theta^2[b_2(a_2{}^2 + b_2{}^2) + 2b_0{}^2 b_2] \cos \theta t \,, \end{aligned}$$

where terms containing higher harmonics have been neglected. Denoting

$$A^2 = a_2{}^2 + b_2{}^2$$

we have

$$\begin{aligned} \Psi_0 &= - \kappa\theta^2 b_0 A^2 \,, \\ \Phi_2 &= - \kappa\theta^2 a_2(A^2 + 2b_0^2) \,, \\ \Psi_2 &= - \kappa\theta^2 b_2(A^2 + 2b_0^2) \,. \end{aligned}$$

Substitution into Eqs. (7.2) gives

$$\begin{aligned} b_0 - \mu b_2 - \kappa n^2 b_0 A^2 &= 0 \,, \\ (1 - n^2)a_2 - \frac{n\Delta}{\pi} b_2 - \kappa n^2 a_2(A^2 + 2b_0{}^2) &= 0 \,, \\ (1 - n^2)b_2 - 2\mu b_0 + \frac{n\Delta}{\pi} a_2 - \kappa n^2 b_2(A^2 + 2b_0{}^2) &= 0 \,. \end{aligned} \tag{7.3}$$

[35] See Bolotin [6].

Here, in contrast to the notation in previous chapters, $n = \theta/\Omega$.

By solving the system of nonlinear equations (7.3), we can determine the amplitude of the steady-state vibrations A and the constant component of the dynamic deflection b_0.

●2. We will first investigate the conservative problem ($\Delta = 0$). In this case Eqs. (7.3) can be satisfied by

$$b_0 = b_2 = 0\,, \qquad a_2 = A \qquad \text{(first solution)},$$

or by

$$a_2 = 0\,, \quad b_0 \neq 0\,, \quad b_2 = A \qquad \text{(second solution)}.$$

The amplitude of the first solution is determined from

$$(1 - n^2)A - \kappa n^2 A^3 = 0\,;$$

hence,

$$A = \frac{\sqrt{1 - n^2}}{n\sqrt{\kappa}} \tag{7.4}$$

The second solution leads to the system of equations

$$b_0 - \mu A - \kappa n^2 b_0 A^2 = 0\,,$$
$$(1 - n^2)A - 2\mu b_0 - \kappa n^2 A(A^2 + 2b_0^2) = 0\,.$$

From the first equation we find

$$b_0 = \frac{\mu A}{1 - \kappa n^2 A^2} \approx \mu A\,;$$

substitution in the second equation yields

$$(1 - n^2 - 2\mu^2)A - \kappa n^2 A^3(1 + 2\mu^2) = 0$$

or

$$A = \frac{1}{n\sqrt{\kappa}}\sqrt{\frac{1 - n^2 - 2\mu^2}{1 + 2\mu^2}}\,. \tag{7.5}$$

It can be shown that only the first of the two solutions is stable; however, this can be seen from the very form of the solutions (Fig. 54).

The identically vanishing solution is unstable in the interval $1 - 2\mu^2 \leqq n^2 \leqq 1$ bounded by the zero solutions of (7.4) and (7.5), and agrees with the results of linear theory.[36]

The resonance curves for the second region of dynamic instability resemble the shapes of the curves obtained for the principal resonance. In particular, here as in the case of the principal resonance, an "overhang" in the direction of lower frequencies can occur (Fig. 54). The figure also shows that the steady-state amplitudes are considerably smaller than for the case of the principal reso-

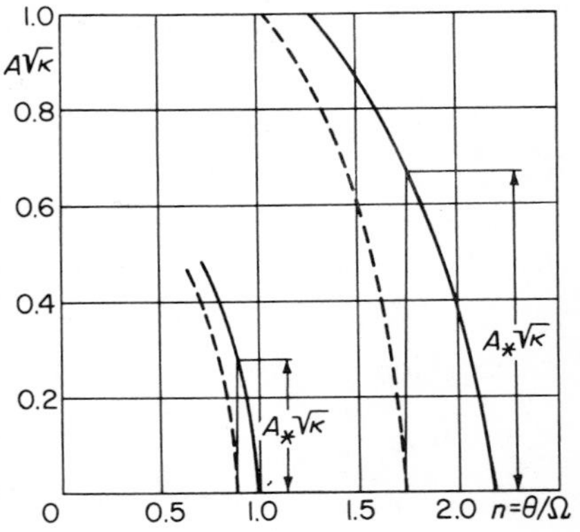

FIG. 54.

[36] The first of the formulas (1.36) results when a greater number of the terms in the series is retained than in (7.1).

nance. Thus, Eq. (7.4) gives

$$A_* = \mu\sqrt{\frac{2}{\kappa(1-2\mu^2)}}$$

for the lower endpoint of the region of instability, whereas for the principal resonance we obtain

$$A_* = \sqrt{\frac{2\mu}{\kappa(1-\mu)}}\,.$$

The dependence of the vibration amplitude on the excitation parameter is shown in Figure 55. One can see that the difference in the amplitudes is particularly large for small values of μ.

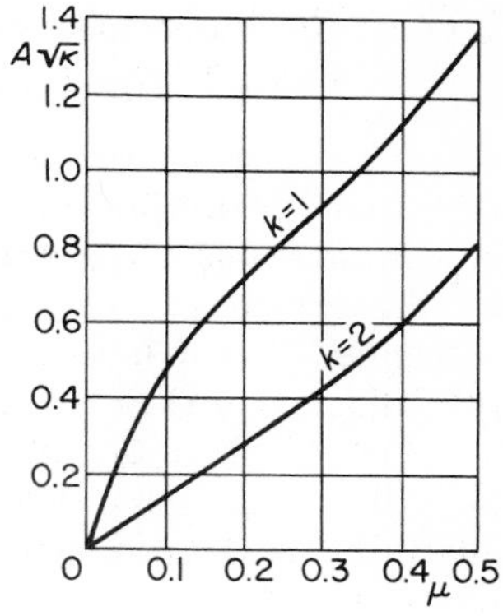

FIG. 55.

●**3.** In considering damping, the differences in the amplitudes prove to be still greater. An equation for determining the steady-state amplitudes is obtained by equating to zero the determinant composed of the coefficients of Eqs. (7.3):

$$\begin{vmatrix} 1-n^2-\kappa n^2(A^2+2b_0^2) & 0 & -\dfrac{n\Delta}{\pi} \\ 0 & 1-\kappa n^2A^2 & -\mu \\ \dfrac{n\Delta}{\pi} & -2\mu & 1-n^2-\kappa n^2(A^2+2b_0^2) \end{vmatrix} = 0\,.$$

This equation contains the constant component of dynamic deflection b_0 in addition to the amplitude A. As in the conservative case, $b_0^2/A^2 \ll 1$. Neglecting the small quantities leads to the equation

$$\begin{vmatrix} 1-n^2-\kappa n^2A^2 & 0 & -\dfrac{\Delta}{\pi} \\ 0 & 1 & -\mu \\ \dfrac{\Delta}{\pi} & -2\mu & 1-n^2-\kappa n^2A^2 \end{vmatrix} = 0\,;$$

its solution gives

$$A = \frac{1}{n\sqrt{\kappa}}\sqrt{1-n^2-\mu^2\pm\sqrt{\mu^4-\left(\frac{\Delta}{\pi}\right)^2}}\,. \qquad (7.6)$$

As long as the expression under the inner radical is positive, Eq. (7.6) gives two real roots for the amplitude. The critical value

$$\mu_* = \sqrt{\frac{\Delta}{\pi}}$$

of the coefficient μ, (the point at which it is still possible to excite a second-order resonance), coincides with the value obtained on the basis of linear theory (§ 9).

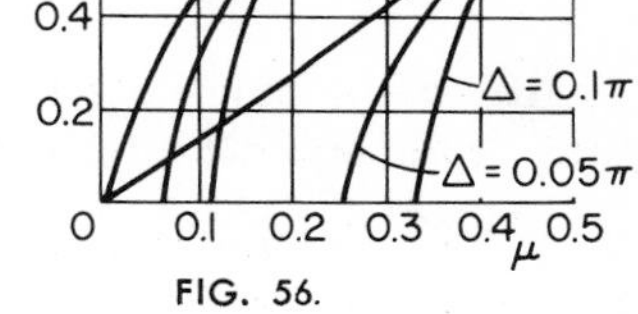

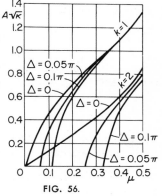

FIG. 56.

The curves showing the dependence of the amplitudes on the excitation parameter and the decrement of damping are given in Figure 56.

§ 27. The Influence of Initial Curvature and Eccentricity. Forced Vibrations

● 1. We have investigated homogeneous equations derived under the assumption that the initial curvature of the rod, the eccentricity of the axial force, and similar nonhomogeneity factors were absent. More exactly, these factors were assumed to be sufficiently small and played the role of "small disturbances" in the initial conditions of the problem. We will now investigate the influence of these factors on the magnitude of the steady-state amplitudes.

The problem of the vibrations of slightly curved rods subjected to a periodic axial force has already been investigated in the literature. An analysis based on linear differential equations (Mettler [2]) has only limited importance.[37]

Let us investigate the problem of the vibrations of a rod having an initial curvature $v_0(x)$ (Fig. 57). The differential equation of the linear vibration problem has the form

$$EJ\frac{\partial^4 v}{\partial x^4} + (P_0 + P_t \cos \theta t)\frac{\partial^2 v}{\partial x^2} + m\frac{\partial^2 v}{\partial t^2} = -(P_0 + P_t \cos \theta t)\frac{\partial^2 v_0}{\partial x^2}$$

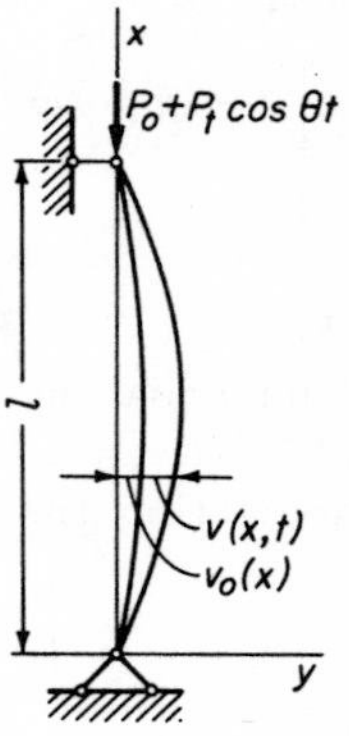

FIG. 57.

(the dynamic deflection is measured from the curved axis of the rod). Assuming that

$$v(x, t) = f(t) \sin \frac{\pi x}{l},$$

$$v_0(x) = f_0 \sin \frac{\pi x}{l},$$

and after substitution and simple transformations, we arrive at the ordinary differential equation

$$f'' + \Omega^2(1 - 2\mu \cos \theta t) f = \frac{\omega^2 f_0}{P_*}(P_0 + P_t \cos \theta t).$$

Adding to this equation terms that take damping and the nonlinearity of the system into account, we obtain

$$f'' + 2\varepsilon f' + \Omega^2(1 - 2\mu \cos \theta t) f + \psi(f, f', f'') = \frac{\omega^2 f_0}{P_*}(P_0 + P_t \cos \theta t). \quad (7.7)$$

In this manner the influence of the initial curvature has been accounted for. The eccentricity will be considered in the following manner. The

[37] The nonlinear transverse vibrations of a slightly curved rod were investigated by F. Weidenhammer [8]**.

expression $M = Pe$ for the additional bending moment resulting from the eccentricicy is expanded in a Fourier series:

$$M = \frac{4Pe}{\pi} \sum_{k=1,3,5}^{\infty} \frac{1}{k} \sin \frac{k\pi x}{l} .$$

Since only the first term of this series can be considered for small eccentricities, we obtain for the "equivalent curvature"

$$f_0 = \frac{4e}{\pi} .$$

●2. Let us now return to Eq. (7.7). Since our purpose is the investigation of the vibrations of the system near $\theta = \Omega$, we will seek the solution in the form of Eq. (7.1) as before. Substituting this expression into Eq. (7.7), we obtain a system of algebraic equations in terms of coefficients b_0, a_2, and b_2:

$$\begin{aligned} b_0 - \mu b_2 - \kappa n^2 b_0 A^2 &= \frac{f_0 P_0}{P_* - P_0} , \\ (1 - n^2)a_2 - \frac{n\Delta}{\pi} b_2 - \kappa n^2 a_2 (A^2 + 2b_0^2) &= 2f_0\mu , \\ (1 - n^2)b_2 - 2\mu b_0 + \frac{n\Delta}{\pi} a_2 - \kappa n^2 b_2 (A^2 + 2b_0^2) &= 0 . \end{aligned} \tag{7.8}$$

This system of equations differs from the homogeneous system (7.3) by the presence of terms on the right-hand side.

We will distinguish three cases:

(a) The frequency of the system is outside the secondary regions of instability. In this case, the determinant of the system of equations obtained from Eqs. (7.8), as a result of neglecting nonlinear terms, is different from zero:

$$\begin{vmatrix} 1 - n^2 & 0 & -\frac{n\Delta}{n} \\ 0 & 1 & -\mu \\ \frac{n\Delta}{\pi} & -2\mu & 1 - n^2 \end{vmatrix} \neq 0 .$$

If, in addition, the nonlinearity of the system is not very large, the linear equations

$$\begin{aligned} b_0 - \mu b_2 &= \frac{f_0 P_0}{P_* - P_0} , \\ (1 - n^2)a_2 - \frac{n\Delta}{\pi} b_2 &= 2f_0\mu , \\ (1 - n^2)b_2 - 2\mu b_0 + \frac{n\Delta}{\pi} a_2 &= 0 \end{aligned} \tag{7.9}$$

give a satisfactory solution of the problem.

(b) The frequency of the system lies within the limits of the second region of instability and moreover, $\mu > 2\mu_*$. The influence of linear damping in this case is sufficiently small so that the magnitudes of the steady-state amplitudes are defined basically by the nonlinear terms. An approximate solution can be obtained by considering the equations

$$
\begin{aligned}
(1-n^2)a_2 - \kappa n^2 a_2(A^2 + 2b_0^2) &= 2f_0\mu\,, \\
b_0 - \mu b_2 - \kappa n^2 b_0 A^2 &= \frac{f_0 P_0}{P_* - P_0}\,, \\
(1-n^2)b_2 - 2\mu b_0 - \kappa n^2 b_2(A^2 + 2b_0^2) &= 0\,.
\end{aligned}
\tag{7.10}
$$

(c) If the frequency of the system lies within the limits of the second region of instability and $\mu \leqq 2\mu_*$, damping and nonlinear factors must be considered.

● **3.** We will dwell briefly on the first case, where the steady-state amplitudes can be determined by a linear approximation. By solving Eqs. (7.9) simultaneously, we obtain the following expressions for the coefficients of Eq. (7.1):

$$
\begin{aligned}
b_0 &= \frac{f_0 P_0}{P_* - P_0} + \frac{1-n^2}{(1-n^2)(1-n^2-2\mu^2) + (n\Delta/\pi)^2}\,\frac{2\mu f_0}{1-(P_0/P_*)}\,, \\
b_2 &= \frac{1-n^2}{(1-n^2)(1-n^2-2\mu^2) + (n\Delta/\pi)^2}\,\frac{2\mu f_0}{1-(P_0/P_*)}\,, \\
a_2 &= \frac{n\Delta/\pi}{(1-n^2)(1-n^2-2\mu^2) + (n\Delta/\pi)^2}\,\frac{2\mu f_0}{1-(P_0/P_*)}\,.
\end{aligned}
$$

In certain cases it is more convenient to measure the constant component of deflection from the axis of the original straight rod, $B_0 = f_0 + b_0$. Then,

$$
B_0 = \frac{f_0}{1-(P_0/P_*)}\left[1 + \frac{2\mu^2(1-n^2)}{(1-n^2)(1-n^2-2\mu^2) + (n\Delta/\pi)^2}\right]. \tag{7.11}
$$

The amplitude of the vibrations which occur near the new zero position is determined by

$$
A = \frac{\sqrt{(1-n^2)^2 + (n\Delta/\pi)^2}}{(1-n^2)(1-n^2-2\mu^2) + (n\Delta/\pi)^2}\,\frac{2\mu f_0}{1-(P_0/P_*)}\,. \tag{7.12}
$$

A curve characterizing the dependence of the amplitudes on the ratio of the frequencies is given in Figure 58. As seen from this figure, the appearance of the curve strongly resembles the ordinary resonance curves of forced vibrations. This does not mean, however, that the amplitudes of the vibrations can be determined from

$$
f'' + \Omega^2 f = \frac{\omega^2 f_0}{P_*}(P_0 + P_t \cos\theta t)
$$

by neglecting the periodic terms on the left-hand side. Such a crude method always gives lower values of the amplitudes. Furthermore, the error rapidly increases as the excitation parameter approaches its critical value. This question is investigated in more detail in an article by Bolotin [6].

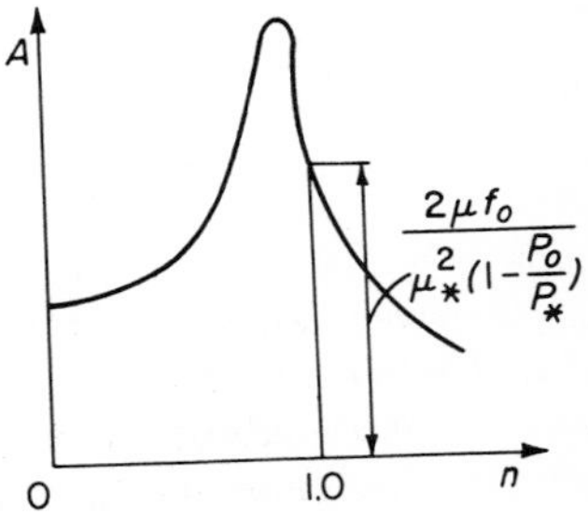

FIG. 58.

● **4.** Let us now investigate the second case. The system of equations (7.10) can be satisfied by setting

$$b_0 = 0\,, \quad b_2 = 0\,, \quad a_2 = A \qquad \text{(first solution)}\,,$$

or

$$a_2 = 0\,, \quad b_0 \neq 0\,, \quad b_2 = B \qquad \text{(second solution)}\,.$$

The first solution corresponds to parametrically excited vibrations and was obtained earlier in Eq. (7.4). For the determination of the second solution, we have the system of equations

$$b_0 - \mu B - \kappa n^2 b_0 B^2 = \frac{f_0 P_0}{P_* - P_0}\,,$$

$$(1 - n^2)B - 2\mu b_0 - \kappa n^2 B(B^2 + 2b_0^2) = 2f_0\mu\,.$$

From the first equation we obtain

$$b_0 = \frac{f_0 P_0}{P_* - P_0} + \frac{\mu B}{1 - \kappa n^2 B^2} \approx \frac{f_0 P_0}{P_* - P_0} + \mu B$$

Substitution in the second equation gives

$$\left[1 - n^2 - 2\mu^2 - 2\kappa n^2\left(\frac{f_0 P_0}{P_* - P_0}\right)^2\right]B - 4\kappa n^2 \frac{f_0 \mu P_0}{P_* - P_0} B^2$$

$$- \kappa n^2(1 + 2\mu^2)\, B^3 = \frac{2 f_0 \mu P_0}{P_* - P_0}\,.$$

Introducing the new unknown

$$x = B + \frac{f_0 \mu P_0}{P_* - P_0}\,\frac{1}{1 + 2\mu^2}\,,$$

we transform the equation obtained to the form

$$x^3 + 3px + 2q = 0\,. \tag{7.13}$$

The coefficients of Eq. (7.13) are determined by formulas that assume the simple forms

$$3p = -\frac{1 - n^2 - 2\mu^2}{\kappa n^2(1 + 2\mu^2)}\,,$$

$$2q = \frac{2 f_0 \mu}{\kappa n^2(1 + 2\mu^2)}\,,$$

for the case where a purely periodic loading $P(t) = P_t \cos \theta t$ is acting on the rod.

The real roots of Eq. (7.13) are determined by making use of the graphical method described in § 18. The corresponding construction is shown in Figure 59. If the exciting frequency is smaller than a critical value, Eq. (7.13) has three real roots, two of which correspond to the steady-state vibration (Fig. 60). If the exciting frequency is greater than this value, Eq. (7.13) has then only one real root.

The resonance curve is bent toward the lower frequencies. During a gradual increase of the frequency θ, the amplitude of the forced vibrations

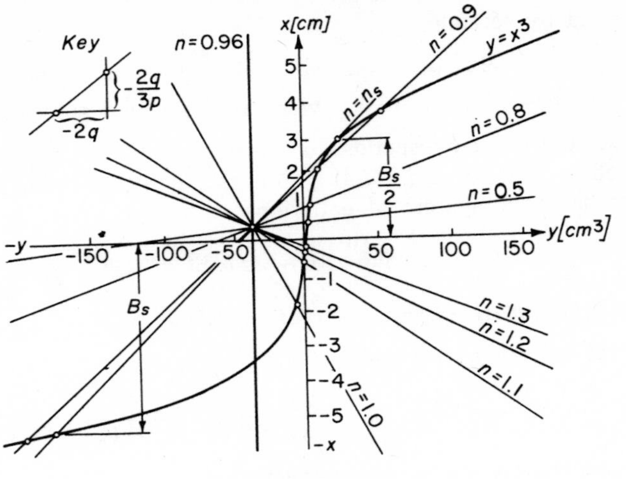

FIG. 59.

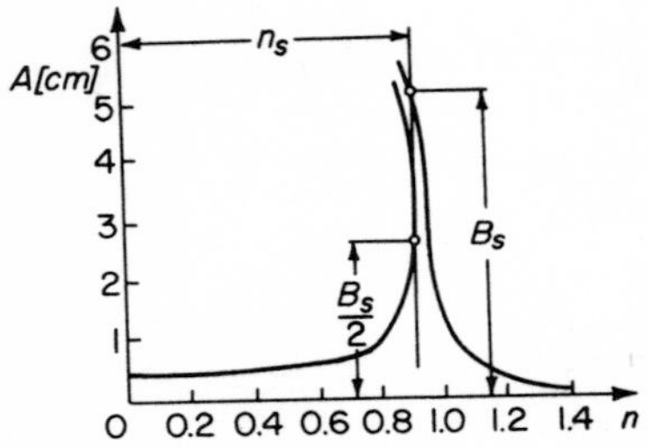

FIG. 60.

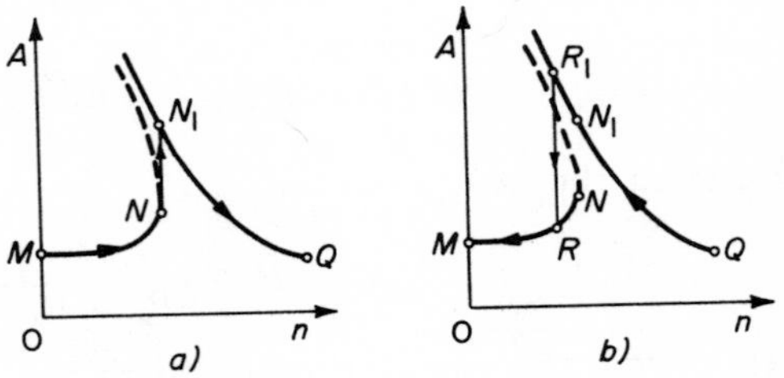

FIG. 61.

increases at first along the curve MN (Fig. 61a) until the amplitude at the point N jumps by the magnitude NN_1. The vibrations which correspond to N and N_1 are therefore of opposite phase. Subsequently the amplitude of the vibrations smoothly decreases along the curve N_1Q. For decreasing frequencies (Fig. 61b), an "overhang" of the steady-state amplitudes may take place up to a certain point R_1, when a sudden disruption of the vibrations by a magnitude RR_1 occurs.

The amplitude of the forced vibrations corresponding to a point N_1 is easily determined analytically by making use of the fact that the discriminant of Eq. (7.13) vanishes for this case,

$$q^2 + p^3 = 0\,, \tag{7.14}$$

and the roots of this equation are

$$x_1 = -2\sqrt[3]{q}\,, \qquad x_2 = x_3 = \sqrt[3]{q} = -\frac{x_1}{2}\,.$$

The amplitudes which correspond to a point N_1 are obtained from the formula

$$B_s = 2\sqrt[3]{\frac{\mu f_0}{\kappa n_s^2(1+2\mu^2)}}\,. \tag{7.15}$$

If one does not take into account the "overhang," this formula gives the maximum value for the steady-state amplitudes. The corresponding frequencies can be found from Eq. (7.14):

$$n_s = \sqrt{\frac{1-2\mu^2}{1-\frac{3}{4}\kappa(1+2\mu^2)B_s^2}}$$

Thus, the frequency at which the jump of the amplitude occurs always lies somewhat below the boundary of the parametric excitation. Equation (7.15) can be simplified by setting $n_s \approx 1$:

$$B_s \approx 2\sqrt[3]{\frac{\mu f_0}{\kappa(1+2\mu^2)}}\,.$$

For further details we refer the reader to the work of Bolotin [6].

§ 28. Resonances of Third and Higher Order

We will consider only briefly resonances of third and higher order, and limit ourselves to the damped-free case.

The amplitudes of parametrically excited vibrations for the kth resonance are determined approximately from the equations

$$(\omega^2 - \tfrac{1}{4}k^2\theta^2)a_k + \Phi_k(a_k) = 0\,, \qquad (k = 1, 2, 3, \cdots)\,. \tag{7.16}$$

These equations are obtained from Eqs. (5.7) and (5.9) by neglecting terms which take into account damping and the mutual influence of the harmonics.

Let us investigate the case of nonlinear inertia,

$$\psi(f, f', f'') = 2\kappa f[(f')^2 + ff'']\,.$$

Substituting the approximate solution for the kth resonance,

$$f(t) = a_k \sin\frac{k\theta t}{2}\,,$$

into the expression for the nonlinear function, we find

$$\psi(f, f', f'') = -\frac{k^2\theta^2}{4}\kappa a_k^3 \sin\frac{k\theta t}{2} + \cdots\,,$$

i.e.,

$$\Phi_k(a_k) = -\tfrac{1}{4}k^2\theta^2\kappa a_k^3\,.$$

Equation (7.16) assumes the form

$$\left(1 - \frac{k^2\theta^2}{4\omega^2}\right)a_k - \frac{k^2\theta^2}{4\omega^2}\kappa a_k^3 = 0\,,$$

and, consequently,

$$a_k = \frac{2\omega}{k\theta\sqrt{\kappa}}\sqrt{\frac{k^2\theta^2}{4\omega^2} - 1}\,, \qquad (k = 1, 2, 3, \cdots)\,. \tag{7.17}$$

Of course, this formula is an approximation. Thus, instead of two solutions which are obtained from a more detailed analysis, the above formula gives only one solution. Nevertheless, Eq. (7.17) makes it possible to draw certain general conclusions on the comparative magnitudes of the amplitudes for resonances of various orders.

First we will compare the maximum amplitudes that can be attained within the corresponding excitation regions. On the basis of the estimates of the width of the regions of instability, Eq. (1.38), we obtain

$$\theta_* = \frac{2\omega}{k} + O(\mu^k) , \qquad (k = 1, 2, 3, \cdots) ,$$

from which

$$a_k \sim \frac{\mu^{k/2}}{\sqrt{\kappa}} , \qquad (k = 1, 2, 3, \cdots) \tag{7.18}$$

follows. The formulas derived earlier for the first two regions of instability (e.g., in § 22 and § 26) are obviously confirmed in the relationship (7.18).

Therefore, the maximum amplitudes rapidly decrease with larger order of the resonance region. For example, even for such a comparatively large excitation parameter as $\mu = 0.05$, the amplitudes attained in the regions from first through fourth order have the approximate ratios 1:0.22:0.05:0.01. In the presence of damping the amplitudes decrease even faster.

Eight

INTERACTION OF FORCED AND PARAMETRICALLY EXCITED VIBRATIONS

§ 29. Preliminary Remarks

● **1.** In the theory previously developed we assumed the deformations to be elastic for determination of both the instability regions and the amplitudes. The results for problems of static stability which are based on these assumptions are applicable only to the case of sufficiently flexible rods. The area of application of the theory of dynamic stability is substantially broader. Thus, the results of linear theory, which considers only very small deviations from the initial motion, are valid under condition that the initial motion lie in the region of elastic deformations. Because of the outer-surface "hardening" of the material, one can compute the steady-state amplitudes in the inelastic region with the formulas of nonlinear theory. (The new equilibrium position remains undetermined.)

This does not mean, however, that the theory is applicable to rods of every slenderness ratio. As the slenderness ratio decreases (the rod becomes less flexible), the influence of the longitudinal vibrations becomes more noticeable. As in almost all studies on dynamic stability, if one assumes that the longitudinal force in the rod is independent of the longitudinal coordinate and equals the external force acting at the end of the rod, the longitudinal vibrations can be neglected. As long as the exciting frequency is small in comparison to the frequency ω_L of the free longitudinal vibrations, such an assumption is justified to a certain extent. For rods of small slenderness ratio the frequency at which a parametric resonance of the transverse vibrations occurs can be of the same order as the natural frequency of the longitudinal vibrations. This particularly refers to the case of the resonance with respect to higher natural frequencies.

● **2.** Let us construct the differential equations that consider the mutual influence of the axial and transverse vibrations.[38]

Let $u(x, t)$ be the axial displacement of the cross sections of the rod developed by the compression deformations (Fig. 2). The entire axial displacement to within quantities of second order is

$$w = u + \tfrac{1}{2}\int_0^x \left(\frac{\partial v}{\partial \xi}\right)^2 d\xi . \tag{8.1}$$

[38] For a general derivation of partial differential equations see Marguerre [1], [2] and Mettler [3] for the corresponding buckling problem.

The axial force at an arbitrary cross section is

$$N = P_0 + P_t \cos \theta t - \int_x^l m \frac{\partial^2 w}{\partial t^2} d\xi \, . \tag{8.2}$$

Considering that

$$\frac{\partial u}{\partial x} = \frac{N}{EF} \tag{8.3}$$

and after making use of Eqs. (8.1) and (8.2) and termwise differentiation, we obtain

$$EF\frac{\partial^2 u}{\partial x^2} - m\frac{\partial^2 u}{\partial t^2} = m\int_0^x \left[\frac{dv}{d\xi} \frac{\partial^3 v}{\partial \xi \partial t^2} + \left(\frac{\partial^2 v}{\partial \xi \partial t} \right)^2 \right] d\xi \, . \tag{8.4}$$

The second equation which relates $u(x, t)$ to $v(x, t)$ is formulated by considering the deformation of bending:

$$EJ\frac{\partial^4 v}{\partial x^4} + \frac{\partial}{\partial x}\left(N\frac{\partial v}{\partial x} \right) + m\frac{\partial^2 v}{\partial t^2} = 0 \, .$$

Using Eq. (8.3), we obtain

$$EJ\frac{\partial^4 v}{\partial x^4} + EF\frac{\partial}{\partial x}\left(\frac{\partial u}{\partial x} \frac{\partial v}{\partial x} \right) + m\frac{\partial^2 v}{\partial t^2} = 0 \, . \tag{8.5}$$

The boundary conditions for $u(x, t)$ will obviously be

$$\begin{aligned} u(0, t) &= 0 \, , \\ EF\frac{\partial u(l, t)}{\partial x} &= P_0 + P_t \cos \theta t \, . \end{aligned} \tag{8.6}$$

The boundary conditions for $v(x, t)$ remain as before.

The solution of the system of equations (8.4) and (8.5) presents severe difficulties. However, if we are interested in the conditions causing undamped transverse vibration, we can neglect the nonlinear terms on the right-hand side of Eq. (8.4) that consider the influence of nonlinear inertia. This equation will then contain only $u(x, t)$ and can be solved independently from Eq. (8.5).

§ 30. Influence of Longitudinal Vibrations on Regions of Dynamic Instability

● **1.** The differential equation

$$EF\frac{\partial^2 u}{\partial x^2} - m\frac{\partial^2 u}{\partial t^2} = 0 \tag{8.7}$$

is easily solved for the boundary conditions (8.6). The solution

$$u(x, t) = \frac{P_0 x}{EF} + u_0(x) \cos \theta t$$

corresponds to the steady-state condition. Substituting into Eq. (8.7), we find that the function $u_0(x)$ must satisfy the equation

$$EF\frac{d^2 u_0}{dx^2} + m\theta^2 u_0 = 0 \, ,$$

or

$$\frac{d^2u_0}{dx} + \nu^2 u_0 = 0 ,$$

where

$$\nu = \theta \sqrt{\frac{m}{EF}} . \tag{8.8}$$

Integrating the equation and using the boundary conditions

$$u_0(0) = 0 , \qquad EF\frac{du_0(l)}{dx} = P_t ,$$

we obtain

$$u_0(x) = \frac{P_t \sin \nu x}{\nu EF \cos \nu l} .$$

Thus

$$u(x, t) = \frac{P_0 x}{EF} + \frac{P_t \cos \theta t \sin \nu x}{\nu EF \cos \nu l} . \tag{8.9}$$

For $\cos \nu l = 0$, the second term in Eq. (8.9) becomes infinite. This corresponds to the resonance of the axial vibrations. By considering Eq. (8.8), we find that the resonance occurs at

$$\theta = \frac{k\pi}{2l}\sqrt{\frac{EF}{m}} , \qquad (k = 1, 3, \cdots) .$$

In the following we will investigate the resonance with respect to the lowest natural frequency

$$\omega_L = \frac{\pi}{2l}\sqrt{\frac{EF}{m}} . \tag{8.10}$$

The expression found for $u(x, t)$ is substituted into Eq. (8.5). The equation obtained is not integrable in its final form; assuming, as before, that

$$v(x, t) = f(t) \sin \frac{\pi x}{l}$$

we will seek the solution with the aid of the Galerkin variational method. The resulting ordinary differential equation is

$$f'' + \omega^2\left(1 - \frac{P_0}{P_*} - \psi\frac{P_t}{P_*} \cos \theta t\right) f = 0$$

or

$$f'' + \Omega^2(1 - 2\mu\psi \cos \theta t) f = 0 . \tag{8.11}$$

Here, in contrast to other notation used in the book,

$$\psi = \frac{2}{l}\int_l^0 \frac{\cos \nu x}{\cos \nu l} \cos^2 \frac{\pi x}{l} dx .$$

The evaluation of the integral yields

$$\psi = \frac{\tan \nu l}{\nu l} \frac{1 - \dfrac{\nu^2 l^2}{2\pi^2}}{1 - \dfrac{\nu^2 l^2}{4\pi^2}} .$$

Since

$$\nu l = \theta l \sqrt{\frac{m}{EF}} = \frac{\theta}{\omega_L} \cdot \frac{\pi}{2} ,$$

the coefficient ψ depends only on the relationship between the exciting frequency of the longitudinal vibrations.

● **2.** For the determination of the boundaries of the regions of instability, one can use the equations of the first two chapters by replacing P_t by ψP_t and μ by $\psi\mu$. The calculations are complicated by the fact that the exciting frequency enters into the expression for ψ in a rather complicated way. However, one can assign values of frequency and solve the equation of the boundaries of the region of instability for P_t.

The results can be presented more clearly in the following manner. The curves in Figure 62 represent the dependence of the coefficient ψ on the ratio of the frequencies θ/ω_L. As can be seen from the curves, this dependence can be approximated with sufficient accuracy by a simpler expression:

$$\psi = \frac{1}{1 - (\theta^2/\omega_L^2)} . \tag{8.12}$$

(This is shown in Figure 62 by dotted curves.) This means that the consideration of longitudinal vibrations leads to the following "effective" axial force

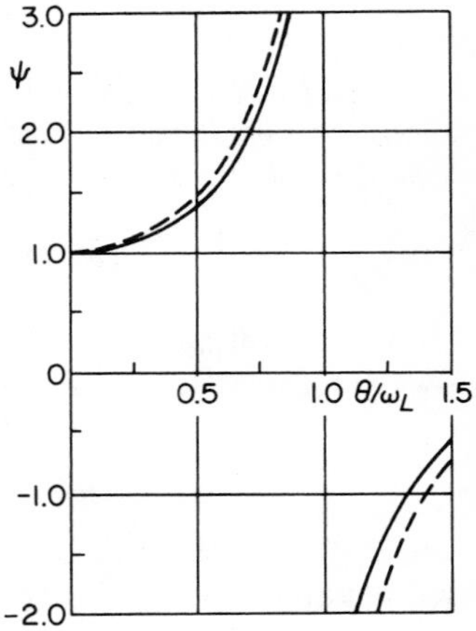

FIG. 62.

$$N(t) = P_0 + \frac{P_t \cos \theta t}{1 - (\theta^2/\omega_L^2)} .$$

The boundaries of the principal region of instability are determined in the first approximation from the condition

$$1 \pm \frac{\mu}{1 - (\theta^2/\omega_L^2)} - \frac{\theta^2}{4\Omega^2} = 0 .$$

Introducing the notation

$$\frac{\theta}{2\Omega} = n , \qquad \frac{4\Omega^2}{\omega_L^2} = \beta ,$$

we obtain

$$(1 - n^2)(1 - \beta n^2) = \mp \mu .$$

Solving this expression with respect to n^2, we obtain the formula

$$n^2 = \frac{1+\beta \pm \sqrt{(1-\beta)^2 \mp 4\mu\beta}}{2\beta} . \qquad (8.13)$$

Generally, Eq. (8.13) gives two regions of instability. As before, one of them lies near $n^2 = 1$, i.e., $\theta = 2\Omega$; the second lies near $n^2 = 1/\beta$, i.e. $\theta = \omega_L$ (Fig. 63). The possible excitation of transverse vibration near $\theta = \omega_L$ is an important fact that cannot be detected within the framework of the usual theory.

For sufficiently large excitation parameters, the regions of instability merge into one. This will obviously take place when

$$(1-\beta)^2 - 4\beta\mu = 0 .$$

Thus, we find

$$\mu_{**} = \frac{(1-\beta)^2}{4\beta}, \qquad n_{**}^2 = \frac{1+\beta}{2\beta} . \qquad (8.14)$$

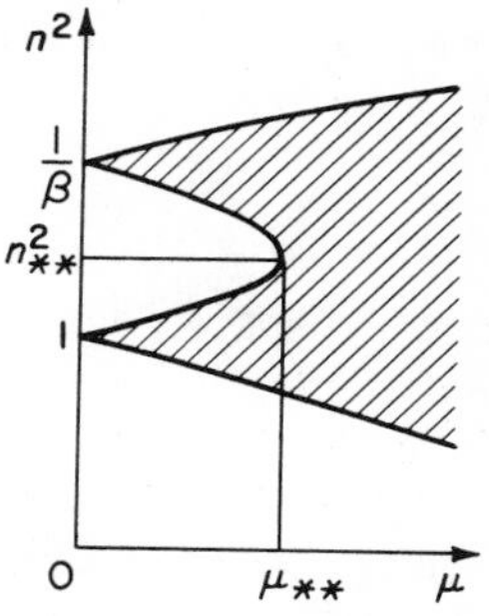

FIG. 63.

Taking into account that

$$\Omega^2 = \frac{\pi^4}{l^4}\frac{EJ}{m}\left(1-\frac{P_0}{P_*}\right), \qquad \omega_L^2 = \frac{\pi^2}{4l^2}\frac{EF}{m},$$

we obtain

$$\beta = \frac{4\Omega^2}{\omega_L^2} = \frac{16\pi^2}{\lambda^2}\left(1-\frac{P_0}{P_*}\right),$$

where $\lambda = l/i$ is the slenderness ratio of the rod ($i^2 = J/F$). The curve of the relationship $\beta(\lambda)$ for $P_0 = 0$ is represented in Figure 64. Even for a flexibility $\lambda = 40$, we have $\beta = 0.10$ and $\mu_{**} = 2.0$. Thus, the merging of the regions of instability is unusual even for rods of small flexibility. The correction to the boundary frequency, however, can be quite large. Expanding the radical in Eq. (8.13) in a binomial series, we obtain an approximate formula for the region lying near $n = 1$:

$$n_*^2 = 1 \pm \frac{\mu}{1-\frac{1}{2}\beta} .$$

For a slenderness ratio $\lambda = 40$ and $\lambda = 0.1$, the width of the region considering the longitudinal vibrations will be approximately 3 percent greater than that obtained according to the usual formulas; for $\lambda = 100$, the influence of the longitudinal vibrations does not exceed 1 percent.

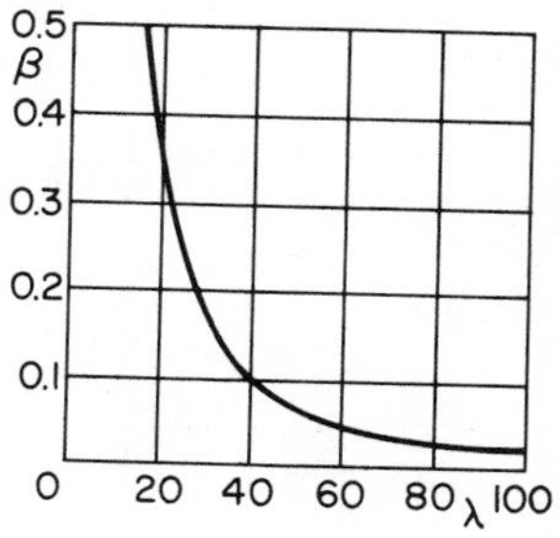

FIG. 64.

● **3.** Damping has not been considered up to this point. The consideration of damping is essential for the explanation of the obvious fact that the instability of the straight form occurs only at sufficiently large parameter μ. We will show that damping exerts a particularly strong influence on the behavior of the system near $\theta = \omega_L$.

First we will introduce into Eq. (8.11) an additional term that takes into account "transverse" damping:

$$f'' + 2\varepsilon f' + \Omega^2(1 - 2\psi\mu \cos \theta t) f = 0 .$$

Furthermore, we will change the method of calculation of the coefficient ψ. In the presence of "longitudinal" damping, Eq. (8. 12) is unusable since it corresponds to an unbounded increase of $u_0(x, t)$ as $t \to \omega_L$. Similar to Eq. (8.12), we write

$$\psi = \frac{1}{\sqrt{(1 - \beta n^2)^2 + \beta n^2(\delta_L/\pi)^2}} ,$$

where δ_L is the decrement of damping of the longitudinal vibrations. This quantity represents the dynamic coefficient which is calculated in a different manner from (8.12) by considering the damping.

For a determination of the boundary of the principal regions of instability, we have the approximate equation (2.12)

$$\begin{vmatrix} 1 - n^2 + \psi\mu & -(n\Delta/\pi) \\ n\Delta/\pi & 1 - n^2 - \psi\mu \end{vmatrix} = 0 .$$

Here Δ is the decrement of damping of the transverse vibrations calculated by considering the force P_0:

$$\Delta = \frac{2\pi\varepsilon}{\Omega} .$$

We will make use of this equation in order to estimate the lowest value of $\mu = \mu_*$ for which the loss of stability is possible. It is easily found that

$$\mu^2 = \left[(1 - n^2)^2 + \left(\frac{n\Delta}{n}\right)^2\right]\left[(1 - \beta n^2)^2 + \beta n^2\left(\frac{\delta_L}{\pi}\right)^2\right].$$

If $\beta \ll 1$, $\Delta \ll 1$, and $\delta_L \ll 1$, then for $n^2 = 1$, as in the usual theory:

$$\mu_* \approx \frac{\Delta}{\pi} .$$

For another resonance ($n^2 = 1/\beta$), we have

$$\mu_{*L} \approx \frac{\delta_L}{\pi\beta} .$$

Let us consider an example. Let $\lambda = 40$; consequently $\beta \approx 0.10$ and $\delta_L = \Delta = 0.03$. For the formation of transverse vibrations near $\theta = 2\Omega$, it is necessary that $\mu \geq 0.01$; for the vibrations to be formed in the neighborhood of $\theta = \omega_L$, it is required that $\mu \approx 0.01$, at least. The latter value corresponds to very large amplitudes of the axial force (for $P_0 = 0$ one must have $P_t \approx 0.2\ P_*$). Therefore one sees that the instability of the straight form near the resonance of longitudinal vibrations can be discovered only for sufficiently large amplitudes of loading. This fact also explains the seemingly paradoxical results of § 30, ● 2, above.

§ 31. Determination of Steady-State Amplitudes Considering Longitudinal Vibrations

● **1.** Since further calculations will be approximate, we shall somewhat simplify the calculation procedure. Let us consider the case where the mass concentrated on the end is sufficiently large compared to the mass of the rod so that the latter can be neglected in constructing the equations of the longitudinal vibrations.

The displacement of the moving end according to Eq. (8.17) will be

$$w = u + \frac{\pi^2 f^2}{4l} . \tag{8.15}$$

The equations of the axial and transverse vibrations have the form

$$M_L w'' = P_0 + P_t \cos \theta t - N ,$$
$$f'' + \omega^2\left(1 - \frac{N}{P_*}\right)f = 0 ,$$

where $N = (EF/l)u$ is the axial force arising in the rod. By considering Eq. (8.15), we obtain the system of equations

$$\begin{aligned} u'' + \omega_L^2 u + \frac{\pi^2}{2l}[(f')^2 + ff''] &= \frac{1}{M_L}(P_0 + P_t \cos \theta t) , \\ f'' + \omega^2\left(1 - \frac{\omega_L^2 M_L}{P_*}u\right)f &= 0 . \end{aligned} \tag{8.16}$$

Here ω_L is the natural frequency of the longitudinal vibrations,

$$\omega_L = \sqrt{\frac{EF}{lM_L}} .$$

We seek the approximate solution of the system (8.16) in the form

$$\begin{aligned} u(t) &= U_0 + U_t \cos \theta t , \\ f(t) &= a \sin \frac{\theta t}{2} \end{aligned} \tag{8.17}$$

where U_0, U_t, and a are constants that are to be determined. Substituting Eq. (8.17) into Eqs. (8.16), and equating the constant terms and also the coefficients of $\cos \theta t$, we obtain

$$\omega_L^2 U_0 = \frac{P_0}{M_L} ,$$
$$(\omega_L^2 - \theta^2)U_t + \frac{\pi^2\theta^2}{8l}a^2 = \frac{P_t}{M_L} .$$

The third equation, which relates U_0, U_t, and a, is obtained by substituting Eqs. (8.17) into the second equation of (8.16) and equating the coefficients of $\sin \theta t/2$:

$$\left(\omega^2 - \frac{\theta^2}{4}\right)a - \frac{\omega^2\omega_L^2 M_L}{P_*}U_0 a + \frac{\omega^2\omega_L^2 M_L}{2P_*}U_t a = 0$$

(terms containing harmonics are neglected). Elimating U_0 and U_t, we arrive at the equation

$$\omega^2 - \frac{\theta^2}{4} - \frac{\omega^2 P_0}{P_*} + \frac{\omega^2 P_t}{2P_*\left(1 - \frac{\theta^2}{\omega_L^2}\right)} - \frac{\pi^2\theta^2\omega^2 M_L a^2}{16P_* l\left(1 - \frac{\theta^2}{\omega_L^2}\right)} = 0\,,$$

or in the notations of the previous paragraphs

$$\kappa = \frac{\pi^4 M_L}{4ml^3}\,.$$

In addition, we denote

$$1 - n^2 + \frac{\mu}{1-\beta n^2} - \frac{\kappa n^2 a^2}{1 - \beta n^2} = 0\,.$$

Hence, we find the amplitude of the steady-state vibrations

$$a^2 = \frac{(1-\beta n^2)(1-n^2)+\mu}{\kappa n^2}\,. \tag{8.18}$$

Another approximate solution of the system (8.16) is obtained by assuming

$$u(t) = U_0 + U_t \cos \theta t\,,$$
$$f(t) = a \cos \frac{\theta t}{2}\,.$$

Having repeated the previous manipulation, we find

$$a^2 = \frac{(1-\beta n^2)(1-n^2)-\mu}{\kappa n^2}\,.$$

● **2.** The two formulas can be combined in

$$a = \sqrt{\frac{\Phi_\pm(n^2, \mu)}{\kappa}}$$

where

$$\Phi_\pm(n^2, \mu) = \frac{(1-\beta n^2)(1-n^2) \pm \mu}{n^2}\,.$$

A graph of these functions is presented in Figure 65, and the general form of resonance curves is depicted in Figure 66. The unstable branches

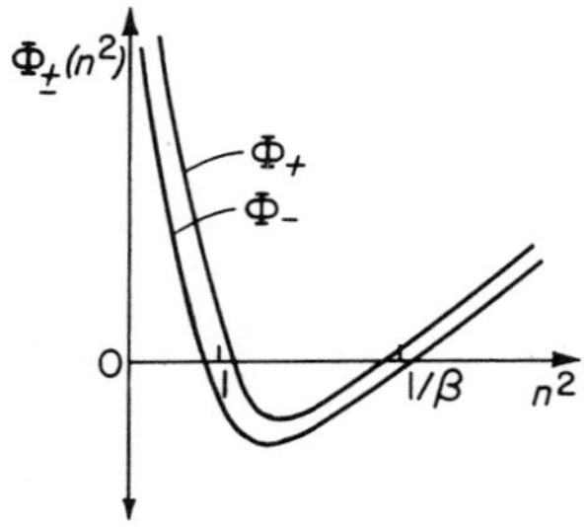

FIG. 65.

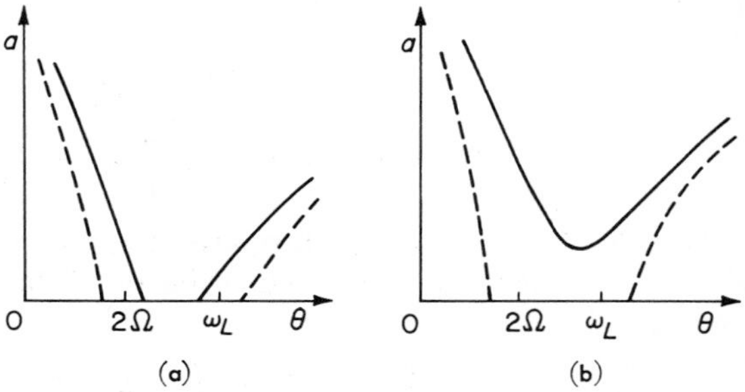

FIG. 66.

are shown by dotted lines. The left-hand resonance curve represents the usual parametrically excited vibrations ($\theta = 2\Omega$). The right-hand curve corresponds to the resonance $\theta = \omega_L$; here the "overhang" of the vibrations occurs towards the larger frequencies. If $\mu \geq \mu_{**}$ (see the preceding paragraphs), then the two resonances merge and the graph takes the form shown in Figure 66b. The "overhang" from the resonance region can take place here on either side.

Let us now give a quantitative estimate for the correction resulting from consideration of the longitudinal vibrations. Consider Eq. (8.18). Setting $\beta = 0$, we obtain the previously known formula

$$a^2 = \frac{1 - n^2 + \mu}{n^2} .$$

Near $n = 1$ (the principal parametric resonance) we will have the following relationships. If $n > 1$, the longitudinal vibrations increase the amplitude of the vibrations; if $n < 1$, then, conversely, the amplitude decreases with regard to the longitudinal vibrations. On the lower boundary of the region of instability, the amplitude is

$$a^2 = \frac{2\mu}{\kappa(1 - \mu)} - \frac{\mu\beta}{\kappa} .$$

For example, for $\beta = 0.10$ ($\lambda = 40$) and $\mu = 0.10$, the influence of longitudinal vibrations is about 3 percent.

● **3.** Let us investigate the more complicated case of an additional elastic coupling with a spring constant c (Fig. 16).

The equations of this problem are

$$M_L w'' = P_0 + P_t \cos \theta t - N - cw ,$$

$$f'' + \omega^2\left(1 - \frac{EF}{lP_*}u\right)f = 0 .$$

Transforming the first of these equations with the help of Eq. (8.15), we obtain

$$u'' + \omega_L^2 u + \frac{\pi^2}{2l}[(f')^2 + ff''] + \frac{\pi^2 cf^2}{4lM_L} = \frac{1}{M_L}(P_0 + P_t \cos \theta t) , \qquad (8.19)$$

where

$$\omega_L^2 = \frac{\dfrac{EF}{l} + c}{M_L} . \qquad (8.20)$$

From Eq. (8.20) it follows that

$$\frac{EF}{l} = \frac{\omega_L^2 M_L}{1 + \xi} , \qquad \left(\xi = \frac{cl}{EF}\right) .$$

On the other hand, $P_*(1 + \xi) = P_{**}$ (P_{**} is the critical force which is calculated with the consideration of the longitudinal coupling). The second equation takes the form

$$f'' + \omega^2\left(1 - \frac{\omega_L^2 M_L}{P_{**}} u\right) f = 0 . \tag{8.21}$$

As before, we seek the solution for the case of steady-state vibrations in the form of Eqs. (8.17). A substitution into Eq. (8.19) gives

$$\omega_L^2 U_0 + \frac{\pi^2 c a^2}{8 l M_L} = \frac{P_0}{M_L} ,$$

$$(\omega_L^2 - \theta^2) U_t + \frac{\pi^2 \theta^2}{8l} a^2 - \frac{\pi^2 c a^2}{8 l M_L} = \frac{P_t}{M_L} .$$

From Eq. (8.21) we obtain

$$\left(\omega^2 - \frac{\theta^2}{4}\right) a - \frac{\omega^2 \omega_L^2 M_L}{P_{**}} U_0 a + \frac{\omega^2 \omega_L^2 M_L}{2 P_{**}} U_t a = 0 .$$

Eliminating U_0 and U_t from these equations, we find

$$1 - \frac{\theta^2}{4\omega^2} - \frac{P_0}{P_{**}} + \frac{P_t}{2P_{**}\left(1 - \dfrac{\theta^2}{\omega_L^2}\right)}$$

$$+ \frac{\pi^2 c a^2}{8 P_{**} l}\left[1 + \frac{1}{2\left(1 - \dfrac{\theta^2}{\omega_L^2}\right)}\right] - \frac{\pi^2 \theta^2 M_L a^2}{16 P_{**} l \left(1 - \dfrac{\theta^2}{\omega_L^2}\right)} = 0 . \tag{8.22}$$

We introduce the notation

$$\frac{\pi^2 \omega^2 c}{4 P_{**} l} = \frac{\pi^4 c}{4 m l^3 (1 + \xi)} = \gamma ,$$

$$\frac{\pi^2 \omega^2 M_L}{4 P_{**} l} = \frac{\pi^4 M_L}{4 m l^3 (1 + \xi)} = \kappa ,$$

$$\omega^2\left(1 - \frac{P_0}{P_{**}}\right) = \Omega^2 , \qquad \frac{P_t}{2(P_{**} - P_0)} = \mu .$$

Equation (8.22) can then be written in the form

$$1 - u^2 + \frac{\mu}{1 - \beta n^2} + \frac{\gamma a^2}{4\Omega^2} \frac{3 - 2\beta n^2}{1 - \beta n^2} - \frac{\kappa n^2 a^2}{1 - \beta n^2} = 0 .$$

Hence

$$a^2 = \frac{(1 - \beta n^2)(1 - n^2) + \mu}{\kappa n^2 - \dfrac{\gamma}{4\Omega^2}(3 - 2\beta n^2)} . \tag{8.23}$$

The solution for the case $f = a \cos \theta t/2$ differs from Eq. (8.23) only by the sign of μ.

As before, we will introduce the two functions

$$\Phi_{\pm}(n^2, \mu) = \frac{(1 - \beta n^2)(1 - n^2) \pm \mu}{n^2 - \dfrac{\gamma}{4\kappa\Omega^2}(3 - 2\beta n^2)} . \tag{8.24}$$

Obviously the zero positions of these functions coincide with boundaries of the regions of dynamic instability (8.13). We denote these zero positions in ascending order by $n_1^2, n_2^2, n_3^2, n_4^2$. The pole, i.e., the root of the equation

$$n^2 - \frac{\gamma}{4\kappa\Omega^2}(3 - 2\beta n^2) = 0$$

will be

$$n_\infty^2 = \frac{3}{4}\frac{\gamma}{\kappa\Omega^2}\frac{1}{1+\frac{\gamma\beta}{2\kappa\Omega^2}}$$

or for $\beta \to 0$, it will be $n_\infty^2 = 3\gamma/4\kappa\Omega^2$. As in § 21, this corresponds to an additional "resonance" at the frequency

$$\theta_\infty = \sqrt{3}\sqrt{\frac{c}{M_L}}\,.$$

Depending on the position of the pole n_∞^2 with respect to the zeros of the function in Eq. (8.24), i.e., depending on the position of the additional resonance relative to the regions of instability, we can distinguish five cases. These cases are represented in Figure 67, where the function Φ_+ is shown as a heavy line and the function Φ_- is shown as a thin line. An approximate

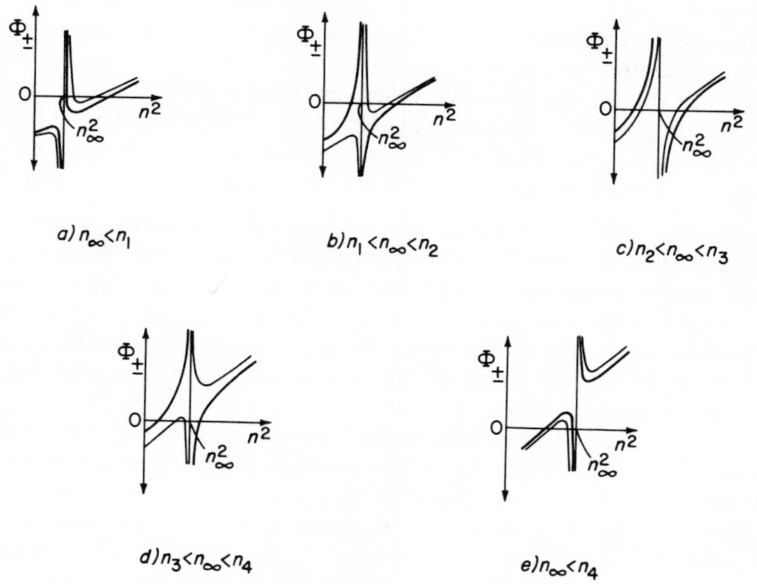

FIG. 67.

form of the resonance curves for these five cases is given in Figure 68. Because of nonlinear damping, the amplitudes at n_∞ will be bounded. The unstable branches are seen as dotted lines. Let us investigate the structure of the left-hand resonance ($\theta \approx 2\Omega$). The first case ($n_\infty < n_1$) corresponds to

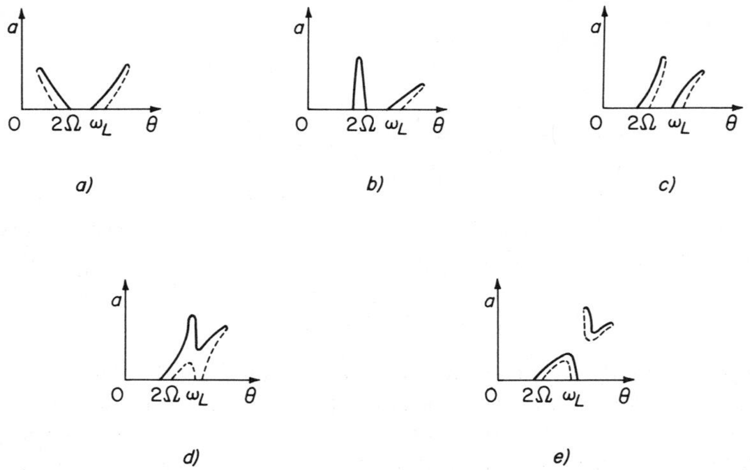

FIG. 68.

the case previously denoted as that of the predominating nonlinear inertia. In the second case ($n_1 < n_\infty < n_2$), the nonlinear elasticity and inertia appear to compensate one another; the resonance curve has the character typical for nonlinear damping. In the remaining cases ($n_\infty > n_2$), nonlinear elasticity is dominant. However, the last two cases are hardly of real value, since the relation $n_\infty > n_3$ can be obtained only for a very rigid longitudinal coupling. Besides, one must keep in mind that in Figures 67 and 68 the scale along the horizontal axis is distorted; in reality we usually have $\omega_L \gg 2\Omega$.

● **4.** *Summary.* The influence of the longitudinal vibration on the principal parametric resonance ($\theta \approx 2\Omega$) is insignificantly small for rods of average and large slenderness ratio. This influence becomes perceptible only for rods of small slenderness ratio. Moreover for $\lambda = 40$ and $\mu = 0.1$, the error in the boundary frequencies and critical amplitudes does not exceed 3 percent. The influence of the longitudinal vibrations on the reasonance regions of higher order is negligible.

However, not in all problems is the correlation between the frequencies ω_L and 2Ω of the same order as in the problem on the parametric resonance of a compressed rod. If one investigates the parametric resonance relative to the *higher* forms of transverse vibrations, even in the problem examined, the frequencies ω_L and 2Ω are convergent. An example of a problem in which the interaction of the parametric and forced vibrations is very essential will be given in § 80 and § 81.

Nine

EXTENSION OF THE APPLICABILITY OF THE THEORY

§ 32. Extension of the Results to Other Problems of Dynamic Stability

●1. The first part of this book was devoted to the problem of parametrically excited vibrations of a compressed rod that is simply supported at the ends. This case was treated in detail for both the linear and nonlinear cases.

Other problems requiring the use of more complicated mathematical methods will be considered in subsequent parts of the book. However, there are problems to which the theory presented heretofore can be applied without any essential changes; we shall briefly dwell upon these problems and confine ourselves to a linear formulation for the sake of simplicity.

Assume that a prismatic rod that is simply supported at both ends lies on a continuous elastic foundation, whose reaction at every point is proportional to the deflection (Winkler foundation). The differential equation of the transverse vibrations of such a rod subjected to a periodic longitudinal force (Fig. 69) is obtained from Eq. (1.2) by the addition of βv to the right-hand side for the foundation reaction. (β is the *foundation coefficient.*) Consequently, the differential equation will be[39]

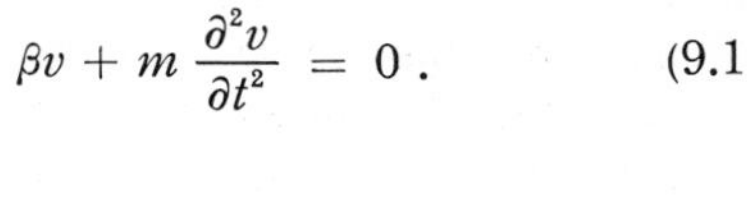

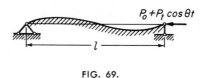

FIG. 69.

$$EJ\frac{\partial^4 v}{\partial x^4} + (P_0 + P_t \cos \theta t)\frac{\partial^2 v}{\partial x^2} + \beta v + m\frac{\partial^2 v}{\partial t^2} = 0\,. \tag{9.1}$$

It is easily seen that Eq. (1.3),

$$v(x, t) = f_k(t) \sin\frac{k\pi x}{l}\,, \qquad (k = 1, 2, 3, \cdots)\,,$$

where $f_k(t)$ are as yet undetermined functions of time, satisfies this equation.

[39] Such a treatment of the vibrations of beams on an elastic foundation is widespread. Note, however, that taking into account the elastic resistance of the foundation and neglecting its inertia is rather illogical. By introducing a more perfect model (an elastic half-space or a layer of finite depth), we find that the "reduced mass" of the foundation depends essentially on the form of the vibrations.

A substitution leads to differential equations (1.4),

$$f_k'' + \omega_k^2\left(1 - \frac{P_0 + P_t \cos \theta t}{P_{*k}}\right) f_k = 0\,, \quad (k = 1, 2, 3, \cdots)\,, \tag{9.2}$$

where the only difference is that

$$\omega_k^2 = \frac{1}{m}\left(\frac{k^4\pi^4 EJ}{l^4} + \beta\right),$$

$$P_{*k} = \frac{k^2\pi^2 EJ}{l^2} + \frac{\beta l^2}{k^2\pi^2}.$$

Analogous equations are obtained by considering the case of an infinitely long beam. In this case, Eq. (9.1) will be satisfied by assuming that

$$v(x, t) = f(t, \lambda) \sin \frac{\pi x}{\lambda}\,,$$

where the length of the half-wave λ can take on arbitrary values from zero to infinity. Substitution leads to Eq. (9.2), where the parameter λ plays the part of the index k; the coefficients of the equations depend on this parameter in the following manner:

$$\omega^2(\lambda) = \frac{1}{m}\left(\frac{\pi^4 EJ}{\lambda^4} + \beta\right),$$

$$P_*(\lambda) = \frac{\pi^2 EJ}{\lambda^2} + \frac{\beta\lambda^2}{\pi^2}.$$

As is to be expected for such a problem, the natural frequencies and the critical forces form a continuous spectrum varying from the minimum values

$$\omega_{\min} = \sqrt{\frac{\beta}{m}}\,, \qquad P_{*\min} = 2\sqrt{EJ\beta} \tag{9.3}$$

to infinity.

For a given length of the half-wave, the boundaries of the principal regions of dynamic instability can be determined by the formulas of Chapter One. Therefore, according to Eq. (1.34), this is

$$\theta_*^2(\lambda) = \frac{4}{m}\left[\frac{\pi^4 EJ}{\lambda^4} + \beta - \frac{\pi^2(P_0 \pm \frac{1}{2} P_t)}{\lambda^2}\right]$$

for harmonic loading. It is evident that the regions of instability corresponding to various values of λ fill out completely a part of the parameter plane (Fig. 70). The equation of the envelope is

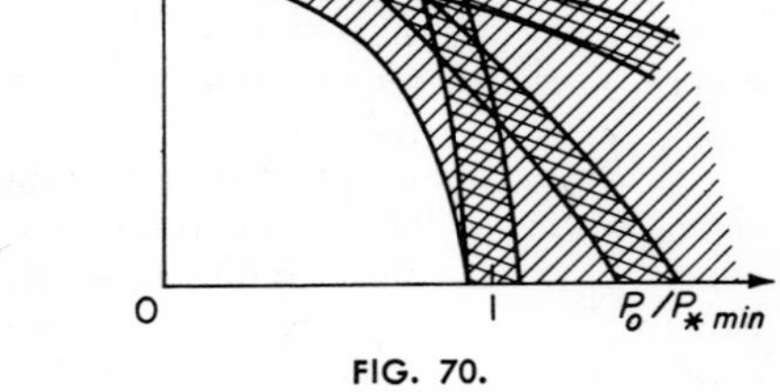

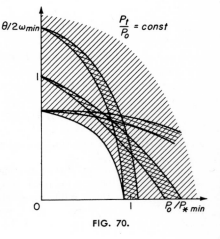

FIG. 70.

$$\theta_*^2 = \frac{4}{m}\left[\beta - \frac{(P_0 \pm \frac{1}{2} P_t)^2}{4EJ}\right]$$

or by considering Eq. (9.3),

$$\theta_* = 2\omega_{\min} \sqrt{1 - \frac{(P_0 \pm \frac{1}{2} P_t)^2}{P_{*\min}^2}}$$

● **2.** Other problems that lead to equations of type (9.2) will be discussed. Examples of these are: the problem of the dynamic stability of a circular ring compressed by a uniformly distributed radial loading (Fig. 1b) and the problem of the stability of a rectangular plate simply supported along all the edges and loaded by periodic forces that are uniformly distributed along all of the sides (Fig. 1c).[40] For example, the first case gives

$$f_k'' + \omega_k^2\left(1 - \frac{q_0 + q_t \cos \theta t}{q_k}\right)f_k = 0\,, \quad (k = 1, 2, 3, \cdots)\,,$$

where ω_k are frequencies of the bending vibrations of the ring and q_k are the critical values for the corresponding static problem.

It would be erroneous to assume, however, that every problem of dynamic stability necessarily reduces to the Mathieu-Hill equation. Rather, the above cases can be considered as exceptions (the so-called *special case*). If any other type of support condition of the rod or a rod of variable cross section, or finally, the case of a varying axial force along the length is taken, the problem cannot be reduced to an equation of the type (9.2). Problems of dynamic stability generally require the investigation of a system of differential equations with periodic coefficients.

It is not difficult to notice the features which are common to the elementary problems indicated above. In all of the cases enumerated, the forms of the free vibration of the system and the corresponding forms of the loss of static stability coincide. Consequently, it is possible to separate the x and t variables in the initial differential equations with the aid of a substitution of the expression

$$v(x, t) = f(t)\varphi(x)\,, \tag{9.4}$$

where $f(t)$ is a function only of t, and $\varphi(x)$ is a function only of x. Such a separation is not generally possible[41]

● **3.** If the forms of the free vibrations of the system and of static buckling are sufficiently close to one another, which is naturally expected in many problems particularly for the first mode, then an approximate solution in the form of Eq. (9.4) can be investigated. The most suitable method for this purpose is the Galerkin variational method.

Consider, for example, a rod of variable cross section compressed by a

[40] A detailed analysis of these problems will be given in the third part of the book (§ 76, § 96, and others).

[41] This was noted first by Brachkovskii [1]; see also the article by Bolotin [5] and the article by Dzhanelidze [1]. This question will be examined in detail in Chapter Twelve.

longitudinally varying axial force $N(x, t)$. The differential equation of this problem has the form

$$\frac{\partial^2}{\partial x^2}\left(EJ\frac{\partial^2 v}{\partial x^2}\right) + \frac{\partial}{\partial x}\left[N(x, t)\frac{\partial v}{\partial x}\right] + m\frac{\partial^2 v}{\partial t^2} = 0 . \tag{9.5}$$

Furthermore, let $N(x, t) = \bar{N}(x)(P_0 + P_t \cos \theta t)$, where P_0 and P_t are parameters that fix the external loading. (In other words, it is assumed that the constant and periodic components vary proportionally to these two parameters.) Substitution of Eq. (9.4) into Eq. (9.5) and the application of the Galerkin method yields

$$\frac{d^2 f(t)}{dt^2}\int_0^l m\varphi^2 dx + f(t)\int_0^l \varphi\frac{d^2}{dx^2}\left(EJ\frac{d^2\varphi}{dx^2}\right)dx$$
$$+ f(t)(P_0 + P_t \cos \theta t)\int_0^l \varphi\frac{d}{dx}\left[\bar{N}(x)\frac{d\varphi}{dx}\right]dx = 0 .$$

With the notation

$$\frac{\int_0^l \varphi\frac{d^2}{dx^2}\left(EJ\frac{d^2\varphi}{dx^2}\right)dx}{\int_0^l m\varphi^2 dx} = \tilde{\omega}^2 , \qquad -\frac{\int_0^l \varphi\frac{d^2}{dx^2}\left(EJ\frac{d^2\varphi}{dx^2}\right)dx}{\int_0^l \varphi\frac{d}{dx}\left[\bar{N}(x)\frac{d\varphi}{dx}\right]dx} = \tilde{P}_* ,$$

the differential equation is written as

$$\frac{d^2 f}{dt^2} + \tilde{\omega}^2\left(1 - \frac{P_0 + P_t \cos \theta t}{\tilde{P}_*}\right)f = 0 . \tag{9.6}$$

It is easily seen that Eq. (9.6) practically coincides with Eq. (9.2). Here, in contrast to Eq. (9.2), $\tilde{\omega}$ and $\tilde{P}_*$ are approximate values (in the sense of the Galerkin method) of the natural frequency and the buckling force, respectively. However if the deflection shape of free vibrations is taken as the function $\varphi(x)$ in Eq. (9.4), then $\tilde{\omega}$ coincides with the exact value; if the buckling deflection shape is taken for $\varphi(x)$, then $\tilde{P}_*$ will be exactly equal to the critical value P_*.[42] If the two forms coincide, then the approximate equation (9.6) becomes exact, corresponding to the case of a *single equation.*

For the problem of the dynamic stability of a compressed rod, the approximate equation (9.6) was first obtained by Krylov and Bogoliubov [2]. An approximate solution of a larger number of special problems was given by Bodner [1], Chelomei [1][43], and others. Recently Dzhanelidze [1] again returned to this question in a more general form.

[42] One must remember that in the solution of an actual problem the results obtained by the Galerkin method are very sensitive to the selection of coordinate functions and depend particularly upon whether or not these functions satisfy all (including the dynamic) boundary conditions. Corresponding corrections must be introduced into this method if the boundary conditions are not satisfied. (See § 48.)

[43] It must be kept in mind that questions on the influence of damping and on the even regions of instability in this work were interpreted incorrectly. (See § 5 and § 7 of this book.)

§ 33. Vibrations of Systems with Periodically Varying Stiffness. Shafts Whose Cross Sections Have Different Principal Moments of Inertia

●1. The theory of dynamic stability can be expanded in still another direction. Elastic systems exist whose investigations also lead to differential equations with periodic coefficients. These are various types of systems with periodically varying stiffness or with periodically varying mass.

Actually, even the straight rod loaded by a periodic axial force, the simplest problem in the theory of dynamic stability, yields a system of such a type. The square of the "instantaneous" value of the natural frequency of a loaded rod

$$\Omega^2(t) = \omega^2\left[1 - \frac{P(t)}{P_*}\right] \tag{9.7}$$

can be interpreted as some quasi-elastic coefficient periodically varying in time, divided by the constant mass m. The linearized equation of dynamic stability then takes the form

$$f'' + \frac{c(t)}{m} f = 0\,; \tag{9.8}$$

i.e., a differential equation for the vibrations of a system with variable stiffness is obtained.

Such an interpretation is far more natural, since Eq. (9.7) reflects the decrease of stiffness of the rod in bending under the influence of a compressive force. In addition to the problems that comprise the nucleus of the book (elastic systems loaded by a periodic parametric load), variable stiffness caused by the construction peculiarities of the systems and, in particular, by the presence of the rotating parts will be discussed in the following examples.

●2. The simplest example of a system with periodically varying stiffness is a straight rotating shaft, whose cross section has different principal moments of inertia. It is known that in a certain range of angular velocities such shafts are subjected to strong vibration (see Timoshenko [1], for example). Consider the problem of a disk of mass M that is placed on the shaft (the distributed mass of the shaft is neglected) and the end supports are such that the disk can vibrate only in one plane (for example the vertical plane).

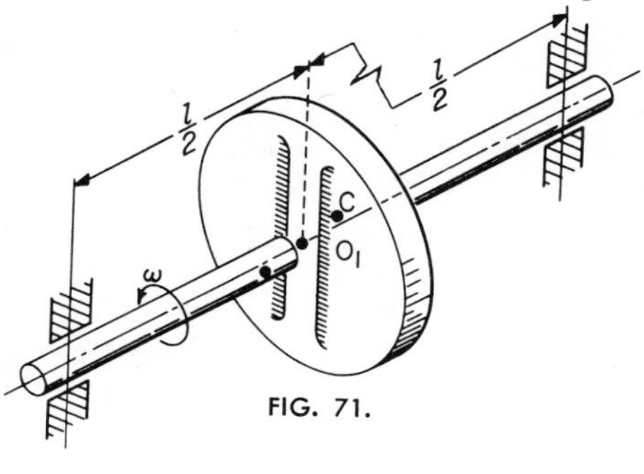

FIG. 71.

The shaft is shown in Figure 71, where O_1 is the point on the axis of the shaft which coincides with the plane of the disk, C is the center of gravity of the disk, and e_1 and e_2 are its coordinates in the direction of the principal axes. Let f be the vertical displacement of the point O_1, M be mass of the disk, c be the spring stiffness of the shaft, and ω be the angular velocity of rotation. Neglecting the torsional deformation leads to the equation of motion of the disk in the form

$$Mf'' = -cf + M\omega^2(e_1 \sin \omega t + e_2 \cos \omega t) - Mg\,. \tag{9.9}$$

In calculating the spring stiffness of the shaft c let J_1 and J_2 be the principal moments of inertia of the cross section ($J_1 > J_2$); then the moment of inertia with respect to the horizontal axis is

$$J_x = \frac{1}{2}(J_1 + J_2) + \frac{1}{2}(J_1 - J_2) \cos 2\omega t\,.$$

Hence,

$$c = \frac{c_1 + c_2}{2} + \frac{c_2 - c_1}{2} \cos 2\omega t\,, \tag{9.10}$$

where c_1 and c_2 are bending stiffnesses of the shaft in the direction of axes 1 and 2 $c_1 < c_2$. For example, for a simply supported shaft with a disk placed in the middle of the shaft, they are

$$c_1 = \frac{48EJ_2}{l^3}\,, \qquad c_2 = \frac{48EJ_1}{l^3}\,.$$

Substituting Eq. (9.10) into Eq. (9.9) and denoting

$$\omega_0{}^2 = \frac{c_1 + c_2}{2M}\,,$$

$$\mu = \frac{c_1 - c_2}{2(c_1 + c_2)} = \frac{J_1 - J_2}{2(J_1 + J_2)}\,,$$

leads to the differential equation

$$f'' + \omega_0{}^2(1 + 2\mu \cos 2\omega t)f = \omega^2(e_1 \sin \omega t + e_2 \cos \omega t) - g. \tag{9.11}$$

A homogeneous equation corresponding to Eq. (9.11) (taking damping into account) takes the form

$$f'' + 2\varepsilon f' + \omega^2(1 + 2\mu \cos 2\omega t)f = 0\,.$$

This equation differs from Eq. (2.1) only by some notation and by a shift in the initial time reference by $\pi/2\omega_0$. Hence, the following results are obtained.

(a) The presence of continuous regions of instability, in the vicinity of angular velocities

$$\omega = \frac{\omega_0}{k}\,, \qquad (k = 1, 2, 3, \cdots)\,;$$

(b) The impossibility of exciting vibrations for values of the parameter μ, smaller than[44]

[44] Details are found in the article of Bolotin [11] where the influence of unbalance and dead weight of the shaft are considered.

$$\mu_* = \sqrt[k]{\frac{\delta}{\pi}}\,, \qquad (k = 1, 2, 3, \cdots)\,.$$

●3. The differential equation of the nonlinear problem is formed by first considering the exact expression of the curvature and then the additional axial force arising from a deviation of the axis of the shaft from the straight position. Moreover, it becomes necessary to consider the shaft as a continuous system, i.e., it becomes necessary to proceed from the equation

$$\frac{\partial^2}{\partial s^2}\left(\frac{EJ_x}{\rho}\right) + \frac{\partial}{\partial s}\left(N\frac{\partial v}{\partial s}\right) + m(s)\frac{\partial^2 v}{\partial t^2} = 0\,. \tag{9.12}$$

Here $v(s, t)$ is the deflection of the shaft at every point, s is the arc length measured along the axis of the shaft, $1/\rho$ is the curvature of the axis, i.e.,

$$\frac{1}{\rho} = \frac{\dfrac{\partial^2 v}{\partial s^2}}{\sqrt{1-\left(\dfrac{\partial v}{\partial s}\right)^2}}\,,$$

and $m(s)$ is the mass per unit length. In the case of a disk placed on the shaft with the concentrated mass M,

$$m(s) = 0 \quad \text{for} \quad 0 \leqq s \leqq \frac{l}{2} - \eta\,,$$

$$\lim_{\eta\to 0}\int_{(l/2)-\eta}^{(l/2)+\eta} m(s)ds = M\,,$$

$$m(s) = 0 \quad \text{for} \quad \frac{l}{2} + \eta \leqq s \leqq l\,.$$

The axial force $N(s, t)$ is computed considering that at the moving end there is an elastic support with a spring stiffness c_L and a longitudinal damper with a resistance coefficient k_L. Denoting the longitudinal displacement of

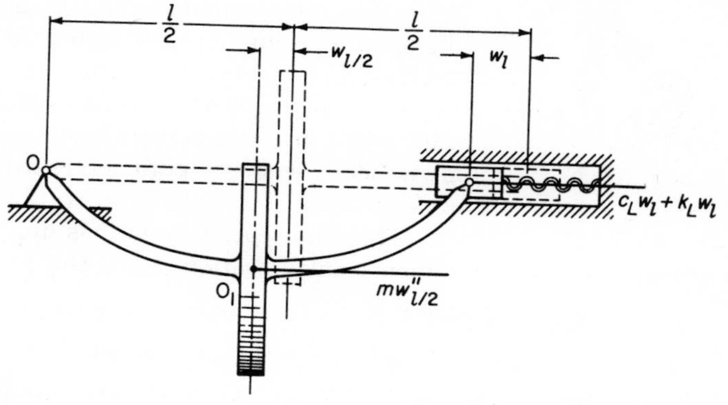

FIG. 72.

the moving end by w_l and the deflection of the middle span for the case represented in Figure 72 by $w_{l/2}$ yields

$$N(s,\,t) \;=\; -\,(c_L w_l + k_L w_l' + m w_{l/2}'') \quad \text{for} \quad 0 \leqq s \leqq \frac{l}{2} - \eta\,,$$
$$-\,(c_L w_l + k_L w_l') \qquad \text{for} \quad \frac{l}{2} + \eta \leqq s \leqq l\,. \tag{9.13}$$

Approximating the deflection shape of the shaft by a suitable curve and applying the Galerkin method leads to

$$f'' + 2\varepsilon f' + \omega_0^2(1 + 2\mu\,\cos\,2\omega t)f + \psi(f, f', f'') \;=\; 0\,,$$

in which

$$\psi(f, f', f'') \;=\; \gamma_0(1 + 2\mu\,\cos\,2\omega t)f^3 + \gamma f^3 + \varepsilon_L(f^2)'f + \kappa(f^2)''f\,. \tag{9.14}$$

The expression for the nonlinear function in (9.14) differs from the usual expression in (5.3) by the presence of the first term, which takes into account the nonlinearity of the curvature. In the case of a simply supported shaft,

$$\gamma_0 = \frac{\pi^2\omega_0^2}{8l^2}\,, \qquad \gamma = \frac{\pi^4 c_L}{8ml^2}\,, \qquad \varepsilon_L = \frac{\pi^4 k_L}{8ml^2}\,, \qquad \kappa = \frac{\pi^4}{32ml^2}\,.$$

If $\gamma_0 \ll \gamma$, i.e., if $\omega_0^2 \ll c_L/m$ (a relatively large stiffness of the elastic support), the first term can then be neglected. Then Eqs. (9.14) and (5.3) coincide and all the results obtained for the problem on the parametric resonance of a compressed rod apply completely to the present problem. The solution for the case where this term cannot be neglected is given in the work of Bolotin [11] where further details can be found.

§ 34. Three-Dimensional Vibrations of a Shaft[45]

● 1. So far we have considered the plane vibrations of a shaft. In the case of three-dimensional vibrations, the linear problem is described by a system of two equations with periodic coefficients of a rather complicated form (Dimentberg [1]). Using a system of coordinates which rotate with the shaft (Fig. 73) leads to differential equations with constant coefficients. Peculiarities which are characteristic of systems with periodically varying parameters are therefore retained.

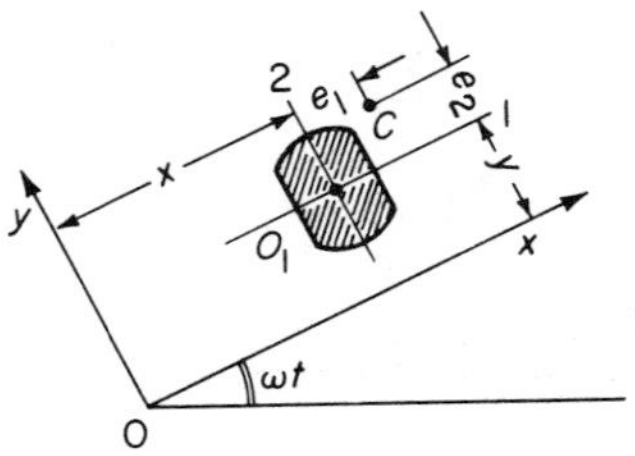

FIG.73.

The differential equations for the three-dimensional vibrations have the form[46]

$$\begin{aligned} x'' - 2\omega y' + (\omega_1^2 - \omega^2)x \;&=\; e_1\omega^2 - g\,\cos\,\omega t\,, \\ y'' + 2\omega x' + (\omega_2^2 - \omega^2)y \;&=\; e_2\omega^2 - g\,\sin\,\omega t\,, \end{aligned} \tag{9.15}$$

where x and y are the displacements of the point O_1 measured along the moving axes of the coordinates. The remaining notations are defined in § 33.

[45] See also Bolotin [17].

[46] The derivation appears in Bolotin [17].

The stability of the zero solution ($x = y = 0$) of a homogeneous system which corresponds to the case of a vertical and completely balanced shaft will now be investigated. The substitution of the expressions

$$x = \xi e^{ht}, \qquad y = \eta e^{ht},$$

leads to the characteristic equation

$$h^4 + (\omega_1^2 + \omega_2^2 + 2\omega^2)h^2 + (\omega_1^2 - \omega^2)(\omega_2^2 - \omega^2) = 0 .$$

The zero solution is stable as long as this equation does not have roots with a positive real part. The stability will obviously be upset in the interval of angular velocities $\omega_1 < \omega < \omega_2$.

The influence of damping, limited to the case of "external" friction will now be considered. Taking such damping into account, the homogeneous system has the form

$$x'' + 2\varepsilon x' - 2\omega y' - (\omega_1^2 - \omega^2)x - 2\varepsilon\omega y = 0 ,$$
$$y'' + 2\varepsilon y' + 2\omega x' + (\omega_2^2 - \omega^2)y + 2\varepsilon\omega y = 0 .$$

If the characteristic equation for this system is formed, the stability condition is

$$(\omega_1^2 - \omega^2)(\omega_2^2 - \omega^2) + 4\varepsilon^2\omega^2 > 0 . \tag{9.16}$$

It is easily seen that damping narrows the region of instability. For sufficiently large damping, as in the problem on the dynamic stability of a compressed rod, loss of stability from the straight-line form is generally impossible (Fig. 74). It is appropriate at this time to introduce the concept of the *critical damping coefficient*, for which it is not difficult to obtain the formula

$$e_* = \frac{\omega_2 - \omega_1}{2} .$$

If the individual frequencies are sufficiently close, i.e., $\omega_1 \approx \omega_2$, then the approximate formula is

$$\delta_* \approx \frac{2\pi\varepsilon_*}{\omega_1} = \pi\left(\frac{\omega_2}{\omega_1} - 1\right) \tag{9.17}$$

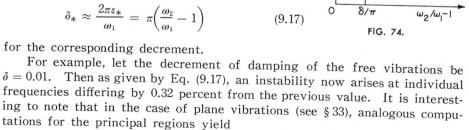

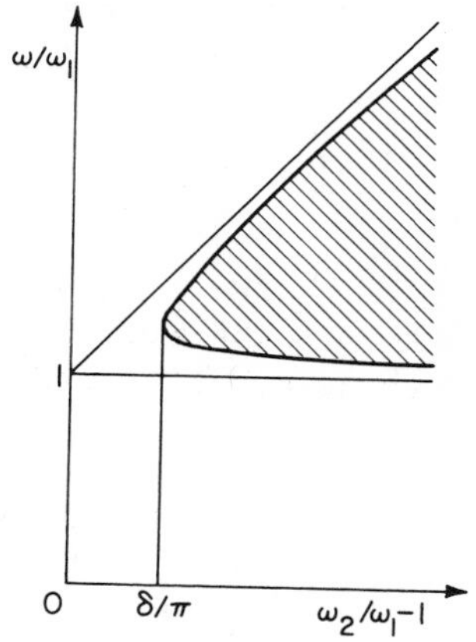

FIG. 74.

for the corresponding decrement.

For example, let the decrement of damping of the free vibrations be $\delta = 0.01$. Then as given by Eq. (9.17), an instability now arises at individual frequencies differing by 0.32 percent from the previous value. It is interesting to note that in the case of plane vibrations (see § 33), analogous computations for the principal regions yield

$$\delta_* = \pi\mu = \frac{\pi}{2}\left(\frac{\omega_2}{\omega_1} - 1\right).$$

In contrast to the problems which have been considered previously, only one region of instability exists here (for a system with one degree of freedom) and not an infinite sequence of instability regions.

●**2.** The nonlinear problem will now be discussed briefly. As in the plane case, in the formulation of the nonlinear equations it is necessary to consider the shaft as the system with an infinite number of degrees of freedom, considering the exact expression for the curvature and the axial force arising from the axial displacements. In the case of a vertical and balanced shaft in the absence of a gyroscopic effect, the equations are

$$\begin{aligned}\frac{\partial^2}{\partial s^2}\left(\frac{EJ_2}{\rho_2}\right) + \frac{\partial}{\partial s}\left(N\frac{\partial u}{\partial s}\right) + m(s)\left(\frac{\partial^2 u}{\partial t^2} - 2\omega\frac{\partial v}{\partial t^2} - \omega^2 u\right) &= 0\,,\\ \frac{\partial^2}{\partial s^2}\left(\frac{EJ_1}{\rho_1}\right) + \frac{\partial}{\partial s}\left(N\frac{\partial v}{\partial s}\right) + m(s)\left(\frac{\partial^2 v}{\partial t^2} + 2\omega\frac{\partial u}{\partial t} - \omega^2 v\right) &= 0\,.\end{aligned} \tag{9.18}$$

Here s is the arc length measured along the deformed axis of the shaft in the direction of the rotating coordinate axes (Fig. 75) and $1/\rho_1$ and $1/\rho_2$ are the principal curvatures of the axis of the shaft (torsion is neglected):

$$\begin{aligned}\frac{1}{\rho_1} &= \frac{\dfrac{\partial^2 v}{\partial s^2}}{\sqrt{1-\left(\dfrac{\partial u}{\partial s}\right)^2-\left(\dfrac{\partial v}{\partial s}\right)^2}} \approx \frac{\partial^2 v}{\partial s^2}\left[1+\frac{1}{2}\left(\frac{\partial u}{\partial s}\right)^2+\frac{1}{2}\left(\frac{\partial v}{\partial s}\right)^2\right],\\ \frac{1}{\rho_2} &= \frac{\dfrac{\partial^2 u}{\partial s^2}}{\sqrt{1-\left(\dfrac{\partial u}{\partial s}\right)^2-\left(\dfrac{\partial v}{\partial s}\right)^2}} \approx \frac{\partial^2 u}{\partial s^2}\left[1+\frac{1}{2}\left(\frac{\partial u}{\partial s}\right)^2+\frac{1}{2}\left(\frac{\partial v}{\partial s}\right)^2\right].\end{aligned} \tag{9.19}$$

The axial force is determined by Eq. (9.13), but the method of calculating $w(s, t)$ is changed. It is easily seen from Figure 75 that

$$w(s, t) = \int_0^s (ds - dz)\,.$$

But

$$dz = ds\sqrt{1-\left(\frac{\partial u}{\partial s}\right)^2-\left(\frac{\partial v}{\partial s}\right)^2},$$

from which it follows that to within the quantities of higher order,

$$w(s, t) \approx \frac{1}{2}\int_0^s\left[\left(\frac{\partial u}{\partial s}\right)^2+\left(\frac{\partial v}{\partial s}\right)^2\right]ds\,.$$

The deflected form of the shaft will be approximated by suitable functions:

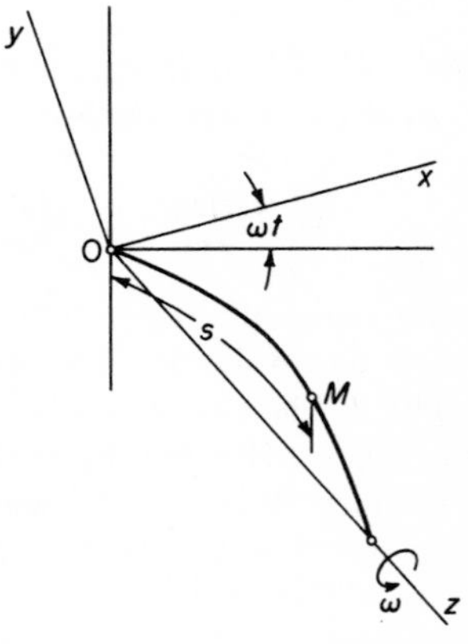

FIG. 75.

$$u(s, t) = x(t)\varphi(s) ,$$
$$v(s, t) = y(t)\varphi(s) ; \tag{9.20}$$

here, as before, x and y are displacements of the point O_1 in the direction of the rotating axes (Fig. 73). Then

$$w(s, t) \approx (x^2 + y^2)\beta(s) \tag{9.21}$$

where $\beta(s)$ is a known function. Substituting Eqs. (9.13), (9.19), (9.20), and (9.21) into the differential equation (9.18) and applying the Galerkin method yields the following system of equations:

$$x'' + 2\varepsilon x' - 2\omega y' + (\omega_1^2 - \omega^2)x - 2\varepsilon\omega y + \psi_1(x, y) = 0 ,$$
$$y'' + 2\varepsilon y' + 2\omega x' + (\omega_2^2 - \omega^2)y + 2\varepsilon\omega x + \psi_2(x, y) = 0 , \tag{9.22}$$

Here damping is taken into account, and $\psi_1(x, y)$ and $\psi_2(x, y)$ are nonlinear functions:

$$\psi_1(x, y) = (\gamma_1 + \gamma)x(x^2 + y^2) + \varepsilon_L x(x^2 + y^2)' + \kappa x(x^2 + y^2)'',$$
$$\psi_2(x, y) = (\gamma_2 + \gamma)y(x^2 + y^2) + \varepsilon_L y(x^2 + y^2)' + \kappa y(x^2 + y^2)''.$$

The first terms on the right-hand side result from the exact expression of the curvature; moreover, for a simply supported shaft in accordance with Eq. (3.16),

$$\gamma_1 = \frac{\pi^2\omega_1^2}{8l^2}, \qquad \gamma_2 = \frac{\pi^2\omega_2^2}{8l^2} .$$

The remaining coefficients retain their previous values.

●3. Let us confine ourselves to the special solution which is of great practical interest. Assume that the shaft performs a steady-state precessed motion with the velocity of rotation. In the rotating x- and y-coordinate system (Fig. 73), such motion is represented in the form $x = \text{const.}$ and $y = \text{const.}$ and, consequently, can be found from the system of algebraic equations

$$(\omega_1^2 - \omega^2)x - 2\varepsilon\omega y + (\gamma_1 + \gamma)x(x^2 + y^2) = 0 ,$$
$$(\omega_2^2 - \omega^2)y + 2\varepsilon\omega x + (\gamma_2 + \gamma)y(x^2 + y^2) = 0 . \tag{9.23}$$

Considering the conservative case ($\varepsilon = 0$) leads to two solutions of the type

$$\text{I.}\quad x^2 = \frac{\omega_1^2}{\gamma_1 + \gamma}\left(\frac{\omega^2}{\omega_1^2} - 1\right), \quad y = 0 ,$$
$$\text{II.}\quad x = 0 , \quad y^2 = \frac{\omega_2^2}{\gamma_2 + \gamma}\left(\frac{\omega^2}{\omega_2^2} - 1\right), \tag{9.24}$$

in addition to the zero solution.

The first solution corresponds to a deflection with respect to the axis of the least stiffness, the second to a deflection with respect to the axis of greatest stiffness (Fig. 76). Additional investigation indicates that only the first solution is stable. This result can be obtained also directly from the form of the derived solutions (Fig. 77).

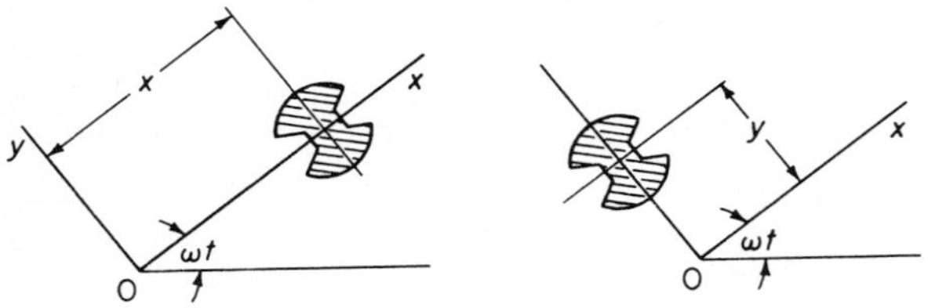

FIG. 76.

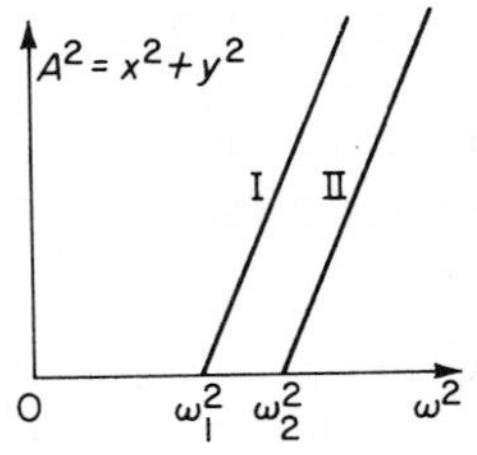

FIG. 77.

The "overhang" occurs in the direction of increasing angular velocities. Moreover, even for close frequencies, the deformations of the shaft can be quite large. Assuming that the supports do not hinder the approach of the ends of the shaft, then $\gamma = 0$, and the formula for the deflection of the shaft takes the form

$$x = \frac{2\sqrt{2l}}{\pi}\sqrt{\frac{\omega^2}{\omega_1^{\ 2}} - 1}\,,$$

which is, incidentally, very similar to the well-known formula of Mises, Eq. (3.8). For $\omega_2 = 1.05\,\omega_1$, the deflection on the upper boundary of the region of instability, i.e., without the consideration of the "overhang," is $0.28l$. (For such large deflections one must generally consider terms of higher order.

Another extreme case is the case where the supports do not allow *any* axial displacements. In this case an axial force

$$N = \frac{EF}{l}w_l$$

results, where EF is the extensional stiffness of the shaft. Consequently, the coefficient of nonlinear elasticity is

$$\gamma = \frac{\pi^4 c}{2\mu l^2} \approx \frac{\omega_1^{\ 2}}{r_2^{\ 2}} = \frac{\omega_2^{\ 2}}{r_1^{\ 2}}$$

(r_1 and r_2 are the principal radii of inertia of the cross section). The formula for deflection of the shaft takes the form ($\gamma \gg \gamma_1$)

$$x = r_2\sqrt{\frac{\omega^2}{\omega_2^{\ 2}} - 1}\,,$$

and, for the case $\omega_2 = 1.05\,\omega_1$, yields $x = 0.32\,r_2$. Actually, the deflection of a shaft can vary within a very wide range.

If damping is considered, the case is limited to the case where $\gamma \gg \gamma_1$. Considering Eqs. (9.23) as a homogeneous algebraic system with respect to x and y and equating its determinant to zero, leads to the equation

$$\begin{vmatrix} \omega_1^{\ 2} - \omega^2 + \gamma a^2 & -2\varepsilon\omega \\ 2\varepsilon\omega & \omega_2^{\ 2} - \omega^2 + \gamma a^2 \end{vmatrix} = 0\,,$$

where $a^2 = x^2 + y^2$. Hence,

$$a^2 = \frac{1}{2\gamma}[2\omega^2 - \omega_1^2 - \omega_2^2 \pm \sqrt{(\omega_1^2 - \omega_2^2)^2 - 16\varepsilon^2\omega^2}] \,. \tag{9.25}$$

The resonance curve is shown in Figure 78. Its base coincides with the interval of instability found from Eq. (9.16). Damping decreases the deflections of the shaft, and the neutral line no longer coincides with the axis of the least stiffness. It is essential that the "overhang" be bounded; the limiting angular velocity is found by equating the expression under the radical in Eq. (9.25) to zero:

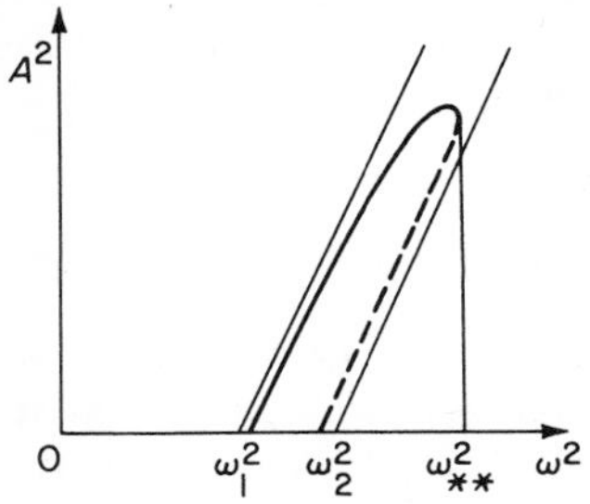

FIG. 78.

$$\omega_{**}^2 = \frac{\omega_2^2 - \omega_1^2}{4\varepsilon} \approx \frac{\delta_*}{\delta}\omega_1 \,.$$

Other questions concerning the considerations of the unbalance, dead weight of the disk, etc., will not be discussed here.

§ 35. Other Examples of Systems with Periodically Varying Stiffness

● **1.** The classical example of a system with a periodically varying stiffness is the drive system of an electric locomotive which uses a coupling rod for force transmission.[47] A simplified diagram of such a system appears in Figure 79.

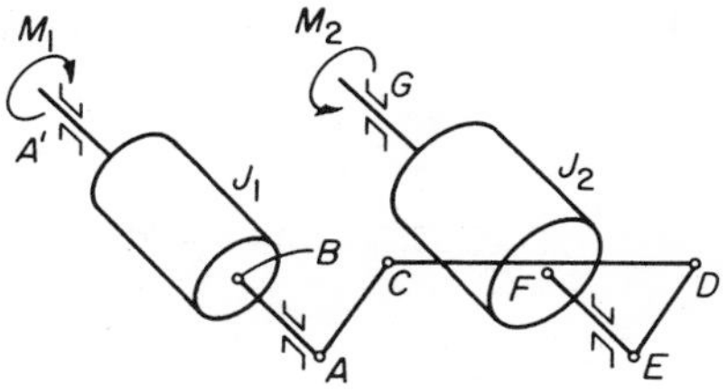

FIG. 79.

Assume that a moment is transmitted from the axis of the engine's rotor AA' to the driving axis EG by a coupling rod CD (usually two coupling rods are installed that are out of phase by $\pi/2$; this condition only slightly complicates the problem). Furthermore, let J_1 and J_2 be the moments of inertia of the masses referred to the first and the second axes respectively, φ_1 and φ_2 the angles of rotation of the masses, M_1 and M_2 the external moments applied to these masses, and c the spring stiffness coefficient of the connection between both axes. The differential equation of motion of the rotor has the form

$$y_1\varphi_1'' + c(\varphi_1 - \varphi_2) = M_1 \,,$$

and the differential equation of motion of the mass referred to the driving axis is

$$y_2\varphi_2'' + c(\varphi_2 - \varphi_1) = -M_2 \,.$$

47 See Timoshenko [1] (further references are contained in this work).

Dividing the first differential equation by J_1, the second by J_2, and subtracting one of the differential equations from the other gives

$$(\varphi_1 - \varphi_2)'' + c\frac{J_1 + J_2}{J_1 J_2}(\varphi_1 - \varphi_2) = \frac{M_1}{J_1} + \frac{M_2}{J_2}. \tag{9.26}$$

The relative angle of rotation of the mass we denote by φ, i.e., $\varphi = \varphi_1 - \varphi_2$ (where $\varphi \ll \varphi_1$). Furthermore, let

$$c\frac{J_1 + J_2}{J_1 J_2} = K, \qquad \frac{M_1}{J_1} + \frac{M_2}{J_2} = Q(t).$$

The differential equation (9.26) then takes the form

$$\varphi'' + K\varphi = Q(t). \tag{9.27}$$

The stiffness c of the system and, therefore, also the coefficient K in Eq. (9.27) depend on the relative position of the parts of the system at a given time, and for the steady-state rotation of the driving axis are periodic functions of time. In fact, near $\varphi_1 = 0$ and $\varphi_2 = \pi$, the stress in the coupling rod and, consequently, its axial deformation become maximum. In contrast, near $\varphi_1 = \pi/2$ or $\varphi_1 = 3\pi/2$, its deformation is equal to zero.

● **2.** The stiffness of the system (Fig. 79) is now calculated. The angle φ of the relative rotation of the masses is composed of the angles of twist $\Delta\varphi_1$ and $\Delta\varphi_2$ of the shafts AB and EF and an additional angle $\Delta\varphi_3$ that appears because of the axial deformation of the coupling rod:

$$\varphi = \Delta\varphi_1 + \Delta\varphi_2 + \Delta\varphi_3. \tag{9.28}$$

Let M be the moment transmitted by one of the shafts to the other shaft, and c_1 and c_2 be the stiffnesses of sections AB and EF. Then,

$$\Delta\varphi_1 = \frac{M}{c_1}, \quad \Delta\varphi_2 = \frac{M}{c_2}. \tag{9.29}$$

Calculate the shortening of the coupling rod with the stiffness EF_K (Fig. 80):

$$\Delta l = \frac{Nl}{EF_K} \approx \frac{M}{r\cos\varphi_1}\frac{l}{EF_K}.$$

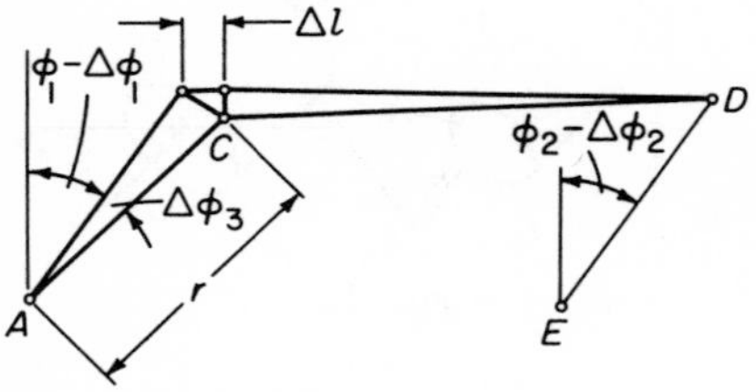

FIG. 80.

From geometric considerations

$$\Delta\varphi_3 \approx \frac{\Delta l}{r\cos\varphi_1} \approx \frac{Ml}{r^2 EF_K \cos^2\varphi_1}. \tag{9.30}$$

Combining Eqs. (9.28), (9.29), and (9.30) yields

$$\varphi = M\left(\frac{1}{c_1} + \frac{1}{c_2} + \frac{l}{r^2 EF_K \cos^2\varphi_1}\right) = \frac{M}{c},$$

where

$$c(\varphi_1) = \frac{c_0(1 + \cos 2\varphi_1)}{1 + \dfrac{c_0}{c_3}(1 + \cos 2\varphi_1)}, \qquad c_0 = \frac{c_1 c_2}{c_1 + c_2}, \qquad c_3 = \frac{r^2 EF_K}{2l}.$$

For a uniform rotation of the driving axis with an angular velocity θ, $\varphi_1 \approx \theta t$, and the stiffness of the system becomes a rather complicated periodic function of time; Eq. (9.27) becomes a Hill differential equation with an additional function on the right-hand side. The regions of instability for the homogeneous equation can be constructed by the known methods (§ 5). If the relation of the change of external moments acting on the rotor and the driving axis is prescribed, then the solution of the nonhomogeneous differential equation can also be found.

In engineering problems it is necessary to take into account the presence of two coupling rods which are out of phase, the clearance between the coupling rod and the pin of the crankshaft, and other additional factors. The treatment of these cases can be found in Timoshenko [1].

In conclusion it might be noted that vibrations induced by a periodically varying stiffness appear to have caused many failures in electric locomotives, especially during the period when electric locomotives were first built.

●3. An example of still another system whose stiffness changes periodically will be discussed briefly.[48] For the transmission of the motion and the output between the intersecting shafts with a gear ratio equal to one, the transmission with the aid of bent rods was proposed (Komarov [1]). Two intersecting shafts forming an angle 2β have rigid disks at their ends with holes uniformly distributed along their peripheries (Fig. 81). Bent rods (for example, the rod ABC in Fig. 81) are inserted into these holes; all the rods can both translate and rotate.

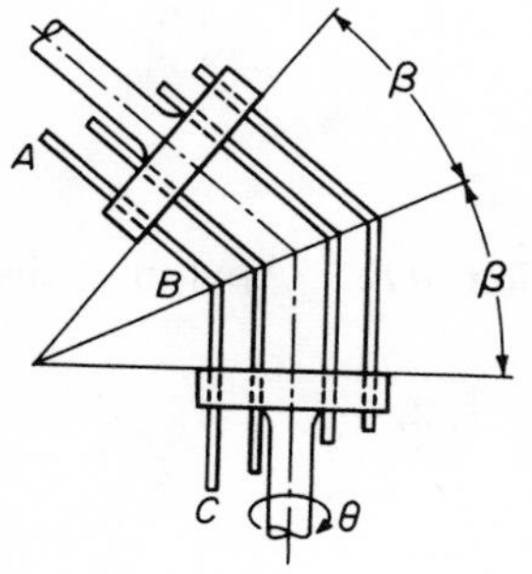

FIG. 81.

The equation of motion for such a system coincides with Eq. (9.26), the only difference being that the coefficient c in this equation is a very complicated function of time with period $2\pi/n\theta$ (θ is the angular velocity and n is the number of rods). The calculation of this function has been carried out in the article by Komarov [1].

§ 36. Vibrations of Systems with Periodically Varying Mass

●1. If the mass of a system (real or reduced) varies periodically with time, then the problem of the vibrations of such a system is not different, in principle, from the problems analyzed previously. In fact, if the mass $m(t) > 0$ and $c = \text{const.}$, then Eq. (9.8) remains practically unchanged. (Certain differences appear only when damping and nonlinear factors are considered.)

The most important engineering problem belonging to this class is the

[48] In addition to this paragraph, see Epishev [1] and Poznyak [1].

problem of the vibrations of crankshafts. It is known (Biezeno and Grammel [1], Vol. II) that the calculation of the vibrations of such shafts is ordinarily reduced to the calculation of a straight shaft with a certain reduced stiffness and a series of concentrated disks (according to the number of cylinders and fly wheels).

The moment of inertia of the mass of every disk is chosen in such a manner that its kinetic energy is equal to the kinetic energy of the rotating parts, the connecting rod, and the piston that this disk replaces. Thus, if the length of the connecting rod l is large in comparison with the length of the crank r (Fig. 82), then the total kinetic energy is

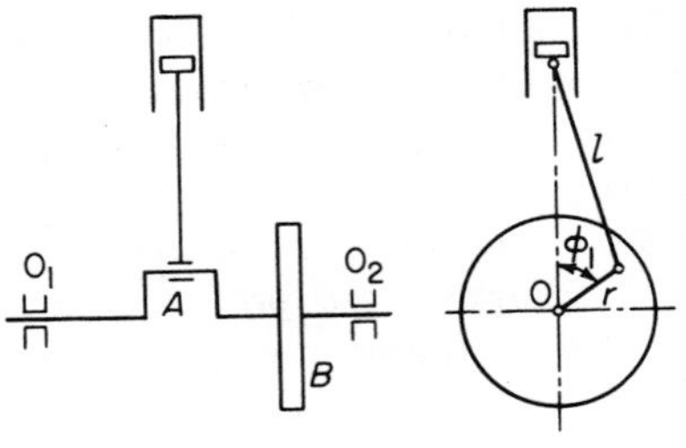

FIG. 82.

$$T \approx \tfrac{1}{2} J_0(\varphi')^2 + \tfrac{1}{2} m(r\varphi' \sin \varphi)^2,$$

where φ is the angle of rotation of the crank, J_0 is the moment of inertia of the rotating parts, and m is the mass of the connecting rod and the piston. The reduced moment of inertia is therefore

$$J(\varphi) = J_0 + mr^2 \sin^2 \varphi \,, \tag{9.31}$$

and consequently for steady-state rotation ($\varphi = \omega t$), the inertia coefficient is a periodic function of time.

The equations of motion will now be formulated; the case will be limited to that of a one-cylinder motor with a flywheel (Fig. 82). Let φ_1 be the angle of rotation of the crank, $J_1(\varphi_1)$ be the moment of inertia calculated from Eq. (9.31), φ_2 be the angle of rotation of the fly wheel, and $J_2 = \text{const.}$ be its moment of inertia. The kinetic energy of the system obviously is

$$T = \tfrac{1}{2} J_1(\varphi_1)\cdot(\varphi_1')^2 + \tfrac{1}{2} J_2\cdot(\varphi_2')^2,$$

and the potential energy of deformation is

$$U = \tfrac{1}{2} c(\varphi_1 - \varphi_2)^2.$$

(Here c is the reduced stiffness of the shaft on section AB.) Applying the Lagrange equations

$$\frac{d}{dt}\left(\frac{\partial T}{\partial \varphi_k'}\right) - \frac{\partial}{\partial \varphi_k}(T - U) = Q_k \,, \qquad (k = 1, 2)$$

leads to the system of equations

$$J_1(\varphi_1)\varphi_1'' + \frac{1}{2}\,\frac{dJ_1(\varphi_1)}{d\varphi_1}(\varphi_1')^2 + c(\varphi_1 - \varphi_2) = M_1(\varphi_1) \,,$$

$$J_2\varphi_2'' + c(\varphi_2 - \varphi_1) = -\,M_2(\varphi_2) \,,$$

where $M_1(\varphi_1)$ and $M_2(\varphi_2)$ are the external moments acting on the crank and fly wheel, respectively. In the case of a two-cycle motor, the moment $M_1(\varphi_1)$ has a period $2\pi/\theta$. In the case of a four-cycle motor, the moment $M_1(\varphi_1)$ has a period $4\pi/\theta$. If the relative angle of twist $\varphi_1 - \varphi_2 = \varphi$ is introduced as in the derivation of the differential equation (9.27), then

$$J_1(\varphi_1)\varphi'' + c\frac{J_1(\varphi_1) + J_2}{J_2}\varphi + \frac{1}{2}\frac{dJ_1(\varphi_1)}{d\varphi_1}(\varphi_1')^2 = M_1(\varphi_1) + \frac{J_1(\varphi_1)}{J_2}M_2(\varphi_2) . \tag{9.32}$$

Some simplifications will now be carried out. Let the moment of inertia of the flywheel be sufficiently large so that we can assume that $J_1(\varphi_1) \ll J_2$ and its rotation is uniform ($\varphi_2 = \theta t$). Since the angle of twist is small ($\varphi \ll \omega t$), it is assumed that[49]

$$\frac{dJ_1(\varphi_1)}{d\varphi_1} \approx \frac{dJ_1(\omega t)}{d(\omega t)} , \qquad J_1(\varphi_1) \approx J_1(\omega t) , \qquad M_1(\varphi_1) \approx M_1(\omega t)$$

and that, $(\varphi_1')^2 \approx \omega^2$. The differential equation (9.32) takes the form

$$J_1(\omega t)\varphi'' + c\varphi = M_1(\omega t) - \frac{\omega^2}{2}\frac{dJ_1(\omega t)}{d(\omega t)} . \tag{9.33}$$

If Eq. (9.31) is considered, the corresponding homogeneous equation is written in the form

$$\varphi'' + \frac{\omega^2}{1 - 2\mu \cos 2\theta t}\varphi = 0 ,$$

where

$$\omega^2 = \frac{c}{J_0 + \frac{1}{2}mr^2} , \qquad \mu = \frac{mr^2}{2(2J_0 + mr^2)} .$$

The problem thus reduces to a Hill differential equation ($\mu < \frac{1}{2}$).

The case of a one-cylinder engine is considered above. For the case of several cylinders, the problem reduces to *systems* of differential equations with perodic coefficients.

The angle of rotation of the kth equivalent disk is denoted by φ_k, the moment of inertia of this disk by $J_k(\varphi_k)$, and the stiffness of the shaft on the section between the $(k-1)^{\text{th}}$ and the kth disks by $c_{k-1,k}$. The approximate equations of motion for the system are written in the form (Kochin [1])[50]

$$J_k(\omega t)\varphi_k'' + c_{k-1,k}(\varphi_k - \varphi_{k-1}) + c_{k,k+1}(\varphi_k - \varphi_{k+1}) = P_k(\omega t) ,$$
$$(k = 1, 2, 3, \cdots, n),$$

where $P_k(\omega t)$ are known functions of time. Part II and Part III of this book are devoted to the methods of investigation of similar equations.

● **2.** Although the division of systems into two classes (with variable stiffness and variable mass) in many cases is physically justified, it is possible only under certain conditions. An example that leads to an equation of the more general form will now be given.

[49] This is equivalent to neglecting along with the nonlinear terms also certain linear terms with respect to φ, which generally must be retained in the "variational equations." A correction can be easily obtained, however.

[50] Another adequate form of the linearization was given by Weidenhammer [6].

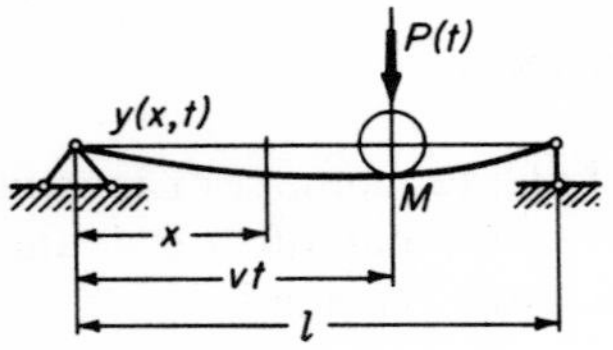

FIG. 83.

Assume that a load with mass M is moving with a constant velocity v along the beam of span l, and that at the time $t = 0$ the load is at one end of the beam (Fig. 83). The differential equation of the vibrations of such a beam is

$$EJ\frac{\partial^4 y}{\partial x^4} + m_0\frac{\partial^2 y}{\partial t^2} = q(x, t)\,, \tag{9.34}$$

where $y(x, t)$ is the deflection of the beam, EJ is its bending stiffness, and m_0 is the mass of the beam per unit length. The function on the right-hand side takes into account the loading $P(t)$ and the inertial force associated with the mass M.

$$q(x, t) = 0 \quad \text{for} \quad x < vt - \eta\,,$$

$$\lim_{\eta\to 0}\int_{vt-\eta}^{vt+\eta} q(x, t)dx = P(t) - M\frac{d^2 y(vt, t)}{dt^2}\,,$$

$$q(x, t) = 0 \quad \text{for} \quad x > vt - \eta\,.$$

For computing the acceleration, the total derivative must be taken:

$$\frac{d^2 y}{dt^2} = \frac{\partial^2 y}{\partial t^2} + 2v\frac{\partial^2 y}{\partial x \partial t} + v^2\frac{\partial^2 y}{\partial x^2}\,.$$

The solution of this problem for the case of a simply supported beam is sought in the form of a series:

$$y(x, t) = \sum_{i=1}^{\infty} f_i(t)\sin\frac{i\pi x}{l}\,, \tag{9.35}$$

where $f_i(t)$ are unknown functions of time. To derive the equation that the function $f(t)$ must satisfy (the index is dropped), only the first term of the series is taken and the Galerkin variational method is used. Calculations yield[51]

$$(1 + 2\alpha\sin^2 kt)f'' + 2\alpha k\sin 2kt\, f'$$
$$+ (\omega_0^{\,2} - 2\alpha k^2\sin^2 kt)f = p(t, kt); \tag{9.36}$$

where

$$\alpha = \frac{M}{m_0 l}\,,\qquad k = \frac{\pi v}{l}\,,\qquad \omega_0^2 = \frac{\pi^2 EJ}{l^2 m_0}\,,\qquad p(t, kt) = \frac{2P(t)}{m_0 l}\sin kt\,.$$

The differential equation (9.36) was obtained by Inglis [1] who gave solutions for a number of special cases. Further generalizations of these results were obtained by Bolotin [1], [3].

Imagine now that a sequence of equidistant loads are moving along a beam. Equation (9.34) then describes the vibration process which, for cer-

[51] The basis of this method in the presence of a discontinuous function $q(x, t)$ can be obtained by the methods of the theory of linear integral equations.

tain parametric relationships, can be accompanied by unboundedly increasing amplitudes.

The homogeneous differential equation corresponding to Eq. (9.36) will now be considered:

$$(1 + 2\alpha \sin^2 kt) f'' + 2\alpha k \sin 2kt f' + (\omega_2 - 2\alpha k^2 \sin^2 kt) f = 0 . \qquad (9.37)$$

All its coefficients are periodic time functions with a period $\pi/k = l/v$. The coefficients of f'' and f, however, are even functions of time and the coefficient of f' is an odd function of time. Therefore the form of Eq. (9.37) does not change if t is replaced by $-t$, and this fact shows that the product of its characteristic roots is equal to unity.[52] Consequently, the boundaries of the regions of instability can be determined from the Mathieu-Hill differential equation by finding the conditions under which the differential equation solutions have periods l/v and $2l/v$.

Through the substitution

$$f = u(t) \exp\left(- \int \frac{\alpha k \sin 2kt}{1 + 2\alpha \sin^2 kt} dt \right),$$

Eq. (9.37) reduces directly to the Hill equation.

The problem can be generalized if one considers, for example, an infinite

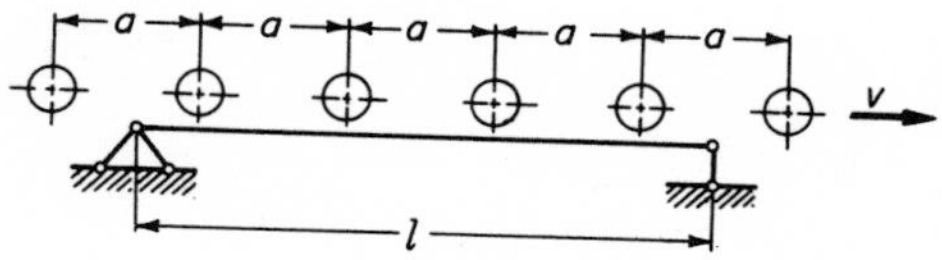

FIG. 84.

sequence of equal loads moving at intervals a. Let the spanwidth be a multiple of the distance a (Fig. 84). Thus the differential equation of the problem has coefficients with a period a/v.

[52] In fact, one of the particular solutions of this differential equation can be presented in the form of Eq. (1.21),

$$f(t) = \chi(t) e^{(t/T)\ln \rho_1},$$

where ρ_1 is one of its characteristic roots. But replacing t by $-t$ must yield another particular solution, from which $\ln \rho_2 = -\ln \rho_1$ and $\rho_2 = 1/\rho_1$.

PART II

GENERAL THEORY OF THE DYNAMIC STABILITY OF ELASTIC SYSTEMS

Ten

ELEMENTS OF MATRIX OPERATIONS

§ 37. Definitions and Basic Operations

●1. Let us consider the following system of linear equations[1]:

$$\begin{aligned} a_{11}x_1 + a_{12}x_2 + \cdots + a_{1n}x_n &= b_1 , \\ a_{21}x_1 + a_{22}x_2 + \cdots + a_{2n}x_n &= b_2 , \\ \cdots\cdots\cdots\cdots\cdots & \\ a_{n1}x_1 + a_{n2}x_2 + \cdots + a_{nn}x_n &= b_n \end{aligned}$$

or, more briefly, $\sum_{k=1}^{n} a_{ik}x_k = b_i, \quad (i = 1, 2, 3, \cdots, n) .$ (10.1)

The corresponding homogeneous system is

$$\sum_{k=1}^{n} a_{ik}x_k = 0 , \quad (i = 1, 2, 3, \cdots, n) . \tag{10.2}$$

Equations (10.1) and (10.2) can be written very compactly if matrix notation is used.

Let us denote the array composed of coefficients a_{ik} by a single letter[2]:

$$\boldsymbol{A} = \begin{pmatrix} a_{11} & a_{12} & \cdots & a_{1n} \\ a_{21} & a_{22} & \cdots & a_{2n} \\ \cdot & \cdot & \cdots & \cdot \\ a_{n1} & a_{n2} & \cdots & a_{nn} \end{pmatrix} .$$

One such array, called a *matrix*, characterizes all of the n^2 coefficients of the system in Eq. (10.1).

Let $x_1, x_2, \cdots, x_n$ be a solution of Eq. (10.1). All of these n numbers can be considered as vectors in n-dimensional space,

$$\boldsymbol{x} = \boldsymbol{x}(x_1 , x_2 , \cdots, x_n) .$$

One may speak about a vector

$$\boldsymbol{b} = \boldsymbol{b}(b_1, b_2, \cdots, b_n)$$

of the "right side" in the same manner.

With this notation the system of equations (10.1) is written in the form

$$\boldsymbol{Ax} = \boldsymbol{b}$$

[1] The information here is reduced to the minimum necessary for the understanding of subsequent material. For a more complete account, see Smirnov [1], Mal'tsev [1], Bulgakov, [1], Pipes [1], Frazer, Duncan and Collar [1], Michal [1].

[2] In contrast to scalar quantities, matrices and vectors are denoted here by boldface type.

where the expanded form of notation

$$\sum_{k=1}^{n} a_{ik}x_k = b_i\,, \qquad (i = 1, 2, \cdots, n)$$

should be regarded as a definition of the rule for the *multiplication of a matrix by a vector.*

With the so-called inverse matrix $\boldsymbol{A}^{-1}$, the solution of Eqs. (10.1) takes the form

$$\boldsymbol{x} = \boldsymbol{A}^{-1}\boldsymbol{b}\,. \tag{10.3}$$

On the other hand, Cramer's rule for the solution of nonhomogeneous equations states that since A_{ik} is the cofactor of the element a_{ik} and the determinant

$$\Delta = \begin{vmatrix} a_{11} & a_{12} & \cdots & a_{1n} \\ a_{21} & a_{22} & \cdots & a_{2n} \\ \cdot & \cdot & \cdot & \cdot \\ a_{n1} & a_{n2} & \cdots & a_{nn} \end{vmatrix}$$

of the system does not disappear, then

$$x_i = \frac{\sum_{k=1}^{n} A_{ik}b_k}{\Delta}\,, \qquad (i = 1, 2, \cdots, n)\,. \tag{10.4}$$

A comparison of Eqs. (10.3) and (10.4) yields

$$\boldsymbol{A}^{-1} = \begin{pmatrix} \frac{A_{11}}{\Delta} & \frac{A_{12}}{\Delta} & \cdots & \frac{A_{1n}}{\Delta} \\ \frac{A_{21}}{\Delta} & \frac{A_{22}}{\Delta} & \cdots & \frac{A_{2n}}{\Delta} \\ \cdot & \cdot & \cdot & \cdot \\ \frac{A_{n1}}{\Delta} & \frac{A_{n2}}{\Delta} & \cdots & \frac{A_{nn}}{\Delta} \end{pmatrix}.$$

An essential requirement for solving a system of linear differential equations is the condition that the determinant Δ not equal zero. If the determinant does equal zero, then the corresponding matrix is called *singular*; otherwise the matrix will be called *regular* or *nonsingular*. An inverse matrix can exist only for a regular matrix.

We also introduce the following definitions. Matrices whose elements are zero will be called *null matrices* and will be denoted simply by $\boldsymbol{O}$.

Of special importance are matrices in which the elements away from the principal diagonal are equal to zero:

$$\boldsymbol{A} = \begin{pmatrix} \alpha_1 & 0 & 0 & \cdots & 0 \\ 0 & \alpha_2 & 0 & \cdots & 0 \\ 0 & 0 & \alpha_3 & \cdots & 0 \\ \cdot & \cdot & \cdot & \cdot & \cdot \\ 0 & 0 & 0 & \cdots & \alpha_n \end{pmatrix}.$$

Such matrices will be called *diagonal matrices* and will be denoted simply by

$$A = \{\alpha_1, \alpha_2, \alpha_3, \cdots, \alpha_n\} .$$

If all diagonal elements are equal to each other,

$$\alpha_1 = \alpha_2 = \alpha_3 = \cdots = \alpha_n = \alpha ,$$

such a matrix is called a *scalar matrix*. In particular, a matrix whose diagonal elements equal unity,

$$E = \{1, 1, 1, \cdots, 1\} ,$$

is called a *unit matrix*; we shall see that this matrix plays the role of unity in matrix algebra.

● **2.** The theory of matrices is more easily developed if one uses a somewhat different treatment of results of linear systems. The relationships

$$\begin{aligned} a_{11}x_1 + a_{12}x_2 + \cdots + a_{1n}x_n &= y_1 , \\ a_{21}x_1 + a_{22}x_2 + \cdots + a_{2n}x_n &= y_2 , \\ \cdots\cdots\cdots\cdots\cdots\cdots\cdots \\ a_{n1}x_1 + a_{n2}x_2 + \cdots + a_{nn}x_n &= y_n \end{aligned} \tag{10.5}$$

will be considered as a *linear transformation* of the n variables $(x_1, x_2, \cdots, x_n)$ to n new variables $(y_1, y_2, \cdots, y_n)$. The matrix $\boldsymbol{A}$ with elements a_{ik} in this case characterizes the linear transformation of the n-dimensional vector $\boldsymbol{x}(x_1, x_2, \cdots, x_n)$ to the new vector $\boldsymbol{y}(y_1, y_2, \cdots, y_n)$:

$$\boldsymbol{y} = \boldsymbol{A}\boldsymbol{x} .$$

The unit matrix $\boldsymbol{E}$ in which every vector $\boldsymbol{x}$ is equal to one corresponds to the identity transformation, and the scalar matrix corresponds to the multiplication of the components of a vector with the same number α (similarity transformation).

Let us now define the fundamental operations of matrices. *The sum* $\boldsymbol{A} + \boldsymbol{B}$ *of two matrices* $\boldsymbol{A}$ *and* $\boldsymbol{B}$ is defined as the matrix through which a vector $\boldsymbol{x}$ is transformed into the sum of the two vectors $\boldsymbol{Ax}$ and $\boldsymbol{Bx}$:

$$\boldsymbol{Ax} + \boldsymbol{Bx} = (\boldsymbol{A} + \boldsymbol{B})\boldsymbol{x} .$$

From Eq. (10.5) it follows that adding two matrices leads to the addition of the corresponding elements:

$$\boldsymbol{A} + \boldsymbol{B} = \begin{pmatrix} a_{11} + b_{11} & a_{12} + b_{12} & \cdots & a_{1n} + b_{1n} \\ a_{21} + b_{21} & a_{22} + b_{22} & \cdots & a_{2n} + b_{2n} \\ \cdots & \cdots & \cdots & \cdots \\ a_{n1} + b_{n1} & a_{n2} + b_{n2} & \cdots & a_{nn} + b_{nn} \end{pmatrix}$$

Somewhat more complicated is the definition of the *product of two matrices*. Let the vector $\boldsymbol{z}$ be obtained by means of the successive transformations of the vector $\boldsymbol{x}$ with the aid of the two matrices:

$$\boldsymbol{y} = \boldsymbol{A}\boldsymbol{x} , \qquad \boldsymbol{z} = \boldsymbol{B}\boldsymbol{y} .$$

The two transformations correspond to a single transformation

$$\boldsymbol{z} = \boldsymbol{C}\boldsymbol{x}$$

with the matrix

$$\boldsymbol{C} = \boldsymbol{B}\boldsymbol{A} .$$

The elements of the matrix $\boldsymbol{C}$ are found by successively applying the transformations

$$y_j = \sum_{k=1}^{n} a_{jk} x_k$$

and

$$z_i = \sum_{j=1}^{n} b_{ij} y_j .$$

Substitution gives

$$z_i = \sum_{j=1}^{n} \sum_{k=1}^{n} b_{ij} a_{jk} x_k ,$$

from which follows

$$c_{ik} = \sum_{j=1}^{n} b_{ij} a_{jk} , \qquad (i, k = 1, 2, \cdots, n) . \tag{10.6}$$

Equation (10.6) should be regarded as the rule for the *multiplication of two matrices.* For example, from the very definition of the inverse matrix, it follows that

$$\boldsymbol{A}\boldsymbol{A}^{-1} = \boldsymbol{A}^{-1}\boldsymbol{A} = \boldsymbol{E} .$$

Still another example is the multiplication by the scalar matrix which reduces to the multiplication of all elements by the same number,

$$\boldsymbol{A}\boldsymbol{B} = \alpha \boldsymbol{B} ,$$

as is easily seen from Eq. (10.6).

The concept of the product of matrices may be extended to the case of three or more factors. In this manner, one can define the mth power of a matrix,

$$\boldsymbol{A}^m = \underbrace{\boldsymbol{A} \cdot \boldsymbol{A} \cdots \boldsymbol{A}}_{m \text{ times}} .$$

●**3.** By using the rules introduced above for the addition and multiplication of matrices, we may construct a matrix algebra which has many of the characteristics of the ordinary algebra of complex numbers. One essential difference exists, however. This difference is caused by the fact that *matrix multiplication is noncommutative,* i.e., the product of two matrices depends upon the order of the factors. In other words, if $\boldsymbol{A}$ and $\boldsymbol{B}$ are two arbitrary matrices, then in general,

$$\boldsymbol{A}\boldsymbol{B} \neq \boldsymbol{B}\boldsymbol{A} .$$

However, there are classes of matrices that are *interchangeable,* i.e., there are classes in which multiplication satisfies the commutative law. For example, powers of the same matrix, or, more generally, functions of the same matrix, are interchangeable. One may perform operations on such matrices, as on ordinary numbers. For example, in complete analogy with the series

$$\frac{1}{1-x} = 1 + x + x^2 + \cdots + x^m + \cdots$$

one may write the expansion

$$(\boldsymbol{E} - \boldsymbol{A})^{-1} = \boldsymbol{E} + \boldsymbol{A} + \boldsymbol{A}^2 + \cdots + \boldsymbol{A}^m + \cdots .$$

Therefore, the convergence of this series must be considered separately.

§ 38. Transformation of Matrices to the Diagonal Form. The Characteristic Equation

●1. Let us consider the transformation

$$\boldsymbol{y} = \boldsymbol{A}\boldsymbol{x} \tag{10.7}$$

and let us investigate how the matrix $\boldsymbol{A}$ changes if we subject the original coordinate system to a linear transformation with a nonsingular matrix $\boldsymbol{U}$. The vector $\boldsymbol{x}(x_1, x_2, \cdots, x_n)$ is transformed into a new vector $\boldsymbol{x}'(x_1', x_2', \cdots, x_n')$, whose components are expressed by the components of the old vector:

$$\boldsymbol{x}' = \boldsymbol{U}\boldsymbol{x} .$$

The vector $\boldsymbol{y}$ is transformed in an analogous manner:

$$\boldsymbol{y}' = \boldsymbol{U}\boldsymbol{y} .$$

Determining the initial values of the vectors from these formulas and substituting them into Eq. (10.7), we obtain

$$\boldsymbol{y}' = \boldsymbol{U}\boldsymbol{A}\boldsymbol{U}^{-1}\boldsymbol{x}' .$$

Thus, in the new coordinate system the transformation (10.7) will be represented by the matrix

$$\boldsymbol{A}' = \boldsymbol{U}\boldsymbol{A}\boldsymbol{U}^{-1} . \tag{10.8}$$

If the two matrices $\boldsymbol{A}$ and $\boldsymbol{A}'$ are connected with a regular matrix $\boldsymbol{U}$ by the relationship in Eq. (10.8), they are called *similar*. Of course they are not identical, but they are equivalent in the geometric sense since they represent the same transformation expressed in different coordinates.

Among the infinite number of existing coordinate systems the ones of special importance are those in which the transformation matrix is simplified to a diagonal form:

$$\boldsymbol{A}' = \{\lambda_1, \lambda_2, \cdots, \lambda_n\} .$$

If such a system of coordinates exists, then the transformation defined in the old system by the matrix $\boldsymbol{A}$ in the new axes reduces simply to an extension (or contraction) along these axes:

$$y'_k = \lambda_k x'_k\,, \qquad (k = 1, 2, \cdots, n)\,.$$

●2. With the new matrix $V = U^{-1}$, we can write Eq. (10.8) in the form

$$AV = VA'$$

or, expanded,

$$\sum_{j=1}^{n} a_{ij} v_{jk} = v_{ik}\lambda_k\,, \qquad (i, k = 1, 2, \cdots, n)\,. \tag{10.9}$$

The vectors that are formed from columns of the matrix

$$V = \begin{pmatrix} v_{11} & v_{12} & \cdots & v_{1n} \\ v_{21} & v_{22} & \cdots & v_{2n} \\ \cdot & \cdot & \cdot & \cdot \\ v_{n1} & v_{n2} & \cdots & v_{nn} \end{pmatrix}$$

are denoted by

$$\boldsymbol{v}_k = \boldsymbol{v}_k(v_{1k}, v_{2k}, \cdots, v_{nk})\,.$$

Equations (10.9) for a fixed k take the form

$$A\boldsymbol{v}_k = \lambda_k \boldsymbol{v}_k\,, \qquad (k = 1, 2, \cdots, n)\,. \tag{10.10}$$

One recognizes from these equations that the determination of the matrix V, which transforms the matrix A into a diagonal form (or, as is said, *on the principal axes*), comes from the determination of the vectors $\boldsymbol{v}_k$. The vectors $\boldsymbol{v}_k$ possess the property that as a result of the linear transformation with the matrix A they remain unchanged to within a constant factor, i.e., they are transformed to collinear vectors. We will call the $\boldsymbol{v}_k$ vectors the eigenvectors of the matrix A.

For determining the eigenvectors, the equation system (10.10) has the form

$$\begin{aligned} (a_{11} - \lambda_k)v_{1k} + a_{12}v_{2k} + \cdots + a_{1n}v_{nk} &= 0\,, \\ a_{21}v_{1k} + (a_{22} - \lambda_k)v_{2k} + \cdots + a_{2n}v_{nk} &= 0\,, \\ \cdots\cdots\cdots\cdots\cdots\cdots\cdots\cdots & \\ a_{n1}v_{1k} + a_{n2}v_{2k} + \cdots + (a_{nn} - \lambda_k)v_{nk} &= 0\,, \\ (k = 1, 2, \cdots, n)\,. & \end{aligned} \tag{10.11}$$

The homogeneous system (10.11) has a non-trivial solution if the condition exists that the determinant composed of its coefficients is equal to zero:

$$\begin{vmatrix} a_{11} - \lambda & a_{12} & \cdots & a_{1n} \\ a_{21} & a_{22} - \lambda & \cdots & a_{2n} \\ \cdot & \cdot & \cdot & \cdot \\ a_{n1} & a_{n2} & \cdots & a_{nn} - \lambda \end{vmatrix} = 0\,. \tag{10.12}$$

Equation (10.12), which may be written in the abbreviated form

$$|A - \lambda E| = 0\,,$$

is called the *characteristic equation of the matrix* $\boldsymbol{A}$; it has n roots $\lambda_1, \lambda_2, \cdots, \lambda_n$, called *characteristic eigenvalues* of the matrix $\boldsymbol{A}$.

If all the characteristic values are different from one another, then the matrix

$$\boldsymbol{A}' = \{\lambda_1, \lambda_2, \cdots, \lambda_n\}$$

represents the diagonal form of the original matrix $\boldsymbol{A}$. The simplest case of the reduction to diagonal form of a linear transformation with two variables has already been discussed in (§ 2, ● 1).

We determine the eigenvectors $\boldsymbol{v}_k$ in the following way. We substitute the characteristic value $\lambda_k = \lambda_1$ into Eq. (10.11) and solve the system with respect to the component v_{i1}; in this way we discard one of the equations (of the n equations only $n-1$ will be linearly independent). The $n-1$ components will then be expressed in terms of one component, for example v_{11}, which remains undetermined. In other words, the components of the eigenvector v_{i1} are determined only to within some constant factor. In order to remove this unknown, the eigenvectors ordinarily are *normalized,* i.e., a multiplier is chosen in such a way that the length of the vector would be equal to unity:

$$\sum_{i=1}^{n} v_{i1}^2 = 1 .$$

The components of the remaining $n-1$ eigenvectors are determined analogously. The matrix formed of columns of the n eigenvectors $\boldsymbol{v}_1, \boldsymbol{v}_2, \cdots, \boldsymbol{v}_n$ is the desired matrix of the transformation $\boldsymbol{V}$.

● 3. The conditions under which the two matrices $\boldsymbol{A}$ and $\boldsymbol{B}$ are simultaneously transformed to the principal axes are of fundamental interest. We will show that two matrices *can be simultaneously transformed into diagonal form only if they are interchangeable.*

Let $\boldsymbol{A}$ and $\boldsymbol{B}$ be two matrices whose characteristic numbers are equal to α and β, respectively. If their principal axes coincide, then the following equations hold:

$$\boldsymbol{A}\boldsymbol{v} = \alpha\boldsymbol{v} , \qquad \boldsymbol{B}\boldsymbol{v} = \beta\boldsymbol{v} ;$$

the $\boldsymbol{v}$'s are the general eigenvectors common to both matrices. We multiply the first equation by $\boldsymbol{B}$ and the second by $\boldsymbol{A}$, and subtract one from the other:

$$(\boldsymbol{B}\boldsymbol{A} - \boldsymbol{A}\boldsymbol{B})\boldsymbol{v} = \alpha\boldsymbol{B}\boldsymbol{v} - \beta\boldsymbol{A}\boldsymbol{v} .$$

The right-hand side obviously is equal to zero; therefore, the matrices must be interchangeable:

$$\boldsymbol{B}\boldsymbol{A} = \boldsymbol{A}\boldsymbol{B} .$$

Conversely, if two matrices are interchangeable we may reduce them to diagonal form by using the same similarity transformation. The interchangeability of two matrices is not only a necessary but a sufficient condition for the feasibility of transforming them simultaneously on the principal axes.

●4. It has been assumed thus far that the characteristic equation (10.12) has different roots. For the case of multiple roots, the investigation is much more difficult. Since this case is also important for subsequent results, we shall mention here some final results and refer the reader to special textbooks[3] for the details.

We will consider the determinant

$$|\boldsymbol{A} - \lambda \boldsymbol{E}| = \begin{vmatrix} a_{11} - \lambda & a_{12} & \cdots & a_{1n} \\ a_{21} & a_{22} - \lambda & \cdots & a_{2n} \\ \cdot & \cdot & \cdot & \cdot \\ a_{n1} & a_{n2} & \cdots & a_{nn} - \lambda \end{vmatrix}$$

which obviously is a polynomial of nth degree. By rules not stated here, this polynomial is split into *elementary divisors*:

$$(\lambda - \lambda_1)^{\rho_1}, \quad (\lambda - \lambda_2)^{\rho_2}, \quad \cdots, \quad (\lambda - \lambda_j)^{\rho_j}$$

where

$$\rho_1 + \rho_2 + \cdots + \rho_j = n\,.$$

If all the characteristic values λ_k are different, then the elementary divisors will have the form

$$(\lambda - \lambda_1), \quad (\lambda - \lambda_2), \quad \cdots, \quad (\lambda - \lambda_n)\,,$$

i.e., they will be linear or, as one also says, *simple*.

If some of the characteristic numbers are equal, then two cases can be considered. Once all elements of the divisor can be shown to be simple, this means that every divisor corresponding to the root of multiplicity r_k occurs exactly r_k times:

$$(\lambda - \lambda_1), (\lambda - \lambda_2), \cdots, \underbrace{(\lambda - \lambda_k), (\lambda - \lambda_k), \cdots, (\lambda - \lambda_k)}_{r_k \text{ times}}, \cdots, (\lambda - \lambda_j)\,.$$

In this case, as in the case of different roots, the matrix $\boldsymbol{A}$ is transformed to the diagonal form

$$\boldsymbol{A} = \begin{pmatrix} \lambda_1 & & & & & & & & 0 \\ & \lambda_2 & & & & & & & \\ & & \ddots & & & & & & \\ & & & \overbrace{\lambda_k \quad \lambda_k \quad \cdots \quad \lambda_k}^{r_k \text{ times}} & & & & & \\ & & & & & \ddots & & & \\ 0 & & & & & & & & \lambda_j \end{pmatrix}.$$

[3] See, for example, V. I. Smirnov [2].

In the second case, the elementary divisors (or only a part of them) can be *nonlinear*.

$$(\lambda - \lambda_1)^{\rho_1},\ (\lambda - \lambda_2)^{\rho_2},\ \cdots,\ (\lambda - \lambda_j)^{\rho_j},$$

where at least one of the exponents ρ_k is greater than 1. In this case the matrix $\boldsymbol{A}$ cannot be transformed to diagonal form. A simple *canonical representation* of the matrix exists, however.[4]

This canonical transformation is

$$\boldsymbol{A} = \begin{pmatrix} \boldsymbol{A}_{\rho_1} & \boldsymbol{0} & \boldsymbol{0} & \cdots & \boldsymbol{0} \\ \boldsymbol{0} & \boldsymbol{A}_{\rho_2} & \boldsymbol{0} & \cdots & \boldsymbol{0} \\ \boldsymbol{0} & \boldsymbol{0} & \boldsymbol{A}_{\rho_3} & \cdots & \boldsymbol{0} \\ \cdot & \cdot & \cdot & \cdot & \cdot \\ \boldsymbol{0} & \boldsymbol{0} & \boldsymbol{0} & \cdots & \boldsymbol{A}_{\rho_j} \end{pmatrix}, \qquad (10.13)$$

which has the form of a matrix whose elements $\boldsymbol{A}_{\rho_1}, \boldsymbol{A}_{\rho_2}, \cdots, \boldsymbol{A}_{\rho_j}$ in turn are matrices. Such matrices are called *quasi matrices.* As was proved in our case, if all quasi elements except the diagonal ones equal zero, then the matrices are called *quasi-diagonal matrices.*

The order of an elementary matrix $\boldsymbol{A}_{\rho_k}$ is equal to the degree of the corresponding elementary divisor. The elementary matrices are of the special form

$$\boldsymbol{A}_{\rho_k} = \begin{pmatrix} \lambda_k & 0 & 0 & \cdots & 0 \\ 1 & \lambda_k & 0 & \cdots & 0 \\ 0 & 1 & \lambda_k & \cdots & 0 \\ \cdot & \cdot & \cdot & \cdot & \cdot \\ 0 & 0 & 0 & \cdots & \lambda_k \end{pmatrix}. \qquad (10.14)$$

In other words, in such a matrix the number λ_k stands everywhere on the principal diagonal, directly below stands a string of ones, and all other elements are equal to zero. If all elementary divisors are linear, then the matrices $\boldsymbol{A}_{\rho_k}$ consist only of the number λ_k, and the canonical transformation is identical to the diagonal form of the matrix.

How are the vectors $\boldsymbol{v}_k$ transformed in the case of nonlinear divisors? Let us consider the group of these vectors corresponding to a determined elementary divisor $(\lambda - \lambda_k)^{\rho_k}$. It follows from the very form of matrices, Eqs. (10.13) and (10.14), that this group of vectors are transformed independently of the others according to the equations

$$\begin{aligned} \boldsymbol{A}\boldsymbol{v}_1^{(k)} &= \lambda_k \boldsymbol{v}_1^{(k)}, \\ \boldsymbol{A}\boldsymbol{v}_2^{(k)} &= \lambda_k \boldsymbol{v}_2^{(k)} + \boldsymbol{v}_1^{(k)}, \\ \boldsymbol{A}\boldsymbol{v}_3^{(k)} &= \lambda_k \boldsymbol{v}_3^{(k)} + \boldsymbol{v}_2^{(k)}, \\ &\cdots\cdots \\ \boldsymbol{A}\boldsymbol{v}_{\rho_k}^{(k)} &= \lambda_k \boldsymbol{v}_{\rho_k}^{(k)} + \boldsymbol{v}_{\rho_k-1}^{(k)}. \end{aligned} \qquad (10.15)$$

If $\rho_k = 1$, then obviously we obtain the relation in Eq. (10.10).

[4] The so-called *Jordan normal form.*

●**5.** Let us go somewhat more extensively into the characteristics of *symmetric* matrices, i.e., matrices in which the corresponding elements on different sides of the principal diagonal are equal,

$$a_{ik} = a_{ki} .$$

Matrix $\boldsymbol{A}^*$, which is the *transpose* of matrix $\boldsymbol{A}$, is obtained if one interchanges the rows and columns of $\boldsymbol{A}$. A symmetric matrix is obviously identical with its transposed matrix:

$$\boldsymbol{A}^* = \boldsymbol{A} .$$

We will now state the important characteristics of symmetric matrices.

All characteristic numbers of symmetric matrices are real, and the elementary divisors are simple. This means that the symmetric matrix may always be reduced to the diagonal form

$$\boldsymbol{A} = \{\lambda_1, \lambda_2, \lambda_3, \cdots, \lambda_n\}$$

where $\lambda_1, \lambda_2, \cdots, \lambda_n$ are real numbers.

Symmetric matrices (the more general *Hermitian matrices*) are therefore of particular interest for applications because the characteristic numbers are real. Symmetric matrices appear in many vibration and elastic stability problems; Hermitian matrices appear in quantum mechanics.

We introduce, further, the following definitions. Two vectors $\boldsymbol{u}(u_1, u_2, \cdots, u_n)$ and $\boldsymbol{v}(v_1, v_2, \cdots, v_n)$ are called *orthogonal* if their scalar product (the sum of the products of corresponding coordinates) is equal to zero:

$$\sum_{k=1}^{n} u_k v_k = 0 .$$

It can be shown that the eigenvectors of symmetric matrices are always mutually orthogonal,

$$\sum_{j=1}^{n} v_{ji} v_{jk} = 0 , \qquad (i \neq k) .$$

If the eigenvectors are normalized

$$\sum_{j=1}^{n} v_{jk}^2 = 1 , \qquad (k = 1, 2, 3, \cdots, n) ,$$

then it is said that they constitute an *orthonormal system.* Using the Kronecker notation

$$\delta_{ik} = \begin{cases} 1 & \text{for } i = k , \\ 0 & \text{for } i \neq k , \end{cases} \tag{10.16}$$

we can write the orthonormal condition of a system in the form

$$\sum_{j=1}^{n} v_{ji} v_{jk} = \delta_{ik} . \tag{10.17}$$

Another way of expressing it is

$$\boldsymbol{V}\boldsymbol{V}^* = \boldsymbol{E} , \tag{10.18}$$

where V is a matrix of v_{ik}. From Eq. (10.17) it is seen that any two columns of the matrix V (and consequently, any two rows) are mutually orthogonal. Such matrices are called *orthogonal*. From Eq. (10.18) it follows that $V^* = V^{-1}$, i.e., for an orthogonal matrix the inverse and transposed matrices are identical.

Thus, a symmetric matrix can be transposed to the diagonal form by means of an orthonormal transformation.

●6. The transformation of a symmetric matrix to diagonal form is closely related to transformation of a quadratic form into the sum of the squares. The *quadratic form* of n variables $x_1, x_2, \cdots, x_n$ is called a homogeneous polynomial of second order,

$$\varphi(x_1, x_2, x_3, \cdots, x_n) = \sum_{i=1}^{n} \sum_{k=1}^{n} a_{ik} x_i x_k \,, \tag{10.19}$$

where it is assumed that $a_{ik} = a_{ki}$. The matrix of coefficients of every quadratic form

$$A = \begin{pmatrix} a_{11} & a_{12} & \cdots & a_{1n} \\ a_{21} & a_{22} & \cdots & a_{2n} \\ \cdot & \cdot & \cdot & \cdot \\ a_{n1} & a_{n2} & \cdots & a_{nn} \end{pmatrix}$$

is obviously symmetrical.

We will investigate how matrix A is transformed from the variables $x_1, x_2, \cdots, x_n$ to new variables $y_1, y_2, \cdots, y_n$:

$$x_i = \sum_{k=1}^{n} b_{ik} y_k \,. \tag{10.20}$$

Substituting Eq. (10.20) into Eq. (10.19), we obtain the transformed form

$$\varphi(y_1, y_2, \cdots, y_n) = \sum_{i=1}^{n} \sum_{k=1}^{n} c_{ik} y_i y_k \tag{10.21}$$

where

$$c_{ik} = c_{ki} = \sum_{r=1}^{n} b_{ri} \sum_{s=1}^{n} a_{rs} b_{sk} \,. \tag{10.22}$$

If we denote the matrices with elements b_{ik} and c_{ik} by B and C, respectively, we write Eq. (10.22) in the form

$$C = B^* A B \,. \tag{10.23}$$

The transformation, Eq. (10.20), can be chosen so that the matrix is diagonal,

$$C = \{c_1, c_2, c_3, \cdots, c_n\} \,.$$

In this case the quadratic form, Eq. (10.21), does not contain any product of different coordinates; one says that it reduces to the sum of squares:

$$\varphi(y_1, y_2, y_3, \cdots, y_n) = \sum_{k=1}^{n} c_k y_k^2 \,.$$

An infinite number of such transformations exists. We will discuss the orthogonal transformation ($\boldsymbol{B}^* = \boldsymbol{B}^{-1}$). Equation (10.23) takes the form

$$\boldsymbol{C} = \boldsymbol{B}^{-1}\boldsymbol{A}\boldsymbol{B}\,.$$

To reduce a quadratic form to the sum of squares with the aid of an orthogonal transformation, it is necessary to transform the relevant matrix to the principal axes. Then

$$\varphi(y_1, y_2, y_3, \cdots, y_n) = \sum_{k=1}^{n} \lambda_k y_k^2\,.$$

We will discuss briefly the classification of quadratic forms. If a quadratic form, Eq. (10.19), is positive for all real values of x_k and vanishes only for $x_1 = x_2 = \cdots = x_n = 0$, then it is called *positive definite.* A quadratic form that assumes only negative values in a corresponding manner is called *negative definite.* If a quadratic form can assume positive and negative values, it is called *indefinite.*

The type of quadratic form is easily determined if it reduces in some way to the sum of squares. Thus, if all coefficients of the squares of the variables were found to be positive (negative), then the form is positive (negative) definite.

The following conclusion, which will be used subsequently, follows from the above assertion: If the quadratic form is positive definite, then all the characteristic numbers of the corresponding matrix are positive.

§ 39. Free Vibrations of Elastic Systems with a Finite Number of Degrees of Freedom

●**1.** The determination of free vibrations of systems with a finite number of degrees of freedom is related to the transformation of matrices to diagonal form. We will investigate this relationship.

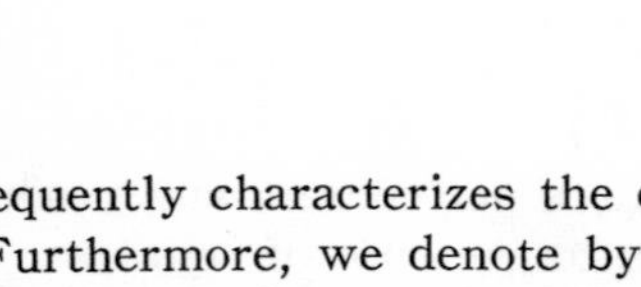

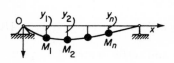

FIG. 85.

Let us consider an elastic system with n degrees of freedom. A suitable model of such a system is a beam supporting n concentrated masses (Fig. 85). The deformed state of the beam is determined if the deflections of its n points, $y_1, y_2, \cdots, y_n$, are known. The vector

$$\boldsymbol{y} = \begin{pmatrix} y_1 \\ y_2 \\ \vdots \\ y_n \end{pmatrix}$$

consequently characterizes the deformation of the system.

Furthermore, we denote by δ_{ik} the displacement of the ith point due to a unit force acting on the kth point.[5] All of these individual displacements form the matrix

[5] Not to be confused with the Kronecker delta! (See Eq. (10.16).)

$$K = \begin{pmatrix} \delta_{11} & \delta_{12} & \cdots & \delta_{1n} \\ \delta_{21} & \delta_{22} & \cdots & \delta_{2n} \\ \cdot & \cdot & \cdot & \cdot \\ \delta_{n1} & \delta_{n2} & \cdots & \delta_{nn} \end{pmatrix},$$

which we denote as the *matrix of the influence of the displacement* or simply the *displacement matrix* for the given system.

The properties of the displacement matrix are well known. Thus, from elementary structural mechanics one knows that displacements away from and symmetric to the principal diagonal are equal to each other:

$$\delta_{ik} = \delta_{ki} .$$

This means that the displacement matrix is a symmetric matrix and, consequently, all of its characteristic numbers, i.e., the roots of the equation

$$\begin{vmatrix} \delta_{11} - \lambda & \delta_{12} & \cdots & \delta_{1n} \\ \delta_{21} & \delta_{22} - \lambda & \cdots & \delta_{2n} \\ \cdot & \cdot & \cdot & \cdot \\ \delta_{n1} & \delta_{n2} & \cdots & \delta_{nn} - \lambda \end{vmatrix} = 0 ,$$

are real.

If the system considered is statically stable then, as can be shown, *all characteristic numbers of the displacement matrix are positive.* For the proof of this important property, we will investigate the potential energy of the external forces.

Let the beam be loaded by the forces $P_1, P_2, \cdots, P_n$ at the n mass points. The deflection of the ith point resulting from these forces is

$$y_i = \sum_{k=1}^{n} \delta_{ik} P_k , \tag{10.24}$$

and the potential energy of the external forces is

$$U = \tfrac{1}{2} \sum_{k=1}^{n} \sum_{j=1}^{n} \delta_{ik} P_i P_k . \tag{10.25}$$

From Eq. (10.25) one recognizes that the potential energy is a quadratic form of the external forces and the matrix of this quadratic form is identical to the displacement matrix. If the potential energy of the external forces is a positive quantity, it then follows that all the characteristic numbers of the displacement matrix are positive.

The assumption that the system shall be stable is essential. If the system is unstable, then the quadratic form, Eq. (10.25), in which the magnitude of δ_{ik} is determined taking into account a parametric loading,[6] may also take on negative values. The quantity of the negative characteristic numbers of the displacement matrix then determines the *degree of instability.*

[6] For example, in the case of a rod compressed by a longitudinal force, for the "unit" displacements δ_{ik}, the longitudinal as well as the the transverse deflections are to be considered.

In what follows, we shall confine ourselves to stable systems.

●2. After these introductory remarks, we now can formulate the equations for free vibrations.

The motion of a system which is deflected from the static equilibrium position can be determined if it is acted upon by inertia forces $-m_i y_i''$ $(i = 1, 2, 3, \cdots, n)$.

Calculating from Eq. (10.24) the deflection at an arbitrary point

$$y_i = -\sum_{k=1}^{n} \delta_{ik} m_k y_k'', \qquad (i = 1, 2, 3, \cdots, n),$$

we obtain the differential equations for free vibrations

$$\sum_{k=1}^{n} m_k \delta_{ik} y_k'' + y_i = 0, \qquad (i = 1, 2, 3, \cdots, n). \tag{10.26}$$

This system of ordinary differential equations can be written in the form of a single matrix equation. For this purpose we introduce the matrix $\boldsymbol{C}$ with the elements

$$C_{ik} = m_k \delta_{ik}.$$

Furthermore, if we denote by $\boldsymbol{y}''$ the vector whose components are equal to the second derivative of the components of the vector $\boldsymbol{y}$, then we can write[7] the differential equation system (10.26) in the form

$$\boldsymbol{C}\boldsymbol{y}'' + \boldsymbol{y} = \boldsymbol{0} \tag{10.27}$$

where $\boldsymbol{0}$ denotes the null vector.

We will seek the free harmonic vibrations

$$\boldsymbol{y} = \boldsymbol{v} \sin(\omega t + \gamma), \tag{10.28}$$

where ω is the vibration frequency, γ is the initial phase angle, and $\boldsymbol{v}$ is the vector whose components equal the vibration amplitudes of the individual point masses:

$$\boldsymbol{v} = \begin{pmatrix} v_1 \\ v_2 \\ \vdots \\ v_n \end{pmatrix}.$$

Substituting Eq. (10.28) into Eq. (10.27) and dividing by $\sin(\omega t + \gamma)$, we obtain the system of n algebraic equations

$$\boldsymbol{v} - \omega^2 \boldsymbol{C}\boldsymbol{v} = \boldsymbol{0} \tag{10.29}$$

or, in the expanded form,

$$v_i - \omega^2 \sum_{k=1}^{n} m_k \delta_{ik} v_k = 0, \qquad (i = 1, 2, 3, \cdots, n). \tag{10.30}$$

The equation system (10.30) has a solution different from zero only if its

[7] We note that the differential equations of free vibrations are often written by using the elements of the matrix $\boldsymbol{C}^{-1}$, i.e., using coefficients of the spring stiffness of the system.

determinant is equal to zero:

$$|\boldsymbol{E} - \omega^2 \boldsymbol{C}| = \boldsymbol{0} . \tag{10.31}$$

In this manner we obtain an algebraic equation from which n natural frequencies $\omega_1, \omega_2, \cdots, \omega_n$ of the system are determined. If one writes down the individual elements of the matrix, then the equations for the natural frequencies are

$$\begin{vmatrix} 1 - m_1\delta_{11}\omega^2 & -m_2\delta_{12}\omega^2 & \cdots & -m_n\delta_{1n}\omega^2 \\ -m_1\delta_{21}\omega^2 & 1 - m_2\delta_{22}\omega^2 & \cdots & -m_n\delta_{2n}\omega^2 \\ \cdot\cdot\cdot & \cdot\cdot\cdot & \cdot\cdot\cdot & \cdot\cdot\cdot \\ -m_1\delta_{n1}\omega^2 & -m_2\delta_{n2}\omega^2 & \cdots & 1 - m_n\delta_{nn}\omega^2 \end{vmatrix} = \boldsymbol{0} .$$

After calculating the natural frequencies, we substitute one of them (for example, ω_j) into Eqs. (10.30). We then find the free vibration shapes, i.e., all of the displacements corresponding to each frequency ω_j,

$$v_{1j},\ v_{2j},\ v_{3j},\ \cdots,\ v_{nj} .$$

From Eq. (10.29) one recognizes that the free vibration shapes are the eigenvectors of the matrix $\boldsymbol{C}$; the natural frequencies are expressed according to Eq. (10.31) by the characteristic numbers λ_k of the matrix:

$$\omega_k = \frac{1}{\sqrt{\lambda_k}} .$$

Moreover, the characteristic numbers $\lambda_1, \lambda_2, \cdots, \lambda_n$ are ordered magnitudes (λ_1 is the largest).

The matric $\boldsymbol{C}$ is generally not symmetric. We will investigate whether or not all of its characteristic roots are real. For this purpose, we will use the diagonal matrix

$$\boldsymbol{M} = \{m_1, m_2, \cdots, m_n\} .$$

Then $\boldsymbol{C} = \boldsymbol{KM}$ and Eq. (10.29) take the form

$$\boldsymbol{v} - \omega^2 \boldsymbol{KMv} = \boldsymbol{0} . \tag{10.32}$$

Introducing a new vector $\boldsymbol{u} = \boldsymbol{M}^{1/2}\boldsymbol{v}$, where

$$\boldsymbol{M}^{1/2} = \{\sqrt{m_1}, \sqrt{m_2}, \cdots, \sqrt{m_n}\} ,$$

we rewrite Eq. (10.32) in the form

$$\boldsymbol{M}^{-1/2}\boldsymbol{u} - \omega^2 \boldsymbol{KM}^{1/2}\boldsymbol{u} = \boldsymbol{0}$$

or, after multiplying the left-hand side by $\boldsymbol{M}^{1/2}$, in the form

$$\boldsymbol{u} - \omega^2 \boldsymbol{M}^{1/2}\boldsymbol{KM}^{1/2}\boldsymbol{u} = \boldsymbol{0} .$$

The characteristic numbers of the matrix $\boldsymbol{M}^{1/2}\boldsymbol{KM}^{1/2}$ are, like the matrix $\boldsymbol{C} = \boldsymbol{KM}$, equal to $1/\omega^2$; in addition, this matrix is symmetric. Consequently, all of the results obtained for symmetrical matrices are valid for matrix $\boldsymbol{KM}$. In particular, the condition of orthogonality, Eq. (10.17), now becomes

$$\sum_{j=1}^{n} m_j v_{ji} v_{jk} = \begin{cases} 1 & \text{for } i = k\,, \\ 0 & \text{for } i \neq k\,, \end{cases} \tag{10.33}$$

and is interpreted in the following way: The work of the inertia forces of the ith vibration form for the deflections of the kth form ($i \neq k$) is always equal to zero.

●3. In a number of cases a somewhat different treatment of the problem of the free vibrations is more suitable. We will begin from the matrix differential equation (10.27),

$$\boldsymbol{C}\boldsymbol{y}'' + \boldsymbol{y} = \boldsymbol{0}\,.$$

We will transform the variables in such a manner that a diagonal matrix results from matrix $\boldsymbol{C}$:

$$\boldsymbol{C}_0 = \left\{\frac{1}{\omega_1^{\,2}},\ \frac{1}{\omega_2^{\,2}},\ \cdots,\ \frac{1}{\omega_n^{\,2}}\right\}.$$

Then the system of equations breaks down into individual equations, each of which contains one of the unknowns:

$$\frac{1}{\omega_k^{\,2}} y_k'' + y_k = 0\,, \qquad (k = 1, 2, 3, \cdots, n)\,.$$

One says that the coordinates (variables) of the matrix differential equation (10.27) are transformed to the principal coordinates.

§ 40. Forced Vibrations of a System with a Finite Number of Degrees of Freedom

●1. Let the system be loaded by n point forces, whose frequencies and phase angles, for the sake of simplicity, will be assumed to be equal (Fig. 86). The dynamic deflection at the ith point, according to Eq. (10.24), will be

$$y_i = \sum_{k=1}^{n} \delta_{ik}(P_k \cos \theta t - m_k y_k'')\,.$$

Hence, we obtain the system of differential equations

$$\sum_{k=1}^{n} m_k \delta_{ik} y_k'' + y_i = \sum_{k=1}^{n} \delta_k P_{ki} \cos \theta t\,,$$

$$(i = 1, 2, 3, \cdots, n)\,,$$

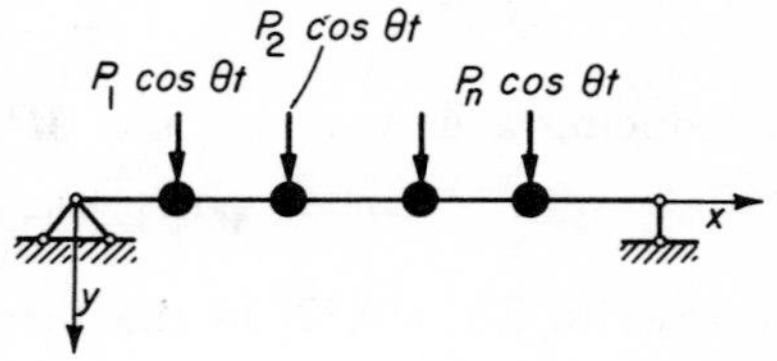

FIG. 86.

or, in matrix form,

$$\boldsymbol{C}\boldsymbol{y}'' + \boldsymbol{y} = \boldsymbol{K}\boldsymbol{p} \cos \theta t\,, \tag{10.34}$$

where $\boldsymbol{p}$ is the vector composed of the amplitudes of the loads P_i.

Let us now introduce the expression

$$\boldsymbol{y} = \boldsymbol{a} \cos \theta t$$

into Eq. (10.34). If we divide by $\cos \theta t$, we find

$$(\boldsymbol{E} - \theta^2 \boldsymbol{C})\boldsymbol{a} = \boldsymbol{K}\boldsymbol{p} \tag{10.35}$$

and, therefore,

$$\boldsymbol{a} = (\boldsymbol{E} - \theta^2 \boldsymbol{C})^{-1}\boldsymbol{K}\boldsymbol{p} \,. \tag{10.36}$$

The solution of Eq. (10.36) exists only in the case where $|\boldsymbol{E} - \theta^2\boldsymbol{C}| \neq 0$. In the case where $|\boldsymbol{E} - \theta^2\boldsymbol{C}| = 0$, θ is obviously equal to the natural frequencies, $\theta = \omega_j$. This case corresponds to the resonance of the forced vibrations.

●**2.** Let us now investigate the problem in still another way. We introduce the new vectors $\boldsymbol{b}$ and $\boldsymbol{q}$, associated with the old vectors $\boldsymbol{a}$ and $\boldsymbol{p}$ by the relations

$$\boldsymbol{a} = \boldsymbol{V}\boldsymbol{b}, \quad \boldsymbol{p} = \boldsymbol{M}\boldsymbol{V}\boldsymbol{q} \,. \tag{10.37}$$

Here $\boldsymbol{V}$ is an orthogonal matrix that transforms the matrix $\boldsymbol{C}$ into the diagonal form

$$\boldsymbol{V}^{-1}\boldsymbol{C}\boldsymbol{V} = \left\{\frac{1}{{\omega_1}^2}, \frac{1}{{\omega_2}^2}, \cdots, \frac{1}{{\omega_n}^2}\right\} . \tag{10.38}$$

If we substitute Eq. (10.37) into Eq. (10.35), multiply the left-hand side by $\boldsymbol{V}^{-1}$ and take into account that $\boldsymbol{K}\boldsymbol{M} = \boldsymbol{C}$, we find

$$\boldsymbol{V}^{-1}(\boldsymbol{E} - \theta^2\boldsymbol{C})\boldsymbol{V}\boldsymbol{b} = \boldsymbol{V}^{-1}\boldsymbol{C}\boldsymbol{V}\boldsymbol{q} \,.$$

But because of Eq. (10.38),

$$\boldsymbol{V}^{-1}(\boldsymbol{E} - \theta^2\boldsymbol{C})\boldsymbol{V} = \left\{1 - \frac{\theta^2}{{\omega_1}^2}, 1 - \frac{\theta^2}{{\omega_2}^2}, \cdots, 1 - \frac{\theta^2}{{\omega_n}^2}\right\} ,$$

from which it follows that

$$b_k = \frac{q_k {\omega_k}^2}{1 - \dfrac{\theta^2}{{\omega_k}^2}} \,. \tag{10.39}$$

The vector components q_k represent "generalized forces," corresponding to the "generalized deflections" b_k. From the second relationship of Eq. (10.37), it follows that

$$\boldsymbol{q} = \boldsymbol{V}^{-1}\boldsymbol{M}^{-1}\boldsymbol{p} \,,$$

or, in expanded form,

$$q_i = \sum_{k=1}^{n} \frac{v_{ki}}{m_k} P_k \,.$$

The deflections a_i are therefore determined by the equation

$$a_i = \sum_{k=1}^{n} \frac{v_{ik} q_k {\omega_k}^2}{1 - \dfrac{\theta^2}{{\omega_k}^2}} \,.$$

Eleven

ELEMENTS OF THE THEORY OF LINEAR INTEGRAL EQUATIONS[8]

§ 41. Basic Definitions

● 1. If one or more variables, i.e., vectors of a space function, are taken in place of the vectors in an n-dimensional space function, then analogous results to the preceding chapter can be obtained.

The function $f(x)$ in the interval $a \leq x \leq b$ can be taken as a vector with an infinite number of "components." The independent variable x plays the role of an index for a component, and the value of the function $f(x)$ gives the magnitude of the corresponding components. We will assume that all the functions encountered, together with their squares, are integrable.

The *scalar product* (φ, ψ) of the two functions $\varphi(x)$ and $\psi(x)$ is defined by the equation

$$(\varphi, \psi) = \int_a^b \varphi(x)\psi(x)\, dx .$$

Two functions whose scalar product is equal to zero,

$$\int_a^b \varphi(x)\, \psi(x)\, dx = 0 ,$$

are called *mutually orthogonal* in the interval $[a, b]$. The scalar product of a function by itself defines the length of a vector in functional space; if the length of a vector is equal to 1,

$$\int_a^b \varphi^2(x)\, dx = 1 ,$$

the corresponding function is called *normalized*.

The above definitions are analogous to the corresponding equations for vectors in n-dimensional space; the only difference is that the summation is now replaced by integration over the interval $[a, b]$.

If the functions $\varphi_1(x), \varphi_2(x), \cdots, \varphi_n(x)$ are orthogonal and normalized,

$$\int_a^b \varphi_i(x)\, \varphi_k(x)\, dx = \delta_{ik} , \tag{11.1}$$

[8] For a more exact study, Privalov [1] and V. I. Smirnov [3] are recommended. (Similar books written in English are Levift [1] and Norse and Feshbach [1].)

(δ_{ik} is the Kronecker delta), then one can say that they form an *orthonormalized system.*

The system of trigonometric functions is a simple example of an orthogonal system. The functions

$$\sin x\,, \quad \sin 2x\,, \quad \sin 3x\,, \cdots$$

are orthogonal in the interval $(0, 2\pi)$. Normalization can be accomplished by dividing each function by $\sqrt{\pi}$.

A system is called *complete (self-contained)*, if no function exists that is orthogonal to all of the functions of this system and does not belong to the system. If such a function does exist, the system is called *incomplete.* For example, the system given above is incomplete since the function $\cos x$ is orthogonal to all the functions of the system in the interval $(0, 2\pi)$. In the Fourier series theory it has been shown that the system

$$1,\ \cos x, \quad \sin x, \quad \cos 2x, \quad \sin 2x, \cdots$$

is complete.

Of greater importance is the problem of representing an arbitrary function $f(x)$ in a series with respect to an orthonormalized system of functions

$$f(x) \sim \sum_{i=1}^{n} a_i \varphi_i(x)\,. \tag{11.2}$$

Such a series is called a *generalized Fourier series.* The Fourier coefficients a_k are determined by a termwise multiplication of the series by $\varphi_k(x)$ and integration over the interval $[a, b]$. By using Eq. (11.1), we obtain

$$a_k = \int_a^b f(x)\,\varphi_k(x)\,dx\,.$$

The coefficients a_k represent in functional space the "projections" of the vector $f(x)$ in the direction of the vectors $\varphi_k(x)$. The convergence of the series in Eq. (11.2) does not mean that its sum is equal to $f(x)$. For such a series to be convergent for an arbitrary function $f(x)$, it is necessary that the system $\varphi_1(x), \varphi_2(x), \cdots, \varphi_n(x) \cdots$ be complete.

●**2.** The integral transformation

$$F(x) = \int_a^b K(x, \xi)\,f(\xi)\,d\xi$$

corresponds to a linear transformation in n-dimensional space. The function of the two variables $K(x, \xi)$ is the analog of the transformation matrix; this function is called the *kernel.* In the following we will consider only kernels which are bounded and continuous with respect to both arguments.

One can construct an algebra of the kernels that is similar to that of matrix algebra. A new kernel which results from the product of the two kernels $K(x, \xi)$ and $L(x, \xi)$ is defined as

$$M(x, \xi) = \int_a^b K(x, \eta) L(\eta, \xi)\,d\eta\,.$$

The "powers"

$$K_2(x, \xi) = \int_a^b K(x, \eta)K(\eta, \xi)\, d\eta ,$$

in more general terms,

$$K_{n+1}(x, \xi) = \int_a^b K_n(x, \eta)K(\eta, \xi)\, d\eta$$

of the kernel $K(x, \xi)$ are called *iterated kernels.* Here, as in matrix algebra, multiplication is generally noncommutative,

$$\int_a^b K(x, \eta)L(\eta, \xi)\, d\eta \neq \int_a^b L(x, \eta)K(\eta, \xi)\, d\eta .$$

●**3.** An equation of the form

$$\int_a^b K(x, \xi)\varphi(\xi)\, d\xi = f(x) ,$$

where $\varphi(x)$ is an unknown and $f(x)$ is a known function, is called a *Fredholm integral equation of the first kind.* The solution of such an equation obviously leads to the determination of a kernel which is inverse to $K(x, \xi)$; this problem is by no means always solvable.

A *Fredholm integral equation of the second kind* is an equation of the form

$$\varphi(x) - \lambda \int_a^b K(x, \xi)\varphi(\xi)\, d\xi = f(x) , \tag{11.3}$$

where λ is a parameter. If $f(x) \equiv 0$, the integral equation is called *homogeneous*:

$$\varphi(x) - \lambda \int_a^b K(x, \xi)\varphi(\xi)\, d\xi = 0 . \tag{11.4}$$

The integral equation (11.4) is satisfied for $\varphi(x) \equiv 0$. In general, non-zero solutions are obtained only for certain values of the parameter λ. These values λ_k are called *eigenvalues of the kernel* $K(x, \xi)$, and the corresponding solutions are called *eigenfunctions.* The eigenvalue (or in more precise terms, its inverse value) and the eigenfunctions form the analog to the characteristic numbers and eigenvectors in matrix algebra.[9]

§ 42. Integral Equations with a Degenerative Kernel. The Fredholm Theorem

●**1.** A class of integral equations exists that directly reduces to a linear equation system. This class consists of integral equations with a degenerative kernel. A kernel is called *degenerative* if it has the form

$$K(x, \xi) = \sum_{k=1}^{n} a_k(x)b_k(\xi) . \tag{11.5}$$

[9] The basis for this analog is given in functional analysis. See Riesz and Sz-Nagy [1]

This essentially means that the kernel consists of a number of components. Substituting Eq. (11.5) into Eq. (11.3) yields

$$\varphi(x) - \lambda \sum_{k=1}^{n} a_k(x) \int_a^b b_k(\xi)\varphi(\xi)\, d\xi = f(x) . \tag{11.6}$$

From Eq. (11.6) we obtain

$$\varphi(x) = f(x) + \lambda \sum_{k=1}^{n} a_k(x) c_k \tag{11.7}$$

where
$$c_k = \int_a^b b_k(\xi)\varphi(\xi)\, d\xi .$$

The constants c_k are determined by multiplying Eq. (11.6) termwise by $b_i(x)$ and integrating over the interval $[a, b]$. As a result of this procedure, we obtain the equation system

$$c_i - \lambda \sum_{k=1}^{n} a_{ik} c_k = f_i . \quad (i = 1, 2, \cdots, n) , \tag{11.8}$$

where the following notation is introduced:

$$a_{ik} = \int_a^b b_i(\xi) a_k(\xi)\, d\xi , \qquad f_i = \int_a^b b_i(\xi) f(\xi)\, d\xi .$$

In this manner the solution of the integral equation (11.3) is given by Eq. (11.7), where the coefficients c_k are determined from the equation system (11.8). The determinant of this equation system has the form

$$D(\lambda) = \begin{vmatrix} 1-\lambda a_{11} & -\lambda a_{12} & \cdots & -\lambda a_{1n} \\ -\lambda a_{21} & 1-\lambda a_{22} & \cdots & -\lambda a_{2n} \\ \cdots & \cdots & \cdots & \cdots \\ -\lambda a_{n1} & -\lambda a_{n2} & \cdots & 1-\lambda a_{nn} \end{vmatrix} .$$

If the determinant $D(\lambda)$ is different from zero, the equation system (11.8) has a unique solution. The homogeneous equation system

$$c_i - \lambda \sum_{k=1}^{n} a_{ik} c_k = 0 , \quad (i = 1, 2, 3, \cdots, n) , \tag{11.9}$$

then has only the trivial zero solution $(c_1 = c_2 = \cdots = c_i = 0)$.

Now let $D(\lambda) = 0$. In this case the homogeneous equation system (11.9) has non-trivial solutions. The equation $D(\lambda) = 0$ obviously has n roots λ_1, λ_2, $\cdots$, λ_n. Consequently, the homogeneous equation system is non-trivially solvable only for n values of the parameter λ.

We will now discuss the integral equations (11.3) and (11.4). For $\lambda \neq \lambda_k$, the nonhomogeneous integral equation has a unique solution and the corresponding homogeneous integral equation admits only the zero solution $\varphi(x) = 0$. For $\lambda = \lambda_k (k = 1, 2, 3, \cdots, n)$, the nonhomogeneous integral equation (11.3) is not solvable with the exception of certain cases that depend on the form of $f(x)$; the corresponding homogeneous integral equation has non-identically disappearing solutions.

● 2. These results are expanded for the general case of an arbitrary kernel and formulated in the following *Fredholm theorems*.

The nonhomogeneous integral equation

$$\varphi(x) - \lambda \int_a^b K(x, \xi)\varphi(\xi)\, d\xi = f(x)$$

has a unique solution for all $\lambda \neq \lambda_k$; the homogeneous integral equation

$$\varphi(x) - \lambda \int_a^b K(x, \xi)\varphi(\xi)\, d\xi = 0$$

has only the zero solution for this case.

For $\lambda = \lambda_k$, the homogeneous integral equation has non-identically disappearing solutions that are related to the transposed integral equation (the transposed kernel $K(\xi, x)$ replaces the kernel $K(x, \xi)$) by:

$$\varphi_k(x) - \lambda_k \int_a^b K(x, \xi)\varphi_k(\xi)\, d\xi = 0,$$

$$\psi_k(x) - \lambda_k \int_a^b K(\xi, x)\psi_k(\xi)\, d\xi = 0.$$

The nonhomogeneous integral equation is solvable only in the case where the condition

$$\int_a^b f(x)\psi_k(x)\, dx = 0 \tag{11.10}$$

is fulfilled for every solution $\psi_k(x)$ of the transposed homogeneous integral equation.

§ 43. Symmetric Integral Equations. Expansion by Eigenfunctions

● 1. A kernel $K(x, \xi)$ and the corresponding integral equation is called *symmetric* if

$$K(x, \xi) \equiv K(\xi, x).$$

The Fredholm theorems naturally also hold true for symmetric kernels; in this case there is no difference between the given and the transposed integral equation. Equation (11.10) becomes

$$\int_a^b f(x)\varphi_k(x)\, dx = 0. \tag{11.11}$$

Additional results will be derived for symmetric integral equations. All eigenvalues of the symmetric kernels are real, and the eigenfunctions are orthogonal to one another,

$$\int_a^b \varphi_i(x)\varphi_k(x)\, dx = \delta_{ik}. \tag{11.12}$$

We will now investigate the problem where a function $f(x)$ is expanded in a series by the eigenfunctions of a symmetric kernel

$$f(x) \sim \sum_{k=1}^{n} f_k \varphi_k(x) , \tag{11.13}$$

where

$$f_k = \int_a^b f(\xi)\varphi_k(\xi)\, d\xi . \tag{11.14}$$

The eigenfunctions of an arbitrary symmetric kernel $K(x, \xi)$ generally do not form a complete system. Therefore the series in Eq. (11.13) is not required to converge to the function $f(x)$. The determination of a class of functions that can be expanded in a series by the eigenfunctions of a kernel $K(x, \xi)$ represents an important problem; this problem is solved by the well-known *Theorem of Hilbert and Schmidt.*

A function $f(x)$ is an *integral transform* of a kernel $K(x, \xi)$ if a continuous function $p(x)$ exists such that

$$f(x) = \int_a^b K(x, \xi)p(\xi)\, d\xi . \tag{11.15}$$

The theorem of Hilbert and Schmidt states that *such a function $f(x)$, which is an integral transform with the help of a symmetric kernel $K(x, \xi)$, is expandable in a uniformly convergent series by the eigenfunctions of this kernel.*

The kernel $K(x, \xi)$ can also be expanded in a series, Eq. (11.13). According to Eq. (11.14)

$$f_k = \int_a^b K(x, \xi)\varphi_k(\xi)\, d\xi = \frac{\varphi_k(x)}{\lambda_k} ;$$

and therefore

$$K(x, \xi) \sim \sum_{k=1}^{n} \frac{\varphi_k(x)\varphi_k(\xi)}{\lambda_k} . \tag{11.16}$$

The above is the so-called *bilinear formula* for the kernel. The series in Eq. (11.16) does not converge for all kernels. The kernel $K(x, \xi)$ is called *positive definite,* if for all continuous functions $p(x)$ the analog of the quadratic form

$$J = \int_a^b \int_a^b K(x, \xi)p(x)p(\xi)\, dx\, d\xi \tag{11.17}$$

takes on only positive values. In this case, all the eigenvalues of the kernel are positive. According to the *Mercer theorem*: if the kernel $K(x, \xi)$ is positive definite, the series (11.16) absolutely and uniformly converges. It is proved in the theory of integral equations that the Mercer theorem is also valid for kernels which have a number of negative eigenvalues.

●2. Let us now consider the nonhomogeneous integral equation (11.3). We will write it in the form

$$\varphi(x) = f(x) + \lambda \int_a^b K(x, \xi)\varphi(\xi)\, d\xi . \tag{11.18}$$

The second sum on the right-hand side is assumed to be an integral transform of the function $\varphi(x)$ with the help of the kernel $K(x, \xi)$. From the theorem of Hilbert and Schmidt one therefore obtains the absolute and uniformly convergent series expansion

$$\varphi(x) = f(x) + \sum_{k=1}^{\infty} a_k \varphi_k(x) .$$

To determine the series coefficients, we write Eq. (11.18) in the form

$$g(x) = \lambda \int_a^b K(x, \xi)[f(\xi) + g(\xi)] \, d\xi ,$$

where $g(x) = \varphi(x) - f(x)$. Multiplying this equation by $\varphi_k(x)$ termwise and integrating over the interval $[a, b]$, we obtain

$$g_k = \frac{\lambda}{\lambda_k}(f_k + g_k) .$$

Here f_k and g_k are the Fourier coefficients for the function $f(x)$ and $g(x)$. This gives

$$g(x) = \sum_{k=1}^{\infty} \frac{\lambda f_k}{\lambda_k - \lambda} \varphi_k(x)$$

and consequently,

$$\varphi(x) = f(x) + \sum_{k=1}^{\infty} \frac{\lambda f_k}{\lambda_k - \lambda} \varphi_k(x) . \tag{11.19}$$

In addition, if the function $f(x)$ is expanded in a series with respect to $\varphi_k(x)$, Eq. (11.19) can be written in the form

$$\varphi(x) = \sum_{k=1}^{\infty} \frac{\lambda_k f_k}{\lambda_k - \lambda} \varphi_k(x) . \tag{11.20}$$

● **3.** The results presented are easily generalized to kernels of the form $m(x) K(x, \xi)$, where $m(\xi)$ is a positive function, i.e., $m(\xi) > 0$ for all $a \leqq \xi \leqq b$. Such kernels are called *weighted.*

If we multiply both sides of the integral equation (11.18) by $\sqrt{m(x)}$ and substitute the new sought-for function $\psi(x) = \sqrt{m(x)}\, \varphi(x)$, we obtain the integral equation

$$\psi(x) = f(x)\sqrt{m(x)} + \lambda \int_a^b L(x, \xi)\, \psi(\xi)\, d\xi$$

with the kernel

$$L(x, \xi) = \sqrt{m(x)m(\xi)}\, K(x, \xi) .$$

The kernel $L(x, \xi)$ is symmetric; therefore, the entire theory presented is applicable to it. The orthogonality condition in Eq. (11.12) is now as follows:

$$\int_a^b \psi_i(x)\psi_k(x)\, dx = \delta_{ik} .$$

If we return to the original functions $\varphi(x)$, we obtain

$$\int_a^b m(x)\varphi_i(x)\varphi_k(x)\,dx = \delta_{ik}\,. \tag{11.21}$$

Therefore, the functions $\varphi_i(x)$ are orthogonal with the *weight*, $m(x)$. Writing the bilinear formula, Eq. (11.16), in the form

$$L(x,\xi) = \sum_{k=1}^{\infty} \frac{\psi_k(x)\psi_k(\xi)}{\lambda_k}$$

and dividing it by $\sqrt{m(x)\,m(\xi)}$, we once more obtain Eq. (11.16).

The theorem of Hilbert and Schmidt is also valid for weighted integral equations; however, the Fourier coefficients are to be calculated with consideration of the weight $m(x)$:

$$a_k = \int_a^b m(\xi) f(\xi)\varphi_k(\xi)\,d\xi\,.$$

● **4.** The theory of integral equations presented here is based on the usual integral definition (Riemann integral). The results are carried over to integral equations where the integrals are interpreted in the Stieltjes sense.

Let us consider a function $M(x)$ that is differentiable everywhere except at a finite number of points $x_1, x_2, \cdots, x_n$. At these points the function $M(x)$ has discontinuities of the first kind:

$$M(x_k+\varepsilon) - M(x_k-\varepsilon) = M_k\,.$$

In the intervals between the discontinuities let

$$\frac{dM}{dx} = m(x)\,.$$

A function with these properties is called a *distribution function.* We will give an example for such a function. Let a beam be loaded by n concentrated masses $M_1, M_2, \cdots, M_n$ (Fig. 85) in addition to the distributed mass $M(x)$. Computing the sum of the masses to the left (or right) of a cross section with an arbitrary coordinate x, we obviously obtain a function that possesses all the characteristics of a distribution function $M(k)$. This function possesses still another important characteristic. One easily recognizes that $M(x_k) > M(x_i)$ if $x_k > x_i$, i.e., the function $M(x)$ increases monotonically.

Let us form the expression

$$J = \int_a^b f(x)m(x)\,dx + \sum_{k=1}^{n} f(x_k)\,M_k\,,$$

consisting of an integral in the ordinary sense and a finite sum; such a generalized integral is called a *Stieltjes integral* and is denoted by

$$J = \int_a^b f(x)\,dM(x)\,.$$

A Stieltjes integral possesses all the basic properties of an ordinary integral.[10]

[10] See, for example, Glivenko [1]. (A similar book written in English is Tricomi [1].)

Applying the formula for integration by parts,

$$\int_a^b f(x)\, dM(x) = f(x)M(x)\Big|_a^b - \int_a^b M(x)\, df(x)\,, \tag{11.22}$$

the result is analogous to the well-known formula for the Riemann integral. If $f(x)$ is a differentiable function, then

$$df(x) = \frac{df}{dx}dx\,;$$

in this case Eq. (11.22) can be used, and the Stieltjes integral can be transformed into a Riemann integral.

Let us now consider the integral equation

$$\varphi(x) - \lambda \int_a^b K(x, \xi)\varphi(\xi)\, dQ(\xi) = f(x)\,,$$

where $K(x, \xi)$ is a symmetric kernel. If the distribution function $Q(x)$ monotonically increases, then all the results of the classical theory of linear integral equations are applicable. One needs only to replace the ordinary differentials dx, $d\xi$, $\cdots$ by the Stieltjes differentials $dQ(x)$, $dQ(\xi)$, $\cdots$ in all the formulas. Therefore, the orthogonality conditions in Eq. (11.12) assume the form

$$\int_a^b \varphi_i(x)\varphi_k(x)\, dQ(x) = \delta_{ik}\,. \tag{11.23}$$

The definition of an integral transform function then changes in the following manner:

$$f(x) = \int_a^b K(x, \xi)\, p(\xi)\, dQ(\xi)\,.$$

The Fourier coefficients are calculated by

$$a_k = \int_a^b f(\xi)\varphi_k(\xi)\, dQ(\xi)\,,$$

instead of by Eq. (11.14). The bilinear formula (11.16) does not change.

If the distribution function is continuous everywhere, then as one easily recognizes, $dQ(\xi) = m(\xi)\, d\xi$ and the integral equation with a Stieltjes integral transforms into a weighted integral equation.

If the distribution function is not monotonic, then the theory becomes more complex. Therefore, in the case where the function $Q(x)$ simply does not decrease, i.e., a partial interval exists where $dQ(x) \equiv 0$, the orthogonality condition in Eq. (11.23) holds; the theorem of Hilbert and Schmidt and the bilinear formula change, however. The series in Eq. (11.16) then converges everywhere with the exception of the intervals in which $dQ(x) \equiv 0$.[11]

[11] The details can be found for example in Nudel'man. See also Krein [1].

§ 44. Free and Forced Vibrations of Systems with Infinite Number of Degrees of Freedom

●**1.** In the same manner, the theory of matrices has been applied to vibration problems for systems with a finite number of degrees of freedom; the theory of linear integral equations represents a suitable mathematical tool for the description of the vibrations of continuous systems. As a model for such a system, we will consider a beam with a distributed mass.

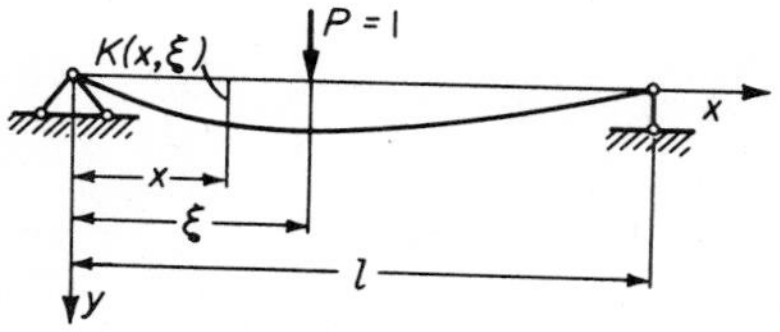

FIG. 87.

As a new concept, let us introduce the influence function of the deflections of an elastic system. As the *influence function* (*Green's function*) $K(x, \xi)$, we denote the analytical expression for the deflection at a point with the coordinate x, which is due to a unit force applied at a point with the coordinate ξ (Fig. 87). The influence function is the analog of the deflection matrix where obviously $\delta_{ik} = K(x_i, \xi_k)$. On the basis of the well-known theorem on the reciprocity of displacements, we have

$$K(x, \xi) \equiv K(\xi, x) ; \tag{11.24}$$

the kernel $K(x, \xi)$ is therefore symmetrical.

With the help of the influence function one can easily form the expression for the deflections of a beam due to an arbitrary load combination. Therefore, if a beam is loaded by a group of forces $P_1, P_2, \cdots, P_n$, then

$$v(x) = \sum_{k=1}^{n} K(x, \xi_k) P_k . \tag{11.25}$$

If a distributed load $q(x)$ acts on the beam, then one can determine the deflection by calculating the integral

$$v(x) = \int_0^l K(x, \xi) q(\xi)\, d\xi . \tag{11.26}$$

One can combine both cases by introducing a distribution function $Q(x)$ such that everywhere except at the points $x_1, x_2, \cdots, x_n$,

$$\frac{dQ}{dx} = q ,$$

and at these points

$$Q(x_k + \varepsilon) - Q(x_k - \varepsilon) = P_k .$$

The function $Q(x)$ obviously represents an ordinary transverse force. We will assume that the transverse force at the ends of the rod equals zero (in the adjacent cross section the force can naturally be different from zero). A consistent sign convention system will now be given. The deflection $v(x)$

and the loading $q(x)$ will be considered positive in the downward direction (along the y-axis). From the definition of the function $Q(x)$, we obtain for the transverse force the rule of signs: the force will be considered positive if it tends to rotate the beam element in a counterclockwise direction.

The function $Q(x)$ generally does not increase monotonically; however, the entire formula apparatus of the theory of the Stieltjes integrals is also applicable in this case. If we combine Eqs. (11.25) and (11.26), we obtain

$$v(x) = \int_0^l K(x, \xi)\, dQ(\xi)\,. \tag{11.27}$$

Moreover, the integral in Eq. (11.27) can be transformed into a Riemann integral. Let us also make use of Eq. (11.22) in Eq. (11.27) for the integration by parts. If we consider that $Q(0) = Q(l) = 0$, we obtain

$$v(x) = -\int_0^l \frac{\partial K(x, \xi)}{\partial \xi} Q(\xi)\, d\xi\,. \tag{11.28}$$

The differentiation of the kernel $K(x, \xi)$ is justified because all of its derivatives, including those up to third order, exist with respect to both arguments. For example.

$$\frac{\partial}{\partial x}\left[EJ(x)\frac{\partial^2 K(x, \xi)}{\partial x^2}\right] = Q(x, \xi)\,,$$

where $Q(x, \xi)$ is the transverse force at any arbitrary cross section caused by a concentrated unit force, and EJ is the bending stiffness.

●2. Let us now derive the equation for the free vibrations of a beam with a distributed mass $m(x)$. If we determine the dynamic deflection due to the inertia loading according to Eq. (11.26), we obtain

$$v(x, t) = \int_0^l K(x, \xi)\left[-m(\xi)\frac{\partial^2 v(\xi, t)}{\partial t^2}\right] d\xi\,. \tag{11.29}$$

The integral differential equation

$$v(x, t) + \int_0^l m(\xi) K(x, \xi)\frac{\partial^2 v(\xi, t)}{\partial t^2} d\xi = 0 \tag{11.30}$$

follows from the above.

If in addition to the distributed mass the beam has the concentrated masses $M_1, M_2, \cdots, M_n$, then in place of Eq. (11.29) we have

$$v(x, t) = \int_0^l K(x, \xi)\left[-m(\xi)\frac{\partial^2 v(\xi, t)}{\partial t^2}\right] d\xi + \sum_{k=1}^{n} K(x, \xi_k)\left[-M_k\frac{\partial^2 v(\xi_k, t)}{\partial t^2}\right],$$

and the integral in Eq. (11.30) can now be thought of as a Stieltjes integral. Therefore, one obtains the integro-differential equation

$$v(x, t) + \int_0^l K(x, \xi)\frac{\partial^2 v(\xi, t)}{\partial t^2} dM(\xi) = 0\,. \tag{11.31}$$

Here, $M(x)$ is the distribution function for the mass introduced earlier (§ 43, ● 4). However, in further investigations we will proceed from the integro-differential equation (11.30), recalling that all the results for the case of additional concentrated masses can be obtained by the direct substitution of $m(\xi)\,d\xi$ by $d\,M(\xi)$.

Let us substitute in Eq. (11.30) the expression

$$v(x, t) = \varphi(x) \sin(\omega t + \gamma)$$

where $\varphi(x)$ are the vibration shapes which are to be determined. After dividing by $\sin(\omega t + \gamma)$, we obtain the integral equation

$$\varphi(x) - \lambda \int_0^l m(\xi)\, K(x, \xi) \varphi(\xi)\, d\xi = 0 \tag{11.32}$$

where

$$\lambda = \omega^2 . \tag{11.33}$$

In this manner we have reduced the problem to an integral equation with a symmetric kernel $K(x, \xi)$ and a positive weight function $m(\xi)$. The spectrum of the eigenfunctions

$$\varphi_1(x),\ \varphi_2(x),\ \cdots,\ \varphi_k(x),\ \cdots$$

yields all of the free vibration forms[12], and the spectrum of the eigenvalues

$$\omega_1^2,\ \omega_2^2,\ \cdots,\ \omega_k^2,\ \cdots$$

yields all the free vibration frequencies. The existence of real frequencies follows from the fact that the kernel $K(x, \xi)$ is, first of all, symmetric and, secondly, positive definite. The last condition results from the consideration of the quadratic integral form, Eq. (11.17), which is equal, within a factor of 1/2, to the potential energy of the system with the loading $p(x)$.

The orthogonality condition Eq. (11.21) has a simple mechanical meaning. The work of the inertia forces of the ith vibration form on the displacements of the kth vibration form is equal to zero. The theorem of Hilbert and Schmidt is also easily interpreted. A function which is an integral transform

$$f(x) = \int_0^l K(x, \xi)\, p(\xi)\, d\xi$$

is nothing else but the deflection under the action of a loading $p(x)$; consequently, the theorem expresses the possibility that the deflections resulting from an arbitrary loading $p(x)$ can be expanded into an absolutely and uniformly convergent series with respect to the free vibration forms. Such series, made up of "beam functions," are often used.

● 3. Let us now consider the problem of forced vibrations. Let the system be loaded by a transverse force

$$q(x, t) = p(x) \cos \theta t .$$

[12] See footnote 14 following.

Applying Eq. (11.26), we obtain the integro-differential equation

$$v(x, t) + \int_0^l m(\xi) K(x, \xi) \frac{\partial^2 v(\xi, t)}{\partial t^2} d\xi = \int_0^l K(x, \xi) p(\xi) \cos \theta t \, d\xi .$$

With the expression

$$v(x, t) = \varphi(x) \cos \theta t ,$$

one obtains the nonhomogeneous Fredholm integral equation

$$\varphi(x) - \lambda \int_0^l m(\xi) K(x, \xi) \varphi(\xi) \, d\xi = f(x) , \tag{11.34}$$

where the parameter $\lambda = \theta^2$ and $f(x)$ is the static deflection resulting from amplitude values of the loading,

$$f(x) = \int_0^l K(x, \xi) p(\xi) \, d\xi . \tag{11.35}$$

The Fredholm theorems (§ 42, ● 2) are easily translated into the language of the theory of vibrations. In particular there arises the possibility that the nonhomogeneous integral equation, for which the value of the parameter λ corresponds to the value λ_k, is not solvable; this corresponds to an ordinary resonance of forced vibrations. In the case of corresponding frequencies it is also possible for no resonance to occur if the external loading satisfies the condition in Eq. (11.11). We will investigate the meaning of this condition. If we substitute Eq. (11.35) into Eq. (11.11), we find that

$$\int_0^l \int_0^l K(x, \xi) \varphi_k(x) p(\xi) \, dx \, d\xi = 0 .$$

Due to the symmetry of the kernel, however, we have

$$\int_0^l K(x, \xi) \varphi_k(x) \, dx = \frac{\varphi_k(\xi)}{\lambda_k} .$$

From this it follows that the external loading must be orthogonal to the corresponding vibration form

$$\int_0^l p(\xi) \varphi_k(\xi) \, d\xi .$$

In other words, the external loading must do no work on the corresponding deflections.

The amplitudes of the forced vibrations are calculated with the aid of Eq. (11.20). If we consider Eq. (11.33), we then find

$$\varphi(x) = \sum_{k=1}^{\infty} \frac{f_k \omega_k^2}{\omega_k^2 - \theta^2} \varphi_k(x) .$$

This equation is essentially a well-known formula from vibration theory.[13] We can obtain the formula in the usual form if we consider that

[13] See, for example, Nudel'man [1], p. 93.

$$f_k\omega_k^2 = \int_0^l p(\xi)\varphi_k(\xi)\,d\xi = Q_k ,$$

where Q_k is the "generalized force" corresponding to the "coordinate" $\varphi(x)$.

§ 45. The Integral Equations for the Boundaries of Static Stability

●1. Let us investigate the bending of a straight rod under the action of a longitudinal loading that induces a longitudinal force $\alpha N(x)$ in the rod. The longitudinal compressive force will be considered positive; the quantity α is an unknown parameter. The fixity of the rod and the dependence of the stiffness on the length can be arbitrarily selected; these quantities influence only the Green's function.

Let us now formulate the equation for the transverse bending of the rod.

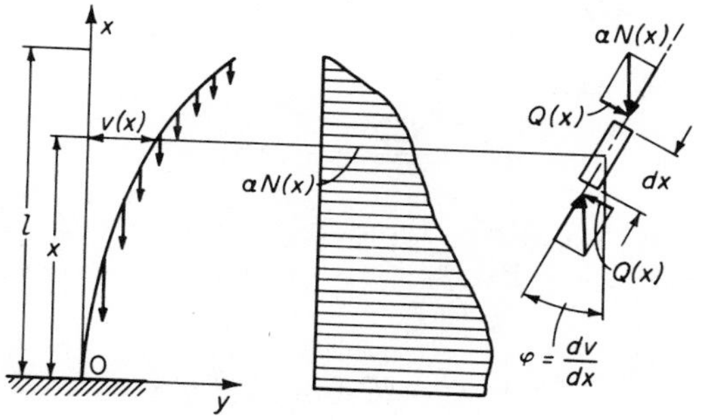

FIG. 88.

If bending causes a rod to change its initial straight line form (Fig. 88), a transverse force[14] then appears at each cross section:

$$Q(x) = -\alpha N(x)\frac{dv(x)}{dx} . \tag{11.36}$$

If we determine the deflection caused by this force by using Eq. (11.28), we find

$$v(x) = -\int_0^l \frac{\partial K(x,\xi)}{\partial \xi}\left[-\alpha N(\xi)\frac{dv(\xi)}{d\xi}\right] d\xi ;$$

with the notation $v(x) \equiv \psi(x)$, we obtain the integro-differential equation

$$\psi(x) - \alpha\int_0^l N(\xi)\frac{\partial K(x,\xi)}{\partial \xi}\frac{d\psi(\xi)}{d\xi}d\xi = 0 . \tag{11.37}$$

This equation can be easily reduced to a Fredholm integral equation. Differentiating Eq. (11.37) termwise with respect to x, we obtain

$$\frac{d\psi(x)}{dx} - \alpha\int N(\xi)\frac{\partial^2 K(x,\xi)}{\partial x\,\partial \xi}\frac{d\psi(\xi)}{d\xi}d\xi = 0 . \tag{11.38}$$

[14] It is assumed that the external loading of the rod does not change its direction during bending, i.e., it remains directed along the x axis. The influence of a different loading behavior will be investigated in Chapter Seventeen.

The spectrum of the eigenfunctions of this equation[15]

$$\frac{d\psi_1}{dx}, \quad \frac{d\psi_2}{dx}, \ldots, \frac{d\psi_k}{dx}, \ldots$$

yields all of the buckling forms; the spectrum of the eigenvalues

$$\alpha_1, \quad \alpha_2, \ldots, \alpha_k, \ldots$$

forms all of the critical parameters.

If the inequality $N(x) > 0$ holds everywhere on the interval $[0, l]$, i.e., if the rod is compressed along its entire length, then all the results of the theory of weighted symmetric integral equations can be applied to the integral equation (11.38). Therefore, the orthogonality condition (11.21) takes the form

$$\int_0^l N(x) \frac{d\psi_i}{dx} \frac{d\psi_k}{dx} dx = \delta_{ik} . \tag{11.39}$$

From Eq. (11.36) we have

$$N(x) \frac{d\psi_k}{dx} = -\frac{1}{\alpha} Q_k(x) ,$$

$Q_k(x)$ denoting the transverse force that corresponds to the kth buckling form. If we substitute this equation into Eq. (11.39) and apply the formula for integration by parts, we find

$$\int_0^l \psi_i(x) \, dQ_k(x) = -\alpha \, \delta_{ik} .$$

The work of the elastic forces of the kth buckling form for the deflections of the ith buckling form is thus equal to zero. This result is analogous to the corresponding result for the free vibration problem.

The kernel expansion (11.16) for the integral equation (11.38) becomes

$$\frac{\partial^2 K(x, \xi)}{\partial x \, \partial \xi} = \sum_{k=1}^{\infty} \frac{1}{\alpha_k} \frac{d\psi_k(x)}{dx} \frac{d\psi_k(\xi)}{d\xi} ,$$

where the series is absolutely and uniformly convergent under the assumptions introduced for $N(x)$. Through integration, we obtain

$$K(x, \xi) = \sum_{k=1}^{\infty} \frac{\psi_k(x) \psi_k(\xi)}{\alpha_k} + C .$$

If the rod, for example, is fixed at a point x_i, then $K(x_i, \xi) = \psi_k(x_i) = 0$ and, consequently, $C = 0$. The kernel expansion then becomes

$$K(x, \xi) = \sum_{k=1}^{\infty} \frac{\psi_k(x) \psi_k(\xi)}{\alpha_k} . \tag{11.40}$$

Further details can be found in the literature.[15]

● **2.** In addition to the longitudinal force acting on the rod, let a transverse

[15] This was obtained for the case of supported ends by E. Trefftz [1] and generalized by J. L. Nudelman [1].

loading $q(x)$ be also present. An equation for bending is obtained for this case by applying Eqs. (11.26) and (11.27):

$$v(x) = -\int_0^l \frac{\partial K(x,\xi)}{\partial \xi}\left[-\alpha N(\xi)\frac{dv(\xi)}{d\xi}\right] d\xi + \int_0^l K(x,\xi)q(\xi)\,d\xi .$$

If we differentiate termwise with respect to x and substitute $v(x) = \psi(x)$, we then obtain the nonhomogeneous Fredholm integral equation

$$\frac{d\psi(x)}{dx} - \alpha\int_0^l N(\xi)\frac{\partial^2 K(x,\xi)}{\partial x \partial \xi}\frac{d\psi(\xi)}{d\xi}d\xi = f(x) ,$$

where

$$f(x) = \int_0^l \frac{\partial K(x,\xi)}{\partial x}q(\xi)\,d\xi .$$

According to Eq. (11.20), its solution is

$$\frac{d\psi(x)}{dx} = \sum_{k=1}^{\infty} \frac{\alpha_k f_k}{\alpha_k - \alpha}\frac{d\psi_k(x)}{dx} ,$$

where

$$f_k = \int_0^l N(x)\frac{d\psi_k(x)}{dx}f(x)\,dx .$$

After termwise integration of the uniformly convergent series, we obtain

$$\psi(x) = \sum_{k=1}^{\infty} \frac{\alpha_k f_k}{\alpha_k - \alpha}\psi_k(x) + C .$$

For example, if one end of the rod is clamped, then the constant C is equal to zero.

Twelve

DIFFERENTIAL EQUATIONS FOR BOUNDARIES OF THE DYNAMIC STABILITY OF RODS

§ 46. Derivation of Differential Equations for Boundaries of Dynamic Stability

● 1. Generalized differential equations for boundaries of regions of dynamic stability of elastic systems can be derived only on the basis of the theory of elasticity of finite deflections. This will be carried out in Chapter Thirteen of this book.

The form of the generalized differential equations and their most important properties can be illustrated by a simplified model. As a suitable model one can use a straight rod compressed by longitudinal forces under very generalized assumptions with respect to the distribution of the loads, masses, and stiffness and with respect to the end fixity of the rod.

Let us investigate the vibrations of a straight rod under the action of a variable (for example, periodic) force. This force, which is distributed in an arbitrary manner over the length of the rod, causes a longitudinal force $N(x, t)$ in the rod cross sections. The fixity of the ends of the rod and the dependence of the mass $m(x)$ and the stiffness $EJ(x)$ on the length of the rod will be taken as arbitrary.

Let $K(x, \xi)$ be the influence function of the rod deflections; the dynamic deflection at every point of the rod is then

$$v(x, t) = \int_0^l K(x, \xi)\left[-m(\xi)\frac{\partial^2 v(\xi, t)}{\partial t^2}\right] d\xi + \int_0^l K(x, \xi) dQ(\xi, t) . \qquad (12.1)$$

The first right-hand term considers the influence of the inertia forces and the second term considers the influence of the longitudinal force. As we found in § 44,

$$Q(\xi, t) = -N(\xi, t)\frac{\partial v(\xi, t)}{\partial \xi} .$$

The second term on the right-hand side is transformed by partical integration by parts to

$$\int_0^l K(x, \xi) dQ(\xi, t) = \int_0^l N(\xi, t)\frac{\partial K(x, \xi)}{\partial \xi}\frac{\partial v(\xi, t)}{\partial \xi} d\xi .$$

Substituting these expressions into Eq. (12.1), we obtain for $v(x, t)$ the integro-differential equation

$$v(x, t) + \int_0^l m(\xi)K(x, \xi) \frac{\partial^2 v(\xi, t)}{\partial t^2} d\xi - \int_0^l N(\xi, t) \frac{\partial K(x, \xi)}{\partial \xi} \frac{\partial v(\xi, t)}{\partial \xi} d\xi = 0 . \tag{12.2}$$

The integro-differential equation (11.30) for the free vibrations and the integral equation (11.38) for the boundaries at static stability are special cases of Eq. (12.2).

We will later consider a loading in the form

$$N(x, t) = \alpha N_0(x) + \beta N_t(x)\Phi(t)$$

where $\Phi(t)$ is a periodic function with the period $T = 2\pi/\theta$ and α and β are unknown parameters; the constant and periodic components of the external loading are given to within these parameters. Therefore, we can write the integro-differential equation in the form:

$$v(x, t) + \int_0^l m(\xi)K(x, \xi) \frac{\partial^2 v(\xi, t)}{\partial t^2} d\xi - \alpha \int_0^l N_0(\xi) \frac{\partial K(x, \xi)}{d\xi} \frac{\partial v(\xi, t)}{d\xi} d\xi - \beta\Phi(t) \int_0^l N_t(\xi) \frac{\partial K(x, \xi)}{\partial \xi} \frac{\partial v(\xi, t)}{\partial \xi} d\xi = 0 . \tag{12.3}$$

● **2.** In Eq. (12.3) let us substitute the expression

$$v(x, t) = \sum_{k=1}^{\infty} f_k(t)\varphi_k(x) \tag{12.4}$$

where $\varphi_k(x)$ are the eigenfunctions of the kernel $m(\xi)K(x, \xi)$, i.e., they are the solutions for the homogeneous integral equation

$$\varphi(x) - \lambda \int_0^l m(\xi)K(x, \xi)\varphi(\xi)d\xi = 0, \qquad (\lambda = \omega^2) , \tag{12.5}$$

and $f_k(t)$ are time functions still to be determined. The eigenfunctions are assumed to be normalized.

Therefore, the series (12.4) represents the often used expansion of an elastic curve with respect to the free vibration form of a rod. The uniform convergence of this series follows from the basic theorems of the theory of linear integral equations; in order to prove the convergence, one needs only to apply the theorem of Hilbert and Schmidt on the right-hand side of Eq. (12.1).

If we substitute the series (12.4) into the integro-differential equation (12.3) and change the order of integration and summation, we obtain

$$\sum_{k=1}^{\infty} \frac{d^2 f_k}{dt^2} \int_0^l m(\xi)K(x, \xi)\varphi_k(\xi)d\xi + \sum_{k=1}^{\infty} f_k\varphi_k(x) - \alpha \sum_{k=1}^{\infty} f_k \int_0^l N_0(\xi) \frac{\partial K(x, \xi)}{\partial \xi} \frac{\partial \varphi_k(\xi)}{\partial \xi} d\xi - \beta\Phi(t) \sum_{k=1}^{\infty} f_k \int_0^l N_t(\xi) \frac{\partial K(x, \xi)}{\partial \xi} \frac{\partial \varphi_k(\xi)}{\partial \xi} d\xi = 0 . \tag{12.6}$$

From the integral equation (12.5) it follows that

$$\int_0^l m(\xi)K(x,\xi)\varphi_k(\xi)d\xi = \frac{\varphi_k(x)}{\omega_k^2} .$$

Furthermore, if we substitute the uniformly convergent series

$$K(x,\xi) = \sum_{i=1}^{\infty} \frac{\varphi_i(x)\varphi_i(\xi)}{\omega_i^2}$$

for $K(x, \xi)$, we then find

$$\int_0^l N_0(\xi)\frac{\partial K(x,\xi)}{\partial \xi}\frac{d\varphi_k(\xi)}{d\xi}d\xi = \sum_{i=1}^{\infty}\frac{\varphi_i(x)}{\omega_i^2}\int_0^l N_0(\xi)\frac{d\varphi_i(\xi)}{d\xi}\frac{d\varphi_k(\xi)}{d\xi}d\xi .$$

Analogously we obtain

$$\int_0^l N_t(\xi)\frac{\partial K(x,\xi)}{d\xi}\frac{d\varphi_k(\xi)}{d\xi}d\xi = \sum_{i=1}^{\infty}\frac{\varphi_i(x)}{\omega_i^2}\int_0^l N_t(\xi)\frac{d\varphi_i(\xi)}{d\xi}\frac{d\varphi_k(\xi)}{d\xi}d\xi .$$

By substituting in Eq. (12.6), we obtain

$$\sum_{k=1}^{\infty}\frac{d^2f_k}{dt^2}\frac{\varphi_k(x)}{\omega_k^2} + \sum_{k=1}^{\infty} f_k\varphi_k(x) - \alpha\sum_{k=1}^{\infty}\sum_{i=1}^{\infty} a_{ik}f_k\varphi_i(x) - \beta\Phi(t)\sum_{k=1}^{\infty}\sum_{i=1}^{\infty} b_{ik}f_k\varphi_i(x) = 0 ,$$

where following notations are introduced for brevity:

$$\begin{aligned} a_{ik} &= \frac{1}{\omega_i^2}\int_0^l N_0(x)\frac{d\varphi_i}{dx}\frac{d\varphi_k}{dx}dx , \\ b_{ik} &= \frac{1}{\omega_i^2}\int_0^l N_t(x)\frac{d\varphi_i}{dx}\frac{d\varphi_k}{dx}dx . \end{aligned} \tag{12.7}$$

The resulting equation can be written in the form

$$\sum_{i=1}^{\infty}\left[\frac{1}{\omega_i^2}\frac{d^2f_i}{dt^2} + f_i - \alpha\sum_{k=1}^{\infty} a_{ik}f_k - \beta\Phi(t)\sum_{k=1}^{\infty} b_{ik}f_k\right]\varphi_i(x) = 0 .$$

In order to satisfy this equation for arbitrary values at x and t, the functions $f_i(t)$ must satisfy the differential equations

$$\begin{gathered} \frac{1}{\omega_i^2}\frac{d^2f_i}{dt^2} + f_i - \alpha\sum_{k=1}^{\infty} a_{ik}f_k - \beta\Phi(t)\sum_{k=1}^{\infty} b_{ik}f_k = 0 \\ (i = 1, 2, 3, \cdots) . \end{gathered} \tag{12.8}$$

The problem of the dynamic stability of a compressed rod leads therefore in the general case to the system (12.8) of ordinary differential equations.

The resulting system consists of an infinite number of differential equations. However, we will limit ourselves to a finite number of equations, where the number of equations is selected from case to case according to the necessary accuracy of the calculations. (More accurately stated, we will compute both indices i and k only up to a finite number n.)

● **3.** Let us introduce the vector

$$\boldsymbol{f} = \begin{pmatrix} f_1(t) \\ f_2(t) \\ \vdots \\ f_n(t) \end{pmatrix}$$

from the coefficients of the series (12.4), and introduce the matrices

$$\boldsymbol{A}_\varphi = \begin{pmatrix} a_{11} & a_{12} & a_{13} & \cdots & a_{1n} \\ a_{21} & a_{22} & a_{23} & \cdots & a_{2n} \\ \cdot & \cdot & \cdot & \cdot & \cdot \\ a_{n1} & a_{n2} & a_{n3} & \cdots & a_{nn} \end{pmatrix},$$

$$\boldsymbol{B}_\varphi = \begin{pmatrix} b_{11} & b_{12} & b_{13} & \cdots & b_{1n} \\ b_{21} & b_{22} & b_{23} & \cdots & b_{2n} \\ \cdot & \cdot & \cdot & \cdot & \cdot \\ b_{n1} & b_{n2} & b_{n3} & \cdots & b_{nn} \end{pmatrix}.$$

By using the diagonal matrix

$$\boldsymbol{C}_\varphi = \left\{ \frac{1}{\omega_1^2}, \frac{1}{\omega_2^2}, \cdots, \frac{1}{\omega_n^2} \right\},$$

we can write the system of differential equations (12.8) in the form

$$\boldsymbol{C}_\varphi \frac{d^2\boldsymbol{f}}{dt^2} + [\boldsymbol{E} - \alpha \boldsymbol{A}_\varphi - \beta \Phi(t) \boldsymbol{B}_\varphi]\boldsymbol{f} = 0 . \tag{12.9}$$

As we will later show, the general equations for the boundaries of the regions of dynamic stability have the same form.

We will clarify the mechanical meaning of the coefficients a_{ik} and b_{ik}. To do this we must return to the problem of the static stability of a rod. The bending of a rod under the action of a longitudinal force $N_0(x)$ leads to the integro-differential equation

$$\psi(x) - \alpha \int_0^l N_0(\xi) \frac{\partial K(x, \xi)}{\partial \xi} \frac{d\psi(\xi)}{d\xi} d\xi = 0 . \tag{12.10}$$

We will seek the solutions of this equation in the form of a series with respect to the eigenfunctions of the kernel $m(\xi)K(x, \xi)$:

$$\psi(x) = \sum_{k=1}^{\infty} f_k \varphi_k(x) . \tag{12.11}$$

The magnitudes f_k are unknown constant coefficients. If we substitute the series (12.11) and the expansion

$$K(x, \xi) = \sum_{i=1}^{\infty} \frac{\varphi_i(x)\varphi_i(\xi)}{\omega_i^2}$$

into Eq. (12.10), we then obtain, by a comparison of the coefficients of $\varphi_i(x)$, the system of homogeneous linear equations

$$f_i - \alpha \sum_{k=1}^{\infty} a_{ik} f_k = 0 , \qquad (i = 1, 2, 3, \cdots) .$$

Here

$$a_{ik} = \frac{1}{\omega^2}\int_0^l N_0(x)\,\frac{d\varphi_i}{dx}\,\frac{d\varphi_k}{dx}\,dx\,.$$

In matrix form the system of equations obtained is written

$$(\boldsymbol{E} - \alpha\boldsymbol{A}_\varphi)\boldsymbol{f} = 0\,.$$

The critical parameters are found from the equation

$$\left|\boldsymbol{A}_\varphi - \frac{1}{\alpha}\boldsymbol{E}\right| = 0$$

or, in the expanded form,

$$\begin{vmatrix} a_{11} - \frac{1}{\alpha} & a_{12} & \cdots & a_{1n} \\ a_{21} & a_{22} - \frac{1}{\alpha} & \cdots & a_{2n} \\ \cdot & \cdot & \cdot & \cdot \\ a_{n1} & a_{n2} & \cdots & a_{nn} - \frac{1}{\alpha} \end{vmatrix} = 0\,.$$

The coefficients a_{ik} therefore form a matrix whose characteristic numbers are equal to the reciprocal values of the critical load parameters α_k.

In an analogous manner one can find the critical parameter of the loading $N_t(x)$ from the equation

$$\left|\boldsymbol{B}_\varphi - \frac{1}{\beta}\boldsymbol{E}\right| = 0\,.$$

§ 47. An Alternate Form of the Differential Equations for Boundaries of Dynamic Stability

● **1.** In the preceding paragraphs we introduced the free vibration shapes in the form of a series expansion for the solution of the dynamic stability problem. Another way is approximating the dynamic deflection by the eigenfunctions of the static stability problem.

The functions

$$\psi_1(x),\ \psi_2(x),\ \cdots,\ \psi_k(x),\ \cdots$$

can form a complete system of solutions of the integro-differential equation

$$\psi(x) - \alpha\int_0^l N_0(\xi)\,\frac{\partial K(x,\xi)}{\partial\xi}\,\frac{d\psi(\xi)}{d\xi}\,d\xi = 0 \tag{12.12}$$

which satisfies the normalizing condition

$$\int_0^l N_0(x)\left(\frac{d\psi_k}{dx}\right)^2 dx = 1\,. \tag{12.13}$$

Let us now substitute the expression

$$v(x, t) = \sum_{k=1}^{\infty} f_k(t)\varphi_k(x) \tag{12.14}$$

in the integro-differential equation (12.3). This yields[16]

$$\begin{aligned}\sum_{k=1}^{\infty} \frac{d^2 f_k}{dt^2} \int_0^l m(\xi)K(x, \xi)\varphi_k(\xi)d\xi + \sum_{k=1}^{\infty} f_k\varphi_k(x) \\ - \alpha \sum_{k=1}^{\infty} f_k \int_0^l N_0(\xi) \frac{\partial K(x, \xi)}{d\xi} \frac{d\varphi_k(\xi)}{d\xi} d\xi \\ - \beta\, \Phi(t) \sum_{k=1}^{\infty} f_k \int_0^l N_t(\xi) \frac{\partial K(x, \xi)}{\partial\xi} \frac{d\varphi_k(\xi)}{d\xi} d\xi = 0\,.\end{aligned} \tag{12.15}$$

From

$$K(x, \xi) = \sum_{i=1}^{\infty} \frac{\varphi_i(x)\varphi_i(\xi)}{\alpha_i} \tag{12.16}$$

it follows that

$$\int_0^l m(\xi)K(x, \xi)\varphi_k(\xi)d\xi = \sum_{i=1}^{\infty} \frac{\varphi_i(x)}{\alpha_i} \int_0^l m(\xi)\varphi_i(\xi)\varphi_k(\xi)d\xi\,,$$

and in an analogous manner,

$$\int_0^l N_t(\xi) \frac{\partial K(x, \xi)}{\partial\xi} \frac{d\varphi_k(\xi)}{d\xi} d\xi = \sum_{i=1}^{\infty} \frac{\varphi_i(x)}{\alpha_i} \int_0^l N_t(\xi) \frac{d\varphi_i(\xi)}{d\xi} \frac{d\varphi_k(\xi)}{d\xi} d\xi\,.$$

With the notation

$$\begin{aligned}\frac{1}{\alpha_i} \int_0^l m(x)\varphi_i\varphi_k dx &= c_{ik}\,, \\ \frac{1}{\alpha_i} \int_0^l N_t(x) \frac{d\varphi_i}{dx} \frac{d\varphi_k}{dx} dx &= b_{ik}\,,\end{aligned} \tag{12.17}$$

these equations take the form

$$\int_0^l m(\xi)K(x, \xi)\varphi_k(\xi)d\xi = \sum_{i=1}^{\infty} c_{ik}\varphi_i(x)\,,$$

$$\int_0^l N_t(\xi) \frac{\partial K(x, \xi)}{\partial\xi} \frac{d\varphi_k(\xi)}{d\xi} d\xi = \sum_{i=1}^{\infty} b_{ik}\varphi_i(x)\,.$$

Finally, on the basis of Eq. (12.16),

$$\int_0^l N_0(\xi) \frac{\partial K(x, \xi)}{\partial\xi} \frac{d\varphi_k(\xi)}{d\xi} d\xi = \frac{\varphi_k(x)}{\alpha_k}\,.$$

If we substitute this expression into Eq. (12.15), we obtain

$$\sum_{i=1}^{\infty} \sum_{k=1}^{\infty} c_{ik} \frac{d^2 f_k}{dt^2} \varphi_i(x) + \sum_{k=1}^{\infty} \left(1 - \frac{\alpha}{\alpha_k}\right) f_k\varphi_k(x) - \beta\, \Phi(t) \sum_{i=1}^{\infty} \sum_{k=1}^{\infty} b_{ik} f_k \varphi_i(x) = 0\,.$$

A comparison of the coefficients of $\varphi_i(x)$ results in the following system of ordinary differential equations:

[16] We are using here, as in many other places, formal computations without proof of their mathematical admissibility.

$$\sum_{k=1}^{\infty} c_{ik} \frac{d^2 f_k}{dt^2} + \left(1 - \frac{\alpha}{\alpha_i}\right) f_i - \beta \Phi(t) \sum_{k=1}^{\infty} b_{ik} f_k = 0 , \qquad (i = 1, 2, 3, \cdots) .$$

We will assume in the following that the indices i and k run from 1 to a *finite* number n so that only a finite number of differential equations exist. Then we can write the differential equation system in the matrix form:

$$\boldsymbol{C}_\psi \frac{d^2 \boldsymbol{f}}{dt^2} + [\boldsymbol{E} - \alpha \boldsymbol{A}_\psi - \beta \Phi(t) \boldsymbol{B}_\psi] \boldsymbol{f} = 0 . \tag{12.18}$$

Here $\boldsymbol{B}_\psi$ and $\boldsymbol{C}_\psi$ are matrices with the elements b_{ik} and c_{ik}, and $\boldsymbol{A}_\psi$ is the diagonal matrix

$$\boldsymbol{A}_\psi = \left\{ \frac{1}{\alpha_1} , \frac{1}{\alpha_2} , \cdots , \frac{1}{\alpha_n} \right\} .$$

● **2.** It is due not only to the selection of the notations that the differential equations (12.9) and (12.18) have the same form. Even if the corresponding elements of the matrices denoted by the same letters are generally different from one another, a well-determined relationship exists between them. For the determination of this relationship we will first give the interpretation of the coefficients c_{ik}.

Let us seek a solution of the integral equation of the free vibrations,

$$\varphi(x) - \omega^2 \int_0^l m(\xi) K(x, \xi) \varphi(\xi) d\xi = 0 . \tag{12.19}$$

in the form of an expanded series

$$\varphi(x) = \sum_{k=1}^{\infty} f_k \psi_k(x) \tag{12.20}$$

with respect to the eigenfunctions of the problem of static stability. Substituting Eq. (12.20) and (12.16) into Eq. (12.19), we obtain

$$\sum_{k=1}^{\infty} f_k \psi_k(x) - \omega^2 \sum_{k=1}^{\infty} \sum_{i=1}^{\infty} c_{ik} f_k \psi_i(x) = 0 ,$$

where again

$$c_{ik} = \frac{1}{\alpha_i} \int_0^l m(x) \psi_i \psi_k \, dx . \tag{12.21}$$

Comparing the coefficients of $\psi_i(x)$, we obtain the following system of homogeneous linear equations:

$$f_i - \omega^2 \sum_{k=1}^{\infty} c_{ik} f_k = 0 .$$

The equation for the natural frequencies is

$$\begin{vmatrix} 1 - \omega^2 c_{11} & -\omega^2 c_{12} & \cdots & -\omega^2 c_{1n} \\ -\omega^2 c_{21} & 1 - \omega^2 c_{22} & \cdots & -\omega^2 c_{2n} \\ \cdots & \cdots & \cdots & \cdots \\ -\omega^2 c_{n1} & -\omega^2 c_{n2} & \cdots & 1 - \omega^2 c_{nn} \end{vmatrix} = 0 ,$$

or, in matrix form,

$$\left| C_\psi - \frac{1}{\omega^2} E \right| = 0 . \tag{12.22}$$

This equation can also be derived from the matrix equation (12.18), if one sets $\alpha = \beta = 0$ and $\boldsymbol{f} = \boldsymbol{a} \sin (\omega t + \gamma)$.

Therefore, the coefficients c_{ik} form a matrix whose characteristic numbers are equal to $1/\omega^2$. This means that $\boldsymbol{C}_\varphi$ and $\boldsymbol{C}_\psi$ are similar matrices: They represent one and the same linear transformation except that they are described in different "coordinate systems" (for a different selection of coordinate functions). An analogous conclusion can be drawn for the matrices $\boldsymbol{A}_\varphi$ and $\boldsymbol{A}_\psi$ as well as $\boldsymbol{B}_\varphi$ and $\boldsymbol{B}_\psi$. Generally one can say that the differential equations

$$\begin{aligned} \boldsymbol{C}_\varphi \frac{d^2 \boldsymbol{f}_\varphi}{dt^2} + [\boldsymbol{E} - \alpha \boldsymbol{A}_\varphi - \beta \Phi(t) \boldsymbol{B}_\varphi] \boldsymbol{f}_\varphi &= 0 , \\ \boldsymbol{C}_\psi \frac{d^2 \boldsymbol{f}_\psi}{dt^2} + [\boldsymbol{E} - \alpha \boldsymbol{A}_\psi - \beta \Phi(t) \boldsymbol{B}_\psi] \boldsymbol{f}_\psi &= 0 , \end{aligned} \tag{12.23}$$

describe one and the same process and differ only in that the matrices and vectors are referred to "different axes." We will derive the equations by which the matrices can be transformed into one another. To do this we will consider the two uniformly convergent series

$$v(x, t) = \sum_{k=1}^{\infty} f_{k\varphi}(t) \varphi_k(x) .$$

$$v(x, t) = \sum_{k=1}^{\infty} f_{k\psi}(t) \psi_k(x) .$$

If we use the orthogonality conditions Eqs. (11.21) and (11.39), we obtain

$$f_{i\varphi} = \sum_{k=1}^{\infty} f_{k\psi} \int_0^l m(x) \varphi_i \psi_k \, dx ,$$

$$f_{i\psi} = \sum_{k=1}^{\infty} f_{k\varphi} \int_0^l N_0(x) \frac{d\psi_i}{dx} \frac{d\varphi_k}{dx} \, dx .$$

The first equation has the matrix form

$$\boldsymbol{f}_\varphi = \boldsymbol{V} \boldsymbol{f}_\psi ,$$

where

$$\{ \boldsymbol{V} \}_{ik} = \int_0^l m(x) \varphi_i \psi_k dx .$$

The inverse transformation will be formed from a matrix with the elements

$$\{ \boldsymbol{V}^{-1} \}_{ik} = \int_0^l N_0(x) \frac{d\psi_i}{dx} \frac{d\varphi_k}{dx} \, dx .$$

The coefficients of both differential equations are transformed in the following manner:

$$\boldsymbol{A}_\psi = \boldsymbol{V}^{-1}\boldsymbol{A}_\varphi \boldsymbol{V},$$
$$\boldsymbol{B}_\psi = \boldsymbol{V}^{-1}\boldsymbol{B}_\varphi \boldsymbol{V},$$
$$\boldsymbol{C}_\psi = \boldsymbol{V}^{-1}\boldsymbol{C}_\varphi \boldsymbol{V}.$$

● **3.** We will discuss briefly a special form of the differential equations for the boundaries of dynamic stability. Let us write the matrix differential equation in the form

$$\frac{d^2\boldsymbol{f}}{dt^2} + \boldsymbol{C}^{-1}(\boldsymbol{E} - \alpha\boldsymbol{A})\boldsymbol{f} - \beta\,\Phi(t)\boldsymbol{C}^{-1}\boldsymbol{B}\boldsymbol{f} = \boldsymbol{0}$$

and select the coordinate system so that the matrix $\boldsymbol{C}^{-1}(\boldsymbol{E} - \alpha\boldsymbol{A})$ will be in a diagonal form. The differential equations for the boundaries of dynamic stability are especially simple for this case:

$$\frac{d^2 f_i}{dt^2} + g_i f_i - \beta\,\Phi(t) \sum_{k=1}^{\infty} h_{ik} f_k = 0\,, \qquad (i = 1, 2, 3, \cdots)\,. \tag{12.24}$$

Such a transformation, as we will show, is equivalent to considering the free vibrations of the rod compressed by the constant component of the longitudinal force as coordinate functions. In fact, the matrix differential equation for the free vibrations of the loaded rod is

$$\boldsymbol{C}\frac{d^2\boldsymbol{f}}{dt^2} + (\boldsymbol{E} - \alpha\boldsymbol{A})\boldsymbol{f} = \boldsymbol{0}\,.$$

If we substitute

$$\boldsymbol{f}(t) = \boldsymbol{u}\sin(\Omega t + \gamma)$$

we obtain the equation

$$(\boldsymbol{E} - \alpha\boldsymbol{A} - \Omega^2\boldsymbol{C})\boldsymbol{u} = \boldsymbol{0}\,.$$

The natural frequencies Ω are obtained from the equation

$$|\,\boldsymbol{C}^{-1}(\boldsymbol{E} - \alpha\boldsymbol{A}) - \Omega^2\boldsymbol{E}\,| = \boldsymbol{0}\,, \tag{12.25}$$

from which $g_i = \Omega_i^2$ follows. The differential equations (12.24) now become

$$\frac{d^2 f_i}{dt^2} + \Omega_i^2\left[f_i - 2\beta\Omega(t)\sum_{k=1}^{n}\mu_{ik} f_k\right] = 0\,, \tag{12.26}$$

where

$$\mu_{ik} = \frac{h_{ik}}{2\Omega_i^2}\,.$$

§ 48. The Application of Variational Methods

● **1.** For the derivation of the differential equations for the boundaries of dynamic stability, variational methods are used in addition to the differential equation method (the Ritz and Galerkin methods) because of the simplicity of the computations. The Galerkin method is most often applied. We will apply this method to the problem of the dynamic stability of straight rods.

As is well known, the differential equation of the bending of a straight rod compressed by a longitudinal force $N(x)$, which is a function of the longitudinal coordinate, is

$$\frac{d^2}{dx^2}\left[EJ(x)\frac{d^2v}{dx^2}\right] + \frac{d}{dx}\left[N(x)\frac{dv}{dx}\right] = 0 .$$

If we substitute into this equation

$$N = \alpha N_0(x) + \beta N_t(x)\Phi(t)$$

and introduce the inertia forces, we obtain

$$\frac{\partial^2}{\partial x^2}\left[EJ(x)\frac{\partial^2 v}{\partial x^2}\right] + \alpha\frac{\partial}{\partial x}\left[N_0(x)\frac{\partial v}{\partial x}\right] + \beta\Phi(t)\frac{\partial}{\partial x}\left[N_t(x)\frac{\partial v}{\partial x}\right] + m\frac{\partial^2 v}{\partial t^2} = 0 . \qquad (12.27)$$

The differential equation (12.27) holds for the case where the functions $N_0(x)$ and $N_t(x)$ are continuous over the total length of the rod. Also the function $J(x)$ together with its derivative is assumed to be continuous. If concentrated forces are acting on the rod or if the stiffness does not change continuously, the differential equation (12.27) then must be replaced between the points of discontinuity (line of action of the concentrated forces and the discontinuities of the stiffness) by differential equations of the same form with additional conditions of the discontinuity points. The integral equation method has in this case the advantage that only one equation is formed for the complete rod including even the discontinuities.

Assume that all coefficients of the differential equation (12.27) are continuous, and apply the Galerkin variational method. With the coordinate functions $(\chi_k)x$, which satisfy the boundary conditions, we can set

$$v(x, t) = \sum_{k=1}^{n} f_k(t)\chi_k(x)$$

as an approximation and introduce this expression into the differential equation (12.27). The Galerkin method requires that the left-hand side of Eq. (12.27) be orthogonal to each of the functions $\chi_i(x)$ after substitution. This condition leads to the following system of ordinary differential equations for the functions $f_k(t)$:

$$\sum_{k=1}^{n}\frac{d^2 f_k}{dt^2}\int_0^l m\chi_i\chi_k dx + \sum_{k=1}^{n} f_k\int_0^l \chi_i\frac{d^2}{dx^2}\left(EJ\frac{d^2\chi_k}{dx^2}\right)dx + \alpha\sum_{k=1}^{n} f_k\int_0^l \chi_i\frac{d}{dx}\left(N_0\frac{d\chi_k}{dx}\right)dx + \beta\Phi(t)\sum_{k=1}^{n} f_k\int_0^l \chi_i\frac{d}{dx}\left(N_t\frac{d\chi_k}{dx}\right)dx = 0 .$$

In addition, we will introduce the matrices $\boldsymbol{F}, \boldsymbol{R}, \boldsymbol{P}$, and $\boldsymbol{Q}$ with the elements

$$\{\boldsymbol{F}\}_{ik} = \int_0^l m\chi_i\chi_k dx ,$$

$$\{\boldsymbol{R}\}_{ik} = \int_0^l \chi_i\frac{d^2}{dx^2}\left(EJ\frac{d^2\chi_k}{dx^2}\right)dx ,$$

$$\{P\}_{ik} = -\int_0^l \chi_i \frac{d}{dx}\left(N_0 \frac{d\chi_k}{dx}\right) dx ,$$

$$\{Q\}_{ik} = -\int_0^l \chi_i \frac{d}{dx}\left(N_t \frac{d\chi_k}{dx}\right) dx .$$

The derived differential equation system then has the matrix form

$$F\frac{d^2 f}{dt^2} + [R - \alpha P - \beta \Phi(t) Q] f = 0 . \tag{12.28}$$

Setting

$$R^{-1}F = C , \qquad R^{-1}P = A , \qquad R^{-1}Q = B ,$$

we obtain

$$C\frac{d^2 f}{dt^2} + [E - \alpha A - \beta \Phi(t) B] f = 0 , \tag{12.29}$$

which is a form analogous to Eq. (12.23).

If one uses the solutions of the differential equation

$$\frac{d^2}{dx^2}\left(EJ\frac{d^2\varphi_k}{dx^2}\right) - m\omega_k^2\varphi_k = 0 , \qquad (k = 1, 2, \cdots, n) ,$$

as coordinate functions of the free vibrations, then the differential equation (12.29) agrees completely with (12.9).

The assumption that the coefficients of the differential equation (12.27) are continuous is essential for the computation described.

The formal extension of the method to individual continuous intervals by piecewise continuous coefficients is not substantiated and can lead to incorrect results. In addition, the formulas for the matrix elements can be shown to be useless if the coordinate functions selected directly satisfy the geometric boundary conditions but not the dynamic conditions containing derivatives higher than first order. However, one can easily transform these equations in such a way that this restriction disappears.

For example, let us consider the matrix element

$$p_{ik} = -\int_0^l \chi_i \frac{d}{dx}\left(N_0 \frac{d\chi_k}{dx}\right) dx .$$

Introducing a distribution function

$$Q_k(x) = N_0 \frac{d\chi_k}{dx}$$

which is equal to the transverse force except for the notation corresponding to the deflection shape $\chi_k(x)$, we can write

$$p_{ik} = -\int_0^l \chi_i dQ_k(x) .$$

Hence, integrating by parts and setting $Q_k(0) = Q_k(1) = 0$, as before, we have

$$p_{ik} = \int_0^l N_0(x) \frac{d\chi_i}{dx} \frac{d\chi_k}{dx} dx .$$

This formula does not contain derivatives higher than first order and is therefore independent of the dynamic boundary conditions for $\chi_k(x)$. The same results can be obtained if the Galerkin method is interpreted in the sense of virtual displacements. The left-hand side of the differential equation (12.27) is interpreted as an expression for the action of the external and internal forces on a unit length of the rod. If we compute the work of these forces on the virtual displacements $\delta f_k \chi_k(x)$ and if the work of the individual forces is added and their sum set equal to zero, we then obtain the given result.

We will note in conclusion that a formal method analogous to the Galerkin variational method can also be applied to the integro-differential equation (12.3). The corresponding variational method is denoted as the "moment method." Let $L_\varphi(v)$ and $L_\psi(v)$ be the expressions appearing on the left-hand side of Eq. (12.3) if the series

$$v(x, t) = \sum_{k=1}^{\infty} f_k(t)\varphi_k(x)$$

and, respectively,

$$v(x, t) = \sum_{k=1}^{\infty} f_k(t)\psi_k(x)$$

are substituted. Then one obtains the differential equation system (12.8) from Eq. (12.3) by the application of the "generalized orthogonality condition"

$$\int_0^l L_\varphi(v) m(x) \varphi_i(x) dx = 0 , \qquad (i = 1, 2, 3, \cdots) .$$

Similarly one obtains the differential equation system (12.17) by the application of the condition

$$\int_0^l \frac{\partial L_\psi(v)}{\partial x} N_0(x) \frac{d\psi_i(x)}{dx} dx = 0 , \qquad (i = 1, 2, 3, \cdots) .$$

For the correct selection of the orthogonality condition, it is useful to consider the Galerkin method as an analog to the principle of virtual displacements.

● **2.** One has complete freedom in the selection of the fundamental functions for the Ritz method.

The variational problem

$$\int_{t_1}^{t_2} (T - U) dt = \min$$

leads, as is well known, to the Lagrangian equations

$$\frac{d}{dt}\left(\frac{\partial T}{\partial q_i'}\right) - \frac{\partial}{\partial q_i}(T - U) = Q_i , \qquad (i = 1, 2, 3, \cdots) . \tag{12.30}$$

In this equation T is the kinetic and U the potential energy of the system, and q_i are the generalized coordinates that will be taken here as the coefficients f_i of the series

$$v(x, t) = \sum_{i=1}^{n} f_i(t)\chi_i(x) , \tag{12.31}$$

and Q_i are the corresponding generalized forces.

The kinetic energy of the system is

$$T = \frac{1}{2}\int_0^l m\left(\frac{\partial v}{\partial t}\right)^2 dx .$$

By the substitution of Eq. (12.31), we obtain

$$T = \frac{1}{2}\sum_{i=1}^{n}\sum_{k=1}^{n}\frac{df_i}{dt}\frac{df_k}{dt}\int_0^l m(x)\chi_i\chi_k dx .$$

The potential energy of deformation is

$$U = \frac{1}{2}\int_0^l EJ(x)\left(\frac{\partial^2 v}{\partial x^2}\right)^2 dx$$

or with Eq. (12.31)

$$U = \frac{1}{2}\sum_{i=1}^{n}\sum_{k=1}^{n} f_i f_k \int_0^l EJ(x)\frac{d^2\chi_i}{dx^2}\frac{d^2\chi_k}{dx^2} dx .$$

In order to determine the generalized forces Q_i, we formulate the expression for the work of the external loading. The longitudinal displacement caused by the deformation of an element of length dx, as is well-known, is a magnitude of third and higher order[17]:

$$dw = \frac{1}{2}\left(\frac{\partial v}{\partial x}\right)^2 dx .$$

The work that the longitudinal force $N(x, t)$ does for this displacement is

$$dV = N(x, t)dw .$$

The total work is

$$V = \frac{1}{2}\int_0^l N(x, t)\left(\frac{\partial v}{\partial x}\right)^2 dx$$

or, after substitution of Eq. (12.31),

$$V = \frac{1}{2}\sum_{i=1}^{n}\sum_{k=1}^{n} f_i f_k \int_0^l N(x, t)\frac{d\chi_i}{dx}\frac{d\chi_k}{dx} dx .$$

The generalized force which corresponds to the coordinate f_i is

$$Q_i = \frac{\partial V}{\partial f_i} = \sum_{k=1}^{n} f_k \int_0^l N(x, t)\frac{d\chi_i}{dx}\frac{d\chi_k}{dx} dx .$$

Substituting the expression obtained into the Lagrangian equation (12.30), it follows that

[17] The beam axis will be assumed to be incompressible.

$$\sum_{k=1}^{n} \frac{d^2 f_k}{dt^2} \int_0^l m(x)\chi_i \chi_k \, dx + \sum_{k=1}^{n} f_k \int_0^l EJ(x) \frac{d^2\chi_i}{dx^2} \frac{d^2\chi_k}{dx^2} \, dx$$
$$= \sum_{k=1}^{n} f_k \int_0^l N(x,t) \frac{d\chi_i}{dx} \frac{d\chi_k}{dx} \, dx \,, \qquad (i = 1, 2, 3, \cdots, n) \,.$$

Setting

$$N(x,t) = \alpha N_0(x) + \beta N_t(x)\Phi(t) \,,$$

as before, we obtain the differential equation system (12.28).

§ 49. The Special Case of Independent Separate Equations and the Criteria for Their Occurrence

● **1.** In the previous paragraphs it was shown that problems of dynamic stability (independent of the selection of eigenfunctions or coordinate functions) can be described by systems of differential equations with periodic coefficients which have one and the same form

$$\boldsymbol{C} \frac{d^2 \boldsymbol{f}}{dt^2} + [\boldsymbol{E} - \alpha \boldsymbol{A} - \beta \Phi(t) \boldsymbol{B}] \boldsymbol{f} = \boldsymbol{0} \,. \tag{12.32}$$

However, the individual coefficients are essentially changed in the case of a transformation of one functional system to another. If one takes the free vibration forms $\varphi(x)$ of a rod as orthogonal functions, then the matrix $\boldsymbol{C}$ becomes a diagonal matrix; however the matrices $\boldsymbol{A}$ and $\boldsymbol{B}$ are generally not diagonal matrices at the same time. Conversely if the eigenfunctions $\psi(x)$ are taken as coordinate functions, then the matrix $\boldsymbol{A}$ is of a diagonal form. If the loading functions $N_0(x)$ and $N_t(x)$ are equal, then the matrix $\boldsymbol{B}$ is also of a diagonal form. For the simplification of further calculations, we will assume that this last condition is fulfilled.

It is now possible for the eigenfunctions of the free vibration problem and the static stability problem to coincide:[18]

$$\varphi_k(x) = \psi_k(x) \,. \tag{12.33}$$

All three matrices $\boldsymbol{A}, \boldsymbol{B}, \boldsymbol{C}$ are then simultaneously transformed into diagonal form, and the differential equation system breaks down into a series of separate equations where each of them depends on only one unknown function:

$$\frac{d^2 f_i}{dt^2} + \omega_i^2 \left[1 - \frac{\alpha}{\alpha_i} - \frac{\beta}{\beta_i} \Phi(t)\right] f_i = 0 \,, \qquad (i = 1, 2, 3, \cdots) \,. \tag{12.34}$$

This *special case*, which is of considerable interest, has already been presented earlier (Chapter Nine). We will now investigate it in detail.

The matrix $\boldsymbol{A}_\varphi$ is a diagonal matrix if

$$\int_0^l N_0(x) \frac{d\varphi_i}{dx} \frac{d\varphi_k}{dx} \, dx = 0 \qquad \text{for} \quad i \neq k \,. \tag{12.35}$$

[18] More accurately one can say that it is possible for them to coincide except for a constant factor since the normalization conditions, Eqs. (11.21) and (11.39), are different

A problem on dynamic stability therefore leads in every case to the differential equations (12.34) if the free vibration forms satisfy the orthogonality conditions. This is also true for the buckling forms.

One obtains still another criterion for the appearance of the special case if one sets the elements outside the principal diagonal of matrix $\boldsymbol{C}$ equal to zero:

$$\int_0^l m(x)\psi_i\psi_k dx = 0 \qquad \text{for} \quad i \neq k\,. \tag{12.36}$$

The requirement expressed by Eq. (12.36) is that the buckling forms satisfy the orthogonality conditions for the vibration forms.

The criteria in Eqs. (12.35) and (12.36) have the advantage over Eq. (12.33) in that they require the knowledge of only one system of eigenfunctions.

● **2.** Some examples for the special case of independent separate equations were given in Chapter Nine. From the following considerations it will be shown that the class of problems that lead to the differential equations of the form in Eq. (12.34), are not exhausted by these examples.

Let us formulate the conditions under which the buckling forms and the free vibration forms coincide. The function $\varphi(x)$ satisfies simultaneously both of the integral equations

$$\varphi(x) - \omega^2 \int_0^l m(\xi)K(x, \xi)\varphi(\xi)d\xi = 0\,,$$

$$\varphi(x) - \alpha \int_0^l S(x, \xi)\varphi(\xi)d\xi = 0\,.$$

The second integral equation is of significance only if the conditions given earlier (§ 45) are fulfilled. We will confine ourselves for simplicity to the case where these conditions are fulfilled.

Two integral operators have the same eigenfunctions if they are interchangeable (compare this with the analogous statement in matrix theory § 38):

$$\int_0^l S(x, \eta)m(\xi)K(\eta, \xi)d\eta = \int_0^l m(\eta)K(x, \eta)S(\eta, \xi)d\eta\,. \tag{12.37}$$

If the ends of the rod are simply-supported and the function $N_0(x)$ is differentiable, the kernel $S(x, \xi)$ can then be written in the form

$$S(x, \xi) = -\frac{\partial}{\partial \xi}\left[N_0(\xi)\frac{\partial K(x, \xi)}{\partial \xi}\right].$$

To simplify the computation, we will set $N_0 = \text{const.}$ which yields

$$S(x, \xi) = -N_0\frac{\partial^2 K(x, \xi)}{\partial \xi^2}\,.$$

From the physical meaning it follows that the load-influence function $K(x, \xi)$ can be expressed in terms of the moment-influence function $M(x, \xi)$:

$$\frac{\partial^2 K(x, \xi)}{\partial x^2} = -\frac{M(x, \xi)}{EJ(x)} .$$

If we use the symmetric property $K(x, \xi) \equiv K(\xi, x)$, then we find

$$S(x, \xi) = N_0 \frac{M(\xi, x)}{EJ(\xi)} . \tag{12.38}$$

According to the well-known formula of structural mechanics, we have

$$K(x, \xi) = \int_0^l \frac{M(\eta, x)M(\eta, \xi)}{EJ(\eta)} d\eta . \tag{12.39}$$

If we substitute Eqs. (12.38) and (12.37) into Eq. (12.37), we then obtain

$$\int_0^l \int_0^l \frac{M(\zeta, x)m(\xi)M(\eta, \zeta)M(\eta, \xi)}{EJ(\zeta)\cdot EJ(\eta)} d\eta d\zeta$$
$$= \int_0^l \int_0^l \frac{m(\eta)M(\zeta, x)M(\zeta, \eta)M(\xi, \eta)}{EJ(\zeta)\cdot EJ(\xi)} d\eta d\zeta .$$

This relationship can be written as follows:

$$\int_0^l \left[\int_0^l \frac{m(\xi)M(\eta, \zeta)M(\eta, \xi)}{EJ(\eta)} d\eta - \int_0^l \frac{m(\eta)M(\zeta, \eta)M(\xi, \eta)}{EJ(\xi)} d\eta\right] \frac{M(\zeta, x)}{EJ(\zeta)} d\zeta = 0 .$$

Since this expression must be satisfied for all values of x, it follows that

$$\int_0^l \frac{m(\xi)M(\eta, \zeta)M(\eta, \xi)}{EJ(\eta)} d\eta = \int_0^l \frac{m(\eta)M(\zeta, \eta)M(\xi, \eta)}{EJ(\xi)} d\eta . \tag{12.40}$$

One easily recognizes that the condition in Eq. (12.40) is fulfilled if the rod has a symmetric moment-influence function,

$$M(x, \xi) \equiv M(\xi, x) , \tag{12.41}$$

and if, in addition, the rod cross sections change in the following manner:

$$J(x)m(x) = \text{const.} \tag{12.42}$$

The condition in Eq. (12.41), as is well known, is satisfied for a rod that is simply supported on both ends.[19] If the cross section of a simply-supported rod (which changes along its length) satisfies the condition in Eq. (12.42), then the problem of the dynamic stability of this rod under the action of periodic end forces leads to differential equations of the form of Eq. (12.34). The problem investigated by Beliaev is obviously a special case of this problem.

The condition in Eq. (12.41) is also satisfied for a prismatic rod of infinite length that is imbedded in a three-dimensional elastic medium.

[19] The condition in Eq. (12.41), in the final analysis, corresponds to the requirement that the deflections of the "imaginary beam" determined by graphic analytical methods must agree with those of the original beam.

Thirteen

DIFFERENTIAL EQUATIONS FOR THE DYNAMIC STABILITY OF ELASTIC SYSTEMS

§ 50. Preliminary Remarks

● 1. The foregoing investigations were carried out essentially for simpler problems of the dynamic stability of straight rods compressed by a longitudinal pulsating load. It can easily be shown, however, that all of the basic results obtained for these simpler problems can be extended without major changes to the general case of vibrations of elastic systems. In this connection, only the form of formulas used in the calculation of coefficients of the differential equations need be changed.

Thus, all of the equations derived in the preceding chapter remain valid for the case of rod systems, for example, for frames with a pulsating loading acting at the node points. If the node points of the frame undergo linear displacements, then additional equations have to be added to the integro-differential equation of the type (12.3); the addition of these equations, however, does not change the structure of the final equations.

In the case of curved rods, and also plates loaded by forces acting in the middle plane, only the method of calculating the matrix of coefficients changes.

Somewhat more complex are problems dealing with the dynamic stability of three-dimensional elastic systems, for example, problems on the dynamic stability of compressed thin-walled rods or beams undergoing bending in the plane of largest rigidity. In this case the vibrations are accompanied by bending in one or two planes and, in addition, by twisting. Therefore, instead of a single equation of the type (12.3), there are two or three equations, and instead of a system of differential equations of the type (12.9), there are two or three analogous systems. These systems, however, can be combined by known methods into one system having the same structure and the same properties as system (12.9).

In general, the problems of vibrations of elastic systems loaded by a pulsating parametric load with parameters α and β always lead to equations of the type

$$L_{\omega}\left(\frac{\partial^2 w}{\partial t^2}\right) + L_0(w) - \alpha L_{\alpha}(w) - \beta\Phi(t)L_{\beta}(w) = 0\,, \tag{13.1}$$

where L_{ω}, L_0, L_{α}, and L_{β} are certain integro-differential operators and the function $w(x, y, z, t)$ describes the deformed state of the system. When this state is characterized by several functions, we regard Eq. (13.1) as a symbolic notation (tensor notation) for a system of integro-differential equations.

The special cases of Eqs. (13.1) are the equations for the free vibrations:

$$(L_0 - \omega^2 L_\omega)\varphi = 0$$

and the equations for static stability:

$$(L_0 - \alpha L_\alpha)\psi_\alpha = 0 \,,$$
$$(L_0 - \beta L_\beta)\psi_\beta = 0 \,.$$

If an appropriate system of linearly independent eigenfunctions is chosen,

$$\chi_1(x, y, z) \,, \quad \chi_2(x, y, z), \cdots , \quad \chi_n(x, y, z) \,,$$

Eqs. (13.1) can be rewritten in matrix form:

$$\boldsymbol{F}\frac{d^2\boldsymbol{f}}{dt^2} + [\boldsymbol{R} - \alpha\boldsymbol{P} - \beta\Phi(t)\boldsymbol{Q}]\boldsymbol{f} = \boldsymbol{0} \,. \tag{13.2}$$

Here $\boldsymbol{f}$ is a vector composed of the coefficients of the series

$$w = \sum_{k=1}^{\infty} f_k(t)\chi_k(x, y, z) \,.$$

The method of calculating the matrices, i.e., the coefficients of Eq. (13.2), will depend on the form of operators entering in (13.1) and on the character of the eigenfunctions χ_k. When the application of the Galerkin variational method is possible, the matrix elements are defined, obviously, in the following way:

$$\{\boldsymbol{F}\}_{ik} = \iiint \chi_i L_\omega(\chi_k)\, dx\, dy\, dz \,,$$

$$\{\boldsymbol{R}\}_{ik} = \iiint \chi_i L_0(\chi_k)\, dx\, dy\, dz \,,$$

$$\{\boldsymbol{P}\}_{ik} = \iiint \chi_i L_\alpha(\chi_k)\, dx\, dy\, dz \,,$$

$$\{\boldsymbol{Q}\}_{ik} = \iiint \chi_i L_\beta(\chi_k)\, dx\, dy\, dz \,.$$

where the integration extends throughout the whole system.

Since the eigenfunctions χ_k are linearly independent, the determinant $|\boldsymbol{R}| \neq 0$, and consequently Eq. (13.2) can be reduced to the form

$$\boldsymbol{C}\frac{d^2\boldsymbol{f}}{dt^2} + [\boldsymbol{E} - \alpha\boldsymbol{A} - \beta\Phi(t)\boldsymbol{B}]\boldsymbol{f} = 0 \,,$$

where

$$\boldsymbol{A} = \boldsymbol{R}^{-1}\boldsymbol{P} \,, \qquad \boldsymbol{B} = \boldsymbol{R}^{-1}\boldsymbol{Q} \,, \qquad \boldsymbol{C} = \boldsymbol{R}^{-1} - \boldsymbol{F} \,.$$

Further investigation leads to results which completely coincide with the results obtained previously for the case of straight rods. These results will not be given here.

● **2.** The general equations for the boundaries of the dynamic stability of elastic systems can be obtained if one starts from the equations of motion for a three-dimensional elastic medium. This problem cannot be solved within the framework of classical theory of small displacements, for which Kirchhoff's uniqueness theorem is valid; here one must consider finite, although sufficiently small, displacements.

The uniqueness of solutions in the classical theory of elasticity is based on the fact that no distinction is made between the geometry of the initial, undeformed state of the medium and the geometry of the medium after deformation; more precisely, the equations of motion, boundary conditions, and equations relating stresses and deformations are constructed in the coordinate systems of the undeformed body without considering the displacements which arise during transition to the deformed condition.

The insufficiency of such a treatment can be seen from a simple example of static transverse bending of a compressed rod. If this problem is formulated on the basis of classical small deflection theory, a unique solution valid for all values of the compressive load is obtained. Only the consideration of additional internal forces arising during the deflection of the rod from the initial position permits us to find the correct solution.

It has been stated above that it is sufficient to restrict oneself to small though finite displacements, in the investigation of stability. This remark is explained as follows. First of all, the perturbed initial state can usually be characterized by small displacements and can usually be determined by the methods of classical theory. An exception to this is the case in which the loss of stability is preceded by large displacements (static or dynamic); here one must consider finite nonlinear displacements (when constructing equations describing the perturbed state).

During the displacement, lengths of linear elements, the areas, and volumes change. The influence of these changes on the stability is usually negligibly small; therefore they can be neglected provided the relative deformations are sufficiently small in comparison to unity. It is not permissible, however, to neglect angles of rotation and the general nondimensional displacements in comparison to unity. Thus, in solving the problems of longitudinal bending of a compressed rod, the changes in cross section and length are not considered; however, the additional forces which arise from rotation of the cross section are taken into account.

Finally, if the problem consists of determining the critical parameters (critical forces or boundary frequencies), these can be found from equations that are obtained from equations for the perturbed state after neglecting the terms in these containing perturbations of order higher than one.

§ 51. Introduction to the Theory of Finite Displacements

There are two methods for describing the finite displacements of an elastic medium.[20] First of all, one can introduce a system of coordinates x_1, x_2, x_3

[20] See, for example, Novozhilov [1] or Kutilin [1].

(rectangular Cartesian or curvilinear) referred to the undeformed medium. If the corresponding displacements of the points of the medium are u_1 u_2, u_3, then the new coordinates will be

$$\begin{aligned} \xi_1 &= x_1 + u_1(x_1, x_2, x_3) , \\ \xi_2 &= x_2 + u_2(x_1, x_2, x_3) , \\ \xi_3 &= x_3 + u_3(x_1, x_2, x_3) . \end{aligned} \tag{13.3}$$

This method of description (the Lagrangian method) contrasts with Euler's method in which the coordinates of points of the deformed medium (ξ_1, ξ_2, ξ_3) are taken as the independent variables. The relationship between the two coordinate systems is given by formulas (13.3).

Assume that the Euler system of coordinates ξ_1, ξ_2, ξ_3 forms a rectangular Cartesian system. The equations of motion have the form

$$\sum_{k=1}^{3} \frac{\partial \sigma_{ik}}{\partial \xi_k} + X_i = \rho \frac{d^2 u_i}{dt^2} , \qquad (i = 1, 2, 3) . \tag{13.4}$$

Here σ_{ik} are components of the stress tensor, X_i are the components of the body force per unit volume in the deformed state, and ρ is the density of the deformed medium. On the right side of the equations, the total (substantial) derivative is taken with respect to time.

As is commonly done in tensor analysis, we will leave out the summation sign whenever the summation is performed over all possible values of the subscript ($k = 1, 2, 3$). The presence of a pair of identical subscripts indicates each time that the summation extends over these subscripts. For example, in accordance with the stated rules, Eqs. (13.4) can be expressed as

$$\frac{\partial \sigma_{ik}}{\partial \xi_k} + X_i = \rho \frac{d^2 u_i}{dt^2} . \tag{13.5}$$

In appearance, Eqs. (13.5) are identical with the equations of motion of the classical theory of elasticity. However, here the differentiation is performed with respect to the coordinates of the deformed state, i.e., with respect to parameters which in the final analysis, depend on the functions u_1, u_2, u_3. Therefore it is expedient to transform equations (13.5) to the Lagrangian variables for the undeformed medium.

Referring the reader to V. V. Novozhilov [1] for details, we can express Eqs. (13.5) for the case of rectangular Cartesian coordinates as

$$\frac{\partial}{\partial x_k}\left[\left(\delta_{ij} + \frac{\partial u_i}{\partial x_j}\right)\overset{*}{\sigma}_{jk}\right] + X_i = \rho \frac{\partial^2 u_i}{\partial t^2} . \tag{13.6}$$

In these equations and in what follows, u_i are the components of the displacement vector in terms of the Lagrangian variables x_1, x_2, x_3; X_i are components of the body force in terms of the same variables; which are referred to the undeformed condition; ρ is the density of the undeformed medium; δ_{ij} is the Kronecker delta symbol; $\overset{*}{\sigma}_{ik}$ is a tensor related to the volumetric density Φ (x_1, x_2, x_3) of the energy for the undeformed state referred to a unit volume of the unstrained body, and related to the deformation tensor in the Lagrangian variables,

$$\varepsilon_{ik} = \frac{1}{2}\left(\frac{\partial u_i}{\partial x_k} + \frac{\partial u_k}{\partial x_i} + \frac{\partial u_j}{\partial x_i}\frac{\partial u_j}{\partial x_k}\right), \tag{13.7}$$

by the equation

$$\sigma^*_{ik} = \frac{\partial \Phi}{\partial \varepsilon_{ik}}.$$

In Eqs. (13.6) the differentiation is performed with respect to the coordinates of the undeformed medium, which leads to certain simplifications. As is known, the tensor σ^*_{ik} can be expressed through a stress tensor σ_{ik} in terms of the Lagrangian variables as

$$\sigma^*_{ik} = \frac{df^*_i}{df_i}\frac{\sigma_{ik}}{\sqrt{1+2\varepsilon_{kk}}}.$$

Here df_i and df^*_i are the areas, before and after the deformation, of an element which is perpendicular to axis x_i. If one considers only small deformations, when it is possible to neglect changes in lengths and areas (deformations are small, but displacements can be large), then tensors σ^*_{ik} and σ_{ik} can be identical. This approximation practically always appears satisfactory, except perhaps in the case of rubber and rubber-like materials. For the purposes of the present work, no distinction will be made between tensors σ^*_{ik} and σ_{ik}.

● **2.** Consider the boundary conditions. On one part of the surface, the displacements may be given, while on another part a surface load may be given. Consider the latter. Let n_i be the direction cosines of the undeformed surface and p_i be the components of the surface load, referred to the Lagrangian coordinate system for the undeformed medium. At each point of the loaded surfaces, it is necessary that

$$\left(\delta_{ij} + \frac{\partial u_i}{\partial x_j}\right)\sigma_{jk}n_k = p_i. \tag{13.8}$$

Thus far we have used rectangular Cartesian coordinates. The reader who is familiar with tensor analysis can easily rewrite the results in a form that is suitable for arbitrary curvilinear coordinates. This can be done by replacing the partial differentiation by tensor differentiation and arranging the subscripts in such a way that the requirement for tensor dimensionality is satisfied.

§ 52. Statement of the Problem on the Dynamic Stability of a Three-Dimensional Elastic Body[21]

● **1.** Let us investigate the motion of an elastic body which is produced by a periodic surface loading

$$p_i = \alpha p_i^{(0)} + \beta p_i^{(t)}\Phi(t)$$

and by periodic body forces

$$X_i = \alpha X_i^{(0)} + \beta X_i^{(t)}\Phi(t).$$

[21] For § 52 through § 54, see Bolotin [16].

Here α and β are arbitrary parameters to within which the constant and variable parts of the loading are given.

We will distinguish two conditions of the body. In the first condition, which we will call unperturbed, the body performs steady-state forced vibrations. For the unperturbed motion, the components of the stress tensor, σ_{ik}, and the components of the displacement vector, v_i, satisfy Eqs. (13.6), that is,

$$\frac{\partial}{\partial x_k}\left[\left(\delta_{ij}+\frac{\partial v_i}{\partial x_j}\right)\sigma_{jk}\right]+X_i = \rho\frac{\partial^2 v_i}{\partial t^2}, \tag{13.9}$$

and the conditions on the surface (13.8),

$$\left(\delta_{ij}+\frac{\partial v_i}{\partial x_j}\right)\sigma_{jk}n_k = p_i . \tag{13.10}$$

In addition to the unperturbed motion, we will investigate the motion differing from it by the presence of small perturbations in the stressed and deformed condition

$$\begin{aligned}\tilde{\sigma}_{ik} &= \sigma_{ik}+\Delta\sigma_{ik},\\ \tilde{p}_i &= p_i+\Delta p_i,\\ \tilde{X}_i &= X_i+\Delta X_i,\\ \tilde{u}_i &= v_i+u_i .\end{aligned}$$

The differential equations for the perturbed motion assume the form

$$\frac{\partial}{\partial x_k}\left[\left(\delta_{ij}+\frac{\partial v_i}{\partial x_j}+\frac{\partial u_i}{\partial x_j}\right)(\sigma_{jk}+\Delta\sigma_{jk})\right]+X_i+\Delta X_i = \rho\frac{\partial^2 v_i}{\partial t^2}+\rho\frac{\partial^2 u_i}{\partial t^2} .$$

Taking into account the fact that the parameters for the unperturbed motion are related by Eqs. (13.9), and neglecting small, second order quantities (for the condition $u_i \ll v_i$, terms of the order $\Delta\sigma_{jk}(\partial u_i/\partial x_j)$ are quantities of this type), we obtain

$$\frac{\partial}{\partial x_k}\left[\left(\delta_{ij}+\frac{\partial v_i}{\partial x_j}\right)\Delta\sigma_{jk}\right]+\frac{\partial}{\partial x_k}\left(\sigma_{jk}\frac{\partial u_i}{\partial x_j}\right)+\Delta X_i = \rho\frac{\partial^2 u_i}{\partial t^2} . \tag{13.11}$$

If the frequencies of forced vibrations lie far from resonance, then the displacements u_i and v_i can be assumed to be quantities of the same order; on this basis the products $\Delta\sigma_{jk}(\partial v_i/\partial x_j)$ can be neglected.

Thus Eqs. (13.11) simplify to

$$\frac{\partial\Delta\sigma_{ik}}{\partial x_k}+\frac{\partial}{\partial x_k}\left(\sigma_{jk}\frac{\partial u_i}{\partial x_j}\right)+\Delta X_i = \rho\frac{\partial^2 u_i}{\partial t^2} . \tag{13.12}$$

● **2.** In Eqs. (13.11) and (13.12), v_i and σ_{ik} are known functions and u_i and $\Delta\sigma_{ik}$ are the unknown functions. To eliminate $\Delta\sigma_{ik}$, it is necessary to use the relationship between stresses and strains.

Since the stability equations are linear with respect to perturbations, we are justified in using Hooke's Law,[22]

[22] Instead of more general nonlinear relationships, as for example Mournaghan's law [1].

$$\Delta\sigma_{ik} = \lambda\delta_{ik}\varepsilon_{jj} + 2\mu\varepsilon_{ik} , \tag{13.13}$$

where λ and μ are Lamé constants, and $\varepsilon_{jj} = \varepsilon_{11} + \varepsilon_{22} + \varepsilon_{33}$. The strains ε_{ik} can be calculated from Eqs. (13.7) with the nonlinear terms omitted,

$$\varepsilon_{ik} = \frac{1}{2}\left(\frac{\partial u_i}{\partial x_k} + \frac{\partial u_k}{\partial x_i}\right). \tag{13.14}$$

Thus, for the additional stresses $\Delta\sigma_{ik}$ the following is obtained:

$$\Delta\sigma_{ik} = \lambda\delta_{ik}\frac{\partial u_j}{\partial x_j} + \mu\left(\frac{\partial u_i}{\partial x_i} + \frac{\partial u_k}{\partial x_i}\right). \tag{13.15}$$

Differentiating (13.15), summing over k, and changing the notation for the doubled subscripts in the last term, we find

$$\frac{\partial}{\partial x_k}(\Delta\sigma_{ik}) = \mu\nabla^2 u_i + (\lambda + \mu)\frac{\partial^2 u_j}{\partial x_i \partial x_j} ,$$

where

$$\nabla^2 = \frac{\partial^2}{\partial x_1{}^2} + \frac{\partial^2}{\partial x_2{}^2} + \frac{\partial^2}{\partial x_3{}^2} .$$

Equations (13.11) assume the form (for $\Delta X_i \equiv 0$)

$$\mu\nabla^2 u_i + (\lambda + \mu)\frac{\partial^2 u_j}{\partial x_i \partial x_j} + \frac{\partial}{\partial x_k}\left\{\left[\lambda\delta_{jk}\frac{\partial u_i}{\partial x_j} + \mu\left(\frac{\partial u_j}{\partial x_k} + \frac{\partial u_k}{\partial x_j}\right)\right]\frac{\partial v_i}{\partial x_j}\right\} + \frac{\partial}{\partial x_k}\left(\sigma_{jk}\frac{\partial u_i}{\partial x_j}\right)$$
$$= \rho\frac{\partial^2 u_i}{\partial t^2} .$$

These are the differential equations for the boundaries of dynamic stability of a homogeneous isotropic medium. For the condition that the displacements in the unperturbed state are small, we obtain

$$\mu\nabla^2 u_i + (\lambda + \mu)\frac{\partial^2 u_j}{\partial x_i \partial x_j} + \frac{\partial}{\partial x_k}\left(\sigma_{jk}\frac{\partial u_i}{\partial x_j}\right) = \rho\frac{\partial^2 u_i}{\partial t^2} . \tag{13.16}$$

One can easily generalize these equations for the case of arbitrary anisotropy and inhomogeneity of a medium. Thus, instead of (13.15), it is necessary to take the general relationship

$$\Delta\sigma_{ik} = \lambda_{ikmn}\varepsilon_{mn} ,$$

where λ_{ikmn} is the tensor of the elastic constants. Then, for example,

$$\frac{\partial}{\partial x_k}(\Delta\sigma_{ik}) = \frac{\partial}{\partial x_k}\left(\lambda_{ikmn}\frac{\partial u_m}{\partial x_n}\right).$$

● **3.** The boundary condition (13.8) for the perturbed motion has the form

$$\left(\delta_{ij} + \frac{\partial v_i}{\partial x_j} + \frac{\partial u_i}{\partial x_j}\right)(\sigma_{jk} + \Delta\sigma_{jk})n_k = p_i + \Delta p_i .$$

Taking into consideration (13.10) and linearizing, we obtain

$$\left(\delta_{ij} + \frac{\partial v_i}{\partial x_j}\right)\Delta\sigma_{jk}n_k + \frac{\partial u_i}{\partial x_j}\sigma_{jk}n_k = \Delta p_i .$$

If the displacements v_i are neglected, then the boundary condition simplifies to

$$\left(\Delta\sigma_{ik} + \frac{\partial u_i}{\partial x_j}\sigma_{jk}\right)n_k = \Delta p_i\,. \tag{13.17}$$

Here Δp_i is the change in the intensity of surface loading for the perturbed motion. The determination of Δp_i will now be considered for various cases.

If the surface loading remains unchanged both in magnitude and direction, then $\Delta p_i \equiv 0$. If the load rotates together with an element of the surface, remaining perpendicular to it, then

$$\Delta p_i = p_k \frac{\partial u_i}{\partial x_k}\,. \tag{13.18}$$

For example, in the case of a hydrostatic loading $p_k = -pn_k$, where p is the pressure. The boundary condition (13.17) then assumes the form

$$\Delta\sigma_{ik}n_k - \frac{\partial u_i}{\partial x_j}(\sigma_{jk} - p\delta_{jk})n_k = 0\,.$$

If a part of the surface of the body rests on an elastic medium which resists displacements (the generalized Winkler foundation), then $\Delta p_i = -c_{ik}u_k$, where c_{ik} is a "foundation tensor."

§ 53. Green's Tensor for a Three-Dimensional Elastic Body. The Integral Equations for Vibrations and Regions of Stability

● **1.** The equation obtained from (13.16) after neglecting parametric terms,

$$\mu\nabla^2 u_i + (\lambda + \mu)\frac{\partial^2 u_j}{\partial x_i \partial x_j} + X_i = 0\,,$$

or in a more general case

$$\frac{\partial}{\partial x_k}\left(\lambda_{ikmn}\frac{\partial u_m}{\partial x_n}\right) + X_i = 0\,, \tag{13.19}$$

corresponds to the usual approximation in the classical theory of elasticity (Lamé equations). In the classical theory, the boundary conditions (13.8) are as follows:

$$\sigma_{ik}n_k = p_i\,. \tag{13.20}$$

Green's tensor for the system of equations (13.19) and for the homogeneous boundary conditions appropriate for the unloaded body is now introduced:

$$G_{ik}(P, Q) = \begin{bmatrix} G_{11}(P, Q) & G_{12}(P, Q) & G_{13}(P, Q) \\ G_{21}(P, Q) & G_{22}(P, Q) & G_{23}(P, Q) \\ G_{31}(P, Q) & G_{32}(P, Q) & G_{33}(P, Q) \end{bmatrix}.$$

In a physical sense the components of Green's tensor represent, within the framework of classical theory, the components of the displacement vector of a point $P = P(x_1, x_2, x_3)$ on the body due to a unit force applied at the point

$Q = Q(\xi_1, \xi_2, \xi_3)$ and directed along one of the vectors of the coordinate system. For example, for a homogeneous and isotropic space, Green's tensor is identical with the well-known Somigliano tensor. The components $G_{ik}(P, Q)$ satisfy the equations

$$\frac{\partial}{\partial x_k}\left[\lambda_{ikmn}\frac{\partial G_{mj}(P, Q)}{\partial x_n}\right] + \delta_{ij}\delta(P - Q) = 0 ,$$

where $\delta(P - Q)$ is a three-dimensional delta function.

With the help of Green's tensor, the solution of Eqs. (13.19) for the boundary conditions (13.20) can be represented in the form

$$u_i(P) = \int_V G_{ik}(P, Q)X_k(Q)dV_Q + \iint_S G_{ik}(P, Q)p_k(Q)dS_Q . \tag{13.21}$$

Here V is the volume of the body, and S is its loaded surface.

● **2.** Let us consider some of the properties of the tensor $G_{ik}(P, Q)$. From the general laws of the classical elasticity theory, it follows that the tensor is symmetrical, i.e.

$$\begin{aligned} G_{kk}(P, Q) &\equiv G_{kk}(Q, P) , \\ G_{ik}(P, Q) &\equiv G_{ki}(Q, P) , \end{aligned} \tag{13.22}$$

and also that it is positive, i.e.

$$\int_V\int_V G_{ik}(P, Q)u_k(P)u_k(Q)dV_P dV_Q > 0 \tag{13.23}$$

for each non-zero vector $u_k(P)$ inside of $\boldsymbol{V}$.

The relationship between the Green's tensor and the problem of small vibrations will now be shown. The differential equations for small vibrations of an elastic body are obtained from (13.19) by applying D'Alembert's principle:

$$\frac{\partial}{\partial x_k}\left(\lambda_{ikmn}\frac{\partial u_m}{\partial x_n}\right) - \rho\frac{\partial^2 u_i}{\partial t^2} = 0 . \tag{13.24}$$

Here ρ is the density of the body at each point. The usual substitution of

$$u_i(P, t) = \varphi_i(P) \cos (\omega t + \delta)$$

into Eq. (13.24) yields a system of differential equations

$$\frac{\partial}{\partial x_k}\left(\lambda_{ikmn}\frac{\partial \varphi_m}{\partial x_n}\right) + \rho\omega^2\varphi_i = 0 .$$

The equivalent system of integral equations, as follows from (13.21), has the form

$$\varphi_i(P) - \lambda\int_V \rho(Q)G_{ik}(P, Q)\varphi_k(Q)dV_Q = 0 \tag{13.25}$$

where $\lambda = \omega^2$. This system is equivalent to a single Fredholm integral equation with a symmetric kernel,

$$\Phi(M) - \lambda\int_{V_1+V_2+V_3} K(M, N)\Phi(N)dV_N = 0 , \tag{13.26}$$

in which the integration is performed three times over the same volume $V = V_1 + V_2 + V_3$, and moreover,

$$K(M, N) = \sqrt{\rho(P)\rho(Q)}G_{ik}(P, Q) , \qquad \text{if} \quad M \in V_i,\ N \in V_k ,$$
$$\Phi(M) = \sqrt{\rho(P)}\varphi_i(P) , \qquad \text{if} \quad M \in V_i .$$

The eigenvalues of the integral equation (13.26), or, which is the same, those of the integral equations (13.25), form a denumerable set $\lambda_1, \lambda_2, \cdots \lambda_m, \cdots$. To each eigenvalue of this set there corresponds an eigenfunction $\Phi_m(M)$ or a "trio" of eigenfunctions $\varphi_1^{(m)}(P)$, $\varphi_2^{(m)}(P)$, $\varphi_3^{(m)}(P)$ which we shall call an *eigenvector* $\varphi_i^{(m)}(P)$ of the integral equation system (13.25). Of course, quantities $\varphi_i^{(m)}(P)$ are not tensors but only vectors designated by the lower subscripts. It is assumed that the usual summation rule for the doubled subscripts does not hold for the superscripts. The latter, which indicate the number of the eigenvector, will be denoted by the letters m and n.

Considering the properties of Green's tensor (13.22) and (13.23) and the fact that the integral equations (13.25) reduces to an integral equation (13.26), we obtain certain important results which we will formulate briefly here.

(1) The eigenvectors $\varphi_i^{(m)}(P)$ form an orthonormal system in the sense that

$$\int_V \varphi_i^{(m)}\varphi_i^{(n)}dV = \delta_{mn} . \tag{13.27}$$

(2) Every vector $u_i(P)$ with continuous components and which can be represented sourcewise with the help of Green's tensor $G_{ik}(P, Q)$ and a vector $X_k(P)$, i.e.,

$$u_i(P) = \int_V G_{ik}(P, Q)X_k(P)dV_Q ,$$

can be expanded in an absolutely and uniformly convergent series with respect to the eigenvectors $\varphi_i^{(m)}(P)$:

$$u_i(P) = \sum_{m=1}^{\infty} a_m\varphi_i^{(m)}(P) .$$

The coefficients of this series are

$$a_m = \int_V u_i(P)\varphi_i^{(m)}dV .$$

(3) The components of Green's tensor $G_{ik}(P, Q)$ can be developed in the bilinear series

$$G_{ik}(P, Q) = \sum_{m=1}^{\infty} \frac{\varphi_i^{(m)}(P)\varphi_k^{(m)}(Q)}{\lambda_m} , \tag{13.28}$$

which converge absolutely and uniformly with respect to both variables.

● **3.** The static problem will now be considered, limited to the case where the external loading is such that during buckling it does not change, with respect to the initial coordinate system, either in direction or in intensity

($\Delta X_i = \Delta p_i = 0$). We will neglect the initial displacements, identifying the latter with the undeformed condition. Under these assumptions, the differential equations for static stability become

$$\frac{\partial}{\partial x_k}\left(\lambda_{ikmn}\frac{\partial u_m}{\partial x_n}\right) - \alpha\frac{\partial}{\partial x_k}\left(s_{jk}\frac{\partial u_i}{\partial x_j}\right) = 0\,, \tag{13.29}$$

and the boundary conditions on the surface of the body are

$$\Delta\sigma_{ik}n_k = \alpha s_{jk}\frac{\partial u_i}{\partial x_k}n_k\,. \tag{13.30}$$

It is assumed here that the external loading, and consequently also all of the components of the initial stressed condition, are given with respect to the parameter α, where $\sigma_{ik} = -\alpha s_{ik}$.

The integral formula (13.21) will now be applied. As a result, a system of integro-differential equations is obtained:

$$u_i(P) + \alpha\int_V G_{ik}(P,Q)\frac{\partial}{\partial\xi_l}\left[s_{jl}(Q)\frac{\partial u_k(Q)}{\partial\xi_j}\right]dV_Q$$
$$- \alpha\int_S\int G_{ik}(P,Q)s_{jl}(Q)\frac{\partial u_k(Q)}{\partial\xi_j}n_l dS_Q = 0\,. \tag{13.31}$$

For further transformations we make use of the Gauss-Ostrogradski formula:

$$\int_V \frac{\partial A_k}{\partial x_k}dV = \int_S\int A_k n_k dS\,.$$

With the help of an identity

$$G_{ik}(P,Q)\frac{\partial}{\partial\xi_l}\left[s_{jl}(Q)\frac{\partial u_k(Q)}{\partial\xi_j}\right]$$
$$\equiv \frac{\partial}{\partial\xi_l}\left[G_{ik}(P,Q)s_{jl}(Q)\frac{\partial u_k(Q)}{\partial\xi_j}\right] - \frac{\partial G_{ik}(P,Q)}{\partial\xi_l}\cdot s_{jl}(Q)\frac{\partial u_k(Q)}{\partial\xi_j}\,,$$

we find that

$$\int_V G_{ik}(P,Q)\frac{\partial}{\partial\xi_l}\left[s_{jl}(Q)\frac{\partial u_k(Q)}{\partial\xi_j}\right]dV_Q$$
$$= \int_S\int G_{ik}(P,Q)s_{jl}(Q)\frac{\partial u_k(Q)}{\partial\xi_j}n_l dS_Q - \int_V \frac{\partial G_{ik}(P,Q)}{\partial\xi_l}s_{jl}(Q)\frac{\partial u_k(Q)}{\partial\xi_j}dV_Q\,.$$

Hence, after substitution in (13.31), the following is obtained:

$$u_i(P) - \alpha\int_V s_{jl}(Q)\frac{\partial G_{ik}(P,Q)}{\partial\xi_l}\,\frac{\partial u_k(Q)}{\partial\xi_j}dV_Q = 0\,.$$

After termwise differentiations, these equations reduce to a system of 3^2 integral equations for $\partial\psi_i/\partial x_g \equiv \partial u_i/\partial x_g$:

$$\frac{\partial\psi_i(P)}{\partial x_g} - \alpha\int_V s_{jl}(Q)\frac{\partial^2 G_{ik}(P,Q)}{\partial x_g\partial\xi_l}\,\frac{\partial\psi_k(Q)}{\partial\xi_j}dV_Q = 0\,. \tag{13.32}$$

This system can be represented in the form of a single integral equation with a symmetric kernel and, generally speaking, a non-monotonic distribution function. The buckling forms (more precisely, their first derivatives with respect to the coordinates) and the critical parameters are essentially the eigenfunctions and eigenvalues of the integral equation. Hence, one obtains the condition of orthogonality for the buckling forms

$$\int_V s_{ij} \frac{\partial \psi_k^{(m)}}{\partial \xi_i} \frac{\partial \psi_k^{(n)}}{\partial \xi_j} dV = \delta_{mn} , \tag{13.33}$$

where $\partial \psi_k^{(m)}/\partial \xi_i$ and $\partial \psi_k^{(n)}/\partial \xi_j$ are the eigenvectors for the static stability problem (trio of eigenfunctions) corresponding to the eigenvalues α_m and α_n respectively. If all the principal values of the tensor s_{ij} are positive, then all $\alpha_m > 0$, and the theorem on expansion and the bilinear formula for components of Green's tensor holds.

Special cases will now be considered. In the problem of the buckling of a compressed straight rod,

$$s_{ij} = \begin{bmatrix} \frac{N}{F} & 0 & 0 \\ 0 & 0 & 0 \\ 0 & 0 & 0 \end{bmatrix} .$$

Assuming, as usual, that during buckling the deformation can be described by transverse displacements of points located on the axis of the rod, we obtain the integral equation (11.32):

$$\frac{d\psi(x)}{dx} - \alpha \int_0^l N(\xi) \frac{\partial^2 G(x, \xi)}{\partial x \partial \xi} \frac{d\psi(\xi)}{d\xi} d\xi = 0 .$$

(Here the subscripts are left out.)

In the problem of the stability of a plate loaded in its middle plane,

$$s_{ij} = \begin{bmatrix} \frac{N_{11}}{h} & \frac{N_{12}}{h} & 0 \\ \frac{N_{21}}{h} & \frac{N_{22}}{h} & 0 \\ 0 & 0 & 0 \end{bmatrix} ,$$

where N_{ik} are the forces per unit length and h is the thickness of the plate. For this case the system of integral equations (13.32) assumes the form

$$\frac{\partial \psi(P)}{\partial x_g} - \alpha \int_\Omega \int N_{jl}(Q) \frac{\partial^2 G(P, Q)}{\partial x_g \partial \xi_l} \frac{\partial \psi(Q)}{\partial \xi_j} d\Omega = 0 , \qquad (g, l, j = 1, 2) ,$$

where $\psi(P)$ is the transverse deflection of the plate, $G(P, Q)$ is its influence function, and $d\Omega$ is an element of area of the middle surface Ω.

The integral equation for buckling of arches can be obtained if we introduce a curvilinear coordinate system which is fixed to the axis of arch, and replace partial integration by tensor integration. The integral equations for stability of shells can be derived similarly.

The way the structure of the equations changes if the vectors of the external loading rotate together with the corresponding elements of the surface (so-called "following" loading) will now be explained. Instead of Eq. (13.30) we have, according to Eqs. (13.17) and (13.18),

$$\Delta\sigma_{ik}n_k = \alpha s_{jk}\frac{\partial u_i}{\partial x_j}n_k + \alpha p_k\frac{\partial u_i}{\partial x_k} .$$

If we construct equations of the type of (13.31) and perform the transformation, then, in place of (13.32), we have

$$\psi_i(P) + \alpha\int_V s_{jl}(Q)G_{ik}(P, Q)\frac{\partial^2\psi_k(Q)}{\partial\xi_j\partial\xi_l}dV_Q = 0 .$$

In contrast to (13.32), this system of integral equations cannot, in general, be reduced to an integral equation with a symmetric (or one that be made symmetric) kernel. Consequently, the static stability problem for the case of the "following" load can have complex eigenvalues together with the real ones. In fact, it may even have no real eigenvalues. This result is clearer if one considers that, generally speaking, "following" loading is not conservative.

§ 54. Transformation to Systems of Ordinary Differential Equations

● **1.** In what follows, we will start from Eqs. (13.16) and the boundary conditions (13.17), letting

$$\sigma_{ik} = -\alpha s_{ik}^{(0)} - \beta\Phi(t)s_{ik}^{(t)} .$$

Here α and β are still arbitrary parameters for the components of stress.

The usual approximation of the theory of dynamic stability is based on the assumption that the initial state can be identified with the equilibrium condition. This is equivalent to saying that the characteristics of the initial condition are determined quasi-statically, i.e., during time t which is considered as a parameter. Then $s_{ik}^{(0)}$ are determined from static loading $p_i^{(0)}$ and $X_i^{(0)}$, given to within the parameter α, and $s_{ik}^{(t)}$ from the value of the amplitude of variable loading $p_i^{(t)}$ and $X_i^{(t)}$, given to within the parameter β.

It is assumed that during the deformation the components of the external loading do not change either in magnitude or direction. Then $\Delta X_i = \Delta p_i = 0$. Applying the integral formula (13.21) and performing the transformations which convert (13.31) to (13.32), we find that Eqs. (13.16) with the boundary conditions (13.17) are equivalent to a system of integro-differential equations:

$$u_i(P, t) - \int_V \rho(Q)G_{ik}(P, Q)\frac{\partial^2 u_k(Q, t)}{\partial t^2}dV_Q$$

$$- \alpha\int_V s_{jl}^{(0)}(Q)\frac{\partial G_{ik}(P, Q)}{\partial\xi_l}\,\frac{\partial u_k(Q, t)}{\partial\xi_j}dV_Q$$

$$- \beta\Phi(t)\int_V s_{jl}^{(t)}(Q)\frac{\partial G_{ik}(P, Q)}{\partial\xi_l}\,\frac{\partial u_k(Q, t)}{\partial\xi_j}dV_Q = 0 . \qquad (13.34)$$

The integro-differential equation (12.3) can therefore be obtained as a special case.

We shall seek the solution of system (13.34) in the form of a series

$$u_i(P, t) = \sum_{m=1}^{\infty} f_m(t)\varphi_i^{(m)}(P) , \tag{13.35}$$

where $\varphi_i^{(m)}(P)$ are the eigenvectors for the problem of free vibrations. Substituting series (13.35) into (13.34), using the expansion theorem (or the bilinear formula for Green's tensor), and finally comparing the coefficients of identical $\varphi_i^{(m)}(P)$, we obtain a system of ordinary differential equations

$$\frac{1}{\omega_m^2}\frac{d^2 f_m}{dt^2} + f_m - \alpha \sum_{n=1}^{\infty} a_{mn} f_n - \beta\Phi(t) \sum_{n=1}^{\infty} b_{mn} f_n = 0 , \quad (m = 1, 2, 3, \cdots) . \tag{13.36}$$

This system differs from (12.8) only in that instead of (12.7) we now have

$$\begin{aligned} a_{mn} &= \frac{1}{\omega_m^2}\int_V s_{jl}^{(0)} \frac{\partial \varphi_k^{(m)}}{\partial \xi_j} \frac{\partial \varphi_k^{(n)}}{\partial \xi_l} dV , \\ b_{mn} &= \frac{1}{\omega_m^2}\int_V s_{jl}^{(t)} \frac{\partial \varphi_k^{(m)}}{\partial \xi_j} \frac{\partial \varphi_k^{(n)}}{\partial \xi_l} dV . \end{aligned} \tag{13.37}$$

● **2.** It is assumed now that the eigenvectors for the problems of free vibrations and static stability coincide for the states $s_{jl}^{(0)}$ and $s_{jl}^{(t)}$. But then $\varphi_k^{(m)}$ must satisfy the orthogonality conditions (13.33) for $\psi_k^{(m)}$. Hence it follows that all a_{mn} and b_{mn} become zero for $m \neq n$, and consequently system (13.36) decomposes into separate equations of the Mathieu-Hill type. This is the *special case* which was investigated in § 49.

Instead of (13.35), it is possible to assume still another expression for $u_i(P, t)$. We will now seek each component $u_i(P, t)$ in the form of a series of functions $\varphi_i^{(m)}(P)$ with undetermined coefficients $f_i^{(m)}(t)$:

$$u_i(P, t) = \sum_{m=1}^{\infty} f_i^{(m)}(t)\varphi_i^{(m)}(P) . \tag{13.38}$$

In contrast to this, the coefficient $f_i^{(m)}(t)$ sought in (13.35) is common to a "trio" of functions. Substitution of (13.38) in (13.34) gives, after transformation,

$$\frac{1}{\omega_m^2}\frac{d^2 f_i^{(m)}}{dt^2} + f_i^{(m)} - \alpha \sum_{n=1}^{\infty}\sum_{k=1}^{3} a_{ik}^{(mn)} f_k^{(n)} - \beta\Phi(t) \sum_{n=1}^{\infty}\sum_{k=1}^{3} b_{ik}^{(mn)} f_k^{(n)} = 0 , \tag{13.39}$$

$$(m = 1, 2, 3, \cdots, \quad i = 1, 2, 3) ,$$

where

$$\begin{aligned} a_{ik}^{(mn)} &= \frac{1}{\omega_m^2}\int_V s_{jl}^{(0} \frac{\partial \varphi_i^{(m)}}{\partial \xi_j} \frac{\partial \varphi_k^{(n)}}{\partial \xi_l} dV , \\ b_{ik}^{(mn)} &= \frac{1}{\omega_m^2}\int_V s_{jl}^{(t)} \frac{\partial \varphi_i^{(m)}}{\partial \xi_j} \frac{\partial \varphi_k^{(n)}}{\partial \xi_l} dV . \end{aligned}$$

If series (13.38) contains as many terms as series (13.35), then the system of differential equations (13.39) contains three times as many differential equation as (3.36).

It is assumed now that although the eigenvectors for the problems of vibrations and stability do not agree, the functions entering into them agree to within a constant factor. In other words, it is assumed that the same functions enter into the eigenvector, but with various "weights".[23] Then the coefficients $a_{ik}^{(mn)}$ become zero for $m \neq n$, but generally they are not equal to zero for $m = n$ and different i and k. The matrix composed of $a_{ik}^{(mn)}$ is a quasi-diagonal matrix; each elementary matrix is of the order three if buckling is described by three functions, and of the order two if it is described by two functions. Assume now that the $b_{ik}^{(mn)}$ matrix possesses the same properties. Then the system (13.39) decomposes into independent systems of third or second order. Such a case can be called quasi-decomposition into independent single equations. If the buckling is described by one function, as for example in the problem of plane vibrations of a straight rod, then the difference between the cases of quasi-decomposition and decomposition vanishes.

The approximate solutions will be considered briefly. If the free vibration forms and the buckling forms differ slightly from one other (this takes place for the first fundamental forms in the majority of cases), then it is possible to neglect the influence of non-diagonal elements in Eqs. (13.36). The approximate equations then assume the form

$$\frac{d^2 f_m}{dt^2} + \omega_m^2[1 - \alpha a_{mm} - \beta\Phi(t) b_{mm}] f_m = 0 , \qquad (m = 1, 2, 3, \cdots) . \qquad (13.40)$$

But with the same degree of accuracy, it follows that

$$a_{mm} \approx \frac{1}{\alpha_m} , \qquad b_{mm} \approx \frac{1}{\beta_m} ,$$

where α_m and β_m are critical parameters of loading. Thus, with the assumptions made and on the basis of the independent individual equations, one obtains an approximate solution for the problem.

Up to now we have made use of the expansion with respect to the free vibration forms. The application of the buckling forms is less convenient. As has already been mentioned, for the expansion theorem to be valid it is necessary that all the principal values of tensor s_{ik} be positive (i.e., in terms of the classical theory of elasticity, that all the principal normal stresses be compressive). And although in one-dimensional and two-dimensional problems this requirement can be relaxed significant limitations remain. Thus if a rod is compressed only on a portion of its length, then, generally speaking, the buckling forms do not constitute a complete system of fundamental functions.

The following practical consideration also points toward the choice of the free vibration forms in the approximation. In reality, the loads encountered are usually sufficiently small in comparison with the critical static value. Consequently the dynamic buckling forms are nearer in character to the free vibration forms than to the static buckling forms. This predetermines the selection of the approximating functions.

[23] For example, the natural vibration forms and the buckling forms for a simply-supported prismatic rod are sinusoidal. However, the relationships between deflection and angle of twist for the indicated forms are generally different (if the center of bending does not coincide with the center of gravity of cross section).

Fourteen

DETERMINATION OF THE REGIONS OF DYNAMIC INSTABILITY

§ 55. Information from the Theory of Differential Equations with Periodic Coefficients[24]

●1. In this chapter we will investigate the methods for determining the regions of dynamic instability for problems which lead to systems of differential equations of the form

$$\boldsymbol{C}\frac{d^2\boldsymbol{f}}{dt^2} + [\boldsymbol{E} - \alpha\boldsymbol{A} - \beta\Phi(t)\boldsymbol{B}]\boldsymbol{f} = \boldsymbol{0} . \tag{14.1}$$

Here $\boldsymbol{A}$, $\boldsymbol{B}$, $\boldsymbol{C}$ are matrices with constant elements, and $\Phi(t)$ is a periodic function of time with period T,

$$\Phi(t + T) = \Phi(t) , \tag{14.2}$$

which can be represented in a Fourier series.

To give greater symmetry to the results presented below, we will consider, in place of a system of n differential equations of the second order (14.1), an equivalent system of $2n$ differential equations of the first order.

For this purpose, we express Eq. (14.1) in the form

$$\frac{d^2f_i}{dt^2} + \sum_{k=1}^{n} \Phi_{ik}(t) f_k = 0 , \qquad (i = 1, 2, \cdots, n) , \tag{14.3}$$

where

$$(\Phi_{ik}) = \boldsymbol{C}^{-1}[\boldsymbol{E} - \alpha\boldsymbol{A} - \beta\Phi(t)\boldsymbol{B}] .$$

Furthermore, we introduce new variables

$$x_j = f_j , \qquad (j = 1, 2, \cdots, n) ,$$

$$x_j = \frac{df_{j-n}}{dt} , \qquad (j = n + 1, n + 2, \cdots, 2n) . \tag{14.4}$$

The system of differential equations (14.3) together with the second group of equations (14.4) constitutes a system of $2n$ equations of the first order:

[24] Chetayev [1], Malkin [2], Nemytskii and Stepanov [1]; also Mettler [5].

$$\begin{aligned} \frac{dx_i}{dt} - x_{n+i} &= 0\,, \qquad (i = 1, 2, \cdots, n)\,, \\ \frac{dx_i}{dt} + \sum_{k=1}^{n} \Phi_{ik}(t)x_k &= 0\,, \qquad (i = n+1, n+2, \cdots, 2n)\,. \end{aligned} \tag{14.5}$$

or, in matrix notation:

$$\frac{d\boldsymbol{x}}{dt} + \boldsymbol{\Phi}(t)\boldsymbol{x} = \boldsymbol{0}\,. \tag{14.6}$$

Here $\boldsymbol{x}$ is a vector with components $x_i (i = 1, 2, \cdots, 2n)$, and $\boldsymbol{\Phi}(t)$ is a matrix of the order $2n$, whose structure is clear from (14.5). From Eq. (14.2) it follows that

$$\boldsymbol{\Phi}(t + T) = \boldsymbol{\Phi}(t)\,. \tag{14.7}$$

For convenience, let $2n = m$.

● **2.** It will be assumed that for Eqs. (14.6) all m linearly independent solutions are known:

$$x_{1k}(t),\ x_{2k}(t),\ x_{3k}(t),\ \cdots,\ x_{mk}(t), \qquad (k = 1, 2, 3, \cdots, m)\,.$$

This systems of solutions, called the *fundamental system,* forms a matrix

$$\boldsymbol{X}(t) = \begin{pmatrix} x_{11}(t) & x_{12}(t) & \cdots & x_{1m}(t) \\ x_{21}(t) & x_{22}(t) & \cdots & x_{2m}(t) \\ \cdot & \cdot & \cdot & \cdot \\ x_{m1}(t) & x_{m2}(t) & \cdots & x_{mm}(t) \end{pmatrix},$$

where the first subscript denotes the number of the function and the second subscript the number of the solution.

Obviously, matrix $\boldsymbol{X}(t)$ satisfies the differential equation

$$\frac{d^2\boldsymbol{X}}{dt^2} + \boldsymbol{X}\boldsymbol{\Phi}(t) = \boldsymbol{0}\,. \tag{14.8}$$

If in the differential equation (14.8) t is replaced by $t + T$, then according to (14.7), its form will be unchanged, Consequently, matrix $\boldsymbol{X}(t + T)$ is also a solution; it can be obtained from $\boldsymbol{X}(t)$ with the help of some nonsingular linear transformation with constant coefficients

$$\boldsymbol{X}(t + T) = \boldsymbol{R}\boldsymbol{X}(t)\,. \tag{14.9}$$

The coefficients r_{ik} for this transformation can be found in the following way. It is assumed that the fundamental system under consideration satisfies the initial conditions

$$x_{ik}(0) = \delta_{ik}\,.$$

Then setting $t = 0$ in Eq. (14.9) gives

$$\boldsymbol{X}(T) = \boldsymbol{R}$$

or

$$r_{ik} = x_{ik}(T)\,.$$

Thus, in order to find the coefficients of transformation (14.9), one must know the fundamental system of solutions, at least in the course of one period.

The characteristic equation will now be constructed:

$$|\boldsymbol{R} - \rho \boldsymbol{E}| = 0 . \tag{14.10}$$

This equation has m roots corresponding to m linearly independent solutions of the differential equation system (14.6).

Let $\rho_1, \rho_2, \cdots, \rho_m$ be the roots of the characteristic equation, among which there are no multiple roots. Then, through an appropriate choice of primary system of functions, the matrix $\boldsymbol{R}$ can be reduced to a diagonal form:

$$\boldsymbol{R} = \begin{pmatrix} \rho_1 & 0 & \cdots & 0 \\ 0 & \rho_2 & \cdots & 0 \\ \cdot & \cdot & \cdot & \cdot \\ 0 & 0 & \cdots & \rho_m \end{pmatrix} .$$

In other words, there exists a fundamental system which upon addition of a period to t can be transformed by the formulas

$$x_{ik}(t + T) = \rho_k x_{ik}(t) , \qquad (i, k = 1, 2, \cdots, m)$$

or, in vector notation,

$$\boldsymbol{x}_k(t + T) = \rho_k \boldsymbol{x}_k(t) , \qquad (k = 1, 2, \cdots, m) . \tag{14.11}$$

Here $\boldsymbol{x}_k(x_{1k}, x_{2k}, \cdots, x_{mk})$ is a vector of the kth solution, i.e., the kth column of the matrix $\boldsymbol{X}(t)$.

From (14.11) it follows that the solutions of the system of differential equations (14.6) can be represented in the form

$$\boldsymbol{x}_k(t) = e^{(t/T)\ln\rho_k} \boldsymbol{\chi}_k(t) ,$$

where $\boldsymbol{\chi}_k(t)$ is a periodic vector with a period T. From (14.12) one can obtain (14.11):

$$\boldsymbol{x}_k(t + T) = e^{((t/T)+1)\ln\rho_k} \boldsymbol{\chi}_k(t + T) = e^{\ln\rho_k} e^{(t/T)\ln\rho_k} \boldsymbol{\chi}_k(t) = \rho_k \boldsymbol{x}_k(t) .$$

One can also write

$$\boldsymbol{x}_k(t) = e^{(t/T)\ln|\rho_k|} \boldsymbol{\varphi}_k(t) , \tag{14.13}$$

where $\boldsymbol{\varphi}_k(t)$, generally speaking, is an almost periodic vector

$$\boldsymbol{\varphi}_k(t) = \boldsymbol{\chi}_k(t) \exp\left(\frac{it}{T} \arg \rho_k\right) .$$

●3. If among the roots of the characteristic equation there are multiple roots, then the form of solutions depends on the structure of elementary divisors of the matrix $\boldsymbol{R} - \rho\boldsymbol{E}$.

In the case where the elementary divisors are simple (§ 38), such as

$$\rho - \rho_1 , \rho - \rho_2 , \cdots , \rho - \rho_m ,$$

the matrix $\boldsymbol{R}$ can be reduced to a diagonal form. The fundamental system of solutions in this case has the form (14.12). On the other hand, if the matrix $\boldsymbol{R}-\rho\boldsymbol{E}$ has nonlinear elementary divisors, such as

$$(\rho-\rho_1)^{\mu_1},\ (\rho-\rho_2)^{\mu_2}.\ \cdots,\ (\rho-\rho_k)^{\mu_k},\ (\mu_1+\mu_2+\cdots+\mu_k=m)\,,$$

where at least one $\mu_i>1$, , then matrix $\boldsymbol{R}$ cannot be reduced to a diagonal form. It can be reduced, however, to the Jordan normal form

$$\boldsymbol{R}=\begin{pmatrix} \boxed{\boldsymbol{R}_1} & & & & \\ & \boxed{\boldsymbol{R}_2} & & & \\ & & \cdot & & \\ & & & \cdot & \\ & & & & \boxed{\boldsymbol{R}_k}\end{pmatrix},\qquad \text{where } R_i=\begin{pmatrix}\rho_i & 0 & 0 & \cdots & 0\\ 1 & \rho_i & 0 & \cdots & 0\\ 0 & 1 & \rho_i & \cdots & 0\\ \cdot & \cdot & \cdot & \cdot & \cdot\\ 0 & 0 & 0 & \cdots & \rho_i\end{pmatrix}.$$

In this case it is possible to find a fundamental system of solutions which decomposes into k groups with μ_k solutions in a group. Upon addition of a period to t, these solutions can be transformed by formulas (10.15):

$$\begin{aligned}
\boldsymbol{x}_{j+1}(t+T) &= \rho_i\boldsymbol{x}_{j+1}(t)\,,\\
\boldsymbol{x}_{j+2}(t+T) &= \boldsymbol{x}_{j+1}(t)+\rho_i\boldsymbol{x}_{j+2}(t)\,,\\
&\cdots\cdots\cdots\\
\boldsymbol{x}_{j+\mu_i}(t+T) &= \boldsymbol{x}_{j+\mu_i-1}(t)+\rho_i\boldsymbol{x}_{j+\mu_i}(t)\\
(i=1,2,\cdots,k,\quad & j=\mu_1+\mu_2+\cdots+\mu_{i-1})\,.
\end{aligned}\tag{14.14}$$

The fundamental system of solutions which satisfies the relationship (14.13) has the form

$$\begin{aligned}
\boldsymbol{x}_{j+1}(t) &= e^{(t/T)\ln\rho_i}\varphi_{j+1}(t)\,,\\
\boldsymbol{x}_{j+2}(t) &= e^{(t/T)\ln\rho_i}\left[\varphi_{j+2}(t)+\frac{1}{\rho_i}\varphi_{j+1}(t)g_1(t)\right],\\
\boldsymbol{x}_{j+3}(t) &= e^{(t/T)\ln\rho_i}\left[\varphi_{j+3}(t)+\frac{1}{\rho_i}\varphi_{j+2}(t)g_1(t)+\frac{1}{\rho_i^2}\varphi_{j+1}(t)g_2(t)\right],\\
&\cdots\cdots\cdots\\
\boldsymbol{x}_{j+\mu_i}(t) &= e^{(t/T)\ln\rho_i}\left[\varphi_{j+\mu_i}(t)+\frac{1}{\rho_i}\varphi_{j+\mu_{i-1}}(t)g_1(t)\right.\\
&\quad\left.+\frac{1}{\rho_i^2}\varphi_{j+\mu_i-2}(t)g_2(t)+\cdots+\frac{1}{\rho_i^{\mu_i-1}}\varphi_{j+1}(t)g_{\mu_i-1}(t)\right].\\
(i=1,2,\cdots,k,\quad & j=\mu_1+\mu_2+\cdots+\mu_{i-1})\,,
\end{aligned}$$

where $\varphi_k(t)$ are periodic vectors with period T, and $g_s(t)$ are polynomials which are defined in the following way:

$$g_1(t)=\frac{t}{T},\qquad g_2(t)=\frac{g_1(g_1-1)}{2!},\ \cdots,$$

$$g_s(t)=\frac{(g_1-1)(g_1-2)\cdots(g_1-s+1)}{s!}\,.$$

The validity of the above solutions can be verified if in the formulas for $\boldsymbol{x}_s(t)$ one makes a direct substitution of variable $t + T$ in place of t.

In the case of nonlinear elementary divisors, the fundamental system of solutions has the form

$$\boldsymbol{x}_{\alpha_i} = e^{(t/T)\ln\rho_i}\boldsymbol{P}_{\alpha_i}(t) , \tag{14.15}$$

where $\boldsymbol{P}_{\alpha_i}(t)$ is a vector which is formed from polynomials in t with periodic coefficients. Here the highest degree of polynomial does not exceed $\mu_i - 1$, and in each group of solutions corresponding to root ρ_i there exists at least one solution of the form

$$\boldsymbol{x}_{j+1} = e^{(t/T)\ln\rho_i}\boldsymbol{\varphi}_{j+1}(t) .$$

●4. The system of differential equations (14.6) has, obviously, an identically vanishing solution

$$x_1 = x_2 = \cdots = x_m = 0 .$$

Besides this trivial solution, to which the initial equilibrium state (the initial motion) corresponds in the mechanical problem under consideration, the system also admits nontrivial solutions, whose form has already been examined.

The characteristic exponent is defined by the equation

$$h = \frac{1}{T}\ln\rho .$$

From the form of solutions (14.12) and (14.15) it follows that if all characteristic exponents have negative real parts, then the general solution of (14.6) will damp out with time. In other words, the initial equilibrium state (the initial motion) is stable. But if among the characteristic exponents there appears even one which has a positive real part, then the system will have particular solutions increasing unboundedly with time; consequently, the initial state is unstable.

Taking into account that

$$\ln\rho = \ln|\rho| + i\arg\rho ,$$

gives the following conclusion. If all the roots of the characteristic equation have absolute values smaller than unity, then stability will take place. If among the characteristic roots there appears even one with an absolute value greater than unity, then instability will take place.

To the characteristic numbers with absolute values equal to one there correspond, obviously, purely imaginary characteristic exponents. In this case either stability or instability can take place.[25] If the characteristic numbers are simple, then the corresponding particular solution will be limited for all time (more exactly, they will be nearly periodic functions). In the case of multiple roots, the character of the solution will depend on the structure of elementary divisors. In fact, if the elementary divisors are

[25] Stability here implies that the solutions remain limited for all time.

simple, then stability takes place; otherwise secular instability, specified by the appearance in the general integral of secular terms of the type $t^m\varphi(t)$, will take place.

§ 56. The Equation for Determination of Characteristic Exponents[26]

Among the solutions corresponding to some characteristic roots, there will always be found at least one solution of the form

$$\boldsymbol{x}(t) = e^{ht}\varphi(t) ,$$

where $\varphi(t)$ is a vector which has periodic components with period T. This solution is continuous, and consequently the components of the vector $\varphi(t)$ can be expanded in a Fourier series. One can use this circumstance to determine the characteristic exponents. This method can be clarified by an example of a system of n differential equations of second order:

$$\boldsymbol{C}\frac{d^2\boldsymbol{f}}{dt^2} + (\boldsymbol{E} - \alpha\boldsymbol{A} - \beta\boldsymbol{B} \cos \theta t)\,\boldsymbol{f} = 0 . \qquad (14.16)$$

We seek the solution of the differential equation system (14.16) in the form

$$\boldsymbol{f}(t) = e^{ht}\left[\tfrac{1}{2}\boldsymbol{b}_0 + \sum_{k=1}^{\infty}(\boldsymbol{a}_k \sin k\theta t + \boldsymbol{b}_k \cos k\theta t)\right], \qquad (14.17)$$

were a_k and b_k are some vectors not dependent on time. Expansion of (14.17) is equivalent, obviously, to n expansions of the type

$$f_i(t) = e^{ht}\left[\tfrac{1}{2}b_{i0} + \sum_{k=1}^{\infty}(a_{ik} \sin k\theta t + b_{ik} \cos k\theta t)\right],$$

where a_{ik} and b_{ik} are time-independent scalar coefficients. Substituting the series (14.17) in the differential equation (14.16) and equating the coefficients of identical e^{ht} sin $k\theta t$ and e^{ht} cos $k\theta t$, we obtain a system of homogeneous algebraic equations:

$$\begin{aligned} h^2\boldsymbol{C}\boldsymbol{b}_0 + (\boldsymbol{E} - \alpha\boldsymbol{A})\boldsymbol{b}_0 - \beta\boldsymbol{B}\boldsymbol{b}_1 &= 0 , \\ (h^2 - k^2\theta^2)\boldsymbol{C}\,\boldsymbol{a}_k + 2h\,k\theta\boldsymbol{C}\,\boldsymbol{b}_k + (\boldsymbol{E} - \alpha\boldsymbol{A})\boldsymbol{a}_k - \tfrac{1}{2}\beta\boldsymbol{B}(\boldsymbol{a}_{k-1} + \boldsymbol{a}_{k+1}) &= 0 , \\ (h^2 - k^2\theta^2)\boldsymbol{C}\,\boldsymbol{b}_k + 2h\,k\theta\boldsymbol{C}\,\boldsymbol{a}_k + (\boldsymbol{E} - \alpha\boldsymbol{A})\boldsymbol{b}_k - \tfrac{1}{2}\beta\boldsymbol{B}(\boldsymbol{b}_{k-1} + \boldsymbol{b}_{k+1}) &= 0 , \\ (k = 1, 2, 3, \cdots, \qquad \boldsymbol{a}_0 = 0) . \end{aligned}$$

In order for this system to have solutions other than the trivial ones, the determinant of the coefficients must be equal to zero. Thus we obtain the equation for determining the characteristic exponents:

$$\begin{vmatrix} (h^2 - \theta^2)\boldsymbol{C} + \boldsymbol{E} - \alpha\boldsymbol{A} & -\tfrac{1}{2}\beta\boldsymbol{B} & 2h\theta\boldsymbol{C} \\ -\beta\boldsymbol{B} & h^2\boldsymbol{C} + \boldsymbol{E} - \alpha\boldsymbol{A} & \boldsymbol{0} \\ -2h\theta\boldsymbol{C} & \boldsymbol{0} & (h^2 - \theta^2)\boldsymbol{C} + \boldsymbol{E} - \alpha\boldsymbol{A} \end{vmatrix} = 0 . \qquad (14.18)$$

26 Bolotin [7].

Eq. (14.18) has been limited to the central matrix elements. It should be kept in mind that each term of the matrix represents n^2 elements. An investigation of stability of the trivial solution leads now to finding the conditions under which Eq. (14.18) does not have any roots with a positive real part. The direct application of Eq. (14.18) is, however, inconvenient for practical calculations.

§ 57. Derivation of Equations for the Boundary Frequencies

● 1. It will be shown, first of all, that the characteristic equation for the problem under consideration is a reciprocal equation, i.e., it has the form

$$\rho^m + a_1\rho^{m-1} + a_2\rho^{m-2} + \cdots + a_{m-2}\rho^2 + a_{m-1}\rho + a_m = 0 ,$$

where $a_k = a_{m-k}$. In other words, if ρ is one of the characteristic roots, then $1/\rho$ is also a characteristic root.

It is simple to show this when $\Phi(t)$ is an even function of time,

$$\Phi(-t) = \Phi(t) . \tag{14.19}$$

Because of (14.19), the differential equation system (14.3) does not change its form when t is replaced by $-t$. Consequently, if

$$\boldsymbol{x}(t) = e^{(t/T)\ln\rho}\boldsymbol{\chi}(t)$$

is one of the solutions of system (14.3), then

$$\boldsymbol{x}(-t) = e^{-(t/T)\ln\rho}\boldsymbol{\chi}(-t) = e^{(t/T)\ln(1/\rho)}\boldsymbol{\chi}(-t)$$

is also one of its solutions, i.e., $1/\rho$ is one of the characteristic roots.

This property is preserved also in the general case of an arbitrary periodic function. The proof is based on the known theorem of Liapunov [1].

If the differential equation system is canonical, i.e.,

$$\frac{dp_k}{dt} = -\frac{\partial H}{\partial q_k} , \qquad \frac{dq_k}{dt} = \frac{\partial H}{\partial p_k} ,$$

or can be reduced to a canonical form by means of a nonsingular linear transformation with constant or periodic coefficients, then the characteristic equation of this system is reciprocal. Here $H(p, q, t)$ denotes a Hamiltonian function.

The differential equation system (12.8) will now be considered:

$$\frac{d^2 f_i}{dt^2} + \omega_i^2\left[f_i - \alpha\sum_{k=1}^{n} a_{ik}f_k - \beta\Phi(t)\sum_{k=1}^{n} b_{ik}f_k\right] = 0 , \qquad (i = 1, 2, \cdots, n) .$$

Setting $f_k = q_k$, $(df_k/dt) = p_k$, we obtain

$$\begin{aligned} \frac{dp_i}{dt} &= -\omega_i^2\left[q_i - \alpha\sum_{k=1}^{n} a_{ik}q_k - \beta\Phi(t)\sum_{k=1}^{n} b_{ik}q_k\right] , \\ \frac{dq_i}{dt} &= p_i , \qquad (i = 1, 2, \cdots, n) . \end{aligned} \tag{14.20}$$

To the differential equations (14.20) there corresponds a Hamiltonian function

$$H(p, q, t) = \tfrac{1}{2}\sum_{i=1}^{n} \omega_i^2 q_i^2 + \tfrac{1}{2}\sum_{i=1}^{n} p_i^2$$
$$- \tfrac{1}{2}\alpha \sum_{i=1}^{n}\sum_{k=1}^{n} a'_{ik} q_i q_k - \tfrac{1}{2}\beta\Phi(t) \sum_{i=1}^{n}\sum_{k=1}^{n} b'_{ik} q_i q_k .$$

This can easily be verified by a direct substitution. Here

$$a'_{ik} = \omega_i^2 a_{ik} = \int_0^l N_0(x) \frac{d\varphi_i}{dx}\frac{d\varphi_k}{dx} dx = a'_{ki} ,$$

and

$$b'_{ik} = \omega_i^2 b_{ik} = \int_0^l N_t(x) \frac{d\varphi_i}{dx}\frac{d\varphi_k}{dx} dx = b'_{ik} .$$

Thus the theorem is valid for the differential equation system (12.8). Moreover, it holds for any other differential equation system which is obtained from (12.8) by means of a linear transformation with constant coefficients.

The Hamiltonian function can also be constructed for a general case of an arbitrary elastic body, since according to (13.37),

$$a'_{ik} = \omega_i^2 a_{ik} = \int_V \sigma_{mn}^{(0)} \frac{\partial \varphi_j^{(i)}}{\partial x_m}\frac{\partial \varphi_j^{(k)}}{\partial x_n} dV = a'_{ki} ,$$

$$b'_{ik} = \omega_i^2 b_{ik} = \int_V \sigma_{mn}^{(t)} \frac{\partial \varphi_j^{(i)}}{\partial x_m}\frac{\partial \varphi_j^{(k)}}{\partial x_n} dV = b'_{ki} .$$

●**2.** Let us now examine the stability of the trivial solutions, limiting ourselves first to the case in which the characteristic equation has no more than one pair of multiple roots at one time. As will be observed, this special case has a definite physical meaning.

Consider a pair of particular solutions which correspond to a pair of reciprocal characteristic roots:

$$f_k(t) = \chi_k(t) \exp\left(\frac{t}{T}\ln \rho_k\right) ,$$

$$f_{n+k}(t) = \chi_{n+k}(t) \exp\left(-\frac{t}{T}\ln \rho_k\right) . \tag{14.21}$$

Let ρ_k be real and different from ± 1; then one of the particular solutions will unboundedly increase with time. Therefore, the region of real ρ will be the region of unboundedly increasing solutions (region of instability).

By varying the coefficients of the system, one can obtain the condition that the characteristic number will remain $\rho_k = 1$ or $\rho_k = -1$ and will be multiple. In the first case the solution will be periodic with period T; in the second case it will be periodic with period $2T$. Upon further variation of coefficients, the considered pair of characteristic roots will become complex conjugates

$$\rho_k = a + ib ,$$
$$\rho_{n+k} = a - ib ,$$

and by virtue of the relation $\rho_k\rho_{n+k} = 1$, will have absolute value equal to one. The region of complex roots is thus simultaneously the region of bounded solutions (region of stability).

Hence it follows that on the boundaries of the regions of instability the differential equation system has periodic solution with period T or $2T$. More precisely, two solutions with the same period confine the region of instability, and two solutions with different periods confine the region of stability. Otherwise, the root $\rho = 0$ would be in the interval between the roots $\rho = 1$ and $\rho = -1$, which is impossible in view of the nonsingularity of transformation (14.9).

The behavior of solutions on the boundaries of the regions of instability depends on the structure of elementary divisors; however, from the practical point of view this question is of no interest. Independently of the character of solutions on the boundary of the region of instability, the systems of equations found on it must be considered as inadmissible.

● **3.** On the basis of the preceding, the finding of the regions of instability reduces to the determination of conditions under which the differential equation system (14.1) has periodic solutions with period T or $2T$.

To simplify the calculations, the following differential equation system will be considered[27]:

$$\boldsymbol{C}\frac{d^2\boldsymbol{f}}{dt^2} + (\boldsymbol{E} - \alpha\boldsymbol{A} - \beta\boldsymbol{B}\cos\theta t)\boldsymbol{f} = \boldsymbol{0} . \tag{14.22}$$

We seek the solution of (14.22) in the form of a series

$$\boldsymbol{f}(t) = \sum_{k=1,3,5}^{\infty}\left(\boldsymbol{a}_k \sin\frac{k\theta t}{2} + \boldsymbol{b}_k \cos\frac{k\theta t}{2}\right), \tag{14.23}$$

where $\boldsymbol{a}_k$ and $\boldsymbol{b}_k$ are vectors which are independent of time. The series (14.23) is obviously equivalent to the n Fourier series for the components of vector $\boldsymbol{f}(t)$. These series converge, since the periodic solutions of the differential equation system (14.22) in all cases satisfy the Dirichlet conditions.

Substituting Eq. (14.23) in (14.22) and comparing coefficients of sin $k\theta t/2$ and cos $k\theta t/2$ gives the following system of matrix equations:

$$(\boldsymbol{E} - \alpha\boldsymbol{A} + \tfrac{1}{2}\beta\boldsymbol{B} - \tfrac{1}{4}\theta^2\boldsymbol{C})\boldsymbol{a}_1 - \tfrac{1}{2}\beta\boldsymbol{B}\boldsymbol{a}_3 = \boldsymbol{0} ,$$
$$(\boldsymbol{E} - \alpha\boldsymbol{A} - \tfrac{1}{4}k^2\theta^2\boldsymbol{C})\boldsymbol{a}_k - \tfrac{1}{2}\beta\boldsymbol{B}(\boldsymbol{a}_{k-2} + \boldsymbol{a}_{k+2}) = \boldsymbol{0}$$
$$(k = 3, 5, \cdots) ;$$
$$(\boldsymbol{E} - \alpha\boldsymbol{A} - \tfrac{1}{2}\beta\boldsymbol{B} - \tfrac{1}{4}\theta^2\boldsymbol{C})\boldsymbol{b}_1 - \tfrac{1}{2}\beta\boldsymbol{B}\boldsymbol{b}_3 = \boldsymbol{0} ,$$
$$(\boldsymbol{E} - \alpha\boldsymbol{A} - \tfrac{1}{4}k^2\theta^2\boldsymbol{C})\boldsymbol{b}_k - \tfrac{1}{2}\beta\boldsymbol{B}(\boldsymbol{b}_{k-2} + \boldsymbol{b}_{k+2}) = \boldsymbol{0} ,$$
$$(k = 3, 5, \cdots) .$$

The condition for the existence of solutions with a period $4\pi/\theta$ has the form

[27] Bolotin [5].

(here two conditions are combined under the $\pm$ sign)

$$\left|\begin{array}{cccc} \boldsymbol{E}-\alpha\boldsymbol{A}\pm\frac{1}{2}\beta\boldsymbol{B}-\frac{1}{4}\theta^2\boldsymbol{C} & -\frac{1}{2}\beta\boldsymbol{B} & \boldsymbol{0} & \cdot \\ -\frac{1}{2}\beta\boldsymbol{B} & \boldsymbol{E}-\alpha\boldsymbol{A}-\frac{9}{4}\theta^2\boldsymbol{C} & -\frac{1}{2}\beta\boldsymbol{B} & \cdot \\ \boldsymbol{0} & -\frac{1}{2}\beta\boldsymbol{B} & \boldsymbol{E}-\alpha\boldsymbol{A}-\frac{25}{4}\theta^2\boldsymbol{C} & \cdot \\ \cdot & \cdot & \cdot & \cdot \end{array}\right| = 0\,. \tag{14.24}$$

If we substitute the series

$$\boldsymbol{f}(t) = \tfrac{1}{2}\boldsymbol{b}_0 + \sum_{k=2,4,6}^{\infty}\left(\boldsymbol{a}_k \sin\frac{k\theta t}{2} + \boldsymbol{b}_k \cos\frac{k\theta t}{2}\right),$$

into the differential equation (14.22), the following conditions for the existence of solutions with a period $2\pi/\theta$ are obtained:

$$\left|\begin{array}{cccc} \boldsymbol{E}-\alpha\boldsymbol{A}-\theta^2\boldsymbol{C} & -\frac{1}{2}\beta\boldsymbol{B} & \boldsymbol{0} & \cdot \\ -\frac{1}{2}\beta\boldsymbol{B} & \boldsymbol{E}-\alpha\boldsymbol{A}-4\theta^2\boldsymbol{C} & -\frac{1}{2}\beta\boldsymbol{B} & \cdot \\ \boldsymbol{0} & -\frac{1}{2}\beta\boldsymbol{B} & \boldsymbol{E}-\alpha\boldsymbol{A}-16\theta^2\boldsymbol{C} & \cdot \\ \cdot & \cdot & \cdot & \cdot \end{array}\right| = 0\,. \tag{14.25}$$

$$\left|\begin{array}{ccccc} \boldsymbol{E}-\alpha\boldsymbol{A} & -\beta\boldsymbol{B} & \boldsymbol{0} & \boldsymbol{0} & \cdot \\ -\frac{1}{2}\beta\boldsymbol{B} & \boldsymbol{E}-\alpha\boldsymbol{A}-\theta^2\boldsymbol{C} & -\frac{1}{2}\beta\boldsymbol{B} & \boldsymbol{0} & \cdot \\ \boldsymbol{0} & -\frac{1}{2}\beta\boldsymbol{B} & \boldsymbol{E}-\alpha\boldsymbol{A}-4\theta^2\boldsymbol{C} & -\frac{1}{2}\beta\boldsymbol{B} & \cdot \\ \boldsymbol{0} & \boldsymbol{0} & -\frac{1}{2}\beta\boldsymbol{B} & \boldsymbol{E}-\alpha\boldsymbol{A}-16\theta^2\boldsymbol{C} & \cdot \\ \cdot & \cdot & \cdot & \cdot & \cdot \end{array}\right| = 0\,. \tag{14.26}$$

We will show that the infinite determinants obtained belong to the class of *normal* determinants. Consider, for example, determinant (14.24). Carrying out the elementary transformations gives

$$\Delta = \left|\begin{array}{cccc} \boldsymbol{E}-\dfrac{4}{\theta^2}\boldsymbol{F}_0 & \dfrac{2\beta}{\theta^2}\boldsymbol{G} & \boldsymbol{0} & \cdot \\ \dfrac{2\beta}{9\theta^2}\boldsymbol{G} & \boldsymbol{E}-\dfrac{4}{9\theta^2}\boldsymbol{F} & \dfrac{2\beta}{9\theta^2}\boldsymbol{G} & \cdot \\ \boldsymbol{0} & \dfrac{2\beta}{25\theta^2}\boldsymbol{G} & \boldsymbol{E}-\dfrac{4}{25\theta^2}\boldsymbol{F} & \cdot \\ \cdot & \cdot & \cdot & \cdot \end{array}\right|,$$

where

$$\boldsymbol{F}_0 = \boldsymbol{C}^{-1}(\boldsymbol{E}-\alpha\boldsymbol{A}\pm\tfrac{1}{2}\boldsymbol{B})\,, \qquad \boldsymbol{F} = \boldsymbol{C}^{-1}(\boldsymbol{E}-\alpha\boldsymbol{A})\,, \qquad \boldsymbol{G} = \boldsymbol{C}^{-1}\boldsymbol{B}\,.$$

Let M_0, M, and N be the upper bounds for the absolute values of the matrix elements $\boldsymbol{F}_0$, $\boldsymbol{F}$, and $\boldsymbol{G}$, respectively. If the determinant Δ is rewritten in the form

$$\Delta = \left|\begin{array}{cccc} 1+a_{11} & a_{12} & a_{13} & \cdot \\ a_{21} & 1+a_{22} & a_{23} & \cdot \\ a_{31} & a_{32} & 1+a_{33} & \cdot \\ \cdot & \cdot & \cdot & \cdot \end{array}\right|,$$

where a_{ik} are elements in the usual sense, we can show that the double series

$$\sum_{i=1}^{\infty}\sum_{k=1}^{\infty} a_{ik}$$

converges absolutely. In fact,

$$\sum_{i=1}^{\infty}\sum_{k=1}^{\infty} |a_{ik}| \leq \frac{4n^2M_0}{\theta^2} + \sum_{k=1}^{\infty}\frac{4n^2(M+\beta N)}{k^2\theta^2},$$

where the series on the right-hand side is a convergent series.

The convergence of the remaining determinants can be proved in an analogous manner.

●4. Comparing the conditions (14.24), (14.25), and (14.26) with the corresponding conditions for a special case of a single equation, we find that the equations are completely analogous. The equations for the special case can be obtained from the general equations by replacing the matrices contained in them by their eigenvalues,

$$\boldsymbol{C} \to \frac{1}{\omega_k^2}, \quad \boldsymbol{A} \to \frac{1}{\alpha_k}, \quad \boldsymbol{B} \to \frac{1}{\beta_k}, \quad \boldsymbol{E} \to 1 .$$

This analogy, as will now be shown, is not limited to the external similarity.

Let us consider some limiting cases. Let the constant component of the parametric loading be absent and the amplitude of the periodic component be very small ($\beta \to 0$). The equations for boundary frequencies assume the form

$$\begin{vmatrix} \boldsymbol{E}-\frac{1}{4}\theta^2\boldsymbol{C} & \boldsymbol{0} & \boldsymbol{0} & \cdot \\ \boldsymbol{0} & \boldsymbol{E}-\frac{9}{4}\theta^2\boldsymbol{C} & \boldsymbol{0} & \cdot \\ \boldsymbol{0} & \boldsymbol{0} & \boldsymbol{E}-\frac{25}{4}\theta^2\boldsymbol{C} & \cdot \\ \cdot & \cdot & \cdot & \cdot \end{vmatrix} = 0,$$

and correspondingly,

$$\begin{vmatrix} \boldsymbol{E}-\theta^2\boldsymbol{C} & \boldsymbol{0} & \boldsymbol{0} & \boldsymbol{0} & \cdot \\ \boldsymbol{0} & \boldsymbol{E}-4\theta^2\boldsymbol{C} & \boldsymbol{0} & \boldsymbol{0} & \cdot \\ \boldsymbol{0} & \boldsymbol{0} & \boldsymbol{E}-16\theta^2\boldsymbol{C} & \boldsymbol{0} & \cdot \\ \boldsymbol{0} & \boldsymbol{0} & \boldsymbol{0} & \boldsymbol{E}-36\theta^2\boldsymbol{C} & \cdot \\ \cdot & \cdot & \cdot & \cdot & \cdot \end{vmatrix} = 0.$$

It is essential that the equations which express the conditions for the existence of solutions with the same period coincide in pairs. This means that regions of instability, bounded by solutions with the same period, degenerate into lines. These regions are determined from the condition

$$\left|\boldsymbol{E} - \frac{k^2\theta^2}{4}\boldsymbol{C}\right| = 0, \qquad (k = 1, 2, 3, \cdots).$$

If we recall that $1/\omega_k^2$ are the characteristic values of matrix $\boldsymbol{C}$, then we find that

$$\theta_* = \frac{2\omega}{k}, \qquad (k = 1, 2, 3, \cdots).$$

In a more general case, where $\alpha \neq 0$, we obtain in an analogous manner

$$|\boldsymbol{E} - \alpha\boldsymbol{A} - \tfrac{1}{4}k^2\theta^2\boldsymbol{C}| = 0, \qquad (k = 0, 1, 2, 3, \cdots). \tag{14.27}$$

These equations are now compared with the equation for determining the free vibration frequencies of a loaded system,

$$|\boldsymbol{E} - \alpha\boldsymbol{A} - \Omega^2\boldsymbol{C}| = 0, \tag{14.28}$$

whence we easily determine that

$$\theta_* = \frac{2\Omega}{k}, \qquad (k = 1, 2, 3, \cdots). \tag{14.29}$$

Note that the equation for boundary frequencies (14.27) includes as a special case (for $k = 0$) the equation

$$|\boldsymbol{E} - \alpha\boldsymbol{A}| = 0$$

for the boundaries of static stability.

Thus, the resonance spectrum of the differential equation system (14.22) is completely analogous to the spectrum of the Mathieu-Hill equation. The difference lies in the method of determining the free vibration frequencies of a loaded system. For problems which reduce to independent single equations, these frequencies are determined from the formula

$$\Omega_k = \omega_k\sqrt{1 - (\alpha/\alpha_k)}, \qquad (k = 1, 2, 3, \cdots);$$

in a general case, to determine the natural frequencies it is necessary to solve Eq. (14.28).

For the exact calculation of the regions of instability, one has to solve Eqs. (14.24) through (14.26).

As before, we define as the *principal instability regions* those regions which correspond to $k = 1$ in formula (14.29). The approximate expression for the boundaries of the principal regions of instability is obtained by equating to zero the determinant of the first matrix element in the principal diagonal of the matrix (14.24):

$$|\boldsymbol{E} - \alpha\boldsymbol{A} \pm \tfrac{1}{2}\beta\boldsymbol{B} - \tfrac{1}{4}\theta^2\boldsymbol{C}| = 0. \tag{14.30}$$

This approximation is equivalent to the assumption that the periodic solutions on the boundaries of principal regions of instability are harmonic functions,

$$\boldsymbol{f}(t) = \boldsymbol{a}\sin\frac{\theta t}{2} + \boldsymbol{b}\cos\frac{\theta t}{2}.$$

Equation (14.30) has a simple interpretation. Let us construct the equations for natural frequencies of a system which is loaded by a constant parametric load with parameters α, $\beta/2$, and α, $-\beta/2$, respectively. These equations have the form

$$|\boldsymbol{E} - \alpha\boldsymbol{A} - \tfrac{1}{2}\beta\boldsymbol{B} - \Omega^2_{\alpha+\frac{1}{2}\beta}\boldsymbol{C}| = 0,$$

$$|\boldsymbol{E} - \alpha\boldsymbol{A} + \tfrac{1}{2}\beta\boldsymbol{B} - \Omega^2_{\alpha-\frac{1}{2}\beta}\boldsymbol{C}| = 0.$$

If we compare these equations with (14.30), we find

$$\theta_* = 2\Omega_{\alpha \pm \frac{1}{2}\beta} .$$

Thus in the first approximation, the frequencies corresponding to the boundaries of the principal regions of instability can be defined as double the natural frequencies of a system loaded by a constant load with parameters α, $\beta/2$ and α, $-\beta/2$, respectively. An attempt to relate the boundary frequencies to the frequencies of natural vibrations of a loaded rod was made by A. F. Smirnov [1].

§ 58. An Example for Determining the Boundaries of the Regions of Dynamic Instability

●1. As an example of the application of the above method, consider the following system of differential equations of second order:

$$\boldsymbol{C}\frac{d^2\boldsymbol{f}}{dt^2} + [\boldsymbol{E} - (\alpha + \beta \cos \theta t)\boldsymbol{A}]\boldsymbol{f} = 0 , \tag{14.31}$$

where

$$\boldsymbol{C} = \begin{pmatrix} 1/\omega_1^{\,2} & 0 \\ 0 & 1/\omega_2^{\,2} \end{pmatrix}, \qquad \boldsymbol{A} = \begin{pmatrix} 0 & a_{12} \\ a_{21} & 0 \end{pmatrix} .$$

As will be seen later, many problems of dynamic stability of plates and those of plane bending lead to the system of differential equations of this form.[28]

The equation for boundaries of static stability

$$| \boldsymbol{E} - \alpha \boldsymbol{A} | = 0$$

has the solution

$$\alpha_* = \pm \frac{1}{\sqrt{a_{12}\, a_{21}}} . \tag{14.32}$$

In the first approximation, the boundaries of the principal regions of instability can be found from the equation

$$| \boldsymbol{E} - (\alpha \pm \tfrac{1}{2}\beta)\, \boldsymbol{A} - \tfrac{1}{4}\theta^2 \boldsymbol{C} | = 0$$

or, in the expanded form,

$$\begin{vmatrix} 1 - (\theta^2/4\omega_1^{\,2}) & -(\alpha \pm \frac{1}{2}\beta)\, a_{12} \\ -(\alpha \pm \frac{1}{2}\beta)\, a_{21} & 1 - (\theta^2/4\omega_2^{\,2}) \end{vmatrix} = 0 .$$

If we expand the determinant and take into account (14.32), there results

$$\left(1 - \frac{\theta^2}{4\omega_1^{\,2}}\right)\left(1 - \frac{\theta^2}{4\omega_2^{\,2}}\right) - \frac{(\alpha \pm \frac{1}{2}\beta)^2}{\alpha_*^{\,2}} = 0 .$$

The solution of this equation gives the expressions for the boundaries of both principal regions of instability:

[28] Bolotin [7].

$$\theta_* = \frac{2\omega_1}{\sqrt{2\gamma}} \sqrt{1 + \gamma - \sqrt{(1-\gamma)^2 + 4\gamma \frac{(\alpha \pm \frac{1}{2}\beta)^2}{\alpha_*^2}}}\,,$$
$$\theta_* = \frac{2\omega_2}{\sqrt{2\gamma}} \sqrt{1 + \gamma + \sqrt{(1-\gamma)^2 + 4\gamma \frac{(\alpha \pm \frac{1}{2}\beta)^2}{\alpha_*^2}}}\,. \tag{14.33}$$

Here we denoted the ratio of the squares of the individual frequencies by

$$\gamma = \frac{\omega_1^2}{\omega_2^2}\,. \tag{14.34}$$

If this ratio differs considerably from unity, for example $\gamma \ll 1$, then one can give formulas (14.33) a simpler form:

$$\theta_* = 2\omega_1 \sqrt{1 - \frac{(\alpha \pm \frac{1}{2}\beta)^2}{(1-\gamma)\alpha_*^2}}\,,$$
$$\theta_* = 2\omega_2 \sqrt{1 + \frac{\gamma}{1-\gamma} \frac{(\alpha \pm \frac{1}{2}\beta)^2}{\alpha_*^2}}\,. \tag{14.35}$$

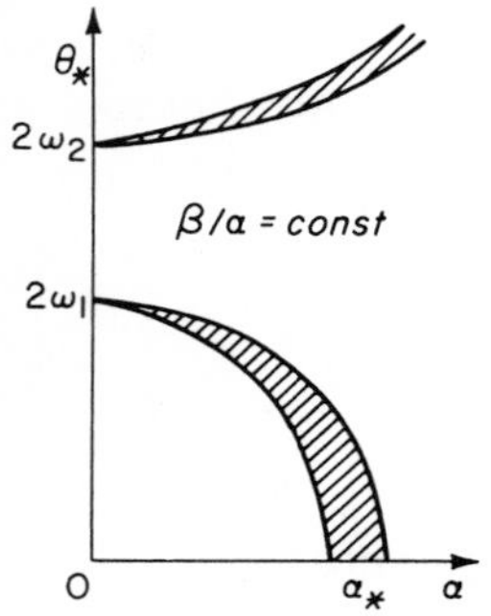

FIG. 89.

According to these formulas, two principal regions of instability exist. For small α/α_* one of these lies near the frequency $2\omega_1$, the other near $2\omega_2$. It is characteristic of the given problem that the resonance frequency of one of the regions increases with an increase of α/α_* (Fig. 89).

●2. We proceed now with the calculation of regions of instability corresponding to $k = 2$ in formula (14.29). For this calculation, consider the equations

$$|\boldsymbol{E} - \alpha \boldsymbol{A} - \theta^2 \boldsymbol{C}| = 0\,,$$
$$\begin{vmatrix} \boldsymbol{E} - \alpha\boldsymbol{A} & -\beta\boldsymbol{A} \\ -\frac{1}{2}\beta\boldsymbol{A} & \boldsymbol{E} - \alpha\boldsymbol{A} - \theta^2\boldsymbol{C} \end{vmatrix} = 0\,, \tag{14.36}$$

which correspond to a harmonic approximation

$$\boldsymbol{f}(t) = \tfrac{1}{2}\boldsymbol{b}_0 + \boldsymbol{a}_2 \sin\theta t + \boldsymbol{b}_2 \cos\theta t\,.$$

Expanded, the first of Eqs. (14.36) has the form

$$\begin{vmatrix} 1 - (\theta^2/\omega_1^2) & -\alpha a_{12} \\ -\alpha a_{21} & 1 - (\theta^2/\omega_2^2) \end{vmatrix} = 0\,.$$

If the determinant is expanded, we obtain

$$\left(1 - \frac{\theta^2}{\omega_1^2}\right)\left(1 - \frac{\theta^2}{\omega_2^2}\right) - \frac{\alpha^2}{\alpha_*^2} = 0\,,$$

or, for $\gamma \ll 1$,

$$\theta_* = \omega_1 \sqrt{1 - \frac{\alpha^2}{(1-\gamma)\alpha_*^2}}\,,$$
$$\theta_* = \omega_2 \sqrt{1 + \frac{\gamma}{1-\gamma}\frac{\alpha^2}{\alpha_*^2}}\,. \tag{14.37}$$

Formulas (14.37) permit the finding of one of the boundaries of each region of instability; for determining the second boundary, the following equation is considered:

$$\begin{vmatrix} 1 & -\alpha a_{12} & 0 & -\beta a_{12} \\ -\alpha a_{21} & 1 & -\beta a_{21} & 0 \\ 0 & -\frac{1}{2}\beta a_{12} & 1-(\theta^2/\omega_1^2) & -\alpha a_{12} \\ -\frac{1}{2}\beta a_{21} & 0 & -\alpha a_{21} & 1-(\theta^2/\omega_2^2) \end{vmatrix} = 0 .$$

Solving this equation, we find for $\gamma \ll 1$:

$$\begin{aligned} \theta_* &= \omega_1 \sqrt{1 - \frac{\mu^2 - 2(1-\gamma)\nu^2 - (\mu^2 - 2\nu^2)^2}{(1-\gamma)(1-\mu^2) - 2\nu^2}} , \\ \theta_* &= \omega_2 \sqrt{1 + \frac{\gamma[\mu^2 - (\mu^2 - 2\nu^2)^2] - 2(1-\gamma)\nu^2}{(1-\gamma)(1-\mu^2) + 2\gamma\nu^2}} , \end{aligned} \tag{14.38}$$

where for brevity we set $\mu = \alpha/\alpha_*$, $\nu = \beta/2\alpha_*$.

3. To find the boundaries of regions of instability for $k = 3$ and also to determine more accurately the boundaries of the principal regions, it is necessary to consider the equation

$$\begin{vmatrix} \boldsymbol{E} - (\alpha \pm \frac{1}{2}\beta)\boldsymbol{A} - \frac{1}{4}\theta^2\boldsymbol{C} & -\frac{1}{2}\beta\boldsymbol{A} \\ -\frac{1}{2}\beta\boldsymbol{A} & \boldsymbol{E} - \alpha\boldsymbol{A} - \frac{9}{4}\theta^2\boldsymbol{C} \end{vmatrix} = 0 ,$$

or, in expanded form,

$$\begin{vmatrix} 1-(\theta^2/4\omega_1^2) & -(\alpha \pm \frac{1}{2}\beta)a_{12} & 0 & -\frac{1}{2}\beta a_{12} \\ -(\alpha \pm \frac{1}{2}\beta)a_{21} & 1-(\theta^2/4\omega_2^2) & -\frac{1}{2}\beta a_{21} & 0 \\ 0 & -\frac{1}{2}\beta a_{12} & \boxed{1-(9\theta^2/4\omega_1^2)} & -\alpha a_{12} \\ -\frac{1}{2}\beta a_{21} & 0 & -\alpha a_{21} & 1-(9\theta^2/4\omega_2^2) \end{vmatrix} = 0 . \tag{14.39}$$

Having set as our goal the determination of the boundaries of region lying near $\theta = \frac{2}{3}\omega_1$, we will substitute this value into all elements of determinant (14.39) except the one enveloped in the frame:

$$\begin{vmatrix} \frac{8}{9} & -(\alpha \pm \frac{1}{2}\beta) a_{12} & 0 & -\frac{1}{2}\beta a_{12} \\ -(\alpha \pm \frac{1}{2}\beta) a_{21} & 1-(\gamma/9) & -\frac{1}{2}\beta a_{21} & 0 \\ 0 & -\frac{1}{2}\beta a_{12} & 1-(9\theta^2/4\omega_1^2) & -\alpha a_{12} \\ -\frac{1}{2}\beta a_{21} & 0 & -\alpha a_{21} & 1-\gamma \end{vmatrix} = 0 .$$

Solving this equation gives a formula for the boundary frequencies:

$$\theta_* = \tfrac{2}{3}\omega_1 \sqrt{1 - \frac{\frac{8}{9}[\mu^2 + \nu^2(1-\gamma)] - [\mu(\mu \pm \nu) + \nu^2]^2}{(1-\gamma)\,[\frac{8}{9} - (\mu \pm \nu)^2] - \nu^2}} . \tag{14.40}$$

In an analogous manner, we can derive the formula for the region $\theta = \frac{2}{3}\omega_2$:

$$\theta_* = \tfrac{2}{3}\omega_2 \sqrt{1 + \frac{\frac{8}{9}[\gamma\mu^2 + \nu^2(1-\gamma)] - \gamma[\mu(\mu \pm \nu) + \nu^2]^2}{(1-\gamma)\,[\frac{8}{9} - (\mu \pm \nu)^2] + \gamma\nu^2}} . \tag{14.40'}$$

The distribution of the first two regions of instability in the plane of parameters β/α_* and $\theta/2\Omega$ is represented in Figure 90.

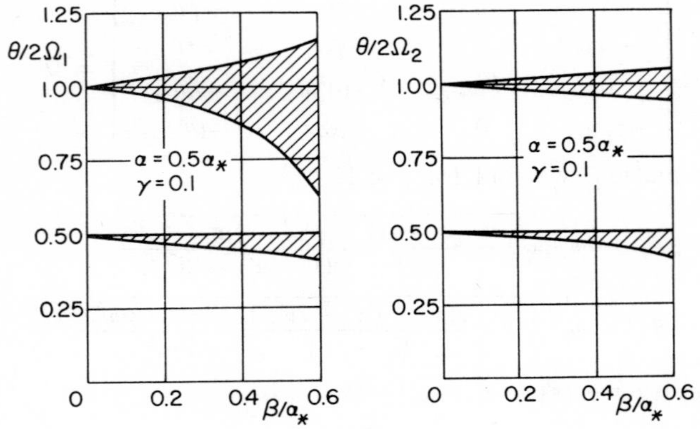

FIG. 90.

The free vibration frequencies of a loaded system can be determined by the approximate formulas

$$\begin{aligned} \Omega_1 &= \omega_1 \sqrt{1 - \frac{\alpha^2}{(1-\gamma)\alpha_*^2}}, \\ \Omega_2 &= \omega_2 \sqrt{1 + \frac{\gamma}{1-\gamma}\frac{\alpha^2}{\alpha_*^2}}. \end{aligned} \tag{14.41}$$

The ratio of individual frequencies was taken as $\gamma = 0.1$.

● **4.** The widths of the first three regions of instability will now be estimated. From formulas (14.35), it can be seen that the width of the first region is of the order of magnitude

$$\frac{\Delta\theta}{\omega_1} \approx \frac{\alpha\beta}{\alpha_*^2}.$$

The second region, as is evident from Eqs. (14.37) and (14.38), has a width of the order

$$\frac{\Delta\theta}{\omega_1} \approx \frac{\beta^2}{\alpha_*^2}.$$

The width of the third region can be estimated from quantities of the order

$$\frac{\Delta\theta}{\omega_1} \approx \frac{\alpha^3\beta}{\alpha_*^4}, \quad \frac{\alpha^2\beta^2}{\alpha_*^4}, \quad \frac{\alpha\beta^3}{\alpha_*^4}.$$

Thus, in contrast to the special case, the widths of the first and second regions in the problem considered here are of the same order of magnitude.

For a given β, the smaller the constant component of loading α, the narrower will be the first region. This means that for small α the second region of instability will have the largest width (Fig. 91).

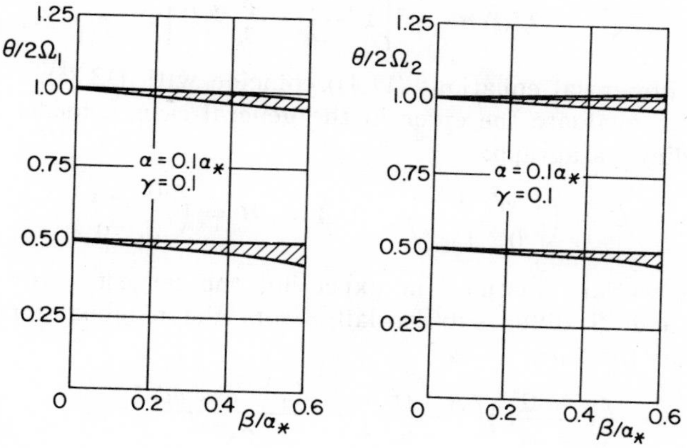

FIG. 91.

§ 59. An Approximate Method for Determining the Regions of Instability

The method described, as we have seen, requires an expansion of determinants of high order. The width of the regions of instability can be estimated by a simpler, approximate method of solution, the idea of which is as follows. The matrix equation

$$\boldsymbol{C}\boldsymbol{f}'' + [\boldsymbol{E} - \alpha\,\boldsymbol{A} - \beta\,\Phi(t)\,\boldsymbol{B}]\,\boldsymbol{f} = \boldsymbol{0} \tag{14.42}$$

describes vibrations of a certain system with variable frequencies of free vibrations. We determine the "instantaneous" frequencies of this system considering the time t as a parameter; these will be the roots of the equation

$$|\,\boldsymbol{E} - \alpha\,\boldsymbol{A} - \beta\,\Phi(t)\,\boldsymbol{B} - \Omega^2(t)\,\boldsymbol{C}\,| = \boldsymbol{0}\,. \tag{14.43}$$

With a known degree of accuracy, to be established below, the matrix equation (14.42) can be replaced by a system of ordinary equations with separable variables,

$$\frac{d^2 f_k}{dt^2} + \Omega_k^{\,2}(t)\,f_k = 0\,, \qquad (k = 1, 2, 3, \cdots)\,. \tag{14.44}$$

It is obvious that functions $\Omega_k(t)$ will have the fundamental period $2\pi/\theta$ and can be represented in the form of a series of the type

$$\Omega_k(t) = \tfrac{1}{2}c_0 + \sum_{k=1}^{\infty} c_k \cos k\theta t\,.$$

Thus we have obtained Hill's differential equation.

If the matrices $\boldsymbol{A}, \boldsymbol{B}, \boldsymbol{C}$ are simultaneously reduced to a diagonal form, the case of independent single equations, then the differential equations (14.44) give an exact solution of the problem. In fact,

$$\Omega_k^2(t) = \omega_k^2\left[1 - \frac{\alpha}{\alpha_k} - \frac{\beta}{\beta_k}\Phi(t)\right],$$

so that the differential equations (14.44) coincide with (12.34).

In order to evaluate the error in the general case, consider the example of the preceding paragraph:

$$\boldsymbol{C} = \begin{pmatrix} 1/\omega_1^2 & 0 \\ 0 & 1/\omega_2^2 \end{pmatrix}, \qquad \boldsymbol{A} = \boldsymbol{B} = \begin{pmatrix} 0 & a_{12} \\ a_{21} & 0 \end{pmatrix}.$$

In this case we are justified in expecting the largest error because the matrices $\boldsymbol{A}$ and $\boldsymbol{B}$ differ substantially from the diagonal form. Equation (14.43) assumes the form

$$\left(1 - \frac{\Omega^2}{\omega_1^2}\right)\left(1 - \frac{\Omega^2}{\omega_2^2}\right) - \frac{(\alpha + \beta \cos \theta t)^2}{\alpha_*^2} = 0,$$

from which it follows that

$$\Omega_{1,2}^2(t) = \frac{\omega^2}{2\gamma}\left[1 + \gamma \mp \sqrt{(1-\gamma)^2 + \frac{4\gamma}{\alpha_*^2}(a + \beta \cos \theta t)^2}\right].$$

If we expand the radical in a series and retain only the first terms, the following results for $\gamma \ll 1$:

$$\Omega_1^2 = \omega_1^2\left[1 - \frac{(\alpha + \beta \cos \theta t)^2}{(1-\gamma)\alpha_*^2}\right] + \cdots,$$

$$\Omega_2^2 = \omega_2^2\left[1 + \frac{\gamma}{1-\gamma}\frac{(\alpha + \beta \cos \theta t)^2}{\alpha_*^2}\right] + \cdots.$$

The problem is thus reduced to two independent differential equations of the form

$$f'' + \omega^2(1 - \nu_0 - \sum_{k=1}^{\infty} \nu_k \cos k\theta t) f = 0.$$

In the first case,

$$\nu_0 = \frac{\alpha^2 + \frac{1}{2}\beta^2}{(1-\gamma)\alpha_*^2}, \qquad \nu_1 = \frac{2\alpha\beta}{(1-\gamma)\alpha_*^2}, \qquad \nu_2 = \frac{\beta^2}{2(1+\gamma)\alpha_*^2}.$$

The instability criterion (1.41) in the new notation assumes the form

$$\theta_*^2 = 4\omega_1^2(1 - \nu_0 \pm \tfrac{1}{2}\nu_k), \qquad (k = 1, 2, 3, \cdots),$$

from which for the fundamental region

$$\theta_*^2 = 4\omega_1^2\left[1 - \frac{\alpha^2 \pm \alpha\beta + \frac{1}{2}\beta^2}{(1-\gamma)\alpha_*^2}\right]. \tag{14.45}$$

Correspondingly, for the second region of instability we obtain

$$\theta_*{}^2 = \omega_1{}^2\left[1 - \frac{\alpha^2 + \frac{3}{4}\beta^2}{(1-\gamma)\alpha_*{}^2}\right],$$
$$\theta_*{}^2 = \omega_1{}^2\left[1 - \frac{\alpha^2 + \frac{1}{4}\beta^2}{(1-\gamma)\alpha_*{}^2}\right]. \tag{14.46}$$

In the second case,

$$\nu_0 = -\frac{\gamma}{1-\gamma}\frac{\alpha^2 + \frac{1}{2}\beta^2}{\alpha_*{}^2},$$
$$\nu_1 = -\frac{2\gamma\,\alpha\,\beta}{(1-\gamma)\alpha_*{}^2},$$
$$\nu_2 = -\frac{\gamma\,\beta^2}{2\alpha_*{}^2(1-\gamma)}.$$

Substitution gives

$$\theta_*{}^2 = 4\omega_2{}^2\left(1 + \frac{\gamma}{1-\gamma}\,\frac{\alpha^2 \pm \alpha\,\beta + \frac{1}{2}\beta^2}{\alpha_*{}^2}\right),$$
$$\theta_*{}^2 = \omega_2{}^2\left(1 + \frac{\gamma}{1-\gamma}\,\frac{\alpha^2 + \frac{3}{4}\beta^2}{\alpha_*{}^2}\right),$$
$$\theta_*{}^2 = \omega_2{}^2\left(1 + \frac{\gamma}{1-\gamma}\,\frac{\alpha^2 + \frac{1}{4}\beta^2}{\alpha^2}\right). \tag{14.47}$$

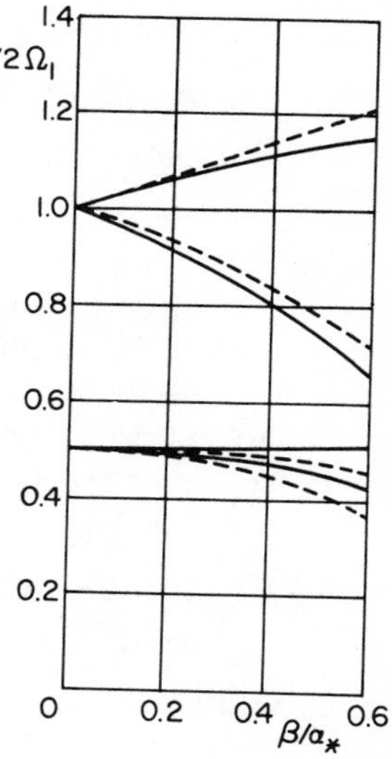

FIG. 92.

Comparison of results calculated by formulas (14.45) and (14.46) and by the formulas of the preceding paragraphs is given in Figure 92 (the solution just obtained is shown by dotted lines).

To explain the character of the approximations made, we proceed in the following way. Let the matrix $\boldsymbol{V}(t)$ be such that it transforms the matrix $\boldsymbol{C}[\boldsymbol{E} - \alpha\boldsymbol{A} - \beta\Phi(t)\boldsymbol{B}]$ to the principal axes (time t is considered as a parameter). Let us make in Eq. (14.42) a substitution $\boldsymbol{f} = \boldsymbol{V}\varphi$. In the new coordinate system, Eq. (14.42) can be written in the following form:

$$\boldsymbol{V}^{-1}\frac{d^2}{dt^2}(\boldsymbol{V}\varphi) + \boldsymbol{V}^{-1}\,\boldsymbol{C}[\boldsymbol{E} - \alpha\,\boldsymbol{A} - \beta\Phi(t)\boldsymbol{B}]\,\boldsymbol{V}\varphi = \boldsymbol{0}.$$

But, according to our condition,

$$\boldsymbol{V}^{-1}\,\boldsymbol{C}[\boldsymbol{E} - \alpha\,\boldsymbol{A} - \beta\Phi(t)\,\boldsymbol{B}]\,\boldsymbol{V} = [\Omega_1{}^2(t), \Omega_2{}^2(t), \cdots, \Omega_n{}^2(t)] = \Omega^2(t),$$

and by the rule for the differentiation of matrices

$$\frac{d^2}{dt^2}(\boldsymbol{V}\varphi) = \boldsymbol{V}\frac{d^2\varphi}{dt^2} + 2\frac{d\boldsymbol{V}}{dt}\frac{d\varphi}{dt} + \frac{d^2\boldsymbol{V}}{dt^2}\varphi.$$

Hence the differential equation (14.42) assumes the form

$$\frac{d^2\varphi}{dt^2} + \underline{2\boldsymbol{V}^{-1}\frac{d\boldsymbol{V}}{dt}\frac{d\varphi}{dt} + \boldsymbol{V}^{-1}\frac{d^2\boldsymbol{V}}{dt^2}\varphi} + \Omega^2(t)\varphi = \boldsymbol{0}. \tag{14.48}$$

If $\boldsymbol{V} =$ const. (this will occur if the matrices $\boldsymbol{A}$, $\boldsymbol{B}$, and $\boldsymbol{C}$ are *simultaneously* brought to principal axes), then the differential equation (14.48) takes the form of (14.44). Otherwise, to obtain Eqs. (14.44) it is necessary to neglect in Eqs. (14.48) the underlined terms. These terms take into consideration the inertial forces arising because of the variation of instantaneous forms of vibrations (they are described by matrix $V(t)$) in the course of one period. The smaller the parameter β, the smaller will be the influence of the rejected terms.

§ 60. The Case of Multiple Roots Different from ±1. Combination Resonance

In §§ 57, 58 we considered a case in which the characteristic equation did not have multiple roots other than ±1. In the case of multiple roots different from ±1, there will be at least two pairs of multiple roots. This case corresponds to combined resonance with respect to two natural frequencies of the system.

Let us return to Eq. (14.18). Assuming that there $\beta \to 0$, we obtain the equations

$$|h^2\boldsymbol{C} + \boldsymbol{E} - \alpha\boldsymbol{A}| = 0,$$

$$\begin{vmatrix} (h^2 - k^2\theta^2)\boldsymbol{C} + \boldsymbol{E} + \alpha\boldsymbol{A} & 2kh\theta\boldsymbol{C} \\ -2kh\theta\boldsymbol{C} & (h^2 - k^2\theta^2)\boldsymbol{C} + \boldsymbol{E} - \alpha\boldsymbol{A} \end{vmatrix} = 0, \qquad (k = 1, 2, 3, \cdots),$$

which in the principal axes of the matrix $\boldsymbol{C}^{-1}(\boldsymbol{E} - \alpha\boldsymbol{A})$ can be written in the following way:

$$\begin{gathered} h^2 + \Omega_p^2 = 0, \\ \begin{vmatrix} h^2 - k^2\theta^2 + \Omega_p^2 & 2hk\theta \\ -2hk\theta & h^2 - k^2\theta^2 + \Omega_p^2 \end{vmatrix} = 0, \\ (p = 1, 2, 3, \cdots, \quad k = 1, 2, 3, \cdots). \end{gathered} \tag{14.49}$$

The solution of Eqs. (14.49) gives

$$h = \pm i(\Omega_p \pm k\theta), \qquad (p = 1, 2, 3, \cdots, \quad k = 0, 1, 2, 3, \cdots),$$

where $i = \sqrt{-1}$. If we equate the values of h for different p and k, the conditions under which the characteristic equation will have multiple roots are obtained:

$$\Omega_p \pm \Omega_q = k\theta, \qquad (p, q = 1, 2, 3, \cdots, \quad k = 0, 1, 2, 3, \cdots). \tag{14.50}$$

For $p = q$ formula (14.50) coincides with formula (14.29); for $p \neq q$ it gives the condition for the appearance of combined resonance.[29]

It is necessary to note that the case of linear elementary divisors corresponds to relationships (14.50). This is evident from the fact that

[29] Relationships of the type of (14.50) for a problem in celestial mechanics were obtained by Artem'ev [1], who investigated a system of equations with periodic coefficients.

we are presupposing the simultaneous existence of two independent solutions of type (14.13).

For canonical systems, only the resonance $\Omega_p + \Omega_q = k\theta$ is possible (Mettler [5], [9], and Andronov and Leontovich [1]). For noncanonical systems the resonance $\Omega_p - \Omega_q = k\theta$ is also significant (Yakubovich [1]). As we have shown (for instance in § 53), most of the systems for which dynamic instability may occur are noncanonical. In a few cases the instability regions for combination resonance may be broader than for the principal resonance (Yakubovich [2], [3]). A detailed investigation is necessary, however, in order to verify completely the practical significance of the combination resonances.

Fifteen

DYNAMIC STABILITY TAKING DAMPING INTO ACCOUNT

§ 61. Introductory Remarks

● 1. The presence of resistance forces in real systems is generally taken into account by introducing into the appropriate differential equations additional terms which contain first derivatives of displacements with respect to time. Thus, the generalization of the usual differential equation for the damped vibrations,

$$f'' + 2\varepsilon f' + \omega^2 f = 0$$

for the case of a system with many degrees of freedom is the matrix differential equation

$$\mathbf{f}'' + 2\boldsymbol{\varepsilon}\mathbf{f}' + \boldsymbol{\omega}^2\mathbf{f} = \mathbf{0}\,, \tag{15.1}$$

where $\mathbf{f}$ is a vector constructed from generalized coordinates f_i, $\boldsymbol{\omega}^2$ is a diagonal matrix

$$\boldsymbol{\omega}^2 = [\omega_1{}^2, \omega_2{}^2, \cdots, \omega_n{}^2]\,,$$

and $\boldsymbol{\varepsilon}$ is the energy dissipation matrix

$$\boldsymbol{\varepsilon} = \begin{pmatrix} \varepsilon_{11} & \varepsilon_{12} & \cdots & \varepsilon_{1n} \\ \varepsilon_{21} & \varepsilon_{22} & \cdots & \varepsilon_{2n} \\ \cdot & \cdot & \cdot & \cdot \\ \varepsilon_{n1} & \varepsilon_{n2} & \cdots & \varepsilon_{nn} \end{pmatrix}. \tag{15.2}$$

The similarity of the method of calculating the resistance forces to one accepted in engineering computations will not be discussed in detail here (a few considerations concerning this can be found in § 15). We will limit ourselves to a remark which will be justified in Chapter Sixteen.

The boundaries of the regions of dynamic instability can be determined by a linear treatment; in the matrix differential equation (15.1), it is possible to retain only the terms which take into account "linear" damping. Exceptions to this rule are the cases where the resistance forces have discontinuous character. Thus in the case where the resistance forces are in the form of "dry" friction, linearization or differential equations is inadmissible (§ 67).

● 2. The fundamental properties of the matrix (15.2) will now be analyzed.

First of all, this matrix must be symmetric. For proof, it is assumed that the matrix is not symmetric. Then, by use of the equation

$$\varepsilon_{ik} = \tfrac{1}{2}(\varepsilon_{ik} + \varepsilon_{ki}) + \tfrac{1}{2}(\varepsilon_{ik} - \varepsilon_{ki}) ,$$

the matrix can be represented as a sum of two matrices. One of these matrices obviously is symmetric; the other with elements

$$\gamma_{ik} = \tfrac{1}{2}(\varepsilon_{ik} - \varepsilon_{ki})$$

is antisymmetric, i.e.,

$$\gamma_{ik} = -\gamma_{ki}, \quad \gamma_{kk} = 0 , \qquad (i, k = 1, 2, \cdots, n) . \tag{15.3}$$

It will be shown that the total work of the forces (to which matrix γ_{ik} corresponds) on the displacements that actually occur is equal to zero. The virtual work of generalized forces Q_i on displacements $f_i (i = 1, 2, 3, \cdots,)$ is

$$dA = \sum_{i=1}^{n} Q_i df_i = \sum_{i=1}^{n} Q_i f_i' dt .$$

If here

$$Q_i = -\sum_{k=1}^{n} \gamma_{ik} f_k' , \qquad (i = 1, 2, 3, \cdots, n) ,$$

is substituted and (15.3) taken into account, the following is obtained:

$$dA = -\sum_{i=1}^{n} \sum_{k=1}^{n} \gamma_{ik} f_i' f_k' dt \equiv 0 .$$

Thus, the matrix $\boldsymbol{\varepsilon}$, which describes the dissipation of energy, is symmetric. Consequently, all of its eigenvalues $\varepsilon_1, \varepsilon_2, \cdots, \varepsilon_n$, i.e., roots of the equation

$$| \boldsymbol{\varepsilon} - \varepsilon \boldsymbol{E} | = 0$$

are real. Furthermore, it is possible to show that all eigenvalues ε_k are positive; for this purpose a quadratic form is constructed:

$$\varphi = \sum_{i=1}^{n} \sum_{k=1}^{n} \varepsilon_{ik} f_i' f_k' .$$

Taken with the opposite sign, this expression represents the work of resistance forces on displacements f_i. If some of $\varepsilon_k < 0$, then the quadratic form φ will be indeterminate and the given system will be self-exciting (for certain relationships between f_i, the resistance forces perform positive work, i.e., they will "build up amplification" of vibrations). Self-exciting systems are excluded from our investigation.

Furthermore, none of the eigenvalues ε_k are equal to zero. Otherwise the system would have incomplete dissipation, i.e., there would exist motions that are not accompanied by a loss of energy. This possibility is also excluded.

● 3. Further conclusions about the character of matrix $\boldsymbol{\varepsilon}$ must be based on experimental data.

It is natural to assume that the dissipation matrix referred to the principal axes of matrix $\boldsymbol{\omega}$ also is a diagonal matrix. In this case, the matrix differential equation (15.1) separates into individual differential equations

$$f_i'' + 2\varepsilon_{ii} f_i' + \omega_i^2 f_i = 0\,, \qquad (i = 1, 2, 3, \cdots, n)\,, \tag{15.4}$$

whose solutions for initial deviations $f_i(0) = a_i$ and initial phases λ_i have the form

$$f_i(t) = a_i e^{-\varepsilon_{ii} t} \cos(\bar{\omega}_i t + \lambda_i)\,, \tag{15.5}$$

where $\bar{\omega}_i$ is the natural frequency with a correction for damping

$$\bar{\omega}_i^2 = \omega_i^2 - \varepsilon_{ii}^2\,.$$

The supposition about the diagonal form of matrix $\boldsymbol{\varepsilon}$ is equivalent to the assumption that there is no transfer of energy between principal forms of vibrations by the resistance forces. Experiments performed on a sufficiently wide class of systems show[30] that this assumption is plausible. In any case, no sharply defined coupling, produced by damping, was detected.

Even if matrix $\boldsymbol{\varepsilon}$ is not a diagonal matrix, then it can easily be shown that the influence of the elements, outside of the principal diagonal, on the damping of free vibrations is very small. Equation (15.1) is now rewritten in the form

$$\frac{d^2 f_i}{dt^2} + 2\varepsilon_{ii} \frac{df_i}{dt} + 2\mu \sum_{k=1}^{n}{}^{*} \varepsilon_{ik} \frac{df_k}{dt} + \omega_i^2 f_i = 0\,, \qquad (i = 1, 2, 3, \cdots, n)\,, \tag{15.6}$$

where the asterisk (*) in the summation sign denotes that during summation the terms with $i = k$ are omitted; μ is a parameter showing the smallness of nondiagonal terms of the dissipation matrix. This parameter is introduced formally and, after completion of the necessary computations, can be made equal to unity. The solution of the system of differential equations (15.6) will be sought in the form of a series in powers of the small parameter μ

$$f_i = f_i^{(0)} + \mu f_i^{(1)} + \mu^2 f_i^{(2)} + \cdots\,. \tag{15.7}$$

Substituting this series into (15.6) and equating the terms with identical μ^k leads to the system of differential equations

$$\begin{aligned}
&\frac{d^2 f_i^{(0)}}{dt^2} + 2\varepsilon_{ii} \frac{df_i^{(0)}}{dt} + \omega_i^2 f_i^{(0)} = 0\,,\\
&\frac{d^2 f_i^{(1)}}{dt^2} + 2\varepsilon_{ii} \frac{df_i^{(1)}}{dt} + \omega_i^2 f_i^{(1)} = -2 \sum_{k=1}^{n}{}^{*} \varepsilon_{ik} \frac{df_k^{(0)}}{dt}\,,\\
&\frac{d^2 f_i^{(2)}}{dt^2} + 2\varepsilon_{ii} \frac{df_i^{(2)}}{dt} + \omega_i^2 f_i^{(2)} = -2 \sum_{k=1}^{n}{}^{*} \varepsilon_{ik} \frac{df_k^{(1)}}{dt}\,,\\
&\cdots\cdots\cdots\cdots\cdots\cdots\cdots\cdots\cdots\\
&\qquad (i = 1, 2, 3, \cdots, n)\,,
\end{aligned} \tag{15.8}$$

which can be solved successively. The zero approximation coincides with (15.5); consequently for all $\lambda_i = 0$,

[30] See Fedorkov [1].

$$f_i^{(0)} = a_i e^{-\varepsilon_{ii}t} \cos \bar{\omega}_i t\,, \qquad (i = 1, 2, 3, \cdots, n) \tag{15.9}$$

Substituting Eq. (15.9) into the right-hand sides of the second group of Eqs. (15.8) gives

$$\frac{d^2 f_i^{(1)}}{dt^2} + 2\varepsilon_{ii}\frac{df_i^{(1)}}{dt} + \omega_i^2 f_i^{(1)} = F_i(t)\,, \qquad (i = 1, 2, 3, \cdots, n)$$

where

$$F_i(t) = 2 \sum_{k=1}^{n}{}^{*} a_k \varepsilon_{ik} e^{-\varepsilon_{kk}t}(\varepsilon_{kk} \cos \bar{\omega}_k t + \bar{\omega}_k \sin \bar{\omega}_k t)\,. \tag{15.10}$$

The solution of this system of differential equations, which for $t = 0$ vanishes together with its first derivative, has the form

$$f_i^{(1)} = \frac{e^{-\varepsilon_{ii}t}}{\bar{\omega}_i}\int_0^t F_i(\tau) e^{\varepsilon_{ii}\tau} \sin \bar{\omega}_i (t - \tau) d\tau\,.$$

Substitution of Eq. (15.10) followed by transformation gives (for $\omega_i \neq \bar{\omega}_k$)

$$f_i^{(1)} = \frac{1}{\bar{\omega}_i}\sum_{k=1}^{n}{}^{*} a_k \varepsilon_{ik} e^{-\varepsilon_{kk}t}(M_{ik} \sin \bar{\omega}_k t + N_{ik} \cos \bar{\omega}_k t)\,, \tag{15.11}$$

where

$$\begin{aligned} M_{ik} &= -\frac{\bar{\omega}_k(\bar{\omega}_k + \bar{\omega}_i) - \varepsilon_{kk}(\varepsilon_{ii} - \varepsilon_{kk})}{(\bar{\omega}_k + \bar{\omega}_i)^2 + (\varepsilon_{ii} - \varepsilon_{kk})^2} + \frac{\bar{\omega}_k(\bar{\omega}_k - \bar{\omega}_i) - \varepsilon_{kk}(\varepsilon_{ii} - \varepsilon_{kk})}{(\bar{\omega}_k - \bar{\omega}_i)^2 + (\varepsilon_{ii} - \varepsilon_{kk})^2}\,, \\ N_{ik} &= \frac{\bar{\omega}_k \varepsilon_{ii} + \varepsilon_{kk}\bar{\omega}_i}{(\bar{\omega}_k + \bar{\omega}_i)^2 + (\varepsilon_{ii} + \varepsilon_{kk})^2} - \frac{\bar{\omega}_k \varepsilon_{ii} - \varepsilon_{kk}\bar{\omega}_i}{(\bar{\omega}_k - \bar{\omega}_i)^2 + (\varepsilon_{ii} - \varepsilon_{kk})^2}\,. \end{aligned} \tag{15.12}$$

It can easily be seen that expression (15.11) contains terms of order ε/ω, $(\varepsilon/\omega)^2$, $(\varepsilon/\omega)^3$, (subscripts in ε_{ik} and $\bar{\omega}_k$ are omitted). For the diagonal elements ε_{ii}

$$\frac{\varepsilon}{\omega} = \frac{\delta}{2\pi}\,,$$

where δ is a decrement of damping of the free vibrations. For metal structures δ lies between 0.005 and 0.05; this permits neglecting the small terms of the second and higher orders in (15.11). This is equivalent to setting

$$\bar{\omega}_i \approx \omega_i\,,$$

$$M_{ik} \approx -\frac{\omega_k}{\omega_k + \omega_i} + \frac{\omega_k}{\omega_k - \omega_i} = \frac{2\omega_i \omega_k}{\omega_k^2 - \omega_i^2}\,,$$

$$N_{ik} \approx 0\,, \qquad (i, k = 1, 2, 3, \cdots, n)\,.$$

Substituting these values into Eq. (15.11), referring back to (15.7), and setting $\mu = 1$ leads to the first approximation

$$f_i(t) = a_i e^{-\varepsilon_{ii}t} \cos \omega_i t + \sum_{k=1}^{n}{}^{*} \frac{a_k \varepsilon_{ik} \omega_k}{\omega_k^2 - \omega_i^2} e^{-\varepsilon_{kk}t} \sin \omega_k t \tag{15.13}$$

$$(i = 1, 2, 3, \cdots, n)\,.$$

First of all, it is seen from (15.13) that the side elements in the first approximation do not influence the damping velocity of vibrations. However, the vibrations are coupled. Thus, the behavior of $f_i(t)$ depends on all $f_k(0) = a_k$

($k = 1, 2, 3, \cdots, n$). This influence, however, can be estimated by quantities of the order $\varepsilon_{ik}/\omega_k$, i.e., it is insignificant even for $\varepsilon_{ik} \approx \varepsilon_{ii}$.

As stated above, $\omega_i \neq \omega_k$. In the case of almost equal natural frequencies, the coupling between forms of the vibrations intensifies.

Consider a case of multiple frequencies $\omega_i = \omega_j$, assuming, however, that $\varepsilon_{ii} \neq \varepsilon_{jj}$. Here formulas (15.12) can be used. Expressions for M_{ik} and N_{ik} obviously contain quantities of order $(\varepsilon/\omega)^{-1}$, 1, ε/ω, $(\varepsilon/\omega)^2$, etc. To within the quantities of the first order,

$$-M_{ij} \approx \frac{2\omega_j^2}{(2\omega_j)^2} + \frac{\varepsilon_{jj}}{\varepsilon_{ii} - \varepsilon_{jj}} = \frac{1}{2} + \frac{\varepsilon_{jj}}{\varepsilon_{ii} - \varepsilon_{jj}},$$

$$N_{ij} \approx -\frac{\omega_i}{\varepsilon_{ii} - \varepsilon_{jj}}.$$

The influence of the elements ε_{ij} increases since the substitution of N_{ij} into Eq. (15.11) gives terms of the type

$$\frac{a_j \varepsilon_{ij}}{\varepsilon_{ii} - \varepsilon_{jj}} e^{-\varepsilon_{jj}} \sin \omega_j t .$$

●4. Therefore, at least in the case of unequal natural frequencies (more precisely, those which are not too close) the dissipation matrix can be considered as a diagonal matrix. A question arises on the relationship between diagonal elements of matrix, i.e., the damping coefficients ε_i.

In certain cases these coefficients can be equal. Thus an oscillogram of damped vibrations is shown in Figure 93 for model of a double hinged arch. (This arch is described in Chapter Eighteen.) The first oscillogram represents damping of the fundamental, antisymmetric form of vibrations; the second represents damping of the symmetrical form. It can be seen at a

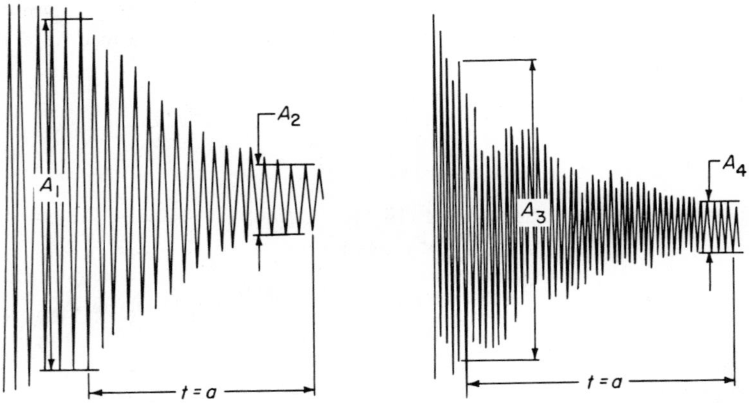

FIG. 93.

glance that for this example both exponents are approximately equal. Calculations give $\varepsilon_1 = 0.114 \text{ sec}^{-1}$ and $\varepsilon_2 = 0.122 \text{ sec}^{-1}$. The difference is about 7 percent. For other systems, the damping coefficients for different forms of vibrations can differ significantly from one another.[31]

Experiments show that in many cases the constant of a system (in the sense of a quantity which does not depend on the number of vibration forms) is not the damping coefficient ε_k but the decrement δ_k. This is justified also by certain theoretical considerations. The decrement of damping is related to the relative energy dissipation during a period by a simple approximate relationship

$$\delta \approx \frac{1}{2}\frac{\Delta W}{W}.$$

For comparable deformations (e.g., for sinusoidal vibrations of a beam with different lengths of half waves), the relative dissipation of internal energy can be considered as a constant quantity. If, in addition, the effect of external resistance forces on the general equilibrium is small, then the damping decrement will be approximately the same for all forms of vibrations of a given system.

Figure 94 presents a graph for variation of $\Delta W/W$ (i.e., double the damping decrement) for a simply-supported beam made of rolled channel section and having various spans. It can be seen from the graph that if the span is doubled, the decrement changes from 0.0095 to 0.007. The decrease of decrement can be explained by the decrease in the amount of external losses in the energy balance. Assuming that

$$\delta = \frac{2\pi\varepsilon}{\omega} = \text{const.}$$

we obtain for the dissipation matrix

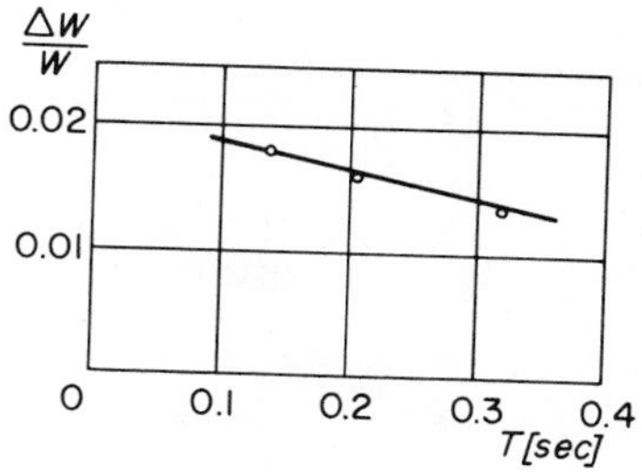

FIG. 94.

$$\boldsymbol{\varepsilon} = \frac{\delta}{\pi} \boldsymbol{C}^{-1/2}, \tag{15.14}$$

where $\boldsymbol{C} = \boldsymbol{\omega}^{-2}$. This formula is valid for an arbitrary choice of coordinates.

Another representation of matrix $\boldsymbol{\varepsilon}$ can be obtained in the following manner. Consider the vibrations of a straight prismatic rod, taking into account internal and external resistance forces. Assume the external resistances to be proportional to velocities of corresponding points. Regarding internal resistance, assume it is proportional to the velocities of deformation of longitudinal fibers. In other words, assume that the rod is a viscoelastic body. The differential equation of free vibrations has the form

$$EJ\frac{\partial^4 v}{\partial x^4} + 2\xi\frac{\partial^5 v}{\partial x^4 \partial t} + 2\eta\frac{\partial v}{\partial t} + m\frac{\partial^2 v}{\partial t^2} = 0,$$

[31] See the work of Fedorkov [1].

where ξ and η are certain constants. The second and third terms take into account internal and external resistances, respectively. Letting

$$v(x, t) = f_k(t)\varphi_k(x) ,$$

where $\varphi_k(x)$ are the vibration forms for the conservative problem and satisfy the equation

$$EJ\frac{d^4\varphi}{dx^4} - m\omega^2\varphi = 0 ,$$

gives an equation of the type in (15.4):

$$f_k'' + 2\varepsilon_k f_k' + \omega_k^2 f_k = 0 , \qquad (k = 1, 2, 3, \cdots) ,$$

where

$$\varepsilon_k = \frac{\eta}{m} + \frac{\xi}{EJ}\omega_k^2 .$$

Consequently, under the assumptions made, the dissipation matrix has the form

$$\boldsymbol{\varepsilon} = \frac{\eta}{m}\boldsymbol{E} + \frac{\xi}{EJ}\boldsymbol{C}^{-1} . \tag{15.15}$$

In general, if matrices $\boldsymbol{\varepsilon}$ and $\boldsymbol{C}$ are simultaneously transformed to a diagonal form, then one of them can be represented as a function of the other. Equations (15.14) and (15.15) are special cases of this. Determination of the general form of the function $\boldsymbol{\varepsilon}(\boldsymbol{C})$ requires a combination of effort in theory and experiment.

§ 62. Determination of the Regions of Dynamic Instability

●1. The equation for the boundaries of dynamic stability, taking damping into account, is obtained by introducing into the matrix differential equation

$$\boldsymbol{f}'' + \boldsymbol{C}^{-1}[\boldsymbol{E} - \alpha\boldsymbol{A} - \beta\Phi(t)\boldsymbol{B}]\boldsymbol{f} = \boldsymbol{0}$$

an additional term with a first derivative of the displacement vector. In what follows the equation will be expressed in the form

$$\boldsymbol{C}\boldsymbol{f}'' + 2\boldsymbol{C}\boldsymbol{\varepsilon}\boldsymbol{f}' + [\boldsymbol{E} - \alpha\boldsymbol{A} - \beta\Phi(t)\boldsymbol{B}]\boldsymbol{f} = \boldsymbol{0} , \tag{15.16}$$

which is valid for an arbitrary choice of coordinate functions.

In order to establish the form of solutions of Eq. (15.16), it is desirable to find a substitution which will eliminate the term with $\boldsymbol{f}'$, i.e., one which leads to equations for which the analytical form of solutions is known.

Let $\boldsymbol{X}$ be some matrix. By analogy with the expansion for a scalar quantity

$$e^x = 1 + \frac{x}{1!} + \frac{x^2}{2!} + \cdots$$

the exponential function of matrix $\boldsymbol{X}$ will be defined by the expansion[32]

[32] V. I. Smirnov [1].

$$e^{X} = E + \frac{X}{1!} + \frac{X^2}{2!} + \cdots = E + \sum_{k=1}^{\infty} \frac{X^k}{k!}\,.$$

Using this definition, we introduce the matrix

$$e^{-\varepsilon t} = E + \sum_{k=1}^{\infty} \frac{\varepsilon^k(-t)^k}{k!}\,.$$

The derivative with respect to t is now constructed for this matrix:

$$\frac{d}{dt}(e^{-\varepsilon t}) = -\sum_{k=1}^{\infty} \frac{\varepsilon^k(-t)^{k-1}}{(k-1)!} = -\varepsilon e^{-\varepsilon t}\,.$$

Thus the exponential function of the matrix possesses the fundamental properties of a scalar exponential function. On the principal axes it is

$$e^{-\varepsilon t} = \{e^{-\varepsilon_1 t}, e^{-\varepsilon_2 t}, \cdots e^{-\varepsilon_n t}\}\,.$$

By analogy with the transformation

$$f = e^{-\varepsilon t}u(t)\,,$$

which reduces the single differential equation (2.1) of the "special" case to the Mathieu-Hill differential equation, we introduce the matrix transformation

$$\boldsymbol{f} = e^{-\varepsilon t}\boldsymbol{u}(t)\,. \tag{15.17}$$

Here $\boldsymbol{u}(t)$ is a vector with components which must be determined. Differentiating twice leads to

$$\boldsymbol{f}' = e^{-\varepsilon t}(\boldsymbol{u}' - \varepsilon \boldsymbol{u})\,,$$
$$\boldsymbol{f}'' = e^{-\varepsilon t}(\boldsymbol{u}'' - 2\varepsilon \boldsymbol{u}' + \varepsilon^2 \boldsymbol{u})\,.$$

Substitution in Eq. (15.16) gives

$$\boldsymbol{C}e^{-\varepsilon t}\boldsymbol{u}'' + [\boldsymbol{E} - \boldsymbol{C}\varepsilon^2 - \alpha \boldsymbol{A} - \beta\Phi(t)\boldsymbol{B}]e^{-\varepsilon t}\boldsymbol{u} = \boldsymbol{0}\,, \tag{15.18}$$

i.e., terms with $\boldsymbol{f}'$ actually vanish. Under the condition that Eq. (15.18) can be written in the form

$$e^{-\varepsilon t}\{\boldsymbol{C}\boldsymbol{u}'' + [\boldsymbol{E} - \boldsymbol{C}\varepsilon^2 - \alpha \boldsymbol{A} - \beta\Phi(t)\boldsymbol{B}]\boldsymbol{u}\} = \boldsymbol{0}\,, \tag{15.19}$$

and taking into account that $e^{-\varepsilon t}$ is a nonsingular matrix (all $e^{-\varepsilon_k t} > 0$, leads to the equation

$$\boldsymbol{C}\boldsymbol{u}'' + [\boldsymbol{E} - \boldsymbol{C}\varepsilon^2 - \alpha \boldsymbol{A} - \beta\Phi(t)\boldsymbol{B}]\boldsymbol{u} = \boldsymbol{0}\,. \tag{15.20}$$

Expressions (15.18) and (15.19) by far are not always equivalent. The product of the two matrices, generally speaking, is noncommutative; therefore factoring matrices $e^{-\varepsilon t}$ outside the brackets is possible only for definite limitations with respect to $\boldsymbol{A}, \boldsymbol{B}, \boldsymbol{C}$, and $\boldsymbol{\varepsilon}$.

If the two matrices $\boldsymbol{X}$ and $\boldsymbol{Y}$ commute,

$$\boldsymbol{XY} = \boldsymbol{YX}\,,$$

we denote this as $\boldsymbol{X} \rightleftarrows \boldsymbol{Y}$. We formulate two theorems about commutative matrices:

I. If $\boldsymbol{X} \rightleftarrows \boldsymbol{Y}$, then $\boldsymbol{f}(\boldsymbol{X}) \rightleftarrows \boldsymbol{Y}$.

II. If $\boldsymbol{X} \rightleftarrows \boldsymbol{Y}$ and $\boldsymbol{Z} \rightleftarrows \boldsymbol{Y}$, then $\boldsymbol{X} \rightleftarrows \boldsymbol{Z}$.

The proof of these theorems follows from the fact that the commutative matrices have coinciding eigenvectors.

Let us return to the differential equation (15.18). On the basis of theorem I, the investigation of commutativity of $e^{-\boldsymbol{\varepsilon} t}$ changes to an investigation of commutativity of matrix $\boldsymbol{\varepsilon}$. Two cases can be distinguished. Matrix $\boldsymbol{\varepsilon}$ commutes with all three matrices $\boldsymbol{A}, \boldsymbol{B}, \boldsymbol{C}$, if these matrices commute with each other and $\boldsymbol{\varepsilon} \rightleftarrows \boldsymbol{C}$ (this follows from theorem II). But in this "special" case the matrix differential equation (15.16) can be reduced to the diagonal form

$$f_k'' + 2\varepsilon_k f_k' + \omega_k^2 \left[1 - \frac{\alpha}{\alpha_k} - \frac{\beta}{\beta_k} \Phi(t)\right] f_k = 0\,, \qquad (k = 1, 2, 3, \cdots)\,,$$

i.e., to ordinary differential equations, which already have been investigated in detail (Chapter Two).

The second case arises when substitution in (15.17) leads to Eq. (15.20), i.e., this is the case of the scalar matrix

$$\boldsymbol{\varepsilon} = \varepsilon \boldsymbol{E}\,, \tag{15.21}$$

which commutes with any other matrix. Here ε is the damping coefficient which is the same for all forms of vibrations. This case will be considered below.

•2. When the elementary divisors in the characteristic equation are simple, the solutions of Eq. (15.20) have the form of (14.12), i.e.,

$$\boldsymbol{u}_k = e^{h_k t} \boldsymbol{\chi}_k(t)\,, \tag{15.22}$$

where $h_k = (\theta/2\pi) \ln \rho_k$ are the characteristic exponents, $\boldsymbol{\chi}_k(t)$ are vectors whose components are periodic functions of time with period $2\pi/\theta$. To each characteristic root ρ_k there corresponds a second root $\rho_{n+k} = 1/\rho_k$; to each solution (15.22), there corresponds a solution

$$\boldsymbol{u}_{n+k} = e^{-h_k t} \boldsymbol{\chi}_{n+k}(t)\,.$$

If all ρ_k are complex numbers, then $|\rho_k| = 1$ and $h_k = i \arg \rho_k$. In this case, as can be seen from Eq. (15.17), all solutions of Eq. (15.16) damp out with the rate of damping of the free vibrations.

Let the characteristic equation for (15.20) have a pair of real roots ρ_k and $\rho_{n+k} = 1/\rho_k$. Consider a pair of corresponding solutions of Eq. (15.16):

$$\begin{aligned} \boldsymbol{f}_k &= e^{(h_k - \varepsilon)t} \boldsymbol{\chi}_k(t)\,, \\ \boldsymbol{f}_{n+k} &= e^{-(h_k + \varepsilon)t} \boldsymbol{\chi}_{n+k}(t)\,. \end{aligned} \tag{15.23}$$

If for definiteness it is assumed that $|\rho_k| > 1$, then the first solution increases without bound for $\operatorname{Re} h_k > \varepsilon$, damps out for $\operatorname{Re} h_k < \varepsilon$, and is periodic for $\operatorname{Re} h_k = \varepsilon$. For the case of $\rho_k > 0$ it is $\operatorname{Im} h_k = 0$; consequently, the first solution has a period $2\pi/\theta$. For the case of $\rho_k < 0$,

$$h_k = \frac{\theta}{2\pi} \ln |\rho_k| + i\pi ,$$

hence the first solution has a period $4\pi/\theta$. As can be seen from (15.23), the second solution damps out for all values of ε. It follows that, as in the conservative case, the periodic solutions with periods $2\pi/\theta$ and $4\pi/\theta$ separate the regions of instability from regions in which the solutions damp out.

The case of multiple roots with nonlinear elementary divisors will now be considered briefly. Let the characteristic equation for (15.20) have a double root; this will obviously be either $\rho_k = \rho_{n+k} = 1$ or $\rho_k = \rho_{n+k} = -1$. In this case the solutions of Eq. (15.20) have the form (14.14), i.e.,

$$\boldsymbol{u}_k = \boldsymbol{\chi}_k(t) ,$$
$$\boldsymbol{u}_{n+k} = \boldsymbol{\chi}_{n+k}(t) + t\boldsymbol{\chi}_k(t) ,$$

where $\boldsymbol{\chi}_k(t)$ and $\boldsymbol{\chi}_{n+k}(t)$ are periodic vectors with period $2\pi/\theta$ or $4\pi/\theta$. If with the help of transformation (15.17) we change over to $\boldsymbol{f}_k(t)$ and consider

$$\lim_{t \to \infty} te^{-\varepsilon t} = 0 ,$$

then the stability for the case of double roots is obtained.

●**3.** Certain qualitative considerations about regions of instability, taking damping into account, will now be examined.

From the preceding presentation it follows that the regions of instability for the differential equation (15.16) always lie within the regions of instability for (15.20). Indeed, the characteristic exponents h_k have a real part only within these regions; consequently, they satisfy the equation

$$\operatorname{Re} h_k = \varepsilon .$$

But Eq. (15.20) describes the vibrations of a conservative system with natural frequencies which were calculated with the correction for damping. To demonstrate this, the terms with $\Phi(t)$ in (15.20) are neglected:

$$\boldsymbol{C}\boldsymbol{f}'' + (\boldsymbol{E} - \boldsymbol{C}\varepsilon^2 - \alpha\boldsymbol{A})\boldsymbol{f} = \boldsymbol{0} .$$

Assuming

$$\boldsymbol{f} = \boldsymbol{a} \sin (\bar{\Omega}t + \lambda) ,$$

where $\bar{\Omega}$ is the frequency of free vebrations, leads to the characteristic equation

$$|\boldsymbol{E} - \alpha\boldsymbol{A} - (\bar{\Omega}^2 + \varepsilon^2)\boldsymbol{C}| = 0 .$$

If this equation is compared with the equation for the natural frequencies of a conservative problem,

$$|\boldsymbol{E} - \alpha\boldsymbol{A} - \Omega^2\boldsymbol{C}| = 0 ,$$

it is found that

$$\bar{\Omega}^2 = \Omega^2 - \varepsilon^2 .$$

Hence it follows that the instability regions for Eq. (15.20) are slightly shifted (in the direction of decreasing frequencies) with respect to the region of instability for the equation

$$\boldsymbol{C}\boldsymbol{f}'' + [\boldsymbol{E} - \alpha\boldsymbol{A} - \beta\Phi(t)\boldsymbol{B}]\boldsymbol{f} = 0 .$$

In certain cases the instability regions for problems with damping may lie outside the limits of corresponding regions for conservative problems. This possibility is shown schematically in Figure 95, where the instability regions taking damping into account are crosshatched, the boundaries of the instability regions for a conservative problem are denoted by solid lines, and the boundaries for instability regions for Eq. (15.20) are denoted by dotted lines. Such a distribution is possible only for sufficiently large damping, however.

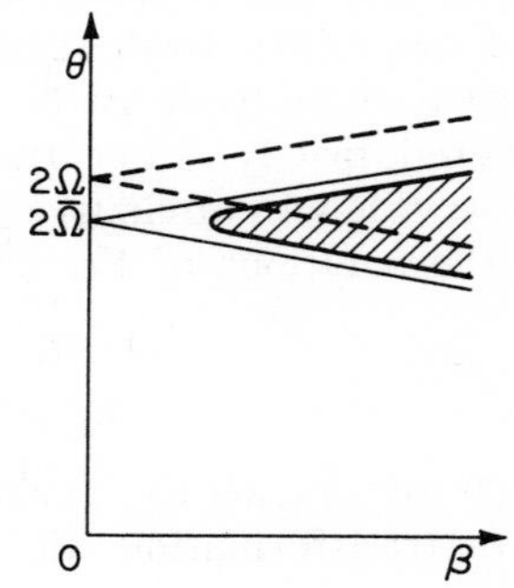

FIG. 95.

§ 63. The Equation for Critical Frequencies

● 1. The derivation of an equation for critical boundary frequencies is analogous to one which was given in § 57 for a conservative problem. For the differential equation (15.16) we seek the periodic solution with period $4\pi/\theta$ in the form of the series

$$\boldsymbol{f}(t) = \sum_{k=1,3,5}^{\infty} \left(\boldsymbol{a}_k \sin \frac{k\theta t}{2} + \boldsymbol{b}_k \cos \frac{k\theta t}{2} \right), \tag{15.24}$$

where $\boldsymbol{a}_k$ and $\boldsymbol{b}_k$ are vectors with constant coefficients. It is assumed that the periodic function $\Phi(t)$ can be represented in the form of the series

$$\Phi(t) = \sum_{k=1}^{\infty} c_k \cos k\theta t .$$

We will now consider the case $\Phi(t) = \cos \theta t$. Substituting (15.24) into (15.16) and equating coefficients of identical $\sin k\theta t/2$ and $\cos k\theta t/2$, we obtain a system of equations

$$\begin{aligned}
(\boldsymbol{E} - \alpha\boldsymbol{A} - \tfrac{1}{2}\beta\boldsymbol{B} - \tfrac{1}{4}\theta^2\boldsymbol{C})\boldsymbol{a}_1 - \theta\boldsymbol{C}\boldsymbol{\varepsilon}\boldsymbol{b}_1 - \tfrac{1}{2}\beta\boldsymbol{B}\boldsymbol{a}_3 &= \boldsymbol{0} ,\\
(\boldsymbol{E} - \alpha\boldsymbol{A} - \tfrac{1}{2}\beta\boldsymbol{B} - \tfrac{1}{4}\theta^2\boldsymbol{C})\boldsymbol{b}_1 + \theta\boldsymbol{C}\boldsymbol{\varepsilon}\boldsymbol{a}_1 - \tfrac{1}{2}\beta\boldsymbol{B}\boldsymbol{b}_3 &= \boldsymbol{0} ,\\
(\boldsymbol{E} - \alpha\boldsymbol{A} - \tfrac{1}{4}k^2\theta^2\boldsymbol{C})\boldsymbol{a}_k - k\theta\boldsymbol{C}\boldsymbol{\varepsilon}\boldsymbol{b}_k - \tfrac{1}{2}\beta\boldsymbol{B}(\boldsymbol{a}_{k-2} + \boldsymbol{a}_{k+2}) &= \boldsymbol{0} ,\\
(\boldsymbol{E} - \alpha\boldsymbol{A} - \tfrac{1}{4}k^2\theta^2\boldsymbol{C})\boldsymbol{b}_k + k\theta\boldsymbol{C}\boldsymbol{\varepsilon}\boldsymbol{a}_k - \tfrac{1}{2}\beta\boldsymbol{B}(\boldsymbol{b}_{k-2} + \boldsymbol{b}_{k+2}) &= \boldsymbol{0} ,\\
(k = 3, 5, 7, \cdots) .&
\end{aligned}$$

In contrast to conservative problems, here the equations for $\boldsymbol{a}_k$ and $\boldsymbol{b}_k$ do not separate. The condition for the existence of solutions with period $4\pi/\theta$

takes the form

$$\begin{vmatrix} \cdots & \cdots & \cdots & \cdots \\ E-\alpha A-\frac{9}{4}\theta^2 C & -\frac{1}{2}\beta B & 0 & -3\theta C\varepsilon \\ -\frac{1}{2}\beta B & E-\alpha A+\frac{1}{2}\beta B-\frac{1}{4}\theta^2 C & -\theta C\varepsilon & 0 \\ 0 & \theta C\varepsilon & E-\alpha A-\frac{1}{2}\beta B-\frac{1}{4}\theta^2 C & -\frac{1}{2}\beta B \\ 3\theta C\varepsilon & 0 & -\frac{1}{2}\beta B & E-\alpha A-\frac{9}{4}\theta^2 C \\ \cdots & \cdots & \cdots & \cdots \end{vmatrix} = 0. \qquad (15.25)$$

For $\varepsilon \to 0$ the determinant (15.25) can be expressed as the product of two determinants which coincide with Eqs. (14.24) for the boundary frequencies in the conservative problem. From (15.25) are obtained the instability regions lying near the frequencies

$$\theta = \frac{2\Omega_j}{k}, \qquad \begin{pmatrix} j = 1, 2, 3, \cdots \\ k = 1, 3, 5, \cdots \end{pmatrix}.$$

Substituting the corresponding eigenvalues

$$A \to \frac{1}{\alpha_k}, \quad B \to \frac{1}{\beta_k}, \quad C \to \frac{1}{\omega_k^2}, \quad E \to 1,$$

in place of the matrices leads to Eqs. (2.7) of the special case of the independent single equations.

●2. Let us establish the condition for the existence of solutions with a period $2\pi/\theta$. Substitute into Eq. (15.16) the series

$$f = \frac{1}{2} b_0 + \sum_{k=2,4,6}^{\infty} \left(a_k \sin \frac{k\theta t}{2} + b_k \cos \frac{k\theta t}{2} \right). \qquad (15.26)$$

After the necessary transformations, a system of linear equations is obtained:

$$\begin{aligned} (E - \alpha A) b_0 - \beta B b_2 &= 0, \\ (E - \alpha A - \theta^2 C) a_2 - 2\theta C \varepsilon b_2 - \tfrac{1}{2}\beta B a_4 &= 0, \\ (E - \alpha A - \theta^2 C) b_2 + 2\theta C \varepsilon a_2 - \tfrac{1}{2}\beta B (b_0 + b_4) &= 0, \\ (E - \alpha A - \tfrac{1}{4} k^2 \theta^2 C) a_k - k\theta C \varepsilon b_k - \tfrac{1}{2}\beta B (a_{k-2} + a_{k+2}) &= 0, \\ (E - \alpha A - \tfrac{1}{4} k^2 \theta^2 C) b_k + k\theta C \varepsilon a_k - \tfrac{1}{2}\beta B (b_{k-2} + b_{k+2}) &= 0, \\ (k = 4, 6, \cdots), \end{aligned}$$

whose determinant, by virtue of the solvability conditions, must be equal to zero:

$$\begin{vmatrix} \cdots & \cdots & \cdots & \cdots & \cdots \\ E-\alpha A-4\theta^2 C & -\frac{1}{2}\beta B & 0 & 0 & -4\theta C\varepsilon \\ -\frac{1}{2}\beta B & E-\alpha A-\theta^2 C & 0 & -2\theta C\varepsilon & 0 \\ 0 & 0 & E-\alpha A & -\beta B & 0 \\ 0 & 2\theta C\varepsilon & -\frac{1}{2}\beta B & E-\alpha A-\theta^2 C & -\frac{1}{2}\beta B \\ 4\theta C\varepsilon & 0 & 0 & -\frac{1}{2}\beta B & E-\alpha A-4\theta^2 C \\ \cdots & \cdots & \cdots & \cdots & \cdots \end{vmatrix} = 0 . \tag{15.27}$$

For $\varepsilon \to 0$ this equation separates into two equations, (14.25) and (14.26); the corresponding instability regions lie near the frequencies

$$\theta = \frac{2\Omega_j}{k}, \qquad \begin{pmatrix} j = 1, 2, 3, \cdots \\ k = 2, 4, 6, \cdots \end{pmatrix}.$$

●**3.** The fact that periodic solutions correspond to the boundaries of the instability regions is not surprising; by their character, the periodic solutions fall between damped solutions and solutions increasing without bound (Fig. 96). The foregoing conclusions, however, pertain to the case in which ε is a scalar matrix. A question arises concerning the extension of results to the case of an arbitrary dissipation matrix.

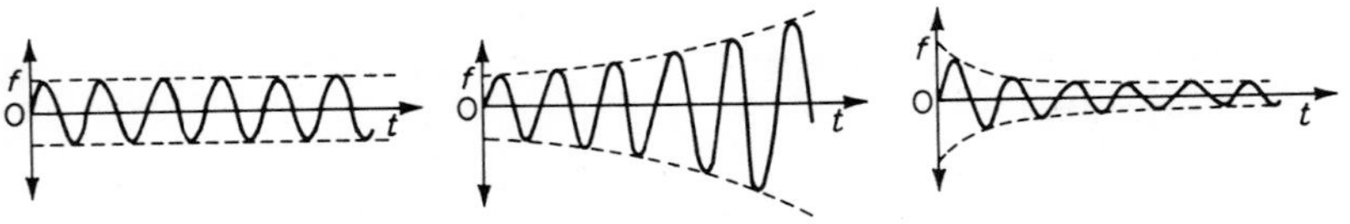

FIG. 96.

Let the damping coefficients for various forms satisfy the inequalities

$$\varepsilon_1 < \varepsilon_2 < \varepsilon_3 < \cdots < \varepsilon_n .$$

Furthermore, assume that by changing one of the parameters of the system (for example β), a transition is made from damped solutions (region of stability) to solutions which increase without bound (instability region). At first glance, the following possibility of transition presents itself.

Within the limits of the stability region, all generalized displacements f_i $(i = 1, 2, 3, \cdots, n)$ damp out. On the boundary of the region, one of the functions (it is possible that this will be displacement f_1, which corresponds to the form with minimum damping) is periodic: the others will, as before, damp out with time. On further increase of the parameter, the function f_1 will increase without bound; moreover, such a value of the parameter can be found for which the function f_2 will be periodic, etc. In this manner it may occur that on the boundaries of the instability region only the one function f_1 is periodic; the remaining functions f_i $(i \geq 2)$ damp out with time.

The above deductions can, nevertheless, be disproved by the following nonrigorous but sufficiently conclusive consideration. To begin with, the series (15.24) and (15.26) formally satisfy Eq. (15.16) for arbitrary assumptions with respect to matrix $\boldsymbol{\varepsilon}$. This means that for sufficiently small ε_{ik}, it is always possible to select real values θ and β such that the determinants (15.25) or (15.27) become zero. This conclusion is obvious for $\boldsymbol{\varepsilon} \rightarrow 0$; for $\boldsymbol{\varepsilon} \neq \mathbf{0}$, it follows from continuous dependence of roots of an algebraic equation on its coefficients. Thus, even in the case of an arbitrary matrix ε_{ik}, there exist values of parameters for which all f_i $(i = 1, 2, 3, \cdots n)$ are periodic; in a sense, these values correspond to the boundaries of the instability regions.

It is possible to introduce still another reason. In Chapter Sixteen a differential equation which can be obtained from (15.16) by addition of nonlinear terms in $\boldsymbol{f}, \boldsymbol{f}'$ and $\boldsymbol{f}''$ will be investigated. It will be shown that besides the trivial solution $f_i = 0$, this nonlinear differential equation admits periodic solutions with period $2\pi/\theta$ and $4\pi/\theta$ in certain regions of variation of parameters. The points of branching out of trivial and periodic solutions give boundaries for the regions of dynamic instability; moreover, the equations for these points coincide with (15.25) and (15.26) and are valid for arbitrary dissipation matrices.

§ 64. Example

Consider a system which is described by the matrices[33]

$$\boldsymbol{A} = \boldsymbol{B} = \begin{pmatrix} 0 & a_{12} \\ a_{21} & 0 \end{pmatrix}, \quad \boldsymbol{C} = \begin{pmatrix} 1/\omega_1^2 & 0 \\ 0 & 1/\omega_2^2 \end{pmatrix},$$

$$\boldsymbol{\varepsilon} = \begin{pmatrix} \varepsilon_1 & 0 \\ 0 & \varepsilon_2 \end{pmatrix}.$$

Let us determine the *principal* regions of instability which lie near the frequencies

$$\theta = 2\Omega_j, \quad (j = 1, 2).$$

If in (15.25) only the central matrix elements are singled out, then the following equation is obtained:

$$\begin{vmatrix} \boldsymbol{E} - \alpha\boldsymbol{A} + \frac{1}{2}\beta\boldsymbol{B} - \frac{1}{4}\theta^2\boldsymbol{C} & -\theta\boldsymbol{C\varepsilon} \\ \theta\boldsymbol{C\varepsilon} & \boldsymbol{E} - \alpha\boldsymbol{A} - \frac{1}{2}\beta\boldsymbol{B} - \frac{1}{4}\theta^2\boldsymbol{C} \end{vmatrix} = 0.$$

Upon expansion, this equation has the form

[33] The corresponding conservative problem was investigated in § 58.

$$\begin{vmatrix} \boxed{1-(\theta^2/4\omega_1^2)} & -(\alpha+\frac{1}{2}\beta)a_{12} & -\varepsilon_1\theta/\omega_1^2 & 0 \\ -(\alpha+\frac{1}{2}\beta)a_{21} & 1-(\theta^2/4\omega_2^2) & 0 & -(\varepsilon_2\theta/\omega_2^2) \\ \varepsilon_1\theta/\omega_1^2 & 0 & \boxed{1-(\theta^2/4\omega_1^2)} & -(\alpha-\frac{1}{2}\beta)a_{12} \\ 0 & \varepsilon_2\theta/\omega_2^2 & -(\alpha-\frac{1}{2}\beta)a_{21} & 1-(\theta^2/4\omega_2^2) \end{vmatrix} = 0\,; \tag{15.28}$$

and is obviously a fourth-order algebraic equation in θ^2. To obtain clear results, assume that

$$\gamma = \frac{\omega_1^2}{\omega_2^2} \ll 1\,, \quad \frac{\alpha^2}{\alpha_*^2} \ll 1\,, \quad \frac{\beta^2}{\alpha_*^2} \ll 1\,,$$

where α_* is determined according to (14.32). Then, for the zero approximation

$$\theta_* \approx 2\omega_1\,, \quad \theta_* = 2\omega_2\,. \tag{15.29}$$

Substitute the first value of (15.29) into all the elements of determinant (15.28) except the first and the third elements of the principal diagonal. Then the following equation is obtained:

$$\begin{vmatrix} \xi & -(\alpha+\frac{1}{2}\beta)a_{12} & -\delta_1/\pi & 0 \\ -(\alpha+\frac{1}{2}\beta)a_{21} & 1-\gamma & 0 & -(\delta_2/\pi)\gamma \\ \delta_1/\pi & 0 & \xi & -(\alpha-\frac{1}{2}\beta)a_{12} \\ 0 & (\delta_2/\pi)\gamma & -(\alpha-\frac{1}{2}\beta)\alpha_{21} & 1-\gamma \end{vmatrix} = 0\,, \tag{15.30}$$

where

$$\xi = 1 - \frac{\theta^2}{4\omega_1^2}\,, \quad \delta_1 = \frac{2\pi\varepsilon_1}{\omega_1}\,, \quad \delta_2 = \frac{2\pi\varepsilon_2}{\omega_2}\,. \tag{15.31}$$

Obviously, δ_1 and δ_2 are decrements of damping of the individual forms of vibrations. If the determinant (15.30) is expanded, we obtain

$$\xi^2\left[(1-\gamma)^2 + \left(\frac{\delta_2}{\pi}\gamma\right)^2\right] - 2\xi(1-\gamma)(\mu^2+\nu^2) + \left[\mu^2 - \nu^2 + \frac{\delta_1\delta_2}{\pi}\gamma\right]^2 + \left(\frac{\delta_1}{\pi}\right)^2(1-\gamma)^2 = 0\,.$$

Here

$$\mu = \frac{\alpha}{\alpha_*}\,, \qquad \nu = \frac{\beta}{2\beta_*}\,.$$

In practical applications, $\delta_1 \ll 1$, $\delta_2 \ll 1$, which permits us to neglect in the above equation terms higher than second order:

$$(1-\gamma)^2\xi^2 - 2\xi(1-\gamma)(\mu^2-\nu^2) + (\mu^2-\nu^2)^2 + \left(\frac{\delta_1}{\pi}\right)^2(1-\gamma)^2 = 0\,.$$

Hence

$$\xi = \frac{\mu^2 + \nu^2 \pm \sqrt{4\mu^2\nu^2 - (\delta_1/\pi)^2(1-\gamma)^2}}{1-\gamma}\,.$$

Taking into account (15.31), the formula for boundary frequencies has the form

$$\theta_* = 2\omega_1 \sqrt{1 - \frac{\mu^2 + \nu^2 \pm \sqrt{4\mu^2\nu^2 - (\delta_1/\pi)^2(1-\gamma)^2}}{1-\gamma}} \,. \qquad (15.32)$$

If

$$4\mu^2\nu^2 - (\delta_1/\pi)^2(1-\gamma)^2 < 0\,,$$

then formula (15.32) gives complex values for the boundary frequency. Thus, the largest value of decrement of damping for which the dynamic instability is still possible is $\delta_{1*} = 2\pi\mu\nu$, or, if the previous notations are used,

$$\delta_{1*} = \frac{\pi\alpha\beta}{\alpha_*^2(1-\gamma)} \,. \qquad (15.33)$$

It is possible to approach the problem differently, by determining for a given damping the minimum value of β for which sustaining of damped free vibrations is possible:

$$\beta_{**} = \frac{\alpha_*^2\delta(1-\gamma)}{\pi\alpha} \,. \qquad (15.34)$$

Let us recall that for the "special" case of a single equation (§ 9) there is the relationship $\mu_* = \Delta/\pi$, where μ is the coefficient of excitation and Δ is the damping decrement of the loaded system,

$$\mu = \frac{\beta}{2(\alpha_* - \alpha)}\,,$$

$$\Delta = \frac{\delta}{\sqrt{1 - \frac{\alpha}{\alpha_*}}} \,.$$

Hence, the formula for β_{**} is obtained:

$$\beta_{**} = \frac{2\alpha_*\delta}{\pi}\sqrt{1 - \frac{\alpha}{\alpha_*}} \,. \qquad (15.35)$$

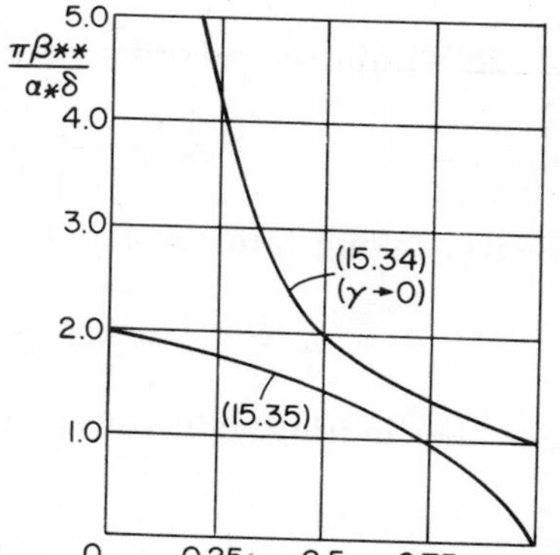

FIG. 97.

The graph in Figure 97 is plotted from formulas (15.34) and (15.35). It can be seen from the graph that for identical α/α_* and identical decrements, the excitation of vibrations in the "special" case of a single equation always requires a smaller amplitude of the load than in the case now being investigated ($\gamma < 0.25$).

● **2.** The instability region for $\theta \approx 2\omega_2$ will now be determined. Inserting this value for θ into all elements of (15.28) except the second and fourth of the principal diagonal gives

$$\begin{vmatrix} -\dfrac{1-\gamma}{\gamma} & -\left(\alpha+\dfrac{1}{2}\beta\right)a_{12} & -\dfrac{\delta_1}{\pi}\dfrac{1}{\gamma} & 0 \\ -\left(\alpha+\dfrac{1}{2}\beta\right)a_{21} & \xi & 0 & -\dfrac{\delta_2}{\pi} \\ \dfrac{\delta_1}{\pi}\dfrac{1}{\gamma} & 0 & -\dfrac{1-\gamma}{\gamma} & -\left(\alpha-\dfrac{1}{2}\beta\right)a_{12} \\ 0 & \dfrac{\delta_2}{\pi} & -\left(\alpha-\dfrac{1}{2}\beta\right)a_{21} & \xi \end{vmatrix} = 0\,.$$

where now

$$\xi = 1 - \frac{\theta^2}{4{\omega_2}^2}\,. \tag{15.36}$$

If the determinant is expanded, the resulting equation is

$$\xi^2\left[\left(\frac{1-\gamma}{\gamma}\right)^2 + \left(\frac{\delta_1}{\pi\gamma}\right)^2\right] + 2\xi\,\frac{1-\gamma}{\gamma}\,(\mu^2+\nu^2)$$
$$+\left(\mu^2-\nu^2+\frac{\delta_1\delta_2}{\pi\gamma}\right)^2 + \left(\frac{1-\gamma}{\gamma}\right)^2\left(\frac{\delta_2}{\pi}\right)^2 = 0\,.$$

It roots are

$$\xi = \frac{1}{\left(\dfrac{1-\gamma}{\gamma}\right)^2+\left(\dfrac{\delta_1}{\pi\gamma}\right)^2}\left\{-\frac{1-\gamma}{\gamma}\,(\mu^2+\nu^2)\right.$$
$$\left.\pm\sqrt{\left(\frac{1-\gamma}{\gamma}\right)^2 4\mu^2\nu^2 - \frac{2\delta_1\delta_2}{\pi^2\gamma}\,(\mu^2-\nu^2) - \left(\frac{\delta_2}{\pi}\right)^2\left[\left(\frac{1-\gamma}{\gamma}\right)^2+\left(\frac{\delta_1}{\pi\gamma}\right)^2\right]}\right\},$$

or, to within second-order terms

$$\xi \approx -\frac{\gamma}{\gamma-1}\left[\mu^2+\nu^2\pm\sqrt{4\mu^2\nu^2-\left(\frac{\delta_2}{\pi}\right)^2}\right].$$

Hence, taking into account Eq. (15.36) gives

$$\theta_* = \sqrt{2\omega_2\, 1 + \frac{\gamma}{\gamma-1}\left[\mu^2+\nu^2\pm\sqrt{4\mu^2\nu^2-\left(\frac{\delta_2}{\pi}\right)^2}\right]}\,. \tag{15.37}$$

For the limiting value of δ_2, a formula analogous to (15.33) is obtained:

$$\delta_{2*} = \frac{\pi\alpha\beta}{{\alpha_*}^2}\,.$$

We note that to within the accuracy of formulas (15.32) and (15.37), a change in the damping decrement of one form of vibration exerts little influence on the boundaries of the instability region for the other form.[34] In fact, δ_2 does not enter into (15.32) and δ_1 does not enter into (15.37).

[34] Since in all except the "special" case of a single independent equation, forms of vibrations are parametrically related, the concept of "instability region for the jth form" has only a limited meaning. It means that for $\alpha = \beta = 0$, the corresponding instability region degenerates into a line $\theta = 2\omega_j/k$.

Finally, we note that if $\delta_1 = \delta_2 = 0$, formulas (15.32) and (15.37) take the form

$$\theta_* = 2\omega_1 \sqrt{1 - \frac{(\mu \pm \nu)^2}{1-\gamma}} ,$$

$$\theta_* = 2\omega_2 \sqrt{1 + \frac{\gamma}{1-\gamma} (\mu \pm \nu)^2} ,$$

i.e., they coincide with formulas (14.35).

§ 65. Approximate Method for the Calculation of Damping

The approximate method developed in § 59 for conservative problems can easily be extended to systems with damping. If we transform Eq. (15.16) to the principal axes of the matrix $\boldsymbol{E} - \alpha \boldsymbol{A} - \beta \Phi(t) \boldsymbol{B}$ and neglect small terms, we obtain scalar equations of the type

$$f_k'' + 2\varepsilon_k f_k' + \Omega_k^2(t) f_k = 0 , \qquad (k = 1, 2, 3, \cdots) . \tag{15.38}$$

Here ε_k is the damping coefficient of the kth form, which can be determined experimentally for $\beta = 0$, and $\Omega_k(t)$ is the "instantaneous" value of the kth frequency of free vibrations; i.e., one of the roots of the equation is

$$| \boldsymbol{E} - \alpha \boldsymbol{A} - \beta \Phi(t) \boldsymbol{B} - \Omega^2(t) \boldsymbol{C} | = 0 ,$$

in whose solution the time t is considered as a parameter. Since the differential equations (15.38) are the Hill equations with dissipating terms, it is proper to use the results of § 10 for their analysis.

Let us demonstrate the application of this method to the example just investigated. For the differential equation of the type (15.38), according to (2.25) the following approximate condition for the formation of the ith resonance of the kth form of vibration is obtained:

$$\mu_{ik} > \frac{\Delta_k}{\pi} , \qquad (i, k = 1, 2, 3, \cdots) . \tag{15.39}$$

Here μ_{ik} is the ith term of the expansion

$$\Omega_k^2(t) = \Omega_k^2 \left(1 - 2 \sum_{i=1}^{\infty} \mu_{ik} \cos i\theta t \right) , \qquad (k = 1, 2, 3, \cdots) ,$$

and Δ_k is damping decrement of the kth form (with the constant component of parametric loading taken into account). Using the notation from § 59 gives

$$\mu_{ik} = \frac{\nu_{ik}}{2(1 - \nu_{0k})} ,$$

$$\Delta_k = \frac{2\pi\varepsilon_k}{\omega_k \sqrt{1 - \nu_{0k}}} = \frac{\delta_k}{\sqrt{1 - \nu_{0k}}} ,$$

from which, instead of (15.39), the following is obtained

$$\nu_{ik} > \frac{2\delta_k}{\pi} \sqrt{1 - \nu_{0k}} , \qquad (i, k = 1, 2, 3, \cdots) . \tag{15.40}$$

Let $k = 1$. Then the largest value of the decrement for which excitation is still possible will be

$$\delta_{*1} = \frac{\pi\alpha\beta}{\alpha_*^{\,2}(1-\gamma)\sqrt{1-\dfrac{\alpha^2+\frac{1}{2}\beta^2}{(1-\gamma)\alpha_*^{\,2}}}}\,. \tag{15.41}$$

It can easily be seen that the difference between formulas (15.41) and (15.33) is in the order of terms which have been neglected during the derivation of formula (15.33) in view of assumption (15.29).

The advantage of this method is that it permits immediate estimation of the order of the limiting decrement for any instability region. Thus, for resonance $\theta = \Omega_1$ the condition for the excitation of vibrations is obtained:

$$\frac{\beta^2}{2(1-\gamma)\alpha_*^{\,2}} > \frac{2\delta_1}{\pi}\sqrt{1-\frac{\alpha^2+\frac{1}{2}\beta^2}{(1-\gamma)\alpha_*^{\,2}}}\,.$$

Consequently, if for the principal resonance region

$$\frac{\beta_{**}}{\alpha_*} \approx \frac{\delta}{\pi}\,\frac{\alpha_*}{\alpha},$$

then, obviously, for the second region

$$\frac{\beta_{**}}{\alpha_*} \approx 2\sqrt{\frac{\delta}{\pi}}\,.$$

For a sufficiently small constant component of loading, the second resonance can occur at smaller values of β than does the first resonance (Fig. 98).

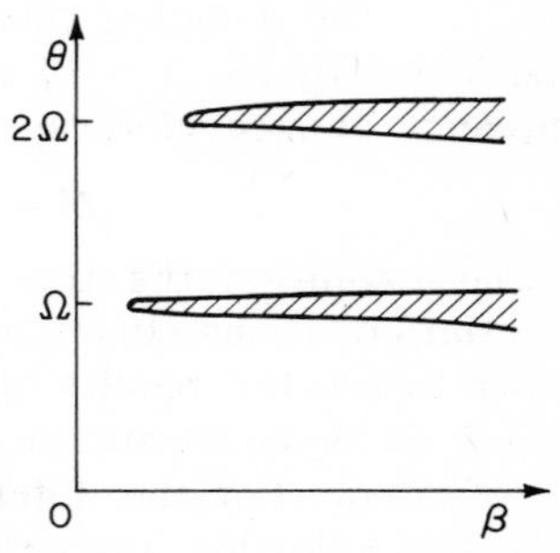

FIG. 98.

Sixteen

THE FUNDAMENTALS OF THE NONLINEAR THEORY OF DYNAMIC STABILITY

§ 66. Methods for Constructing the Differential Equations for a Nonlinear Problem

●**1.** In each problem on dynamic stability, it is possible to separate the fundamental motion which exists for all values of the parameters from an additional motion which arises for only certain parameter values. The first motion corresponds to ordinary forced vibrations, the second to parametrically excited vibration.

The construction of linear equations for the boundaries of dynamic stability reduces to the following. Besides the fundametnal motion, perturbed motion is considered which differs from the former by the presence of a qualitatively new type of deformation. (In problems on the vibrations of a compressed rod, the transverse deflection of the rod belongs to this new type of deformation.) As a result, one obtains differential equations in terms of the variation of the given motion, i.e., "variational equations." If these variations are damped out with time, then the given motion is stable; unlimited increase of the variations, however, corresponds to dynamic instability for the given form of motion.

The following considerations must be added. Although in all problems of dynamic stability the steady-state forced vibrations appear as the initial form, it is customary to perturb the underformed state of the system. This has been done in most of the published works; unfortunately, the necessary assumptions were frequently absent. This was done also in the first part of the present book; the methods for a more complete solution of the problem were not indicated until Chapter Eight.

In most of the special cases (but not in all!), the replacement of initial forced motion by the equilibrium state can be justified. If the external loading is such that the frequency of the forced vibrations of the system does not lie near the resonance frequency, then the amplitudes of the forced vibrations are sufficiently small and the unperturbed motion can be identified with the undeformed state with sufficient accuracy. In the cases where the resonance of forced vibrations is near the parametric resonance, a simultaneous consideration of both forms of motion is necessary. For the simplest problems, this was carried out in Chapter Eight; in addition, an estimate of the error for the approximate solutions was made.

●2. The construction of nonlinear differential equations for dynamic stability can be carried out by two methods. The first method, developed in Chapters Three through Seven, consists of adding the nonlinear terms, found from additional considerations, to the ordinary linear differential equations. The second method is based on a simultaneous consideration of forced and parametrically excited vibrations. We will now consider the first method.

Let $u_1, u_2, \cdots, u_m$ be the generalized coordinates which correspond to the given motion, and $v_1, v_2, \cdots, v_n$ be the generalized coordinates of parametrically excited vibrations. Thus, in problems on the vibrations of a compressed straight rod, u_k and v_k are the generalized coordinates of the longitudinal and transverse displacements, respectively; in the problems on dynamic

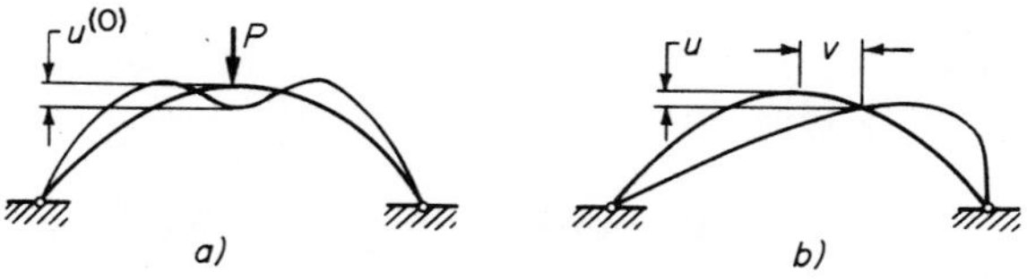

FIG. 99.

stability of the symmetrical form of vibrations of an arch (Fig. 99), u_k and v_k are the generalized coordinates for symmetric and antisymmetric deformations.

For the unperturbed motion, $u_k = u_k^{(0)}$ and $v_k = 0$ for all k. For the perturbed motion $v_k \neq 0$, and in the first approximation, as before, $u_k = u_k^{(0)}$. It can be easily shown, however, that

$$u_k = u_k^{(0)} + \frac{1}{2} \sum_{p=1}^{n} \sum_{q=1}^{n} h_{pq}^{(k)} v_p v_q + O(v_i^4), \tag{16.1}$$

where $h_{pq}^{(k)}$ are certain constants and the symbol $O(v_i^4)$ denotes terms of fourth and higher order. In the majority of problems, the deformations imparted by the initial motion can be neglected by setting $u_k^{(0)} = 0$.

For example, the longitudinal displacement of the movable end of a straight rod is

$$w = \frac{1}{2} \int_0^l \left(\frac{\partial v}{\partial x} \right)^2 dx + O(v^4)$$

(compressive deformations are neglected). Hence, if

$$v(x, t) = \sum_{k=1}^{n} f_k(t) \varphi_k(x),$$

it is found to within the second order terms that

$$w = \frac{1}{2} \sum_{p=1}^{n} \sum_{q=1}^{n} h_{pq} f_p f_q. \tag{16.2}$$

Here
$$h_{pq} = \int_0^l \frac{d\varphi_p}{dx}\frac{d\varphi_q}{dx}\,dx\,. \qquad (16.3)$$

Relations analogous to Eq. (16.2) can be obtained also for other elastic systems. Thus, in purely antisymmetric deformation of the arch, the crown acquires a vertical displacement u (i.e., a symmetric component) which is small of the second order in comparison with the crown's horizontal displacement v (Fig. 99b). If a narrow strip is subjected to bending-torsional deformations out of the plane of the largest rigidity, then the centers of gravity of its cross sections acquire vertical displacements. These displacements are small quantities of second order in comparison with the components of the antisymmetric deformation. The number of examples can easily be increased. Equation (16.1), however, follows directly from the statement of the dynamic stability problem.

It should be recalled that dynamic stability problems have been classified as problems on the vibrations of systems subjected to periodic parametric loading. The loading has been defined as parametric (with respect to displacements v_k) when it enters into the differential equations for the perturbed motion as a multiplier of $v_1, v_2, \cdots, v_n$.

Another definition for parametric loading will now be given. The loading will be called parametric (with respect to displacements v_k) if it performs work on displacements u_k, which by Eq. (16.1) are small quantities of the second order in comparison with v_k.

The two definitions are equivalent. To prove this, let us set up the Lagrangian equations for the perturbed motion:
$$\frac{d}{dt}\left(\frac{\partial T}{\partial v_k'}\right) - \left(\frac{\partial}{\partial v_k}\right)(T - U) = \frac{\partial V}{\partial v_k}, \qquad (k = 1, 2, \cdots, n)\,. \qquad (16.4)$$

Here T and U are the kinetic and the potential energies of the system, and V is the force function. Let Q_k be the generalized forces of the parametric loading corresponding to the displacements u_k; then, to within the second-order terms, the force function is
$$V = \tfrac{1}{2}\sum_{k=1}^{n}\sum_{p=1}^{n}\sum_{q=1}^{n} h_{pq}^{(k)} Q_k v_p v_q\,.$$

If this expression is substituted into (16.4), the "parametric" terms on the right-hand side are
$$\frac{\partial V}{\partial v_i} = \sum_{p=1}^{m}\sum_{q=1}^{n} h_{iq}^{(p)} Q_p v_q\,.$$

When displacements $u_1, u_2, \cdots, u_m$ occur, elastic, resistance, and inertial forces arise that are nonlinearly related to displacements $v_1, v_2, \cdots, v_n$. It is evident that these forces are parametric with respect to $v_1, v_2, \cdots, v_n$, and consequently enter into the differential equations of perturbed motion as coefficients of $v_1, v_2, \cdots, v_n$. This gives nonlinear expressions beginning with terms of the third order.

If the specific nonlinearities connected with the structure of the system (clearances, one-sided coupling, dry friction) are neglected, then the nonlinearities introduced above permit the description of a large class of elastic systems. If the nonlinear terms are introduced into the differential equations for the boundaries of dynamic stability, then the differential equations for the nonlinear problem are obtained.

●3. The latter procedure will be explained by an example of a straight rod which is compressed by an arbitrary load

$$N(z,\ t) = \alpha N_0(z) + \beta \Phi(t) N_t(z)\,.$$

The differential equations for the linear problem have the form

$$\boldsymbol{C}\boldsymbol{f}'' + \boldsymbol{C}\boldsymbol{\varepsilon}\boldsymbol{f}' + [\boldsymbol{E} - \alpha\boldsymbol{A} - \beta\Phi(t)\boldsymbol{B}]\boldsymbol{f} = \boldsymbol{0}\,. \tag{16.5}$$

If the normalized forms of free vibrations are taken as the eigenfunctions (as was shown in Chapter Thirteen), then

$$c_{ik} = \frac{\delta_{ik}}{\omega_i^2}\,, \qquad a_{ik} = \frac{1}{\omega_i^2}\int_0^l N_0(x)\frac{d\varphi_i}{dx}\frac{d\varphi_k}{dx}dx\,,$$

$$b_{ik} = \frac{1}{\omega_i^2}\int_0^l N_t(x)\frac{d\varphi_i}{dx}\frac{d\varphi_k}{dx}dx\,.$$

Let us assume that at the end of the rod there is a concentrated mass, longitudinal viscous friction, and longitudinal elastic coupling. If the distributed inertial forces are neglected, the additional longitudinal force is obtained

$$\Delta N(t) = -cw - k_L\frac{dw}{dt} - M\frac{d^2w}{dt^2}\,. \tag{16.6}$$

Furthermore, introducing this force into the differential equation (16.5) leads to

$$\boldsymbol{C}\boldsymbol{f}'' + \boldsymbol{C}\boldsymbol{\varepsilon}\boldsymbol{f}' + [\boldsymbol{E} - \alpha\boldsymbol{A} - \beta\Phi(t)\boldsymbol{B}]\boldsymbol{f} + \boldsymbol{V}(\boldsymbol{f}, \boldsymbol{f}', \boldsymbol{f}'')\boldsymbol{f} = \boldsymbol{0}\,, \tag{16.7}$$

where the matrix $\boldsymbol{V}$ by analogy to matrices $\boldsymbol{A}$ and $\boldsymbol{B}$ has the components

$$v_{ik} = -\frac{1}{\omega_1^2}\int_0^l \Delta N(x,t)\frac{d\varphi_i}{dx}\frac{d\varphi_k}{dx}\,.$$

Successive differentiation of Eq. (16.2) yields

$$\frac{dw}{dt} = \sum_{i=1}^n\sum_{k=1}^n h_{ik}f_if'_k\,, \qquad \frac{d^2w}{dt^2} = \sum_{i=1}^n\sum_{k=1}^n h_{ik}(f'_if''_k + f'_if'_k)\,.$$

Hence, taking Eq. (16.6) into account gives

$$v_{ik} = \frac{h_{ik}c}{2\omega_i^2}\sum_{p=1}^n\sum_{q=1}^n h_{pq}f_pf_q + \frac{h_{ik}k_L}{\omega_i^2}\sum_{p=1}^n\sum_{q=1}^n h_{pq}f_pf'_q$$
$$+ \frac{h_{ik}M_L}{\omega_i^2}\sum_{p=1}^n\sum_{q=1}^n h_{pq}(f'_pf'_q + f_pf''_q)\,.$$

The matrix differential equation (16.7) can be rewritten in the form

$$\boldsymbol{C}\boldsymbol{f}'' + \boldsymbol{C}\boldsymbol{\varepsilon}\boldsymbol{f} + [\boldsymbol{E} - \alpha\boldsymbol{A} - \beta\Phi(t)\boldsymbol{B}]\boldsymbol{f} - \boldsymbol{\psi}(\boldsymbol{f}, \boldsymbol{f}', \boldsymbol{f}'') = \boldsymbol{0}\,. \tag{16.8}$$

Here $\boldsymbol{\psi}$ is a vector with the components

$$\psi_i = \sum_{r=1}^{n} v_{ir} f_r = \frac{c}{2\omega_i^2} \sum_{p=1}^{n} \sum_{q=1}^{n} \sum_{r=1}^{n} h_{ir} h_{pq} f_p f_q f_r + \frac{k_L}{2\omega_i^2} \sum_{p=1}^{n} \sum_{q=1}^{n} \sum_{r=1}^{n} h_{ir} h_{pq} f_p f_p f'_q f_r$$
$$+ \frac{M_L}{\omega_i^2} \sum_{p=1}^{n} \sum_{q=1}^{n} \sum_{r=1}^{n} h_{ir} h_{pq} (f'_p f'_q + f_p f''_q) f_r \, .$$

The first group of terms represents "nonlinear elasticity," the second "nonlinear damping," and the last "nonlinear inertia" of the system. All of these terms are homogeneous, third-power functions of f_i, f'_i, f''_i; if subsequent terms are retained in the expansion, then, obviously, they will be of the fifth order.

●4. The method described above for constructing the nonlinear differential equations is based on separate considerations of forced and parametrically excited vibrations. More precisely, as in the construction of differential equations for linear problems, the unperturbed motion is identified with the underformed state; only the reactions of the "longitudinal" system are considered for displacements w_i which are related to deflections of the rod purely by geometry.

An approximate method for the simultaneous investigation of forced and parametrically excited oscillations for nonlinear problems was presented briefly in § 31. This method can be developed for an arbitrary elastic system; its application to general problems of dynamic stability of straight rods will be shown.

Start with the differential equations

$$\begin{aligned} \frac{\partial}{\partial x}\left(EF\frac{\partial u}{\partial x}\right) - m\frac{\partial^2 u}{\partial t^2} - \int_0^x m(\xi)\left[\frac{\partial v}{\partial \xi}\frac{\partial^3 v}{\partial \xi\, \partial t^2} + \left(\frac{\partial^2 v}{\partial \xi\, \partial t}\right)^2\right] d\xi &= -p(x, t) \, , \\ \frac{\partial^2}{\partial x^2}\left(EJ\frac{\partial^2 v}{\partial x^2}\right) + \frac{\partial}{\partial x}\left(EF\frac{\partial u}{\partial x}\frac{\partial v}{\partial x}\right) + m\frac{\partial^2 v}{\partial t^2} &= 0 \, , \end{aligned} \tag{16.9}$$

which are a generalization of Eqs. (8.4) and (8.5) for the case of a rod of variable cross section. Here $u(x, t)$ is the longitudinal displacement which will be considered positive if it is directed opposite to the x axis; $p(x, t)$ is the distributed compressive loading so that everywhere, with the exception of points of application of concentrated forces,

$$dN = p\,dx \, .$$

The lower end of the rod is fixed to prevent longitudinal displacements, and at the upper end a concentrated force

$$N(l, t) = P_0 + P_t \cos \theta t - cw - k_L \frac{dw}{dt} - M_L \frac{d^2 w}{dt^2} \, . \tag{16.10}$$

is applied, where $w(t)$ is determined from Eq. (16.2). Consequently, the boundary conditions for $u(x, t)$ are

$$\begin{aligned} u(0, t) &= 0 \, , \\ EF\frac{\partial u(l, t)}{\partial x} &= N(l, t) \, . \end{aligned} \tag{16.11}$$

The boundary conditions for the transverse deflections $v(x, t)$ can be arbitrary. The solution of the problem is sought in the form of the series

$$u(x, t) = \sum_{k=1}^{m} u_k(t)\,\psi_k(x)\,,$$
$$v(x, t) = \sum_{k=1}^{n} f_k(t)\,\varphi_k(x)\,, \tag{16.12}$$

where u_k and f_k are the functions of time which have to be determined and $\psi_k(x)$ and $\varphi_k(x)$ are the forms of longitudinal and transverse free vibrations. The functions $\psi_k(x)$ satisfy the differential equation

$$\frac{d}{dx}\left(EF\frac{d\psi}{dx}\right) + m\,\omega_L^2\,\psi = 0 \tag{16.13}$$

and the boundary conditions

$$\psi(0) = \frac{d\psi(l)}{dx} = 0 \tag{16.14}$$

(ω_L are frequencies of the longitudinal free vibrations), and functions $\varphi_k(x)$ satisfy the differential equation

$$\frac{d^2}{dx^2}\left(EJ\frac{d^2\varphi}{dx^2}\right) - m\,\omega^2\,\varphi = 0 \tag{16.15}$$

and boundary conditions established for the transverse displacements.

Let us transform the boundary conditions (16.11) to homogeneous boundary conditions of the type (16.14). The longitudinal loading is introduced:

$$\bar{p}(x, t) = p\,, \qquad (0 \le x \le l - \varepsilon)\,,$$
$$\lim_{\varepsilon\to 0}\int_{l-\varepsilon}^{l} \bar{p}(x, t)\,dx = N(l, t)\,.$$

It is necessary to introduce this loading into the right-hand side of the first differential equation (16.9) for $p(x, t)$. If series (16.12) is substituted into the differential equations (16.9) and the Galerkin method is applied, the following is obtained:

$$\int_0^l L_1(u, v)\,\psi_i(x)\,dx = \int_0^l \bar{p}(x, t)\,\psi_i(x)\,dx\,, \quad (i = 1, 2, 3, \cdots, m)\,,$$
$$\int_0^l L_2(u, v)\,\varphi_k(x)\,dx = 0\,, \qquad (k = 1, 2, 3, \cdots, n)\,,$$

where L_1 and L_2 are the left-hand sides of differential equations (16.9). Calculations give

$$u_i'' + \omega_{Li}^2\,u_i + \sum_{p=1}^{n}\sum_{q=1}^{n} g_{pq}^{(i)}\,(f_p f_q'' + f_p' f_q') = \int_0^l p\psi_i dx + \psi_i(l)N(t)\,,$$
$$(i = 1, 2, 3, \cdots, m)\,, \tag{16.16}$$
$$f_k'' + \omega_k^2 f_k + \sum_{p=1}^{m}\sum_{q=1}^{n} s_{pq}^{(k)}\,u_p f_q = 0\,, \qquad (k = 1, 2, 3, \cdots, n)\,.$$

Here, relationships (16.13) and (16.15) are used and, in addition, the condition for orthonormality of the eigenfunctions,

$$\int_0^l m\,\varphi_i \varphi_k\,dx = \int_0^l m\,\psi_i \psi_k\,dx = \delta_{ik}\,.$$

Further, the following notations are introduced:

$$g_{pq}^{(i)} = \int_0^l m \frac{d\varphi_p}{dx}\frac{d\varphi_q}{dx}\psi_i\,dx\,,$$

$$s_{pq}^{(k)} = -\int_0^l \frac{d}{dx}\left(EF\frac{d\psi_p}{dx}\frac{d\varphi_q}{dx}\right)\varphi_k\,dx\,.$$

Integrating the last formula by parts and taking into account (16.14) leads to

$$s_{pq}^{(k)} = \int_0^l EF\frac{d\varphi_k}{dx}\frac{d\varphi_q}{dx}\frac{d\psi_p}{dx}\,dx\,. \tag{16.17}$$

In place of $N(t)$, it is necessary to substitute the following expression in the first group of differential equations:

$$N(t) = P_0 + P_t\cos\theta t - \sum_{p=1}^{n}\sum_{q=1}^{n} h_{pq}\left[\frac{c}{2}f_p f_q + k_L f_p' f_q' + M(f_p f_q'' + f_p' f_q')\right].$$

●5. The system of differential equations (16.16) takes into account the interaction of forced and parametrically excited vibrations. Even for a linear approximation with respect to $v(x,t)$, these types of vibrations do not separate:

$$\begin{aligned} &u_i'' + \omega_{Li}^2 u_i = \int_0^l p\psi_i\,dx + \psi_i(l)(P_0 + P_t\cos\theta t)\,, && (i = 1, 2, \cdots, m)\,,\\ &f_k'' + \omega_k^2 f_k - \sum_{p=1}^{m}\sum_{q=1}^{m} s_{pq}^{(k)} u_p f_q = 0\,, && (k = 1, 2, \cdots, n)\,. \end{aligned} \tag{16.18}$$

However, here a successive solution of the equations is possible. Finding a solution for the problem of longitudinal oscillation $u(x,t)$ and substituting it into the equations for dynamic stability gives

$$N(x,t) = EF\frac{\partial u(x,t)}{\partial t}\,.$$

This corresponds to taking into account "linear" interaction between a given and a parametrically excited motion. The application of this method to a simple problem was shown in § 30.

If the terms with u_i'' in Eqs. (16.18) are omitted, then a "quasi-statical" value for $u(x,t)$ is found:

$$u(x,t) = \sum_{i=1}^{m}\frac{\psi_i(x)}{\omega_{Li}^2}\left[\int_0^l p\psi_i d\xi + \psi_i(l)(P_0 + P_t\cos\theta t)\right].$$

This gives, as a final result, the usual approximation of linear theory. If $u(x,t)$ is determined from Eqs. (16.16), then the approximate nonlinear equations (16.8) for $u_i'' = 0$ are obtained.

The proper choice of an approximation is based on the following. Let ω_L be the lower natural frequency of the motion whose stability is to be investigated (for a compressed rod this is the frequency of free longitudinal vibrations). If

$$\beta = \frac{\theta^2}{\omega_L^2} \ll 1 ,$$

then the transverse forces arising in the system can be determined "quasi-statically," i.e., without considering the forced oscillations. In the third part of this book, problems will be discussed in which simultaneous consideration of given and perturbed motion is necessary.

§ 67. The Relationship Between Linear and Nonlinear Theories

● 1. The problems of dynamic stability are essentially nonlinear problems; hence the question arises concerning the extent of applicability of the linear theory. The proper relationship between linear theory and theory based on nonlinear differential equations can be understood on the basis of the Liapunov theory[1] of the stability of motion.

Let the motion of the system be described by the differential equations of the form

$$\frac{dx_i}{dt} = F_i(t, x_1, x_2, \cdots, x_n), \qquad (i = 1, 2, \cdots, n), \tag{16.19}$$

where $F_i(t, x_1, x_2, \cdots, x_n)$ are some continuous nonlinear functions of time and of the generalized coordinates $x_1, x_2, \cdots, x_n$.

Let us consider any particular solution of system (16.19)

$$x_i = f_i(t) , \qquad (i = 1, 2, \cdots, n) ,$$

which corresponds to the unperturbed motion. Besides the unperturbed motion, consider also other neighboring motions

$$x_i = f_i(t) + \xi_i(t) , \qquad (i = 1, 2, \cdots, n) ,$$

whose initial conditions differ very little from the initial conditions for $f_i(t)$. These motions will be called *perturbed* and the differences

$$f_i(t) - x_i(t)$$

will be called *perturbations*.

The definition of stability (instability) of motion as formulated by Liapunov will now be stated. Let $\varepsilon_1, \varepsilon_2, \cdots, \varepsilon_n$ be arbitrary positive numbers. If for any arbitrarily small ε_k, positive numbers exist such that for any initial perturbations which satisfy the conditions

$$| \xi_i(t_0) | \leqq \eta_i , \qquad (i = 1, 2, \cdots, n) ,$$

and for any $t > t_0$, the inequality

$$| \xi_i(t) | < \varepsilon_i , \qquad (i = 1, 2, \cdots, n) , \tag{16.20}$$

[1] Liapunov [1] and also Chetayev [1].

holds, then the unperturbed motion is stable; otherwise it is unstable. In other words, the motion is called *stable* if small changes in the initial conditions slightly deviate the system from the unperturbed motion; by decreasing the initial perturbations, it is possible to make the deviations for $t > t_0$ arbitrarily small.

If a stronger condition than (16.20) is satisfied, namely, if the perturbations damp out asymptotically with time,

$$\lim_{t \to \infty} |\xi_i(t)| = 0 , \qquad (i = 1, 2, \cdots, n) ,$$

then the motion is called *asymptotically stable.*

● **2.** Frequently, in judging the stability of unperturbed motion, the "*variational equations*" which correspond to the given system of differential equations have decisive importance. To obtain the variational equations, the following method will be used. The perturbed values of x_i are substituted in (16.19):

$$\frac{d}{dt}(f_i + \xi_i) = F_i(t, f_1 + \xi_1, f_2 + \xi_2, \cdots, f_n + \xi_n) , \qquad (i = 1, 2, \cdots, n) .$$

If the right-hand side of a power series is expanded with respect to perturbations and it is taken into account that f_i satisfies the differential equations of unperturbed motion, then it is found that

$$\frac{d\xi_i}{dt} = \sum_{k=1}^{n} p_{ik}\xi_k + R_i(t, \xi_1, \xi_2, \cdots, \xi_n) .$$

Here

$$p_{ik} = \frac{\partial F_i(t, f_1, f_2, \cdots, f_n)}{\partial f_k} ,$$

and R_i are terms of the expansion which contain powers of ξ_k higher than one. If these terms are neglected, then the *variational equations* are obtained:

$$\frac{d\xi_i}{dt} = \sum_{k=1}^{n} p_{ik}\xi_k , \qquad (i = 1, 2, \cdots, n) . \tag{16.21}$$

If in the initial system (16.19) F_i depends periodically on time and if the stability of periodic solution is investigated, then the system (16.21) has periodic coefficients. The problem of the stability of a given motion is then is reduced to a system of linear differential equations with periodic coefficients.

The clarification of cases in which the differential equations of the first approximation completely solve the problem of the stability of nonlinear systems is due to Liapunov. An important role is played here by the roots of the characteristic equation of system (16.21), which will be referred to simply as "the characteristic equation" in subsequent discussions.

The following theorem results from the above.

If all of the roots of the characteristic equation are smaller in absolute value than unity, then the unperturbed motion is asymptotically stable regardless of the terms of higher order in the equations of perturbed motion. But if the characteristic equation has roots larger in absolute value than unity, then the unperturbed motion is unstable.

If the characteristic equation has no roots larger in absolute value than unity but has roots equal in absolute value to unity, then the stability remains uncertain (critical case); in this case the first approximation does not solve the problem of the stability of motion. For the solution of this problem, it is necessary to consider higher order terms in the differential equations of perturbed motion; the stability or instability of motion will depend on the magnitudes of these terms.

● **3.** Let us return to the differential equations of dynamic stability. It can easily be seen that the differential equations for the linear problem (16.5) are the variational equations for the system of differential equations (16.8), constructed under the condition that the undeformed state of the system is perturbed.

Indeed, the system of differential equation (16.8) has the trival solution $\boldsymbol{f} = \boldsymbol{0}$. If in (16.8) the perturbed value $\boldsymbol{f} + \boldsymbol{\xi}$ is substituted for $\boldsymbol{f}$ and the nonlinear terms are neglected, this leads to (16.5), where $\boldsymbol{f}$ is used in place of $\boldsymbol{\xi}$.

It follows from the Liapunov theorem that the trivial solution of the nonlinear system is stable everywhere except in the regions of excitation of the linear system (i. e., in the regions of dynamic instability). Within the limits of these regions, the trivial solution is unstable. Consequently, the linear theory completely answers the question on the stability of the initial form of motion (which is identified with the undeformed state).

Certain difficulties can arise is connection with the conservative problem. In this case, outside the limits of the excitation regions the roots of the characteristic equation are equal in absolute value to unity; therefore, at first glance it seems that here a critical case must be dealt with, where the first approximation does not resolve the question on the stability of solutions.

However, one must take into account the case of roots which are equal in absolute value to unity and which belongs exclusively to conservative systems, and must be considered as a result of the idealization of real systems. The introduction of infinitesimal damping (complete dissipation) into the corresponding differential equations gives the asymptotic stability of trivial solutions everywhere except in the region of excitation.

The generalized differential equations (16.16) will now be considered. If "longitudinal" and "transverse" damping are introduced with coefficients ε_L and ε, Eqs. (16.16) can be rewritten in the form

$$\begin{gathered} u_i'' + 2\varepsilon_L u_i' + \omega_{Li}^2 u_i + F_i(f_p, f_p', f_p'') \\ = \int_0^l p\Psi_i \, dx + \phi_i(l)(P_0 + P_t \cos \theta t) , \\ f_k'' + 2\varepsilon f_k' + \omega_k^2 f_k - \sum_{p=1}^{m} \sum_{q=1}^{n} s_{pq}^{(k)} u_p f_q = 0 , \\ (i = 1, 2, \cdots, m , \qquad k = 1, 2, \cdots, n) , \end{gathered} \tag{16.22}$$

where F_i is the *sum* of the second-order terms on the left-hand and right-hand sides of the differential equations (16.16). For the given unperturbed motion all $f_i = 0$, and u_i are determined from the linear system

$$u_i'' + 2\varepsilon_L u_i' + \omega_{Li}^2 u_i = \int_0^l p\Psi_i\,dx + \psi_i(l)(P_0 + P_t \cos\theta t)\,,$$
$$(i = 1, 2, \cdots, m)\,. \qquad (16.23)$$

Let us denote the solution of (16.23) by $u_{0i}(t)$. Then, for the perturbed motion

$$\begin{aligned} u_i &= u_{0i} + \bar{u}_i\,, \\ f_j &= \bar{f}_i\,, \end{aligned} \qquad (16.24)$$

where the bars denote small perturbations. If (16.24) is substituted into (16.22) and it is taken into account that the functions u_{0i} satisfy (16.23), then the following differential equations for the perturbed motion are obtained:

$$\bar{u}_i'' + 2\varepsilon_L \bar{u}_i' + \omega_{Li}^2 \bar{u}_i + F_i(\bar{f}_p, \bar{f}_p', \bar{f}_p'') = 0\,,$$
$$\bar{f}_k'' + 2\varepsilon \bar{f}_k' + \omega_k^2 \bar{f}_k - \sum_{p=1}^{m}\sum_{q=1}^{n} s_{pq}^{(k)}(u_{0p} + \bar{u}_p)\bar{f}_p = 0\,,$$
$$(i = 1, 2, \cdots, m, \qquad k = 1, 2, \cdots, n)\,.$$

The variational equations take the following form (the bars are omitted in further discussions):

$$u_i'' + 2\varepsilon_L u_i' + \omega_{Li}^2 u_i = 0\,,$$
$$f_k'' + 2\varepsilon f_k' + \omega_k^2 f_k - \sum_{p=1}^{m}\sum_{q=1}^{n} s_{pq}^{(k)} u_{0p} f_q = 0$$
$$(i = 1, 2, \cdots, m\,, \qquad k = 1, 2, \cdots, n)\,.$$

From the first group of differential equations, it is evident that perturbations damp out asymptotically with time. The second group of differential equations can be represented in the form

$$f_k'' + 2\varepsilon f_k' + \omega_i^2 f_i - \sum_{k=1}^{n} r_{ik} f_k = 0\,, \qquad (i = 1, 2, \cdots, n)\,, \qquad (16.25)$$

where
$$r_{ik} = \sum_{p=1}^{m} s_{pk}^{(i)} u_{0p}\,.$$

Taking Eq. (16.17) into account leads to[2]

$$r_{ik} = \sum_{p=1}^{m} u_{0p} \int_0^l EF \frac{d\varphi_i}{dx}\frac{d\varphi_k}{dx}\frac{d\psi_p}{dx}\,dx = \int_0^l N_d(x, t)\frac{d\varphi_i}{dx}\frac{d\varphi_k}{dx}\,dx\,.$$

Here
$$\begin{aligned} N_d(x, t) &= EF\frac{\partial u_0(x, t)}{\partial x}\,, \\ u_0(x, t) &= \sum_{p=1}^{m} u_{0p}\psi_p(x)\,. \end{aligned} \qquad (16.26)$$

Thus, the problem reduces to the usual linear differential equations for the boundaries of dynamic stability, the difference being that the dynamic force

[2] Translators' footnote: The subscript d in $N_d(x, t)$ denotes the dynamic force.

(16.26) is introduced in place of the force $N(x, t)$ which is determined from quasi-statical considerations.

Let

$$\int_0^l p\psi_i \, dx + \psi_i(l)(P_0 + P_t \cos \theta t) = (\alpha + \beta \cos \theta t) Q_i ,$$

where Q_i is a generalized force corresponding to the displacement u_i. From Eq. (16.23) it follows that

$$u_{0i}(t) = \frac{\alpha Q_i}{\omega_{Li}^2} + \frac{\beta Q_i \cos \theta t}{\sqrt{(\omega_{Li}^2 - \theta^2)^2 + 4\theta^2 \varepsilon_L^2}} .$$

Hence, taking into account (16.26) yields

$$N_d(x, t) = \alpha EF \sum_{i=1}^{m} \frac{Q_i}{\omega_{Li}^2} \frac{d\psi_i}{dx} + \beta EF \cos \theta t \sum_{i=1}^{m} \frac{Q_i \dfrac{d\psi_i}{dx}}{\sqrt{(\omega_{Li}^2 - \theta^2)^2 + 4\theta^2 \varepsilon_L^2}} .$$

For the case where the forced vibrations can be described by a single generalized coordinate, an approximate equation results:

$$N_d(x, t) \approx \alpha N_0(x) + \frac{\beta N_t(x) \cos \theta t}{\sqrt{\left(1 - \dfrac{\theta^2}{\omega_L^2}\right)^2 + \dfrac{4\theta^2 \varepsilon_L^2}{\omega_L^4}}} .$$

In conclusion note that the results of this subsection are based on the assumption that the nonlinear functions in Eq. (16.19) are continuous for all arguments. Otherwise the theorem on stability from the first approximation becomes inapplicable. As an example of a system with discontinuous nonlinear functions, consider a system with dry friction. As is known, the resistance force in this case is

$$R_i = -k_i \operatorname{sign} f_i' ;$$

consequently, nonlinear functions have a discontinuity of the first kind for $f_i' = 0$.

§ 68. Periodic Solutions of Nonlinear Differential Equations with Periodic Coefficients

●1. To find periodic solutions of nonlinear differential equations, simple approximate methods based on expansion into trigonometric series are used in the first part of the book (§§ 19–20). The disadvantage of this method lies in the fact that the existence of periodic solutions must be postulated but the convergence of the series remains unproved.

General methods for finding periodic solutions for a system of differential equations were given by Poincaré and Liapunov[3]. On the basis of these methods, Mandel'shtam and Papaleksi developed a theory for the periodic solutions of systems with periodic coefficients and small nonlinearities[4]. A periodic solution of a linear system with periodic coefficients is taken as a

[3] Liapunov [1] and Poincaré [1]; see also Malkin [1].

[4] Mandel'shtam and Papeleksi [2].

starting point. On the basis of this solution, an approximate periodic solution of a nonlinear system is found by the method of successive approximations. Simultaneously, the conditions for the existence of periodic solutions are established.

Consider a system of equations

$$\frac{dx_i}{dt} + \sum_{k=1}^{n} p_{ik} x_k + \mu V_i(x_1, x_2, \cdots, x_n, t) = 0, \quad (i = 1, 2, 3, \cdots, n), \tag{16.27}$$

where p_{ik} are periodic functions of time with period T, V_i are the nonlinear functions of $x_1, x_2, \cdots, x_n$ and are periodic functions of time (with period T), and μ is a small parameter. It is assumed that these functions are continuous with respect to their arguments.

In contrast to functions ψ_i in the differential equations (16.8), the functions V_i can also contain linear terms. The latter are chosen in such a way that the system

$$\frac{d\xi_i}{dt} + \sum_{k=1}^{n} p_{ik}\xi_k = 0, \quad (i = 1, 2, 3, \cdots, n), \tag{16.28}$$

has a periodic solution. The system of differential equations (16.28) which is obtained from (16.27) for $\mu = 0$ is called the *abbreviated system.*

Besides system (16.28), also consider its *conjugate*, i.e., a system obtained from (16.28) by means of replacing the matrix p_{ik} by the transposed matrix taken with the opposite sign:

$$\frac{d\eta_i}{dt} - \sum_{k=1}^{n} p_{ki}\eta_k = 0, \quad (i = 1, 2, 3, \cdots, n), \tag{16.29}$$

As is known, the solutions of the given and the conjugate system satisfy the condition

$$\xi_1\eta_1 + \xi_2\eta_2 + \cdots + \xi_n\eta_n = \text{const.} \tag{16.30}$$

To verify this condition, it is sufficient to differentiate (16.30) with respect to time and make use of Eqs. (16.28) and (16.29). The following theorem, established by Liapunov, results from (16.30):

If ρ_k is a root of the characteristic equation for the system of differential equations (16.28), then $1/\rho_k$ is a root of the characteristic equation for the conjugate system. Therefore, the multiplicity of both roots and the structure of the elementary divisors in both systems are the same.

It also follows from (16.30) that if a complete solution of the system of differential equations (16.28) is known, then the determination of solutions for the conjugate system reduces to the solution of linear algebraic equations.

● 2. It is known from the theory of linear differential equations with periodic coefficients (Chapters Fourteen and Fifteen) that a periodic solution of the system of differential equations (16.28), if it exists, has a period T or $2T$. The problem consists in establishing whether or not a periodic solution of the nonlinear system (16.27) with the same period as in the linear system

(16.28) exists for sufficiently small values of μ; if such a solution exists, it is found by various approximation methods. We must now find those solutions of the nonlinear system of differential equations which for sufficiently small μ differ slightly from the corresponding solutions of the abbreviated system, or more precisely, those solutions which for $\mu = 0$ reduce to the corresponding solution of system (16.28).

Let

$$\xi_i = \xi_i(t), \qquad (i = 1, 2, 3, \cdots, n), \tag{16.31}$$

be an arbitrary periodic solution of the abbreviated system that satisfies the initial conditions

$$\xi_1(0) = C, \qquad \xi_i(0) = 0, \qquad (i = 2, 3, \cdots, n). \tag{16.32}$$

This solution is called a *generating* solution. The periodic solution of a nonlinear system, if it exists, will depend on the small parameter μ and, in addition, on n parameters β_i:

$$x_i = x_i(t, \beta_1, \beta_2, \cdots, \beta_n, \mu), \qquad (i = 1, 2, 3, \cdots, n). \tag{16.33}$$

The parameters β represent small changes of initial conditions:

$$\begin{aligned} x_1(0, \beta_1, \beta_2, \cdots, \beta_n, \mu) &= C + \beta_1, \\ x_i(0, \beta_1, \beta_2, \cdots, \beta_n, \mu) &= \beta_i, \qquad (i = 2, 3, \cdots, n). \end{aligned} \tag{16.34}$$

The values of β_i as functions of μ will be selected in such a way that they vanish for $\mu = 0$ and that the solution (16.33) is periodic with a period T (or $2T$). In other words, β_i will be selected so that (16.33) will be a periodic solution that reduces to a generating solution (16.31) for $\mu = 0$. The condition for periodicity of the functions x_i has the form

$$x_i(T, \beta_1, \beta_2, \cdots, \beta_n, \mu) - x_i(0, \beta_1, \beta_2, \cdots, \beta_n, \mu) = 0 \qquad (i = 1, 2, 3, \cdots, n). \tag{16.35}$$

The left-hand sides of (16.35) are denoted by ψ_i; they are expanded in a series of $\beta_1, \beta_2, \beta_3, \cdots, \beta_n$. From the periodicity of the generating solution, it follows that for $\beta_1 = \beta_2 = \cdots = \beta_n = \mu = 0$, all ψ_i vanish. Hence

$$\psi_i(\beta_1, \beta_2, \cdots, \beta_n, \mu) = \frac{\partial\psi_i}{\partial\beta_1}\beta_1 + \frac{\partial\psi_i}{\partial\beta_2}\beta_2 + \cdots + \frac{\partial\psi_i}{\partial\beta_n}\beta_n + \frac{\partial\psi_i}{\partial\mu}\mu + \cdots,$$

where the terms of higher orders are not written out. (The derivatives $\partial\psi_i/\partial\beta_k$ and $\partial\psi_i/\partial\mu$ are formed for $\beta_1 = \beta_2 = \cdots = \beta_n = \mu = 0$.) The determinant of the coefficients of the first powers of β_1 has the form

$$\frac{\partial(\psi_1, \psi_2, \cdots, \psi_n)}{\partial(\beta_1, \beta_2, \cdots, \beta_n)} = \begin{vmatrix} \frac{\partial\psi_1}{\partial\beta_1} & \frac{\partial\psi_1}{\partial\beta_2} & \cdots & \frac{\partial\psi_1}{\partial\beta_n} \\ \frac{\partial\psi_2}{\partial\beta_1} & \frac{\partial\psi_2}{\partial\beta_2} & \cdots & \frac{\partial\psi_2}{\partial\beta_n} \\ \cdot & \cdot & \cdots & \cdot \\ \frac{\partial\psi_n}{\partial\beta_1} & \frac{\partial\psi_n}{\partial\beta_2} & \cdots & \frac{\partial\psi_n}{\partial\beta_n} \end{vmatrix}. \tag{16.36}$$

If the determinant (16.36) differs from zero, then a unique system of functions $\beta_i(\mu)$ exists which satisfies conditions (16.35) and vanishes for $\mu = 0$. These functions are analytical for sufficiently small values of μ. Thus the following *theorem of Poincaré* is obtained.

If the functional determinant (16.36) of the considered generating solution does not vanish for $\beta_1 = \beta_2 = \cdots = \beta_n = \mu = 0$, *then for sufficiently small values of* μ *one and only one periodic solution of the nonlinear system exists which for* $\mu = 0$ *reduces to the generating solution.*

●3. The actual computation of periodic solutions presents serious difficulties. The functions x_i will be sought in the form of a series in integers of positive powers of $\beta_1, \beta_2, \cdots, p_n, \mu$. Considering the fact that generating solution must be obtained for $\beta_1 = \beta_2 = \cdots = \beta_n = \mu = 0$ leads to the assumption

$$x_i = \xi_i + \mu A_i(t) + \sum_{k=1}^{n} \beta_k B_{ik}(t) + \cdots, \qquad (i = 1, 2, 3, \cdots n) \qquad (16.37)$$

(terms of higher order are not written out). Here in accordance with the initial conditions (16.34),

$$A_i(0) = 0, \qquad B_{ik}(0) = \delta_{ik}. \qquad (16.38)$$

For the determination of functions $A_i(t)$ and $B_{ik}(t)$, the series (16.37) is substituted into the basic differential equation (16.27). By virtue of (16.28), after comparing the coefficients of μ and β_i, we obtain the differential equation system

$$\begin{aligned} \frac{dA_i}{dt} + \sum_{k=1}^{n} p'_{ik} A_k &= 0, \qquad (i = 1, 2, 3, \cdots, n), \\ \frac{dB_{ij}}{dt} + \sum_{k=1}^{n} p'_{ik} B_{kj} &= 0, \qquad (i, j = 1, 2, 3, \cdots, n), \end{aligned} \qquad (16.39)$$

and an analogous system for determining coefficients of higher terms of the expansion (16.37). In the differential equations (16.39) we have

$$p'_{ik} = p_{ik} + \frac{\partial V_i(\xi_1, \xi_2, \cdots, \xi_n, t)}{\partial \xi_k}. \qquad (16.40)$$

It is evident from formula (16.40) that the coefficients p'_{ik} are periodic functions of time. Thus, the determination of functions $A_i(t)$ and $B_{ik}(t)$ requires the solution of a system of linear differential equations with periodic coefficients.

The difficulties in finding the periodic solution do not end here. The coefficients of series (16.37) and, consequently, the solutions x_i as functions of n parameters $\beta_1, \beta_2, \cdots, \beta_n$ can be found when the system of differential equations (16.39) is solved. These parameters must be determined from conditions (16.35).

Here the following must be taken into consideration. It is seen from the initial conditions (16.32) that the generating solution is determined to within a constant C. The presence of only one constant is quite natural: the periodic solution of the linear abbreviated system can be determined only to within a constant multiplier. This corresponds to the well-known fact from mechanics that the amplitude of the linear system remains indeterminate.

The consideration of nonlinear terms will remove this indeterminancy. The first question that arises here is: near which solution of the linear system does the periodic solution of the nonlinear system lie? In other words, it is necessary first to find the value of the constant multiplier in the solution of the abbreviated system of differential equations. This will be the zero approximation for the "amplitude" of the nonlinear system. For practical purposes, the zero approximation frequently turns out to be sufficient.

● **4.** For further calculations the system of differential equations (16.27) will be transformed so that [the abbreviated system (16.28) has constant coefficients. Such a transformation is always possible, in view of the following theorem:

An arbitrary system of linear differential equations with periodic coefficients can be transformed into a system of linear differential equations with constant coefficients, with the aid of some nonsingular linear transformation with periodic coefficients.

This will be shown in the example of the abbreviated system (16.28). For the case where this system has one periodic solution with a period T and all of the elementary divisors are simple, the complete system of solutions has the form

$$\begin{aligned} \xi_{i1} &= \varphi_{i1}(t)\,, &\quad (i &= 1,\,2,\,3,\cdots,\,n)\,, \\ \xi_{ik} &= e^{-h_k t}\varphi_{ik}(t) &\quad (k &= 2,\,3,\,\cdots,\,n)\,, \end{aligned}$$

where $\varphi_{ik}(t)$ are the periodic funtions with the period T, and $h_k = \ln \rho_k / T$ are the characteristic exponents. The first index denotes the number of the function; the second denotes the number of the solution.

For the conjugate system, the following is obtained on the basis of the Liapunov theorem (see p. 261):

$$\begin{aligned} \eta_{i1} &= \psi_{i1}(t)\,, &\quad (i &= 1,2,3,\cdots,n) \\ \eta_{ik} &= e^{-h_k t}\psi_{ik}(t) &\quad (k &= 2,\,3,\,\cdots,\,n)\,, \end{aligned} \tag{16.41}$$

where $\psi_{ik}(t)$ are periodic functions. Formula (16.30) yields

$$\sum_{i=1}^{n} \xi_{i1}\psi_{i1} = \text{const.}\,,$$

$$e^{-h_k t}\sum_{i=1}^{n} \xi_{ik}\psi_{ik} = \text{const.}\,, \qquad (k = 2,3,\cdots,n)\,.$$

Differentiating with respect to time and denoting

$$\sum_{i=1}^{n} \xi_{ik}\psi_{ik} = \zeta_k\,, \qquad (1,\,2,\,3,\,\cdots,\,n)\,, \tag{16.42}$$

gives the following differential equations with constant coefficients:

$$\begin{aligned} &\frac{d\zeta_1}{dt} = 0\,, \\ &\frac{d\zeta_i}{dt} - h_i\zeta_i = 0\,, \qquad (i = 2, 3, \cdots, n)\,. \end{aligned} \tag{16.43}$$

Thus, the system of differential equations with periodic coefficients (16.28) was transformed to the form (16.43) by using substitution (16.42).

Let us return to the initial system of nonlinear differential equations

$$\frac{dx_i}{dt} + \sum_{k=1}^{n} p_{ik}x_k + \mu V_i(x_1, x_2, \cdots, x_n, t) = 0\,, \quad (i = 1, 2, 3, \cdots, n)\,. \tag{16.44}$$

It will be transformed in such a way that the abbreviated system for the transformed equations coincides with (16.43). Together with (16.44), consider the system of differential equations

$$\frac{d\eta_i}{dt} - \sum_{k=1}^{n} p_{ki}\eta_k = 0\,, \qquad (i = 1, 2, 3, \cdots, n)\,. \tag{16.45}$$

Multiplying the ith equation of (16.44) by η_i, the ith equation of (16.45) by x_i, and adding the results leads to

$$\frac{d}{dt}\sum_{i=1}^{n} x_i\eta_i + \mu \sum_{i=1}^{n} \eta_i V_i(x_1, x_2, \cdots, x_n, t) = 0\,.$$

Substitution of (16.41) gives for n independent solutions

$$\frac{d}{dt}\sum_{i=1}^{n} x_i\psi_{i1} + \mu \sum_{i=1}^{n} \psi_{i1} V_i(x_1, x_2, \cdots, x_n, t) = 0\,,$$

$$\frac{d}{dt}\sum_{i=1}^{n} x_i\psi_{ik} - h_k \sum_{i=1}^{n} x_i\psi_{ik} + \mu \sum_{i=1}^{n} \psi_{ik} V_i(x_1, x_2, \cdots, x_n, t) = 0\,,$$

$$(k = 2, 3, \cdots, n)\,.$$

Introducing the notation

$$\begin{aligned} &\sum_{i=1}^{n} x_i\psi_{ik} = z_k\,, \\ &\sum_{i=1}^{n} \psi_{ik} V_i(x_1, x_2, \cdots, x_n, t) = F_k(z_1, z_2, \cdots, z_n, t)\,, \\ &(k = 1, 2, 3, \cdots, n)\,, \end{aligned} \tag{16.46}$$

yields the transformed system

$$\begin{aligned} &\frac{dz_1}{dt} + \mu F_1(z_1, z_2, \cdots, z_n, t) = 0\,, \\ &\frac{dz_i}{dt} - h_i z_i + \mu F_i(z_1, z_2, \cdots, z_n, t) = 0\,, \\ &(i = 2, 3, \cdots, n)\,. \end{aligned} \tag{16.47}$$

Its abbreviated system coincides, obviously, with (16.43). It is evident that periodic solutions of system (16.47) correspond to periodic solutions x_i.

● 5. The periodic solution of the abbreviated system of differential equations can be determined without difficulty; it has the form

$$\zeta_1 = C\,, \; \zeta_i = 0\,, \qquad (i = 2,\, 3,\, \cdots,\, n)\,. \tag{16.48}$$

A solution of the system of differential equations (16.47) which satisfies the initial conditions will now be constructed:

$$z_1(0) = C + \beta_1\,, \quad z_i(0) = \beta_i\,, \qquad (i = 2,\, 3,\cdots,\, n)\,.$$

Integrating Eqs. (16.47) gives

$$\begin{aligned} z_1(t) &= C + \beta_1 - \mu \int_0^t F_1(z_1\,, z_2\,,\cdots,\, z_n\,, \tau)\, d\tau\,, \\ z_i(t) &= \beta_i e^{h_i t} - \mu e^{h_i t} \int_0^t e^{-h_i \tau} F_i(z_1\,, z_2\,,\cdots,\, z_n\,, \tau)\, d\tau\,, \\ &\qquad (i = 2,\, 3,\, \cdots,\, n)\,. \end{aligned} \tag{16.49}$$

The condition of the periodicity of solution requires that

$$\begin{aligned} z_1(T) - z_1(0) &= -\mu \int_0^T F_1(z_1\,, z_2\,, \cdots,\, z_n\,, t)\, dt = 0\,, \\ z_i(T) - z_i(0) &= \beta_i(e^{h_i T} - 1) - \mu e^{h_i T} \int_0^T e^{-h_i t} F_i(z_1\,, z_2\,, \cdots,\, z_n\,, t)\, dt = 0 \\ &\qquad (i = 2,\, 3,\, \cdots,\, n)\,. \end{aligned} \tag{16.50}$$

The first of Eqs. (16.50) can be used for determining the "amplitude" C of the zero approximation. The condition

$$\int_0^T F_1(z_1\,, z_2\,,\cdots,\, z_n\,, t)\, dt = 0$$

must be fulfilled for arbitrary, sufficiently small values of μ. But for $\mu \to 0$, in accordance with (16.48), $z_1 = C$, $z_i = 0$ $(i = 2, 3,\cdots, n)$. Hence the equation for C is obtained

$$\int_0^T F_1(C,\, 0,\, 0,\cdots,\, t)\; dt = 0\,. \tag{16.51}$$

Solving this equation yields the "amplitude" of the zero approximation.

The conditions for the existence of the periodic solution will now be considered. Denote

$$\begin{aligned} \psi_1 &= \int_0^T F_1(z_1\,, z_2\,, \cdots,\, z_n\,, t)\, dt\,, \\ \psi_i &= -\mu e^{h_i T} \int_0^T e^{-h_i t} F_i(z_1\,, z_2\,, \cdots,\, z_n\,, t)\, dt + \beta_i(e^{h_i T} - 1)\,, \\ &\qquad (i = 2,\, 3,\, \cdots,\, n)\,, \end{aligned}$$

and construct the functional determinant (16.36) for

$$\beta_1 = \beta_2 = \cdots = \beta_n = \mu = 0\,.$$

It is clear from (16.49) that the parameter β_1 enters into the expression for ψ_1 in the first power and with the coefficients $[\partial\psi_1/\partial z]$ (the brackets indicate the fact that, after differentiation, it is necessary to set $z_1 = C$ and $z_i = 0$

for $i = 2, 3, \cdots, n$). The determinant (16.36) assumes the form

$$\frac{\partial(\psi_1, \psi_2, \cdots, \psi_n)}{\partial(\beta_1, \beta_2, \cdots, \beta_n)} = \begin{vmatrix} \left[\frac{\partial \psi_1}{\partial z_1}\right] & 0 & 0 & \cdots & 0 \\ 0 & e^{h_2 T} - 1 & 0 & \cdots & 0 \\ 0 & 0 & e^{h_3 T} - 1 & \cdots & 0 \\ \vdots & \vdots & \vdots & & \vdots \\ 0 & 0 & 0 & \cdots & e^{h_n T} - 1 \end{vmatrix} .$$

Consequently,

$$\frac{\partial(\psi_1, \psi_2, \cdots, \psi_n)}{\partial(\beta_1, \beta_2, \cdots, \beta_n)} = \left[\frac{\partial \psi_1}{\partial z_1}\right] \prod_{k=2}^{n} (e^{h_k T} - 1) .$$

From the fact that the abbreviated system of differential equations (16.28) has a unique periodic solution, it is found that all h_k ($k \geq 2$) are different from zero. Hence, the condition for the existence of the periodic solution of the nonlinear differential equation system is

$$\left[\frac{\partial \psi_1}{\partial z_1}\right] \neq 0 .$$

If the functions ψ_1 and $\partial\psi_1/\partial z_1$ vanish simultaneously from $z_1 = C$, then C is a multiple root of Eq. (16.51).

If the abbreviated system of differential equations (16.28) has a unique periodic solution and Eq. (16.51) has simple real roots, then for sufficiently small values of μ the nonlinear system of differential equations (16.27) has a periodic solution which reduces to the generating solution for $\mu = 0$. The zero approximation is determined from the linear system of equations

$$\sum_{k=1}^{n} x_k \psi_{k1} = C ,$$

$$\sum_{k=1}^{n} x_k \psi_{ki} = 0 , \qquad (i = 2, 3, \cdots, n) , \tag{16.52}$$

where C is a root of Eq. (16.51).

§ 69. Example. The Case of a System of Second Order

●1. Consider the differential equation of the second order

$$\frac{d^2 f}{dt^2} + 2\varepsilon \frac{df}{dt} + \Omega^2(1 - 2\mu \cos \theta t) f + \gamma f^3 = 0 . \tag{16.53}$$

Equation (16.53) will be rewritten in such a way that its "linear" part admits a periodic solution. This can be accomplished by various methods, by varying ε, μ, and Ω. Thus, for a fixed μ it is always possible to find an appropriate frequency Ω_* and an appropriate damping coefficient ε_*. Then Eq. (16.53) takes the form

$$\frac{d^2 f}{dt^2} + 2\varepsilon_* \frac{df}{dt} + \Omega_*^2(1 - 2\mu \cos \theta t) f + V\left(f, \frac{df}{dt}, t\right) = 0 , \tag{16.54}$$

where

$$V\left(f, \frac{df}{dt}, t\right) = \gamma f^3 + (\Omega^2 - \Omega_*^2)(1 - 2\mu \cos \theta t) f + 2(\varepsilon - \varepsilon_*) \frac{df}{dt} . \quad (16.55)$$

It is assumed here that the small parameter is included in expression

$$V\left(f, \frac{df}{dt}, t\right).$$

Consequently, all three components in (16.55) must be small i.e., Ω and Ω_*, and ε and ε_* must be sufficiently close in magnitude. The values of ε_* and Ω_* will now determined. For this purpose, the differential equation (16.54) is transformed to a nondimensional form and a new variable $\theta t = 2\tau$ is introduced:

$$\frac{d^2 f}{d\tau^2} + \frac{4\varepsilon_*}{\Theta} \frac{df}{d\tau} + \frac{4\Omega_*^2}{\Theta^2}(1 - 2\mu \cos 2\tau) f + V\left(f, \frac{df}{d\tau}, \tau\right) = 0 . \quad (16.56)$$

Compare this differential equation with the linear differential equation of dynamic stability expressed in a nondimensional form:

$$\frac{d^2 f}{d\tau^2} + \frac{4\varepsilon}{\theta} \frac{df}{d\tau} + \frac{4\Omega^2}{\theta^2}(1 - 2\mu \cos 2\tau) f = 0 . \quad (16.57)$$

Equation (16.57) has a periodic solution for $\theta = \theta_*$, where θ_* is the boundary frequency. Comparing the coefficients gives

$$\Omega_* = \Omega(\theta/\theta_*) , \qquad \varepsilon_* = \varepsilon(\theta/\theta_*) . \quad (16.58)$$

The condition that the function (16.55) has to be small thus leads to a requirement that the excitation frequency θ, for which a solution of the nonlinear system is sought, be sufficiently close to one of the boundary frequencies θ_*.

● **2.** If $f = x_1$ and $df/dt = x_2$, then the differential equation (16.54) can be written in the following form:

$$\begin{aligned} \frac{dx_1}{dt} - x_2 &= 0 , \\ \frac{dx_2}{dt} + 2\varepsilon_* x_2 + \Omega_*^2(1 - 2\mu \cos \theta t) x_1 + V(x_1, x_2, t) &= 0 . \end{aligned} \quad (16.59)$$

The corresponding abbreviated system is

$$\begin{aligned} \frac{d\xi_1}{dt} - \xi_2 &= 0 , \\ \frac{d\xi_2}{dt} + 2\varepsilon_* \xi_2 + \Omega_*^2(1 - 2\mu \cos \theta t) \xi_1 &= 0 , \end{aligned} \quad (16.60)$$

and its conjugate is

$$\begin{aligned} \frac{d\eta_1}{dt} - \Omega_*^2(1 - 2\mu \cos \theta t) \eta_2 &= 0 , \\ \frac{d\eta_2}{dt} + \eta_1 - 2\varepsilon_* \eta_2 &= 0 . \end{aligned} \quad (16.61)$$

Observe that the following differential equation for η_2 results from (16.61):

$$\frac{d^2\eta_2}{dt^2} - 2\varepsilon_* \frac{d\eta_2}{dt} + \Omega_*^2(1 - 2\mu \cos \theta t)\,\eta_2 = 0\,.$$

Thus the differential equation for η_2 differs from the differential equation for ξ_1,

$$\frac{d^2\xi_1}{dt^2} + 2\varepsilon_* \frac{d\xi_1}{dt} + \Omega_*^2(1 - 2\mu \cos \theta t)\,\xi_1 = 0\,, \qquad (16.62)$$

only by the sign in front of the second term. One equation can be obtained from the other by changing t to $-t$. Consequently, between the solutions of conjugate differential equation systems the following relationship exists:

$$\eta_2(t) = \xi_1(-t)\,. \qquad (16.63)$$

The next problem is determination of the periodic solution of the system of differential equations (16.60) and (16.61). As is known (§ 7), the solutions of Eq. (16.62) have the form

$$\xi_1 = u(t)\,e^{-\varepsilon_* t},$$

where $u(t)$ are solutions of the Mathieu differential equation

$$\frac{d^2u}{dt^2} + \Omega_*^2\left(1 - \frac{\varepsilon_*^2}{\Omega_*^2} - 2\mu \cos \theta t\right)u = 0\,. \qquad (16.64)$$

The linearly independent solutions of the Mathieu differential equation are

$$u_1(t) = e^{ht}\varphi(t)\,, \qquad u_2(t) = e^{-ht}\varphi(-t)\,,$$

where h is a characteristic exponent and $\varphi(t)$ is a periodic function of time with a period $T = 2\pi/\theta$ or $2T$. The condition of the periodicity for ξ_{11} and ξ_{12} requires that

$$h = \varepsilon_*\,,$$

Hence, it is found that the first (periodic) solution of the system of differential equations (16.60) has the form

$$\xi_{11} = \varphi(t)\,, \qquad \xi_{21} = \frac{d\varphi(t)}{dt}\,. \qquad (16.65)$$

The second (damping) solution is

$$\xi_{12} = e^{-2\varepsilon_* t}\varphi(-t)\,, \qquad \xi_{22} = \frac{d}{dt}[e^{-2\varepsilon_* t}\varphi(-t)]\,.$$

Using (16.63) for the conjugate differential equations leads to

$$\eta_{21}(t) = \xi_{11}(-t) = \varphi(-t)\,,$$
$$\eta_{22}(t) = \xi_{12}(-t) = e^{2\varepsilon_* t}\varphi(t)\,,$$

Hence with the aid of the second of equations (16.61),

$$\eta_{11} = 2\varepsilon_*\varphi(-t) - \frac{d\varphi(-t)}{dt}\,,$$

$$\eta_{12} = -e^{2\varepsilon_* t}\frac{d\varphi(t)}{dt}\,.$$

Recalling the notation (16.41) gives

$$\psi_{11} = 2\varepsilon_* \varphi(-t) - \frac{d\varphi(-t)}{dt}, \qquad \psi_{21} = \varphi(-t),$$
$$\psi_{12} = -\frac{d\varphi(t)}{dt}, \qquad \psi_{22} = \varphi(t). \tag{16.66}$$

The relationship between the constant C in Eq. (16.51) for zero approximation and the periodic solution of the nonlinear system of differential equations (16.59) will now be established. Equations (16.52) for the case of the system of second order have the form

$$x_1\psi_{11} + x_2\psi_{21} = C,$$
$$x_1\psi_{12} + x_2\psi_{22} = 0.$$

Solving these equations gives

$$x_1 = C\frac{\psi_{22}}{\Delta},$$
$$x_2 = -C\frac{\psi_{12}}{\Delta}, \tag{16.67}$$

where

$$\Delta = \psi_{11}\psi_{22} - \psi_{12}\psi_{21}.$$

From comparison of (16.66) with (16.65), it follows that

$$\psi_{22} = \xi_{11}, \qquad \psi_{12} = -\xi_{21}.$$

It is obvious that

$$\psi_{11} = \eta_{11}, \qquad \psi_{21} = \eta_{21}.$$

Therefore,

$$\Delta = \xi_{11}\eta_{11} + \xi_{21}\eta_{21};$$

moreover, on the basis of (16.10), $\Delta = \text{const}$. The value of this constant can easily be found if the initial conditions for η and ξ are specified. Let

$$\xi_1(0) = \eta_1(0) = 1,$$
$$\xi_2(0) = \eta_2(0) = 0.$$

Then $\Delta = 1$, and the first of Eqs. (16.67) take the form

$$x_1 = f(t) = C\varphi(t). \tag{16.68}$$

Substituting into Eq. (16.51) and using (16.46) and (16.66) yields

$$\int_0^T V\left[C\varphi(t), C\frac{d\varphi(t)}{dt}, t\right]\varphi(-t)\,dt = 0, \tag{16.69}$$

where, as is evident from (16.68), the constant C is actually the amplitude of the zero approximation.

● **3.** In determining the function $\varphi(t)$, the known results pertaining to the

Mathieu differential equation can be used[5]. Let us express the differential equation (16.64) in the form

$$\frac{d^2u}{d\tau^2} + (a - 2q \cos 2\tau)u = 0 ,$$

where

$$a = \frac{4\Omega_*^2}{\theta^2}\left(1 - \frac{\varepsilon^2}{\Omega_*^2}\right), \qquad q = \mu\frac{4\Omega_*^2}{\theta^2}, \qquad \theta t = 2\tau .$$

Its solution has the form

$$u_1(\tau) = e^{\nu\tau}\varphi(\tau, \sigma) , \qquad (\nu = \tfrac{1}{2}\theta h) ,$$

where

$$\begin{aligned}\varphi(\tau, \sigma) = \sin(\tau - \sigma) &+ s_3 \sin(3\tau - \sigma) + s_5 \sin(5\tau - \sigma) + \cdots \\ &+ c_3 \cos(3\tau - \sigma) + c_5 \cos(5\tau - \sigma) + \cdots .\end{aligned}$$

All quantities s_k and c_k, and also σ, depend on a and q:

$$\begin{aligned} s_3 &= -\tfrac{1}{8}q + \tfrac{1}{64}q^2 \cos 2\sigma + O(q^3) , \\ s_5 &= \tfrac{1}{192}q^2 + O(q^3) , \\ &\cdots\cdots\cdots \\ c_3 &= \tfrac{3}{64}q^2 \sin 2\sigma + O(q^3) , \\ &\cdots\cdots\cdots \end{aligned}$$

(the remaining coefficients have the order q^3 and higher). For determination of the parameters σ and of the characteristic exponent, the following equations are obtained:

$$\begin{aligned} a &= 1 - q \cos 2\sigma + 4q^2(-1 + \tfrac{1}{2}\cos 4\sigma) + O(q^3) , \\ \nu &= -\tfrac{1}{2}q \sin 2\sigma + O(q^3) . \end{aligned}$$

Setting $\nu = \frac{1}{2}\theta\varepsilon_*$ gives the parameter σ from the second equation. The function $\varphi(\tau, \sigma)$ if determined in the same way, and calculation of the amplitude C reduces to evaluation of definite integrals.

The calculations become simpler in the case of a conservative problem. The function $\varphi(\tau, \sigma)$ degenerates here into one of the Mathieu functions of integer order (depending on the region of excitation in which the periodic solution is sought). Thus, for the principal instability region it is necessary to take

$$\varphi(\tau) = \mathrm{ce}_1(\tau)$$

or

$$\varphi(\tau) = \mathrm{se}_1(\tau) ,$$

where

$$\begin{aligned} \mathrm{ce}_1(\tau) &= \cos\tau - \tfrac{1}{8}q \cos 3\tau + \tfrac{1}{64}q^2(-\cos 3\tau + \tfrac{1}{3}\cos 5\tau) + O(q^3) , \\ \mathrm{se}_1(\tau) &= \sin\tau - \tfrac{1}{8}q \sin 3\tau + \tfrac{1}{64}q^2(\sin 3\tau + \tfrac{1}{3}\sin 5\tau) + O(q^3) . \end{aligned}$$

For the case where $q \ll 1$, the following is taken:

$$\mathrm{ce}_1(\tau) \approx \cos\tau , \qquad \mathrm{se}_1(\tau) \approx \sin\tau .$$

For the first case and with (16.55) and (16.58) taken into account, Eq. (16.69) becomes

[5] See, for example, McLachlan [1].

$$\int_0^{2\pi/\theta}\left[\gamma C^3 \cos^2\frac{\theta t}{2} + \Omega^2 C\left(1 - \frac{\theta^2}{\theta_*^{\,2}}\right)(1 - 2\mu\cos\theta t)\right]\cos^2\frac{\theta t}{2}\,dt = 0\,.$$

Evaluating the integrals yields

$$\int_0^{2\pi/\theta}\cos^4\frac{\theta t}{2}dt = \frac{3}{4}\frac{\pi}{\theta}\,, \qquad \int_0^{2\pi/\theta}\cos\theta t\cos^2\frac{\theta t}{2}dt = \frac{1}{2}\frac{\pi}{\theta}\,,$$

$$\int_0^{2\pi/\theta}\cos^2\frac{\theta t}{2}\,dt = \frac{\pi}{\theta}\,,$$

from which

$$\tfrac{3}{4}\gamma C^3 + \Omega^2\left(1 - \frac{\theta^2}{\theta_*^{\,2}}\right)(1-\mu)C = 0\,.$$

If this equation is solved, in addition to the trivial root $C = 0$ one obtains

$$C = \pm\frac{2\Omega}{\sqrt{3\gamma}}\sqrt{\left(\frac{\theta^2}{\theta_*^{\,2}} - 1\right)(1-\mu)}\,. \qquad (16.70)$$

Here, instead of θ_* it is necessary to take the boundary frequency at the lower boundary of the principal region of instability:

$$\theta_*^{\,2} \approx 4\Omega^2(1-\mu)\,. \qquad (16.71)$$

If the generating solution is taken in the form $\mathrm{se}_1(\tau)$, then in Eqs. (16.70) and (16.71) the sign of μ must be changed to the opposite. It can easily be seen that the amplitude calculated by Eq. (16.70) differs from that found in § 20 only by terms of the order μ^2. These terms characterize higher approximations.

It is noted that the theory presented in the previous paragraph applies, strictly speaking, only to nonconservative problems. In fact, the assumption of the linear character of the elementary divisors is essential; in the case of a conservative problem, however, double characteristic roots of the nonlinear elementary divisors correspond to the periodic solutions.

§ 70. The Method of Formal Expansion into Trigonometric Series

● **1.** Consider the general system of nonlinear differential equations of dynamic stability:

$$\boldsymbol{Cf}'' + 2\boldsymbol{Kf}'[\boldsymbol{E} - \alpha\boldsymbol{A} - \beta\Phi(t)\boldsymbol{B}]\boldsymbol{f} + \boldsymbol{\psi}(\boldsymbol{f}, \boldsymbol{f}', \boldsymbol{f}'') = \boldsymbol{0}\,. \qquad (16.72)$$

Here $\boldsymbol{f}(t)$ is an n-dimensional vector, $\boldsymbol{A}$, $\boldsymbol{B}$, $\boldsymbol{C}$, $\boldsymbol{K} = \boldsymbol{C}\varepsilon$ are n^{th} order matrices whose properties were investigated previously, and $\Phi(t)$ is a periodic function of time with a period $T = 2\pi/\theta$. Assume that this function can be expanded into a uniformly convergent series

$$\Phi(t) = \sum_{k=1}^{n} c_k \cos k\theta t\,. \qquad (16.73)$$

The components of the vector $\boldsymbol{\psi}$ are the sums of expressions of the type

$$f_p f_q f_r\,, \qquad f_p f_q f'_r\,, \qquad f_p f'_q f'_r\,, \qquad f'_p f'_q f'_r\,, \qquad f_p f_q f''_r\,,$$

multiplied by some constant coefficients, i.e., they are homogenous third-order functions of the components of vectors $\boldsymbol{f}$, $\boldsymbol{f}'$, $\boldsymbol{f}''$:

$$\varphi_i(f, f', f'') = \sum_{p=1}^{n} \sum_{q=1}^{n} \sum_{r=1}^{n} (A_{pqr}^{(i)} f_p f_q f_r + B_{pqr}^{(i)} f_p f_q f_r' + \cdots) . \tag{16.74}$$

The method presented above for constructing periodic solutions requires numerous calculations and, thus, is not suitable for the practical calculation of solutions. In the following, a method of formal expansion in a trigonometric series will be developed. Moreover, a correlation between methods of investigating linear and nonlinear problems will be preserved.

The periodic solution of the type

$$\boldsymbol{f}\left(t + \frac{4\pi}{\theta}\right) = \boldsymbol{f}(t)$$

will be sought in the form of a series

$$\boldsymbol{f} = \sum_{k=1,3,5}^{\infty} \left(\boldsymbol{a}_k \sin \frac{k\theta t}{2} + \boldsymbol{b}_k \cos \frac{k\theta t}{2}\right), \tag{16.75}$$

where $\boldsymbol{a}_k$ and $\boldsymbol{b}_k$ are vectors with constant components. It can easily be seen that series (16.75), with a proper choice of coefficients, formally satisfies the differential equation (16.72) with a nonlinear part (16.74). This will also be true for the case where homogenous algebraic forms of fifth, seventh, and generally uneven orders are added to functions φ_i.

First of all, substitute series (16.75) into the expressions for φ_i. Then, obviously,

$$\varphi_i(f, f', f'') = \sum_{k=1,3,5}^{n} \left(v_{ik} \sin \frac{k\theta t}{2} + w_{ik} \cos \frac{k\theta t}{2}\right), \tag{16.76}$$

where

$$v_{ik} = v_{ik}(\boldsymbol{a}_1, \boldsymbol{a}_3, \cdots, \boldsymbol{b}_1, \boldsymbol{b}_3, \cdots),$$
$$w_{ik} = w_{ik}(\boldsymbol{a}_1, \boldsymbol{a}_3, \cdots, \boldsymbol{b}_1, \boldsymbol{b}_3, \cdots)$$

are homogenous third-order functions of the components of vectors $\boldsymbol{a}_k$ and $\boldsymbol{b}_k$. The vectors composed of v_{ik} and w_{ik} will be denoted by $\boldsymbol{v}_i$ and $\boldsymbol{w}_i$, respectively.

Substitute (16.75) and (16.76) into the matrix differential equation (16.72) and compare the coefficients of

$$\sin \frac{k\theta t}{2} \text{ and } \cos \frac{k\theta t}{2} .$$

The result is a system of vector equations, which for the case $\boldsymbol{\Phi}(t) = \cos \theta t$ assume the form

$$\begin{aligned}
(\boldsymbol{E} - \alpha \boldsymbol{A} + \tfrac{1}{2}\beta \boldsymbol{B} - \tfrac{1}{4}\theta^2 \boldsymbol{C})\, \boldsymbol{a}_1 - \theta \boldsymbol{K} \boldsymbol{b}_1 - \tfrac{1}{2}\beta \boldsymbol{B} \boldsymbol{a}_3 + \boldsymbol{v}_1 &= \boldsymbol{0}, \\
(\boldsymbol{E} - \alpha \boldsymbol{A} - \tfrac{1}{2}\beta \boldsymbol{B} - \tfrac{1}{4}\theta^2 \boldsymbol{C})\, \boldsymbol{b}_1 + \theta \boldsymbol{K} \boldsymbol{a}_1 - \tfrac{1}{2}\beta \boldsymbol{B} \boldsymbol{b}_3 + \boldsymbol{w}_1 &= \boldsymbol{0}, \\
(\boldsymbol{E} - \alpha \boldsymbol{A} - \tfrac{1}{4}k^2\theta^2 \boldsymbol{C})\boldsymbol{a}_k - k\theta \boldsymbol{K} \boldsymbol{b}_k - \tfrac{1}{2}\beta \boldsymbol{B}(\boldsymbol{a}_{k-2} + \boldsymbol{a}_{k+2}) &= \boldsymbol{0}, \\
(\boldsymbol{E} - \alpha \boldsymbol{A} - \tfrac{1}{4}k^2\theta^2 \boldsymbol{C})\boldsymbol{b}_k + k\theta \boldsymbol{K} \boldsymbol{a}_k - \tfrac{1}{2}\beta \boldsymbol{B}(\boldsymbol{b}_{k-2} + \boldsymbol{b}_{k+2}) &= \boldsymbol{0}, \\
(k = 3, 5, \cdots) .&
\end{aligned} \tag{16.77}$$

If the first m terms are retained in series (16.73), then system (16.77) obviously has 6 mn equations.

In the case of a conservative problem, system (16.77) separates into two independent systems, one of which,

$$\begin{aligned}(\boldsymbol{E} - \alpha \boldsymbol{A} + \tfrac{1}{2}\beta \boldsymbol{B} - \tfrac{1}{4}\theta^2 \boldsymbol{C})\,\boldsymbol{a}_1 - \tfrac{1}{2}\beta \boldsymbol{B}\boldsymbol{a}_3 + \boldsymbol{v}_1 &= \boldsymbol{0}\,,\\ (\boldsymbol{E} - \alpha \boldsymbol{A} - \tfrac{1}{4}k^2\theta^2 \boldsymbol{C})\,\boldsymbol{a}_k - \tfrac{1}{2}\beta \boldsymbol{B}(\boldsymbol{a}_{k-2} + \boldsymbol{a}_{k+2}) + \boldsymbol{v}_k &= \boldsymbol{0}\,,\\ (k = 3,\ 5,\cdots)\,,\end{aligned}$$

contains only a_k; the other system,

$$\begin{aligned}(\boldsymbol{E} - \alpha \boldsymbol{A} - \tfrac{1}{2}\beta \boldsymbol{B} - \tfrac{1}{4}\theta^2 \boldsymbol{C})\,\boldsymbol{b}_1 - \tfrac{1}{2}\beta \boldsymbol{B}\boldsymbol{b}_3 + \boldsymbol{w}_1 &= \boldsymbol{0}\,,\\ (\boldsymbol{E} - \alpha \boldsymbol{A} - \tfrac{1}{4}k^2\theta^2 \boldsymbol{C})\,\boldsymbol{b}_k - \tfrac{1}{2}\beta \boldsymbol{B}(\boldsymbol{b}_{k-2} + \boldsymbol{b}_{k+2}) + \boldsymbol{w}_k &= \boldsymbol{0}\,,\\ (k = 3,\ 5,\cdots)\,,\end{aligned}$$

contains only $\boldsymbol{b}_k$.

Here $\boldsymbol{v}_k = \boldsymbol{v}_k(\boldsymbol{a}_1, \boldsymbol{a}_3, \cdots)$ and $\boldsymbol{w}_k = \boldsymbol{w}_k(\boldsymbol{b}_1, \boldsymbol{b}_3, \cdots)$. In fact, for $\boldsymbol{K} = \boldsymbol{0}$, the differential equation (16.72) is satisfied by the formal expansion

$$\sum_{k=1,3,5}^{\infty} \boldsymbol{a}_k \sin \frac{k\theta t}{2} \quad \text{and} \quad \sum_{k=1,3,5}^{\infty} \boldsymbol{b}_k \cos \frac{k\theta t}{2}\,.$$

Analogously, a solution of the following type is sought:

$$\boldsymbol{f}\left(t + \frac{2\pi}{\theta}\right) = \boldsymbol{f}(t)\,.$$

Substituting into Eq. (16.72) the series

$$\boldsymbol{f}(t) = \tfrac{1}{2}\boldsymbol{b}_0 + \sum_{k=2,4,6}^{\infty}\left(\boldsymbol{a}_k \sin \frac{k\theta t}{2} + \boldsymbol{b}_k \cos \frac{k\theta t}{2}\right) \tag{16.78}$$

yields, after analogous transformations, the system of equations:

$$\begin{aligned}(\boldsymbol{E} - \alpha \boldsymbol{A})\,\boldsymbol{b}_0 - \beta \boldsymbol{B}\boldsymbol{b}_2 + 2\boldsymbol{v}_0 &= \boldsymbol{0}\,,\\ (\boldsymbol{E} - \alpha \boldsymbol{A} - \theta^2 \boldsymbol{C})\,\boldsymbol{a}_2 - 2\theta \boldsymbol{K}\boldsymbol{b}_2 - \tfrac{1}{2}\beta \boldsymbol{B}\boldsymbol{a}_4 + \boldsymbol{v}_2 &= \boldsymbol{0}\,,\\ (\boldsymbol{E} - \alpha \boldsymbol{A} - \theta^2 \boldsymbol{C})\,\boldsymbol{b}_2 + 2\theta \boldsymbol{K}\boldsymbol{a}_2 - \tfrac{1}{2}\beta \boldsymbol{B}(\boldsymbol{b}_0 + \boldsymbol{b}_4) + \boldsymbol{w}_2 &= \boldsymbol{0}\,,\\ (\boldsymbol{E} - \alpha \boldsymbol{A} - \tfrac{1}{4}k^2\theta^2 \boldsymbol{C})\,\boldsymbol{a}_k - 2k\theta \boldsymbol{K}\boldsymbol{b}_k - \tfrac{1}{2}\beta \boldsymbol{B}(\boldsymbol{a}_{k-2} + \boldsymbol{a}_{k+2}) + \boldsymbol{v}_k &= \boldsymbol{0}\,,\\ (\boldsymbol{E} - \alpha \boldsymbol{A} - \tfrac{1}{4}k^2\theta^2 \boldsymbol{C})\,\boldsymbol{b}_k + 2k\theta \boldsymbol{K}\boldsymbol{a}_k - \tfrac{1}{2}\beta \boldsymbol{B}(\boldsymbol{b}_{k-2} + \boldsymbol{b}_{k+2}) + \boldsymbol{w}_k &= \boldsymbol{0}\,,\\ (k = 4,\ 6,\ \cdots)\,.\end{aligned} \tag{16.79}$$

Here

$$\begin{aligned}\boldsymbol{v}_k &= \boldsymbol{v}_k(\boldsymbol{a}_2, \boldsymbol{a}_4, \cdots, \boldsymbol{b}_0, \boldsymbol{b}_2, \boldsymbol{b}_4, \cdots)\,,\\ \boldsymbol{w}_k &= \boldsymbol{w}_k(\boldsymbol{a}_2, \boldsymbol{a}_4, \cdots, \boldsymbol{b}_0, \boldsymbol{b}_2, \boldsymbol{b}_4, \cdots)\,.\end{aligned}$$

In the case where all four matrices $\boldsymbol{A}$, $\boldsymbol{B}$, $\boldsymbol{C}$, and $\boldsymbol{K}$ simultaneously reduce to the diagonal form, the system of equations which was investigated in the first part of the book (Chapters Five and Six) is obtained. Thus, if the matrices are replaced by their characteristic numbers

$$\boldsymbol{A} \to \frac{1}{\alpha_*}\,, \quad \boldsymbol{B} \to \frac{1}{\beta_*}\,, \quad \boldsymbol{C} \to \frac{1}{\omega^2}\,, \quad \boldsymbol{K} \to \frac{\varepsilon}{\omega^2}\,, \quad \boldsymbol{E} \to 1\,,$$

the following is obtained instead of (16.77):

$$\left(1-\frac{\alpha}{\alpha_*}+\tfrac{1}{2}\frac{\beta}{\beta_*}-\tfrac{1}{4}\frac{\theta^2}{\omega^2}\right)\boldsymbol{a}_1-\frac{\varepsilon\theta}{\alpha\omega^2}\boldsymbol{b}_1-\tfrac{1}{2}\frac{\beta}{\beta_*}\boldsymbol{a}_3+\boldsymbol{v}_1=0\,,$$
$$\left(1-\frac{\alpha}{\alpha_*}-\tfrac{1}{2}\frac{\beta}{\beta_*}-\tfrac{1}{4}\frac{\theta^2}{\omega^2}\right)\boldsymbol{b}_1+\frac{\varepsilon\theta}{\alpha\omega^2}\boldsymbol{a}_1-\tfrac{1}{2}\frac{\beta}{\beta_*}\boldsymbol{b}_3+\boldsymbol{w}_1=0\,,$$
$$\left(1-\frac{\alpha}{\alpha_*}-\tfrac{1}{4}\frac{k^2\theta^2}{\omega^2}\right)\boldsymbol{a}_k-\frac{k\varepsilon\theta}{\omega^2}\boldsymbol{b}_k-\tfrac{1}{2}\frac{\beta}{\beta_*}(\boldsymbol{a}_{k-2}+\boldsymbol{a}_{k+2})+\boldsymbol{v}_k=0\,,$$
$$\left(1-\frac{\alpha}{\alpha_*}-\tfrac{1}{4}\frac{k^2\theta^2}{\omega^2}\right)\boldsymbol{b}_k+\frac{k\varepsilon\theta}{\omega^2}\boldsymbol{a}_k-\tfrac{1}{2}\frac{\beta}{\beta_*}(\boldsymbol{b}_{k-2}+\boldsymbol{b}_{k+2})+\boldsymbol{w}_k=0\,,$$
$$(k=3,\,5,\,\cdots)\,.$$

This system corresponds to a single differential equation of a "special" case

$$\frac{d^2f}{dt^2}+2\varepsilon\frac{df}{dt}+\omega^2\left(1-\frac{\alpha}{\alpha_*}-\frac{\beta}{\beta_*}\cos\theta t\right)f+\varphi(f,\,f',\,f'')=0\,,$$

and differs from system (5.7) only in notation.

The amplitudes of the steady-state vibrations near the principal region of excitation can be determined with the aid of the harmonic approximation

$$\boldsymbol{f}(t)\approx\boldsymbol{a}\sin\frac{\theta t}{2}+\boldsymbol{b}\cos\frac{\theta t}{2}\,. \tag{16.80}$$

The vectors $\boldsymbol{a}$ and $\boldsymbol{b}$ are determined from the system of $6n$ equations

$$\begin{aligned}(\boldsymbol{E}-\alpha\boldsymbol{A}+\tfrac{1}{2}\beta\boldsymbol{B}-\tfrac{1}{4}\theta^2\boldsymbol{C})\,\boldsymbol{a}-\theta\boldsymbol{K}\boldsymbol{b}+\boldsymbol{v}(\boldsymbol{a},\,\boldsymbol{b})&=\boldsymbol{0}\,,\\(\boldsymbol{E}-\alpha\boldsymbol{A}-\tfrac{1}{2}\beta\boldsymbol{B}-\tfrac{1}{4}\theta^2\boldsymbol{C})\,\boldsymbol{b}-\theta\boldsymbol{K}\boldsymbol{a}+\boldsymbol{w}(\boldsymbol{a},\,\boldsymbol{b})&=\boldsymbol{0}\,.\end{aligned} \tag{16.81}$$

●2. As an example, consider a system of equations characterized by matrices

$$\boldsymbol{C}=\begin{pmatrix}1/\omega_1^{\ 2} & 0\\ 9 & 1/\omega_2^{\ 2}\end{pmatrix},\quad \boldsymbol{A}=\boldsymbol{B}=\begin{pmatrix}0 & \alpha_{12}\\ \alpha_{21} & 0\end{pmatrix},\quad \boldsymbol{K}=\begin{pmatrix}\varepsilon_1/\omega_1^{\ 2} & 0\\ 0 & \varepsilon_2/\omega_2^{\ 2}\end{pmatrix}.$$

Furthermore, let

$$\begin{aligned}\varphi_1(f,\,f',\,f'')&=\frac{2\kappa}{\omega_1^{\ 2}}f_1[(f_1')^2+f_1f_1'']\,.\\ \varphi_2(f,\,f',\,f'')&=\frac{2\kappa}{\omega_2^{\ 2}}f_2[(f_1')^2+f_1f_1'']\,,\end{aligned} \tag{16.82}$$

where κ is a constant ($\kappa>0$). Substituting the expressions

$$\boldsymbol{f}_1=\boldsymbol{a}_1\sin\frac{\theta t}{2}+\boldsymbol{b}_1\cos\frac{\theta t}{2}\,,$$
$$\boldsymbol{f}_2=\boldsymbol{a}_2\sin\frac{\theta t}{2}+\boldsymbol{b}_2\cos\frac{\theta t}{2}\,,$$

into Eqs. (16.82) yields

$$\varphi_1=-\frac{\kappa\theta^2}{4\omega_1^{\ 2}}a_1(a_1^{\ 2}+b_1^{\ 2})\sin\frac{\theta t}{2}-\frac{\kappa\theta^2}{4\omega_1^{\ 2}}b_1(a_2^{\ 2}+b_2^{\ 2})\cos\frac{\theta t}{2}+\cdots\,,$$
$$\varphi_2=-\frac{\kappa\theta^2}{4\omega_2^{\ 2}}a_2(a_1^{\ 2}+b_1^{\ 2})\sin\frac{\theta t}{2}-\frac{\kappa\theta^2}{4\omega_2^{\ 2}}b_2(a_1^{\ 2}+b_1^{\ 2})\cos\frac{\theta t}{2}+\cdots$$

(dots denote terms which contain higher harmonics). Consequently,

$$\boldsymbol{v} = -\frac{\kappa\theta^2}{4} A_1^2 \begin{pmatrix} a_1/\omega_1^2 \\ a_2/\omega_2^2 \end{pmatrix} = -\frac{\kappa\theta^2}{4} A_1^2 \boldsymbol{Ca} ,$$

$$\boldsymbol{w} = -\frac{\kappa\theta^2}{4} A_1^2 \begin{pmatrix} b_1/\omega_1^2 \\ b_2/\omega_2^2 \end{pmatrix} = -\frac{\kappa\theta^2}{4} A_1^2 \boldsymbol{Cb} ,$$

where $A_1 = \sqrt{a_1^2 + b_1^2}$ is the amplitude of the first component of the vector $\boldsymbol{f}$. Substitution of the above expressions into Eqs. (16.81) yields

$$\begin{aligned} &[\boldsymbol{E} - (\alpha - \tfrac{1}{2}\beta)\boldsymbol{B} - \tfrac{1}{4}\theta^2\boldsymbol{C}(1 + \kappa A_1^2)]\,\boldsymbol{a} - \theta\boldsymbol{Kb} = \boldsymbol{0} , \\ &[\boldsymbol{E} - (\alpha + \tfrac{1}{2}\beta)\boldsymbol{B} - \tfrac{1}{4}\theta^2\boldsymbol{C}(1 + \kappa A_1^2)]\,\boldsymbol{b} + \theta\boldsymbol{Ka} = \boldsymbol{0} . \end{aligned} \tag{16.83}$$

In addition to the trivial solution $\boldsymbol{a} = \boldsymbol{b} = 0$, the system of equations (16.83) has solutions which can be determined from the condition

$$\begin{vmatrix} \boldsymbol{E} - (\alpha - \tfrac{1}{2}\beta)\boldsymbol{B} - \tfrac{1}{4}\theta^2 C(1 + \kappa A_1^2) & -\theta\boldsymbol{K} \\ \theta\boldsymbol{K} & \boldsymbol{E} - (\alpha + \tfrac{1}{2}\beta)\boldsymbol{B} - \tfrac{1}{4}\theta^2\boldsymbol{C}(1 + \kappa A_1^2) \end{vmatrix} = 0 . \tag{16.84}$$

Thus a fourth-order algebraic equation for the amplitude A_1 has been obtained. Expanding this equation gives

$$\begin{vmatrix} 1 - \dfrac{\theta^2}{4\omega_1^2}(1 + \kappa A_1^2) & -\dfrac{\alpha - \frac{1}{2}\beta}{a_{12}} & -\dfrac{\varepsilon_1\theta}{\omega_1^2} & 0 \\ -\dfrac{\alpha - \frac{1}{2}\beta}{a_{21}} & 1 - \dfrac{\theta^2}{4\omega_2^2}(1 + \kappa A_1^2) & 0 & -\dfrac{\varepsilon_2\theta}{\omega_2^2} \\ \dfrac{\varepsilon_1\theta}{\omega_1^2} & 0 & 1 - \dfrac{\theta^2}{4\omega_1^2}(1 + \kappa A_1^2) & -\dfrac{\alpha + \frac{1}{2}\beta}{a_{12}} \\ 0 & \dfrac{\varepsilon_2\theta}{\omega_2^2} & -\dfrac{\alpha + \frac{1}{2}\beta}{a_{21}} & 1 - \dfrac{\theta^2}{4\omega_2^2}(1 + \kappa A_1^2) \end{vmatrix} = 0 .$$

Besides (16.84), the equation will also be considered for the boundary frequencies

$$\begin{vmatrix} \boldsymbol{E} - (\alpha - \tfrac{1}{2}\beta)\boldsymbol{B} - \tfrac{1}{4}\theta^2\boldsymbol{C} & -\theta\boldsymbol{K} \\ \theta\boldsymbol{K} & \boldsymbol{E} - (\alpha + \tfrac{1}{2}\beta)\boldsymbol{B} - \tfrac{1}{4}\theta^2\boldsymbol{C} \end{vmatrix} = 0 . \tag{16.85}$$

Its roots will be denoted by θ_*. When (16.84) and (16.85) are compared, the first equation is satisfied for

$$\theta^2(1 + \kappa A_1^2) = \theta_*^2 .$$

Therefore,

$$A_1 = \frac{1}{\sqrt{\kappa}}\sqrt{\frac{\theta_*^2}{\theta^2} - 1} .$$

§ 71. Derivation of Differential Equations for Nonsteady-State Vibrations

An approximate solution to a problem of nonsteady-state vibrations can be obtained by assuming that the components of vectors $\boldsymbol{a}_k$ and $\boldsymbol{b}_k$ in expressions (16.75) and (16.78) are slowly changing functions of time:

$$|a'_{ik}|\frac{2\pi}{\theta} \ll |a_{ik}|, \quad |b'_{ik}|\frac{2\pi}{\theta} \ll |b_{ik}|,$$
$$|a''_{ik}|\frac{2\pi}{\theta} \ll |a'_{ik}|, \quad |b''_{ik}|\frac{2\pi}{\theta} \ll |b'_{ik}|, \tag{16.86}$$

The solution with the period $4\pi/\theta$ is sought in the form of a series

$$\boldsymbol{f}(t) = \sum_{k=1,3,5}^{\infty}\left(\boldsymbol{a}_k(t)\sin\frac{k\theta t}{2} + \boldsymbol{b}_k(t)\cos\frac{k\theta t}{2}\right).$$

When (16.86) is taken into account, an approximate value for $\boldsymbol{f}'$ is obtained:

$$\boldsymbol{f}' \approx \sum_{k=1,3,5}^{\infty}\frac{k\theta}{2}\left(\boldsymbol{a}_k\cos\frac{k\theta t}{2} - \boldsymbol{b}_k\sin\frac{k\theta t}{2}\right).$$

For the second derivative $\boldsymbol{f}''$, the expression is

$$\boldsymbol{f}'' \approx -\sum_{k=1,3,5}^{\infty}\frac{k^2\theta^2}{4}\left[\left(\boldsymbol{a}_k + \frac{4}{k\theta}\boldsymbol{b}'_k\right)\sin\frac{k\theta t}{2} + \left(\boldsymbol{b}_k - \frac{4}{k\theta}\boldsymbol{a}'_k\right)\cos\frac{k\theta t}{2}\right].$$

By substituting expressions that contain the small parameter into the nonlinear terms, this expression can be simplified:

$$\boldsymbol{f}'' \approx -\sum_{k=1,3,5,}^{\infty}\frac{k^2\theta^2}{4}\left(\boldsymbol{a}_k\sin\frac{k\theta t}{2} + \boldsymbol{b}_k\cos\frac{k\theta t}{2}\right).$$

Substitute these series into Eq. (16.72). Comparing coefficients $\sin k\theta t/2$ and $\cos k\theta t/2$ leads to

$$-\theta\boldsymbol{C}\boldsymbol{b}'_1 + (\boldsymbol{E} - \alpha\boldsymbol{A} + \tfrac{1}{2}\beta\boldsymbol{B} - \tfrac{1}{4}\theta^2\boldsymbol{C})\boldsymbol{a}_1 - \theta\boldsymbol{K}\boldsymbol{b}_1 - \tfrac{1}{2}\beta\boldsymbol{B}\boldsymbol{a}_3 + \boldsymbol{v}_1 = \boldsymbol{0},$$
$$\theta\boldsymbol{C}\boldsymbol{a}'_1 + (\boldsymbol{E} - \alpha\boldsymbol{A} + \tfrac{1}{2}\beta\boldsymbol{B} - \tfrac{1}{4}\theta^2\boldsymbol{C})\boldsymbol{b}_1 + \theta\boldsymbol{K}\boldsymbol{a}_1 - \tfrac{1}{2}\beta\boldsymbol{B}\boldsymbol{b}_3 + \boldsymbol{w}_1 = \boldsymbol{0},$$
$$-k\theta\boldsymbol{C}\boldsymbol{b}'_k + (\boldsymbol{E} - \alpha\boldsymbol{A} - \tfrac{1}{4}k^2\theta^2\boldsymbol{C})\boldsymbol{a}_k - k\theta\boldsymbol{K}\boldsymbol{b}_k - \tfrac{1}{2}\beta\boldsymbol{B}(\boldsymbol{a}_{k-2} + \boldsymbol{a}_{k+2}) + \boldsymbol{v}_k = \boldsymbol{0},$$
$$k\theta\boldsymbol{C}\boldsymbol{a}'_k + (\boldsymbol{E} - \alpha\boldsymbol{A} - \tfrac{1}{4}k^2\theta^2\boldsymbol{C})\boldsymbol{b}_k + k\theta\boldsymbol{K}\boldsymbol{a}_k - \tfrac{1}{2}\beta\boldsymbol{B}(\boldsymbol{b}_{k-2} + \boldsymbol{b}_{k+2}) + \boldsymbol{w}_k = \boldsymbol{0}$$
$$(k = 3, 5, \cdots).$$

In harmonic approximation, this is

$$-\theta\boldsymbol{C}\boldsymbol{b}' + (\boldsymbol{E} - \alpha\boldsymbol{A} + \tfrac{1}{2}\beta\boldsymbol{B} - \tfrac{1}{4}\theta^2\boldsymbol{C})\boldsymbol{a} - \theta\boldsymbol{K}\boldsymbol{b} + \boldsymbol{v} = 0,$$
$$\theta\boldsymbol{C}\boldsymbol{a}' + (\boldsymbol{E} - \alpha\boldsymbol{A} - \tfrac{1}{2}\beta\boldsymbol{B} - \tfrac{1}{4}\theta^2\boldsymbol{C})\boldsymbol{b} + \theta\boldsymbol{K}\boldsymbol{a} + \boldsymbol{w} = 0 \tag{16.87}$$

(subscripts of $\boldsymbol{a}_1$, $\boldsymbol{b}_1$, $\boldsymbol{v}_1$, and $\boldsymbol{w}_1$ are omitted).

For problems investigated in the preceding paragraph, the differential equations (16.87) for the nonsteady-state motion have the form

$$\frac{\theta}{\omega_1^2}\frac{db_1}{dt} = \left[1 - \frac{\theta^2}{4\omega_1^2}(1 + \kappa A_1^2)\right] a_1 - \frac{\alpha - \frac{1}{2}\beta}{a_{12}} a_2 - \frac{\varepsilon_1\theta}{\omega_1^2} b_1 ,$$

$$\frac{\theta}{\omega_2^2}\frac{db_2}{dt} = -\frac{\alpha - \frac{1}{2}\beta}{a_{21}} a_1 + \left[1 - \frac{\theta^2}{4\omega_2^2}(1 + \kappa A_1^2)\right] a_2 - \frac{\varepsilon_1\theta}{\omega_2^2} b_2 ,$$

$$\frac{\theta}{\omega_1^2}\frac{da_1}{dt} = -\frac{\varepsilon_1\theta}{\omega_1^2} a_1 - \left[1 - \frac{\theta^2}{4\omega_1^2}(1 + \kappa A_1^2)\right] b_1 + \frac{\alpha + \frac{1}{2}\beta}{a_{12}} b_2 ,$$

$$\frac{\theta}{\omega_2^2}\frac{da_2}{dt} = -\frac{\varepsilon_2\theta}{\omega_2^2} a_2 + \frac{\alpha + \frac{1}{2}\beta}{a_{21}} b_1 - \left[1 - \frac{\theta^2}{4\omega_2^2}(1 + \kappa A_1^2)\right] b_2 .$$

The equations obtained can be numerically integrated in steps.

PART III

APPLICATIONS OF THE GENERAL THEORY

Seventeen

DYNAMIC STABILITY OF STRAIGHT RODS

§ 72. Different Cases of Supports and Influence of Load Behavior

● **1.** The case of a straight prismatic rod freely supported on both ends was investigated in detail in the first part of the book. This problem led to the special case of individual differential equations with periodic coefficients. Other cases of end support also lead to systems of differential equations with periodic coefficients; the methods for constructing and investigating these systems were previously described.

Consider the problem of the dynamic stability of a straight prismatic rod, fixed on one end and freely supported on the other end, and compressed by a periodic longitudinal force $P(t)$ (Fig. 100). The shapes of the free vibrations of an unloaded rod are taken as the eigenfunctions:

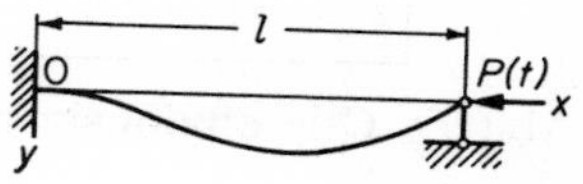

FIG. 100.

$$\varphi_k(x) = \sin \frac{n_k x}{l} - \frac{\sin n_k}{\sinh n_k} \sinh \frac{n_k x}{l} \tag{17.1}$$

where n_k denote the roots of the characteristic equation

$$\tan n_k = \tanh n_k . \tag{17.2}$$

Through normalizing, the eigenfunctions assume the form

$$\bar{\varphi}_k(x) = \frac{\varphi_k(x)}{\sqrt{m \int_0^l \varphi_k^2(x) dx}} \tag{17.3}$$

(the normalized functions are denoted with bars). The basic equation of the problem is expressed as

$$\boldsymbol{C f}'' + [\boldsymbol{E} - \boldsymbol{P}(t)\boldsymbol{A}]\boldsymbol{f} = 0 .$$

The elements of matrix $\boldsymbol{A}$ can be determined from formula (12.7):

$$a_{ik} = \frac{1}{\omega_i^2} \int \frac{d\bar{\varphi}_i}{dx} \frac{d\bar{\varphi}_k}{dx} dx ,$$

where the natural frequencies are

$$\omega_i^2 = \frac{n_i^4 EJ}{ml^4} .$$

Substitution of Eq. (17.3) into the above expression for a_{ik} yields

$$a_{ik} = \frac{l^4}{n_i^4 EJ} \frac{\int_0^l \frac{d\varphi_i}{dx} \frac{d\varphi_k}{dx} dx}{\sqrt{\int_0^l \varphi_i^2 dx \int_0^l \varphi_k^2 dx}} .$$

For calculating the coefficients a_{ik}, the well-known tables of integrals of "beam functions" can be used. An extract from such a table[1] follows, where the values of the first three roots of Eq. (17.2) are also given.

	n_i	$\frac{1}{l}\int_0^l \varphi_i^2 dx$	$l\int_0^l \frac{d\varphi_i}{dx}\frac{d\varphi_k}{dx}dx$		
			$k = 1$	$k = 2$	$k = 3$
$i = 1$	3.927	0.4996	5.5724	2.1424	− 1.900
$i = 2$	7.069	0.5010	2.1424	21.451	3.909
$i = 3$	10.210	0.5000	− 1.900	3.909	47.017

Matrix $\boldsymbol{C}$ is obviously a diagonal matrix with elements

$$c_{ik} = \delta_{ik} \frac{ml^4}{n_i^4 EJ} .$$

Let $P(t) = P_0 + P_t \cos\theta t$. Then for the boundary frequencies Eq. (14.30) can be written in the form

$$| \boldsymbol{C}^{-1} - (P_0 \pm \tfrac{1}{2}P_t)\boldsymbol{C}^{-1}\boldsymbol{A} - \tfrac{1}{4}\theta^2\boldsymbol{E} | = 0 .$$

Substituting here the values for matrix elements we obtain to within a matrix of third order

$$\begin{vmatrix} 231 - 11.1\alpha - \lambda & -4.29\alpha & 3.80\alpha \\ -4.29\alpha & 2500 - 42.9\alpha - \lambda & -7.82\alpha \\ 3.80\alpha & -7.82\alpha & 10840 - 94.0\alpha - \lambda \end{vmatrix} = 0 . \qquad (17.4)$$

Here for brevity we have denoted

$$\alpha = \frac{(P_0 \pm \frac{1}{2}P_t)l^2}{EJ} , \qquad \lambda = \frac{ml^4\theta^2}{4EJ} . \qquad (17.5)$$

Consider now a numerical example. Let $P_0 = 10EJ/l^2$, and $P_t = 0.2\ P_0 = 2EJ/l^2$. Substituting the value $\alpha = 11.0$ into (17.4) and solving the obtained equation for λ yields

$$\lambda_1 = 113.9 , \qquad \lambda_2 = 2030 , \qquad \lambda_3 = 9806 .$$

Substitution of another value, $\alpha = 9.0$, yields

$$\lambda_1 = 136.3 , \qquad \lambda_2 = 2115 , \qquad \lambda_3 = 9993 .$$

[1] Sorokin [1].

The boundaries of the three principal regions of instability are found from the notations (17.5) (resonances with respect to the first three natural frequencies):

$$\frac{21.4}{l^2}\sqrt{\frac{EJ}{m}} \leq \theta \leq \frac{23.3}{l^2}\sqrt{\frac{EJ}{m}} ,$$
$$\frac{90.1}{l^2}\sqrt{\frac{EJ}{m}} \leq \theta \leq \frac{92.0}{l^2}\sqrt{\frac{EJ}{m}} ,$$
$$\frac{198.0}{l^2}\sqrt{\frac{EJ}{m}} \leq \theta \leq \frac{200}{l^2}\sqrt{\frac{EJ}{m}} .$$

Compare these results with the first approximation based on the Galerkin method, which is obtained by equating to zero the "determinants" of the first order:

$$\omega_k^{\,2} - (P_0 \pm \tfrac{1}{2}P_t)\omega_k^{\,2} a_{kk} - \frac{\theta^2}{4} = 0 , \qquad (k = 1, 2, 3, \cdots) .$$

Hence, solving for θ leads to

$$\theta_* = 2\omega_k\sqrt{1 - (P_0 \pm \tfrac{1}{2}P_t)a_{kk}} , \qquad (k = 1, 2, 3, \cdots) .$$

For the first three regions, the difference in comparison with the more exact solution found above does not exceed 1 percent. The explanation for this is the small difference between the forms of free vibrations and the forms of the loss of static stability.

● **2.** Problems in which the vector of the periodic load rotates together with the corresponding section, remaining at all times directed along the tangent to the elastic curve (following load), are encountered in practical applications. Such a problem occurs, for example, in the case where the periodic load is produced by unbalanced rotating masses and the exciter of the vibrations is rigidly connected with the vibrating rod. The constant component (weight force) does not change its direction (Fig. 101).

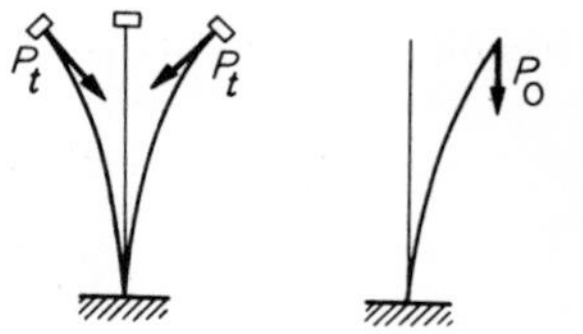

FIG. 101.

The equations of vibrations for a rod subjected to a load whose vectors remain tangent to the elastic curve will now be set up. The difference here from problems analyzed previously (§ 46 and others) consists in the method of calculating the reduced load. It is assumed, first of all, that the rod is loaded only by a distributed longitudinal force $\beta n(x)\Phi(t)$. The influence of rotation, aside from the previously introduced shear forces of the type in (11.36), will be taken into account if a distribution load

$$q_1(x, t) = \beta n(x)\Phi(t)\frac{\partial v(x, t)}{\partial x}$$

is considered or, expressed differently,

$$q_1(x, t) = \beta\Phi(t)\frac{\partial v(x, t)}{\partial x}\,\frac{dN_t(x)}{dx} ,$$

since in this case the longitudinal force is a differentiable function.

For the calculation of concentrated forces, a Stieltjes differential is introduced by substituting

$$q_1(x, t)dx \rightarrow dQ_1(x, t) .$$

Here,

$$dQ_1(x, t) = \beta\Phi(t)\frac{\partial v(x, t)}{\partial x}dN_t(x) . \tag{17.6}$$

For example, if the rod is fixed on one end and is loaded on the free end by the "following" force (Fig. 101), then the influence of the rotation is indicated by the appearance of a transverse component

$$P_t\Phi(t)\frac{\partial v(l, t)}{\partial x} .$$

This component is also taken into account by formula (17.6).

The equation of the problem under investigation is obtained by adding to the right-hand side of the integro-differential equation (12.3) an additional term which takes into account the force dQ_1:

$$v(x, t) + \int m(\xi)K(x, \xi)\frac{\partial^2 v(\xi, t)}{\partial t^2}d\xi - \int N(\xi, t)\frac{\partial K(x, \xi)}{\partial \xi}\frac{\partial v(\xi, t)}{\partial \xi}d\xi$$

$$= \beta\Phi(t)\int K(x, \xi)\frac{\partial v(\xi, t)}{\partial \xi}dN_t(\xi) .$$

Let us transform the added component by integrating it by parts:

$$\int K(x, \xi)\frac{\partial v(\xi, t)}{\partial \xi}dN_t(\xi) = - \int N_t(\xi)\frac{\partial}{\partial \xi}\left[K(x, \xi)\frac{\partial v(\xi, t)}{\partial \xi}\right]d\xi$$

(recall that on the ends $Q_1 = N_t = 0$!). Substitution and cancellation lead to

$$v(x, t) + \int m(\xi)K(x, \xi)\frac{\partial^2 v(\xi, t)}{\partial t^2}d\xi - \alpha\int N_0(\xi)\frac{\partial K(x, \xi)}{\partial \xi}\frac{\partial v(\xi, t)}{\partial \xi}d\xi$$

$$+ \beta\Phi(t)\int N_t(\xi)K(x, \xi)\frac{\partial^2 v(\xi, t)}{\partial \xi^2}d\xi = 0 .$$

The methods of §§ 46—47 can be applied to this equation. Without pausing to perform the intermediate calculations, we will just give the formulas for the matrix elements. If the normalized forms of free vibrations of the unloaded rod are taken as the fundamental functions, then

$$b_{ik} = - \frac{1}{\omega_i^2}\int N_t(x)\varphi_i\int\frac{d^2\varphi_k}{dx^2}dx .$$

If the buckling forms under the action of a load which does not change its direction are taken as fundamental functions, then the following formula is obtained:

$$b_{ik} = - \frac{1}{a_i}\int N_t(x)\psi_i\frac{d^2\psi_k}{dx^2}dx . \tag{17.7}$$

Here, obviously, $a_{ik} = \delta_{ik}/\alpha_k$.

● **3.** As an example, consider the problem depicted in Figure 101. This example will also be used to show the application of ψ functions.

As is known, the buckling forms and the critical buckling forces for a prismatic rod fixed at one end and loaded by a concentrated force applied at the other (free) end are

$$\psi_k(x) = 1 - \cos \frac{k\pi x}{2l},$$
$$P_* = \frac{k^2\pi^2 EJ}{4l^2} \qquad (k = 1, 3, 5, \cdots).$$

Normalizing the functions according to (12.13) and introducing continuous numbering gives

$$\bar{\psi}_k(x) = \frac{2\sqrt{2l}}{(2k-1)\pi}\left[1 - \cos \frac{(2k-1)\pi x}{2l}\right],$$
$$P_k = \frac{(2k-1)^2\pi^2 EJ}{4l^2}, \qquad (k = 1, 2, 3, \cdots).$$

Consequently,

$$\boldsymbol{A} = \frac{4l^2}{\pi^2 EJ}\{1, \tfrac{1}{9}, \tfrac{1}{25}, \cdots\}.$$

Take the force P_t as parameter β. Then $N_t = 1$, and formula (17.7) takes the form

$$b_{ik} = -\frac{8l(2k-1)}{(2i-1)^3\pi^2 EJ}\int_0^l \left[1 - \cos \frac{(2i-1)\pi x}{2l}\right] \cos \frac{(2k-1)\pi x}{2l}\, dx.$$

Evaluating the integral leads to

$$b_{ik} = \begin{cases} \dfrac{8l^2}{(2k-1)^2\pi^2 EJ}\left[\dfrac{1}{2} + \dfrac{2}{\pi}\,\dfrac{(-1)^k}{(2k-1)}\right], & (i = k), \\[2ex] \dfrac{16l^2(-1)^k}{\pi^3(2i-1)^3 EJ}, & (i \neq k), \end{cases}$$

The calculations which follow are confined to third-order matrices:

$$\boldsymbol{B} = \frac{4l^2}{\pi^2 EJ}\begin{pmatrix} -0.2732 & 1.2732 & -1.2732 \\ -0.0472 & 0.1582 & -0.0472 \\ -0.0102 & 0.0102 & 0.0302 \end{pmatrix}.$$

The elements of matrix $\boldsymbol{C}$, according to formulas (12.17), have the form

$$c_{ik} = \begin{cases} \dfrac{32ml^4}{(2k-1)^4\pi^4 EJ}\left[\dfrac{3}{2} + \dfrac{4}{\pi}\,\dfrac{(-1)^k}{2k-1}\right], & (i = k), \\[2ex] \dfrac{32ml^4}{(2i-1)^3(2k-1)\pi^4 EJ}\left[1 + \dfrac{2}{\pi}\,\dfrac{(-1)^i}{2i-1} + \dfrac{2}{\pi}\,\dfrac{(-1)^k}{2k-1}\right], & (i \neq k), \end{cases}$$

or, after integration

$$c_{ik} = \frac{32ml^3}{(2i-1)^3(2k-1)\pi^4 EJ}\int_0^l\left[1 - \cos\frac{(2i-1)\pi x}{2l}\right] \times\left[1 - \cos\frac{(2k-1)\pi x}{2l}\right]dx\,.$$

In this way,

$$\boldsymbol{C} = \frac{ml^4}{\pi^4 EJ}\begin{pmatrix} 7.2576 & 6.1408 & 1.5004 \\ 0.6816 & 0.7584 & 0.2592 \\ 0.0608 & 0.0928 & 0.0608 \end{pmatrix}.$$

The expansion in ψ functions gives the largest error in the absence of parametric loading. Use is made of this fact in estimating the magnitudes of the possible errors. From the equation $|\boldsymbol{E} - \omega^2\boldsymbol{C}| = 0$, and taking the first-order "determinant" in the first approximation, leads to the minimum critical frequency:

$$\omega_1 = \frac{3.66}{l^2}\sqrt{\frac{EJ}{m}}\,.$$

The deviation from the exact value[2] is about 4 percent. If the second-order determinant is taken, then the following are obtained for the first two frequencies:

$$\omega_1 = \frac{3.52}{l^2}\sqrt{\frac{EJ}{m}}\,, \qquad \omega_2 = \frac{24.2}{l^2}\sqrt{\frac{EJ}{m}}\,.$$

The first frequency practically coincides with the exact value, while the error for the second frequency is still sufficiently large.

● **4.** The matrix differential equation for the boundaries of dynamic stability is of the form

$$\boldsymbol{C}\boldsymbol{f}'' + [\boldsymbol{E} - P_0\boldsymbol{A} - P_t\Phi(t)\boldsymbol{B}]\boldsymbol{f} = 0\,.$$

Let $\Phi(t) = \cos\theta t$. Then the following equation for the determination of the principal boundaries of instability is obtained:

$$|\,\boldsymbol{E} - P_0\boldsymbol{A} \pm \tfrac{1}{2}P_t\boldsymbol{B} - \tfrac{1}{4}\theta^2\boldsymbol{C}\,| = 0.$$

Limited to second order matrices, this equation can be written

$$\begin{vmatrix} 1 - \alpha \mp 0.1366\beta - 7.2576\lambda & \pm 0.6366\beta - 6.1408\lambda \\ \mp 0.0236\beta - 0.6816\lambda & 1 - 0.1111\alpha \pm 0.0791\beta - 0.7584\lambda \end{vmatrix} = 0\,,$$

where, for brevity, the following notation is used:

$$\frac{4P_0l^2}{\pi^2 EJ} = \alpha\,, \qquad \frac{4P_tl^2}{\pi^2 EJ} = \beta\,, \qquad \frac{ml^4\theta^2}{4\pi^4 EJ} = \lambda\,.$$

In what follows, the case of the purely periodic load ($\alpha = 0$) will be con-

[2] The exact values for the first two frequencies are

$$\omega_1 = \frac{3.516}{l^2}\sqrt{\frac{EJ}{m}}\,, \qquad \omega_2 = \frac{22.035}{l^2}\sqrt{\frac{EJ}{m}}\,.$$

sidered. Expanding the determinant leads to

$$1.319\lambda^2 - (8.016 \pm 0.1815\beta)\lambda + 1 \mp 0.0575\beta + 0.0042\beta^2 = 0 . \quad (17.8)$$

The graph depicted in Figure 102 shows the first two principal regions of instability. For comparison, the boundaries for the region of instability in the case of a load which does not change its direction are also plotted on this graph. These boundaries are found from the equation

$$| \boldsymbol{E} \pm \tfrac{1}{2}P_t \boldsymbol{A} - \tfrac{1}{4}\theta^2 \boldsymbol{C} | = 0 .$$

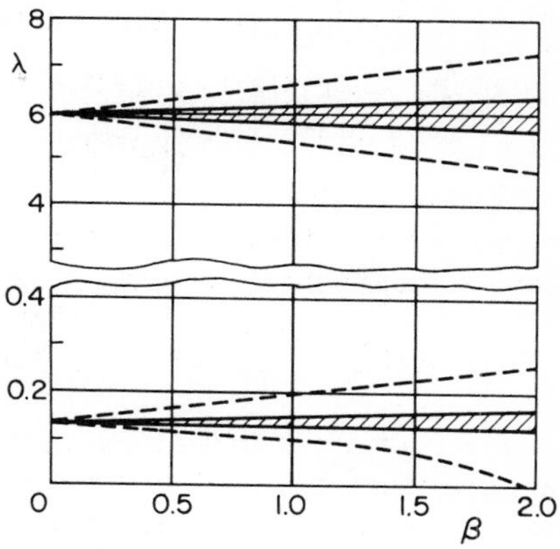

FIG. 102.

Thus, the consideration of load behavior leads to a narrowing of the regions of dynamic instability. This result becomes somewhat clearer if the corresponding statics problem is considered. It is known[3] that under the action of "following" load, loss of static stability in the Euler sense generally is impossible (this discussion obviously concerns stability in the elastic range). Consequently in the given case the static stability problem does not have any real eigenvalues; this fact could have been foreseen from a consideration of the general equations.

The integro-differential equation for the transverse bending in the case of a load which does not change direction has the form (§ 45)

$$\frac{dv(x)}{dx} - \alpha\int N(\xi)\frac{\partial^2 K(x, \xi)}{\partial x \partial \xi}\,\frac{dv(\xi)}{d\xi}d\xi = 0 , \quad (17.9)$$

and can easily be made symmetrical by introducing a new unknown,

$$\psi(x) = \sqrt{N(x)}\frac{dv}{dx} .$$

For the case of a rotating load, the integro-differential equation is

$$v(x) + \beta\int N(\xi)K(x, \xi)\frac{d^2 v(\xi)}{d\xi^2}d\xi = 0 \quad (17.10)$$

which after double differentiation with respect to x is reduced to an integral equation:

$$u(x) + \beta\int N(\xi)\,\frac{\partial^2 K(x, \xi)}{\partial x^2}u(\xi)\,d\xi = 0 , \quad (17.10')$$

where $u = (d^2v/dx^2)$. In general, the kernel of this equation is not symmetric; consequently the boundary value problem need not have any real eigenvalues.[4]

[3] See for example, Feodosiev [1].

[4] This follows also from general equations of § 53 based on equations of the nonlinear theory of elasticity.

We will consider one exception. Let the rod be loaded by concentrated forces $N_1, N_2, \cdots, N_n$, which are applied at points having coordinates $a_1, a_2, \cdots, a_n$. Then, obviously, $dN/dx = 0$ everywhere except at the above points, where discontinuities take place:

$$N(a_k + 0) - N(a_k - 0) = -N_k, \qquad (k = 1, 2, 3, \cdots, n). \tag{17.11}$$

Applying integration by parts to the integral in Eq. (17.10) gives

$$\int N(\xi)K(x, \xi)\frac{d^2v(\xi)}{d\xi^2}d\xi = -\int \frac{dv(\xi)}{d\xi}d[N(\xi)K(x, \xi)].$$

Hence, if the definition of Stieltjes integral and formula (17.11) are taken into account, the following is obtained:

$$\int N(\xi)K(x, \xi)\frac{d^2v(\xi)}{d\xi^2}d\xi = \sum_{k=1}^{n} N_kK(x, a_k)\frac{dv(a_k)}{dx} - \int N(\xi)\frac{\partial K(x, \xi)}{\partial \xi}\frac{dv(\xi)}{d\xi}d\xi.$$

If $v = 0$ or $dv/dx = 0$ at all of the points where the concentrated forces are applied, then the sum in the last formula vanishes. In this case Eq. (17.10) reduces to Eq. (17.9) with a kernel which can be made symmetrical, and there is essentially no difference between the two problems considered. The physical meaning of the two cases is obvious. At the points where $dv/dx = 0$, the additional reduced load is equal to zero; at points where $v = 0$, this load is taken by the support.

● **5.** If the static stability problem does not have real eigenvalues, then this fact must be reflected also in the position of the region of stability. This can be seen because the frequency of free vibrations of a loaded rod, the rule for variation of which is specified by the path of "skeletal curves" of the instability region, must be different from zero for arbitrary values of parameter α (reduction of it to zero would mean the loss of static stability).

Consequently, in contrast to loading which does not change direction, the region of instability located in the λ, β plane does not intersect axis β but remains in the upper half-plane. An example of the distribution of the instability regions is shown in Figure 103a.

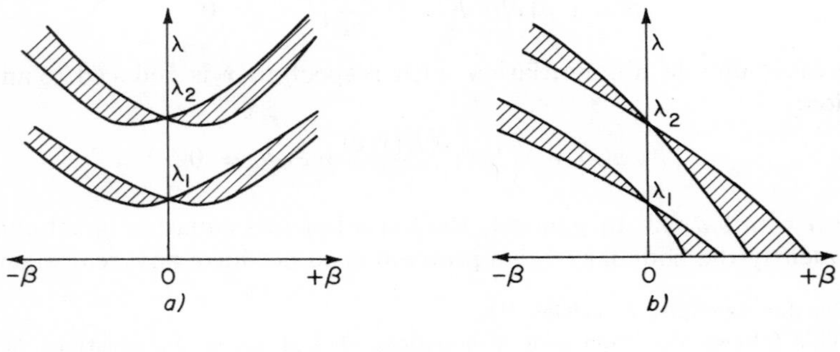

FIG. 103.

In evaluating this graph one must consider that it was obtained from an equation which was based on the harmonic approximation and the approximation of the forms of vibrations with the help of two functions, i.e., from an equation which holds for not too large values of β. This graph seems to convey accurately the essential features of the principal regions of instability for a "following" loading. For comparison, Figure 103b shows the distribution of the instability regions for the case where the load direction does not change during vibrations.

● **6.** We will now consider in greater detail the problem of the stability of the straight form of equilibrium of a compressed rod subjected to the action of a "following" force which is constant in magnitude. The fact that the critical force in the Euler sense does not exist for this problem does not mean that the elastic equilibrium of the straight rod is stable for all the values of the force $\boldsymbol{P}$.

In the classical treatment of the elastic stability concept, it is assumed that the perturbations are small and independent of time. The critical parameters are determined from the condition that there exist, together with the given form of equilibrium, other adjoining forms. Even if one confines himself to the stability with small perturbations, such a treatment seems to be insufficient.

Let us consider the equation for small vibrations of a system with respect to the previously given equilibrium position:

$$\boldsymbol{f}'' + \boldsymbol{C}^{-1}(\boldsymbol{E} - \alpha\boldsymbol{A})\boldsymbol{f} = \boldsymbol{0}.$$

Assuming

$$\boldsymbol{f} = \boldsymbol{a}e^{i\rho t}$$

leads to the characteristic equation

$$|\, \boldsymbol{C}^{-1}(\boldsymbol{E} - \alpha\boldsymbol{A}) - \rho^2\boldsymbol{E}\,| = 0.$$

If all ρ are real or have positive imaginary parts, then the given position is stable. If among the roots ρ there is at least one which has a negative imaginary part, then the perturbations will increase unboundedly with time. The equilibrium which is stable in the Euler sense, is unstable in the dynamic sense.

When all the external forces are conservative, matrices $\boldsymbol{C}$ and $\boldsymbol{C}^{-1}\boldsymbol{A}$ are symmetric and, consequently, all ρ^2 are real. A transition from real to imaginary values of ρ is possible only through the value $\rho = 0$, i.e., through neutral equilibrium in the Euler sense. Thus for elastic systems which are loaded by conservative forces, the classical treatment of the static stability concept appears to be sufficient.

The "following" forces generally are nonconservative. For example, the work of force $\boldsymbol{P}$ (Fig. 101) depends on the choice of the path through which the rod is brought to the final position. In the case of nonconservative parametric forces, the matrix $\boldsymbol{C}^{-1}\boldsymbol{A}$ is not symmetric and consequently the quantities ρ^2 can be real or also complex. Of special importance is the fact that the transition from real to complex roots can proceed through multiple values which are different from zero, i.e., by passing through neutral equilibrium.[5]

The problem of the stability of an elastic rod fixed at one end and loaded at the other end by a "following" force is exactly a problem of this type. It was previously assumed that a straight form of the rod remains stable for all values of the force $\boldsymbol{P}$.[6] Recently it has been shown[7] that for sufficiently large values of the force, a loss of stability in the dynamic sense is possible. This follows also from the equations given above.

The equation for "free vibrations" has the form

$$\begin{vmatrix} 1 + 0.2732\beta - 7.2576\lambda & -1.2732\beta - 6.1408\lambda \\ 0.0472\beta - 0.6816\lambda & 1 - 0.1582\beta - 0.7584\lambda \end{vmatrix} = 0 ,$$

where

$$\beta = \frac{4Pl^2}{\pi^2 EJ} , \qquad \lambda = \frac{ml^4 \rho^2}{\pi^4 EJ} .$$

Expanding the determinant gives the following equation:

$$1.3186\lambda^2 - (8.0160 - 0.3630\beta)\lambda + 1 + 0.1150\beta + 0.0169\beta^2 = 0$$

whose roots are all real and simple as long as

$$(8.0160 - 0.3630\beta)^2 - 4 \times 1.3186(1 + 0.1150\beta + 0.0169^2) > 0 .$$

Hence two values of β correspond to an appearance of a pair of multiple roots: $\beta_1 = 0.9942$, $\beta_2 = -140.5$ (in view of the approximation of the equation, the second value hardly appears reliable). If $\beta > \beta_1$, then among ρ there appear roots which have a negative imaginary part. The minimum value of the critical force is

$$P_* = 24.43 \frac{EJ}{l^2} ,$$

which is 20 percent larger than the exact value which was obtained in the works of Beck, Deineko, and Leonov cited above.

The above analysis, however, is insufficient. The problem of the stability of equilibrium forms of a rod is essentially *nonlinear*, and that which was qualified as stability actually appears to be a questionable case, according to Liapunov. For a certain class of problems in the theory of elastic stability, such a rough approach can be justified. If it is proved that the introduction of an arbitrarily small damping transforms the questionable case to asymptotic stability, then it is not necessary to make a strict analysis where only an approximate solution is required. Here, generally, this does not take place. Thus, Ziegler [1] has shown that in the case of a simple system subjected to the action of a "following" force, the introduction of damping lowers the critical value in comparison with the value which is obtained

[5] See Nikolai [2].

[6] Pflüger [1] and Feodosiev [1].

[7] Beck [1] and Deineko and Leonov [1].

from the simplified analysis. At first glance this result seems paradoxical. It must be considered, however, that damping can exert a destabilizing influence in nonconservative systems (an example of such is the instability of rotating shafts due to internal friction).

Thus problems involving the stability of equilibrium positions of elastic systems subjected to the action of "following" forces must be investigated on the basis of damping considerations and, in certain cases, on the basis of nonlinear considerations. The character and the magnitude of resistance forces have essential influence on the magnitude of critical parameters. This problem requires a thorough investigation.[8]

§ 73. The Equations for the Boundaries of Dynamic Stability for Thin-Walled Rods

● 1. Thus far, only the plane vibrations of rods have been investigated. The results obtained can be generalized to a considerable extent if one considers a case of the spatial dynamic stability of thin-walled rods.

The static stability of thin-walled rods with open profile and with undeformed cross section was investigated in detail by Vlasov [1]. The differential equations which he derived for the case where the longitudinal force is constant along the length of bar have the form

$$\begin{aligned}
EJ_y\frac{d^4u}{dz^4} + N\frac{d^2u}{dz^2} + (a_y - e_y)N\frac{d^2\varphi}{dz^2} &= 0\,, \\
EJ_x\frac{d^4v}{dz^4} + N\frac{d^2v}{dz^2} - (a_x - e_x)N\frac{d^2\varphi}{dz^2} &= 0\,, \\
(a_y - e_y)N\frac{d^2u}{dz^2} - (a_x - e_y)\frac{d^2v}{dz^2} + EJ_\omega\frac{d^4\varphi}{dz^4} & \\
+ [(r^2 + 2\beta_x e_x + 2\beta_y e_y)N - GJ_d]\frac{d^2\varphi}{dz^2} &= 0\,.
\end{aligned} \tag{17.12}$$

The notation used in these equations is as follows: u and v are the displacements of the center of bending A in the directions of the Ox and Oy axes; φ is the angle of twist; EJ_x, EJ_y, EJ_ω, and GJ_d are bending, warping, and torsional rigidities of the cross section; a_x and a_y are coordinates of the center of bending; e_x and e_y are the coordinates of the point of application of the axial force; r, β_x and β_y geometric characteristics which can be calculated from the formulas

$$\begin{aligned}
r^2 &= \frac{J_x + J_y}{F} + a_x^{\,2} + a_y^{\,2}\,, \\
\beta_x &= \frac{1}{2J_y}\int_F x(x^2 + y^2)\,dF - a_x\,, \\
\beta_y &= \frac{1}{2J_x}\int y(x^2 + y^2)\,dF - a_y\,,
\end{aligned}$$

Axis Oz is directed along the rod; axes Ox and Oy coincide with the principal

[8] Bolotin [20].

axes of inertia of the cross section (Fig. 104).

To obtain the equations for the vibrations of a thin-walled rod which is loaded by variable longitudinal force $N(t)$, inertial terms are introduced into Eq. (17.12). In calculating the inertial forces, we take into account, as is generally done, the influence of components which arise from the rotation of the cross section with respect to its principal axes and also their non-remaining in the plane. Then for the projections of inertial forces on axes Ox and Oy and for the inertial moment with respect to the axis of the centers of bending, the following expressions (per unit length of the rod) are obtained:

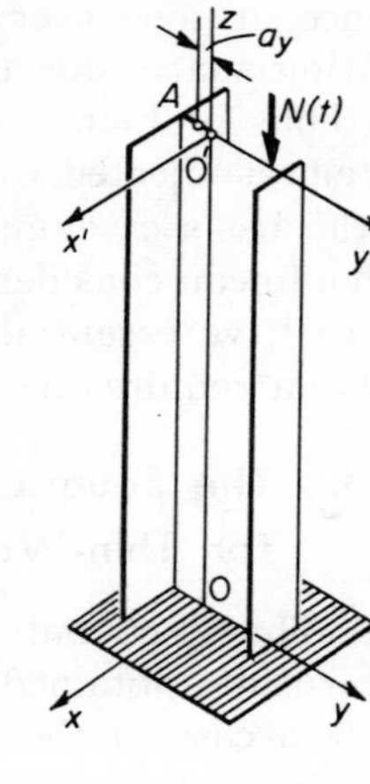

FIG. 104.

$$q_x = -m\frac{\partial^2 u}{\partial t^2} - ma_y\frac{\partial^2 \varphi}{\partial t^2},$$

$$q_y = -m\frac{\partial^2 v}{\partial t^2} + ma_x\frac{\partial^2 \varphi}{\partial t^2},$$

$$m_A = -mr^2\frac{\partial^2 \varphi}{\partial t^2} - ma_y\frac{\partial^2 u}{\partial t^2} + ma_x\frac{\partial^2 v}{\partial t^2}.$$

After substituting these expressions into Eq. (17.12), the system of differential equations is obtained

$$\begin{aligned}
&EJ_y\frac{\partial^4 u}{\partial z^4} + N(t)\frac{\partial^2 u}{\partial z^2} + N_t(a_y - e_y)\frac{\partial^2 \varphi}{\partial z^2} + m\frac{\partial^2 u}{\partial t^2} + ma_y\frac{\partial^2 \varphi}{\partial t^2} = 0,\\
&EJ_x\frac{\partial^4 v}{\partial z^4} + N(t)\frac{\partial^2 v}{\partial z^2} - N_t(a_x - e_x)\frac{\partial^2 \varphi}{\partial z^2} + m\frac{\partial^2 v}{\partial t^2} - ma_x\frac{\partial^2 \varphi}{\partial t^2} = 0,\\
&N(t)(a_y - e_y)\frac{\partial^2 u}{\partial z^2} - N(t)(a_x - e_x)\frac{\partial^2 v}{\partial z^2} + EJ_\omega\frac{\partial^4 \varphi}{\partial z^4} +\\
&\quad [N(t)(r^2 + 2\beta_x e_x + 2\beta_y e_y) - GJ_d]\frac{\partial^2 \varphi}{\partial z^2} + mr^2\frac{\partial^2 \varphi}{\partial t^2} +\\
&\quad ma_y\frac{\partial^2 u}{\partial t^2} - ma_x\frac{\partial^2 v}{\partial t^2} = 0.
\end{aligned} \tag{17.13}$$

The case of a rod simply-supported at both ends (generalization for other types of support is trivial) will now be considered. The boundary conditions

$$u(0) = v(0) = \varphi(0) = \frac{\partial^2 u(0)}{\partial z^2} = \frac{\partial^2 v(0)}{\partial z^2} = \frac{\partial^2 \varphi(0)}{\partial z^2} = 0,$$

$$u(l) = v(l) = \varphi(l) = \frac{\partial^2 u(l)}{\partial z^2} = \frac{\partial^2 v(l)}{\partial z^2} = \frac{\partial^2 \varphi(l)}{\partial z^2} = 0$$

can be satisfied by assuming

$$\begin{aligned}
&u(z, t) = \sum_{k=1}^{\infty} U_k(t) \sin\frac{k\pi z}{l}, \qquad v(z, t) = \sum_{k=1}^{\infty} V_k(t) \sin\frac{k\pi z}{l}\\
&\varphi(z, t) = \sum_{k=1}^{\infty} \Phi_k(t) \sin\frac{k\pi z}{l},
\end{aligned} \tag{17.14}$$

where $U_k(t)$, $V_k(t)$, and $\Phi_k(t)$ are unknown functions of time. The formal substitutions of series (17.14) into Eqs. (17.13) leads to a system of ordinary differential equations:

$$
\begin{aligned}
&m\frac{d^2U_k}{dt^2} + ma_y\frac{d^2\Phi_k}{dt^2} + EJ_y\lambda_k^4U_k - \lambda_k^2N(t)[U_k + (a_y - e_y)\Phi_k] = 0\,, \\
&m\frac{d^2V_k}{dt^2} - ma_x\frac{d^2\Phi_k}{dt^2} + EJ_x\lambda_k^4V_k - \lambda_k^2N(t)[V_k - (a_x - e_x)\Phi_k] = 0\,, \\
&ma_y\frac{d^2U_k}{dt^2} - ma_x\frac{d^2V_k}{dt^2} + mr^2\frac{d^2\Phi_k}{dt^2} + (EJ_\omega\lambda_k^4 + GJ_d\lambda_k^2)\Phi_k \\
&\quad - \lambda_kN(t)][(a_y - e_y)U_k - (a_x - e_x)V_k + (r^2 + 2\beta_xe_x + 2\beta_ye_y)\Phi_k] = 0\,, \\
&\qquad (k = 1, 2, 3, \cdots)\,,
\end{aligned}
\tag{17.15}
$$

where we let $\lambda_k = k\pi/l$. Equations (17.15) were established by Vlasov [1] in connection with the problems of free vibrations; their application to dynamic stability problems was discussed by Gol'denblat [1].

For $k = 1, 2, 3, \cdots$, each of the systems (17.15) contains only those functions U_k, V_k, Φ_k, which have the same index k. Instead of a system of infinite equations, as in the general case, we obtain an infinite sequence of systems of differential equations, each of which consists of three differential equations. We have here an example of the case introduced in §54, namely, the case of quasi-separation into independent individual equations.

● 2. The differential equations (17.15) can be expressed in a more compact form if the following matrix notation is introduced:

$$
\boldsymbol{f}_k = \begin{pmatrix} U_k \\ V_k \\ \Phi_k \end{pmatrix}, \qquad \boldsymbol{F} = \begin{pmatrix} 1 & 0 & a_y \\ 0 & 1 & -a_x \\ a_y & -a_x & r^2 \end{pmatrix},
$$

$$
\boldsymbol{R}_k = \begin{pmatrix} EJ_y\lambda_k^4 & 0 & 0 \\ 0 & EJ_x\lambda^4 & 0 \\ 0 & 0 & EJ_\omega\lambda_k^4 + GJ_d\lambda_k^2 \end{pmatrix},
$$

$$
\boldsymbol{S} = \begin{pmatrix} 1 & 0 & a_y - e_y \\ 0 & 1 & -(a_x - e_x) \\ a_y - e_y & -(a_x - e_x) & r^2 + 2\beta_xe_x + 2\beta_ye_y \end{pmatrix}.
$$

Then system (17.15) takes the form

$$
m\boldsymbol{F}\frac{d^2\boldsymbol{f}}{dt^2} + [\boldsymbol{R}_k - \lambda_k^2N(t)\boldsymbol{S}]\boldsymbol{f} = \boldsymbol{0}\,. \tag{17.16}
$$

If we write

$$
m\boldsymbol{R}_k^{-1}\boldsymbol{F} = \boldsymbol{C}\,, \qquad \lambda_k^2\boldsymbol{R}_k^{-1}\boldsymbol{S} = \boldsymbol{A}\,,
$$

then the resulting Eq. (17.15) agrees completely with (14.1). Hence it follows directly that the problem concerning the determination of frequencies of free vibrations of an unloaded rod leads to the equation

$$
|\,\boldsymbol{R}_k - m\omega^2\boldsymbol{F}\,| = 0\,,
$$

while the problem of the determination of critical forces leads to the equation

$$| \boldsymbol{R}_k - \lambda_k^2 N\boldsymbol{S} | = 0 ,$$

and the problem of the determination of frequencies of free vibrations of a rod loaded by a constant longitudinal force leads to

$$| \boldsymbol{R}_k - \lambda_k^2 N\boldsymbol{S} - m\Omega^2\boldsymbol{F} | = 0 . \tag{17.17}$$

Furthermore, it can easily be shown that the problem of the determination of odd regions of dynamic instability for the case of a rod loaded by periodic longitudinal force $N_0 + N_t \cos \theta t$ leads to the equation

$$\begin{vmatrix} \boldsymbol{R}_k - \lambda_k^2\left(N_0 \pm \frac{1}{2}N_t\right)\boldsymbol{S} - \frac{1}{4}m\theta^2\boldsymbol{F} & -\frac{1}{2}\lambda_k^2 N_t\boldsymbol{S} & \boldsymbol{0} \\ -\frac{1}{2}\lambda_k^2 N_t\boldsymbol{S} & \boldsymbol{R}_k - \lambda_k^2 N_0\boldsymbol{S} - \frac{9}{4}m\theta^2\boldsymbol{F} & -\frac{1}{2}\lambda_k^2 N_t\boldsymbol{S} \\ \boldsymbol{0} & -\frac{1}{2}\lambda_k^2 N_t\boldsymbol{S} & \boldsymbol{R}_k - \lambda_k^2 N_0\boldsymbol{S} - \frac{25}{4}m\theta^2\boldsymbol{F} \\ \cdots & \cdots & \cdots \end{vmatrix} = 0 \tag{17.18}$$

and to analogous equations for determining even instability regions.

It is possible to make the following general deductions on the character of the distribution of instability regions. For sufficiently small values of the amplitude of the longitudinal force, the regions of instability lie near frequencies

$$\theta = \frac{2\Omega}{j} , \qquad (j = 1, 2, 3, \cdots) ,$$

where Ω are the frequencies of free bending-torsional vibrations of the rod loaded by a constant component of the longitudinal force, i.e., the roots of Eq. (17.17). In addition, a combination resonance can occur at frequencies which satisfy the condition

$$\Omega_{k1} \pm \Omega_{k2} = n\theta , \qquad (n = 0, 1, 2, 3, \cdots) ,$$

where Ω_{k1} and Ω_{k2} are two roots of Eq. (17.17) calculated for one and the same k.

The boundaries of the instability regions lying near $\theta = 2\Omega$ can be determined with sufficient accuracy from the equation

$$\left| \boldsymbol{R}_k - \left(N_0 \pm \frac{1}{2}N_t\right)\lambda_k^2\boldsymbol{S} - \frac{1}{4}m\theta^2\boldsymbol{F} \right| = 0 . \tag{17.19}$$

The application of Eq. (17.19) to an analysis of various special problems is given in the next paragraph.

§ 74. Special Problems in Dynamic Stability of Thin-Walled Rods

● **1.** Begin with the case where the cross section of the bar has two axes of symmetry and the longitudinal force is applied at the center of gravity of the cross section:

$$(a_x = a_y = \beta_y = \beta_y = e_x = e_y = 0) .$$

In this case all three matrices $\boldsymbol{F}, \boldsymbol{R}$, and $\boldsymbol{Q}$ are diagonal; consequently, the unknowns in Eqs. (17.15) separate:

$$\frac{d^2V}{dt^2} + \omega_x^2\left[1 - \frac{N(t)}{N_x}\right]U = 0 , \qquad \frac{d^2V}{dt^2} + \omega_y^2\left[1 - \frac{N(t)}{N_y}\right]V = 0 ,$$

$$\frac{d^2\Phi}{dt^2} + \omega_\varphi^2\left[1 - \frac{N(t)}{N_\varphi}\right]\Phi = 0 .$$

The following notations are introduced here for the individual natural frequencies:

$$\omega_x = \frac{k^2\pi^2}{l^2}\sqrt{\frac{EJ_y}{m}} , \qquad \omega_y = \frac{k^2\pi^2}{l^2}\sqrt{\frac{EJ_x}{m}} ,$$

$$\omega_\varphi = \frac{k\pi}{lr}\sqrt{\frac{1}{m}\left(EJ_\omega\frac{n^2\pi^2}{l^2} + GJ_d\right)} , \tag{17.20}$$

and for the individual critical forces (index n is omitted)

$$N_x = \frac{k^2\pi^2 EJ_y}{l^2} , \qquad N_y = \frac{k^2\pi^2 EJ_x}{l^2} ,$$

$$N_\varphi = \frac{1}{r^2}\left(EJ_\omega\frac{k^2\pi^2}{l^2} + GJ_d\right) . \tag{17.21}$$

Thus, the bending vibrations in two principal planes and torsional vibrations take place independently of each other, satisfying the conditions mentioned. This fact was noted by Vlasov for free vibrations and by Gol'denblat for parametrically excited vibrations.

If $N(t) = N_0 + N_t \cos \theta t$, then the boundaries of principal regions of instability can be approximately determined from the formulas

$$\theta_* = 2\omega_x\sqrt{1 - \frac{N_0}{N_x} \pm \frac{N_t}{2N_x}} ,$$

$$\theta^* = 2\omega_y\sqrt{1 - \frac{N_0}{N_y} \pm \frac{N_t}{2N_y}} ,$$

$$\theta_* = 2\omega_\varphi\sqrt{1 - \frac{N_0}{N_\varphi} \pm \frac{N_t}{2N_\varphi}} .$$

An example for the distribution of instability regions in the plane of parameters (N_0, θ) is shown in Figure 105.

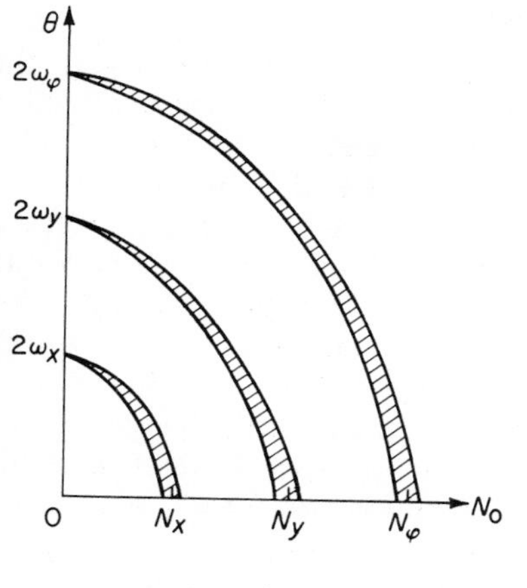

FIG. 105.

● **2.** Proceed now to a more complicated case where the cross section has two axes of symmetry and is loaded by a longitudinal force applied off-center.

Let the eccentricity, e_y be in the plane of largest rigidity (Fig. 106).

In this case the second of Eqs. (17.15) contains only $V_k(t)$ and drops out from the general system of equations. Since this equation describes the forced vibrations of a rod in the plane of largest rigidity (to this equation there correspond nonhomogeneous boundary conditions $EJ_y(\partial^2 v/\partial z^2) = Ne$ for $z = 0$ and $z = l$), it requires special consideration (see § 27 in Part I).

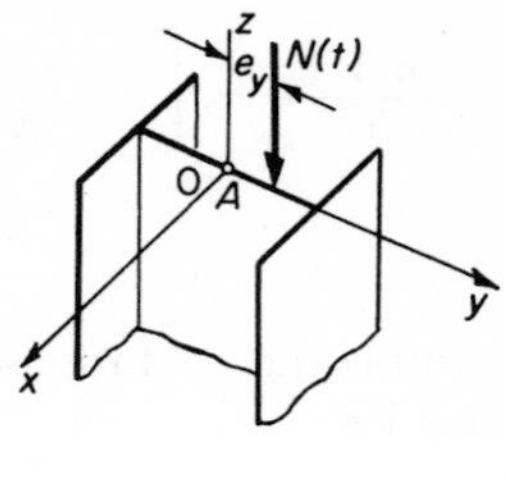

FIG. 106.

The remaining equations form a system of two differential equations of the type in (17.16) with matrices

$$\boldsymbol{F} = \begin{pmatrix} 1 & 0 \\ 0 & r^2 \end{pmatrix},$$

$$\boldsymbol{R}_k = \begin{pmatrix} EJ_y\lambda_k^4 & 0 \\ 0 & EJ_\omega\lambda_k^4 + GJ_d\lambda_k^2 \end{pmatrix},$$

$$\boldsymbol{S} = \begin{pmatrix} 1 & -e_y \\ -e_y & r^2 \end{pmatrix}.$$

For the given problem Eq. (17.19) takes the form

$$\begin{vmatrix} 1-(\mu\pm\nu)-n^2 & (\mu\pm\nu)e_y \\ (\mu\pm\nu)\dfrac{\gamma e_y}{r^2} & 1-(\mu\pm\nu)\gamma-\gamma n^2 \end{vmatrix} = 0,$$

where we have denoted

$$\mu = \frac{N_0}{N_x}, \qquad \nu = \frac{N_t}{2N_x}, \qquad n = \frac{\theta^2}{4\omega_x^2},$$
$$\gamma = \frac{\omega_x^2}{\omega_\varphi^2} = \frac{N_x}{N_\varphi} = \frac{k^2\pi^2 r^2}{l^2}\,\frac{EJ_y}{EJ_\omega(k^2\pi^2/l^2)+GJ_d}. \tag{12.22}$$

This equation makes it possible to evaluate the effect of eccentricity in the plane of largest rigidity on the parametrically excited vibrations which emanate from this plane. Apart from the magnitude of the eccentricity itself, the degree of this influence depends essentially also on parameter γ, i.e., on the ratio of the individual natural frequencies (individual critical forces). For the case of a rod with zero warping rigidity, parameter γ can be larger than unity (for sufficiently short bars) and smaller than unity (for long, flexible bars). If the warping rigidity is not equal to zero, then as the length of the bar becomes shorter parameter γ approaches a certain constant value, which is of the order of unity for an I-beam with thin flanges.

Consider the case of a sufficiently flexible bar for which it is possible to assume $\gamma \ll 1$. The following approximate formulas are easily obtained:

$$\theta_* = 2\omega_x\sqrt{1-(\mu\pm\nu)-\frac{\gamma}{1-\gamma}\,\frac{e_y^2}{r^2}(\mu\pm\nu)^2},$$
$$\theta_* = 2\omega_\varphi\sqrt{1-(\mu\pm\nu)-\frac{\gamma}{1-\gamma}\,\frac{e_y^2}{r^2}(\mu\pm\nu)^2}. \tag{17.23}$$

The first formula gives boundaries of the region which degenerates into a line. $\theta_* = 2\omega_x$ for $\mu = \nu = 0$. Inside this region the vibrations have primarily a bending character. In fact, taking the first row of the matrix equation[9]

$$[\boldsymbol{R}_k - (N_0 \pm \tfrac{1}{2}N_t)\lambda_k{}^2\boldsymbol{S} - \tfrac{1}{4}m\theta^2\boldsymbol{F}]\boldsymbol{f} = \boldsymbol{0}\,,$$

gives

$$[1 - (\mu \pm \nu) - n^2]U_0 + (\mu \pm \nu)e_y\Phi_0 = 0\,.$$

Hence for the region under consideration,

$$\Phi_0 \approx \frac{\gamma}{1-\gamma}\,\frac{\mu e_y}{r^2}U_0\,,$$

i.e., even for $e_y \approx r$ we have, by virtue of $\gamma \ll 1$, $\mu \ll 1$, the relationship $\Phi_0 \ll U_0/r$.

In analogous manner, it can be shown that inside the second region the vibrations have primarily a torsional character. Therefore, in the following, a resonance of bending and torsional vibrations, respectively, will be discussed; it should be kept in mind, however, that these vibrations are coupled (bending-torsional vibrations) and also that such a division is meaningful only for the case $\gamma \ll 1$ (or $\gamma \gg 1$). It is evident from formulas (17.23) that the influence of eccentricity increases as γ approaches unity.

● 3. As the next example, we consider the problem of dynamic stability of a rod whose cross section has one axis of symmetry. This axis will be designated Oy (Fig. 104).

As before, the second equation of system (17.15) is separated out for this case. The coefficients of the remaining equations form the matrices:

$$\boldsymbol{F} = \begin{pmatrix} 1 & a_y \\ a_y & r^2 \end{pmatrix}, \qquad \boldsymbol{R}_k = \begin{pmatrix} EJ_y\lambda_k{}^4 & 0 \\ 0 & EJ_\omega\lambda_k{}^4 + GJ_d\lambda_k{}^2 \end{pmatrix},$$

$$\boldsymbol{S} = \begin{pmatrix} 1 & a_y - e_y \\ a_y - e_y & r^2 + 2\beta_y e_y \end{pmatrix}.$$

For determining the boundaries of the principal regions of instability, the equation

$$[\,\boldsymbol{R}_k - (N_0 \pm \tfrac{1}{2}N_t)\lambda_k{}^2\boldsymbol{S} - \tfrac{1}{4}m\theta^2\boldsymbol{F}\,| = 0$$

is obtained or, in expanded form,

$$\begin{vmatrix} 1-(\mu\pm\nu)-n^2 & -(\mu\pm\nu)(a_y-e_y)-n^2a_y \\ -(\mu\pm\nu)\dfrac{a_y-e_y}{r^2} - \gamma n^2\dfrac{a_y}{r^2} & 1-(\mu\pm\nu)\gamma\left(1+\dfrac{2\beta_y e_y}{r^2}\right)-\gamma n^2 \end{vmatrix} = 0\,, \qquad (17.24)$$

where notation (17.22) has been used. If $\gamma \ll 1$, then, assuming for the region of bending vibrations that

$$n_*^2 = 1 - (\mu \pm \nu)$$

[9] See equation (17.19).

and substituting this expression into all of the elements of determinant (17.24) except the first element of the main diagonal leads to the following (for $e_y = 0$).

$$\begin{vmatrix} 1-(\mu \pm \nu)-n^2 & -a_y \\ -\frac{a_y \gamma}{r^2} & 1-\gamma \end{vmatrix} = 0 .$$

For the nondimensional boundary frequency one obtains

$$n_* = \frac{1}{\sqrt{\gamma}} \sqrt{1-(\mu \pm \nu)+\frac{\gamma}{1-\gamma}\frac{a_y{}^2}{r^2}} . \tag{17.25}$$

Similarly, for the other principal region of instability,

$$n_* = \sqrt{1-(\mu \pm \nu)-\frac{\gamma}{1-\gamma}\frac{a^2{}_y}{r^2}} .$$

Thus far, we have dealt only with the principal regions of dynamic instability. To determine the regions of higher order, it is necessary to refer back to general equations (17.18). Of course, these equations can no longer be solved in a general form for boundary frequencies; only numerical solution for some particular values of parameters is possible.

§ 75. The Problem of the Dynamic Stability of Thin-Walled Rods on a Nonlinear Basis

● **1.** In contrast to the nonlinear problem considered in the first part of the book, dynamic stability problems of thin-walled rods require investigation of a system of two or three nonlinear differential equations with periodic coefficients. Particular difficulties arise also in determination of the nonlinear characteristics of the system. Further investigation will be carried out considering the basic nonlinear factor, i.e., the nonlinear inertia term; the investigation is limited to the case where the cross section has one axis of symmetry (Fig. 104).

The longitudinal displacements

$$w(z, t) = \tfrac{1}{2}\int_0^z \left(\frac{\partial u}{\partial \zeta}\right)^2 d\zeta \tag{17.26}$$

give rise to a longitudinal inertia force which must be taken into account during the construction of nonlinear equations. But in contrast to the plane problems, here nonlinear inertia forces of another type also occur. The bending-torsional vibrations of the bar out of plane Oyz are described by linear displacement $u(z, t)$ and the angle of twist $\varphi(z, t)$. In addition, the centers of gravity of cross sections also undergo displacement $v(z, t)$ in the direction of axis Oy (Fig. 107); this displacement is measured by quantities of the second order of smallness and is related nonlinearly

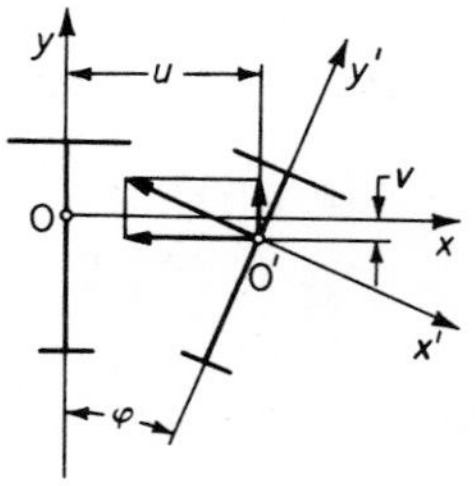

FIG. 107.

to the fundamental displacements $u(z, t)$ and $\varphi(z, t)$. This relationship will be determined first.

Projecting the curvature of the rod in the plane $O'x'z'$ on the axis Oy leads to the curvature in the plane Oyz:

$$\frac{\partial^2 v}{\partial z^2} \approx \frac{\partial^2 u}{\partial z^2}\varphi .$$

Integrating twice leads to

$$v(z, t) = \iint \frac{\partial^2 u}{\partial z^2}\varphi dz dz_1 + Cz + C_1 , \qquad (17.27)$$

where the constants are determined from the boundary contitions. In the case of a rod supported on both ends, it is possible to assume

$$\begin{aligned} u(z, t) &= U(t) \sin \frac{\pi z}{l} , \\ \varphi(z, t) &= \Phi(t) \sin \frac{\pi z}{l} . \end{aligned} \qquad (17.28)$$

Then according to (17.27),

$$v(z, t) = -\frac{\pi^2}{l^2} U(t)\Phi(t)\left(\frac{z^2}{4} + \frac{l^2}{8\pi^2} \cos \frac{2\pi z}{l} + Cz + C_1\right).$$

From boundary conditions

$$v(0, t) = v(l, t) = 0$$

it follows that

$$C = -\tfrac{1}{4}l , \qquad C_1 = -\frac{l^2}{8\pi^2} .$$

Finally, the following is obtained:

$$v(z, t) = \frac{\pi^2}{4l^2} U(t)\Phi(t)\left[z(l - z) + \frac{l^2}{\pi^2} \sin^2 \frac{\pi z}{l} .\right] \qquad (17.29)$$

In a similar way the deflections for other types of support can be determined. Thus, during bending-torsional vibrations the following inertia load results:

$$\Delta q(z, t) = -m\frac{\partial^2 v(z, t)}{\partial t^2}$$

or

$$\Delta q(z, t) = -\frac{m\pi^2}{4l^2}(U''\Phi + 2U'\Phi' + U\Phi'')\left[z(l - z) + \frac{l^2}{\pi^2} \sin^2 \frac{\pi z}{l}\right]. \qquad (17.30)$$

In the general case,

$$\Delta q(z, t) = -(U''\Phi + 2U'\Phi' + U\Phi'')f(z) , \qquad (17.31)$$

where $f(z)$ is some function characterizing the forms of vibrations of the beam and the manner of mass distribution along its length. The additional bending moment induced by this load obviously will be

$$\Delta M(z, t) = -(U''\Phi + 2U'\Phi' + U\Phi'')F(z) , \qquad (17.32)$$

where

$$F(z) = -\iint f(z)dzdz_1 + Dz + D_1 .$$

The constants D and D_1 are determined from the boundary conditions. The longitudinal inertia force is calculated from the formula

$$\Delta N(z, t) = -\int_l^{l-z} m\frac{\partial^2 w}{\partial t^2}d\zeta . \tag{17.33}$$

Using (17.26) and (17.28) leads to

$$w(z, t) = \frac{U^2\pi^2}{2l^2}\left(z + \frac{l}{2\pi}\sin\frac{2\pi z}{l}\right).$$

Application of Eq. (17.33) gives

$$\Delta N(z, t) = -\frac{\pi^2 m}{4}[(U')^2 + UU'']\left(1 - \frac{z^2}{l^2} - \frac{1}{\pi^2}\sin^2\frac{\pi z}{l}\right).$$

If a mass M_L is located on the movable end of the rod, then, as in the case of plane vibrations,

$$\Delta N(z, t) = -\frac{\pi^2 m}{4}[(U')^2 + UU'']\left(1 - \frac{z^2}{l^2} - \frac{1}{\pi^2}\sin^2\frac{\pi z}{l} + \frac{2M_L}{ml}\right); \tag{17.34}$$

and generally,

$$\Delta N(z, t) = -[(U')^2 + UU''[G(z) . \tag{17.35}$$

The function $G(z)$ depends on the boundary conditions and on the distribution of mass along the length of the rod.

● **2.** The differential equations for bending-torsional vibrations of a beam with cross section having one axis of symmetry (axis Oy) and loaded by a longitudinal force $N(t)$, an additional force[10] $\Delta N(z, t)$, and also by load $\Delta q(z, t)$ which produces a moment $\Delta M(z, t)$, have the form

$$\begin{gathered}
EJ_y\frac{\partial^4 u}{\partial z^4} + N(t)\frac{\partial^2 u}{\partial z^2} + N(t)(a_y - e_y)\frac{\partial^2 \varphi}{\partial z^2} + m\frac{\partial^2 u}{\partial t^2} \\
+ ma_y\frac{\partial^2 \varphi}{\partial t^2} + \frac{\partial^2}{\partial z^2}(\Delta M\varphi) + \frac{\partial}{\partial z}\left[\Delta N\left(\frac{\partial u}{\partial z} + a_y\frac{\partial \varphi}{\partial z}\right)\right] = 0 , \\
N(t)(a_y - e_y)\frac{\partial^2 u}{\partial z^2} + EJ_\omega\frac{\partial^4 \varphi}{\partial z^4}[N(t)(r^2 + 2\beta_y e_y) \\
- GJ_d]\frac{\partial^2 \varphi}{\partial z^2} + mr^2\frac{\partial^2 \varphi}{\partial t^2} + ma_y\frac{\partial^2 u}{\partial t^2} + \frac{\partial}{\partial z}\left\{\Delta N\left[r^2\frac{\partial \varphi}{\partial z} + a_y\frac{\partial u}{\partial z}\right]\right\} \\
+ \Delta M\frac{\partial^2 u}{\partial z^2} - 2\beta_y\frac{\partial}{\partial z}\left(\Delta M\frac{\partial \varphi}{\partial z}\right) - \Delta q a_y\varphi = 0 .
\end{gathered} \tag{17.36}$$

These equations can be easily obtained from the well-known equations of Vlasov [1]; in contrast to the latter, they take into account inertial com-

[10] In contrast to $N(t)$ this force is central, which is reflected in the differential equations.

ponents ΔN, Δq, ΔM, which are nonlinearly related to the principal displacements u and φ.

Assuming for the case of the hinged rod that

$$u(z,t) = U(t)\sin\frac{\pi z}{l},$$

$$\varphi(z,t) = \Phi(t)\sin\frac{\pi z}{l},$$

an approximate solution will be sought with the aid of the Galerkin method. The following system of ordinary differential equations results:

$$\begin{gathered} U'' + a_y\Phi'' + \omega_x^2\left\{U - \frac{N(t)}{N_x}[U + (a_y - e_y)\Phi]\right\} \\ + \psi_x(U, U', U'', \Phi, \Phi'\, \Phi'') = 0, \\ \frac{a_y}{r^2}U'' + \Phi'' + \omega_\varphi^2\left\{\Phi - \frac{N(t)}{N_\varphi}\left[\frac{a_y - e_y}{r^2}U + \left(1 + \frac{2\beta_y e_y}{r^2}\right)\Phi\right]\right\} \\ + \psi_\varphi(U, U', U'', \Phi, \Phi', \Phi'') = 0, \end{gathered} \tag{17.37}$$

where in addition to the notation of § 74, the following notation has been used:

$$\begin{aligned} \psi_x &= \frac{2\Phi}{ml}\int_0^l \frac{\partial^2}{\partial z^2}\left(\Delta M \sin\frac{\pi z}{l}\right)\sin\frac{\pi z}{l}dz \\ &+ \frac{2\pi}{ml^2}(U + a_y\Phi)\int_0^l \frac{\partial}{\partial z}\left(\Delta N\cos\frac{\pi z}{l}\right)\sin\frac{\pi z}{l}dz, \\ \psi_\varphi &= -\frac{2\pi^2 U}{ml^3}\int_0^l \Delta M\sin^2\frac{\pi z}{l}dz \\ &+ \frac{2\pi}{ml^2}\left(\frac{a_y}{r^2}U + \Phi\right)\int_0^l \frac{\partial}{\partial z}\left(\Delta N\cos\frac{\pi z}{l}\right)\sin\frac{\pi z}{l}dz \\ &- \frac{2\Phi}{ml}\int_0^l \sin\frac{\pi z}{l}\left[\frac{2\pi\beta_y}{l}\frac{\partial}{\partial z}\left(\Delta M\cos\frac{\pi z}{l}\right) + \Delta q a_y\sin\frac{\pi z}{l}\right]dz. \end{aligned}$$

Taking into account (17.31), (17.32), and (17.35) leads to

$$\begin{aligned} \psi_x &= I_1\Phi(U''\Phi + 2U'\Phi' + U\Phi'') + 2\kappa(U + a_y\Phi)[(U')^2 + UU''], \\ \psi_\varphi &= \frac{1}{r^2}(I_1U - 2\beta_y I_2\Phi + a_y I_3\Phi)(U''\Phi + 2U'\Phi' + U\Phi'') \\ &\quad + 2\kappa\left(\frac{a_y}{r^2}U + \Phi\right)[(U')^2 + UU''], \end{aligned}$$

where

$$\begin{aligned} I_1 &= \frac{2\pi^2}{ml^3}\int_0^l F(z)\sin^2\frac{\pi z}{l}dz = -\frac{2}{ml}\int_0^l \frac{d^2}{dz^2}\left[F(z)\sin\frac{\pi z}{l}\right]\sin\frac{\pi z}{l}dz, \\ I_2 &= \frac{2\pi^2}{ml^3}\int_0^l F(z)\cos^2\frac{\pi z}{l}dz = -\frac{2\pi}{ml^2}\int_0^l \frac{d}{dz}\left[F(z)\cos\frac{\pi z}{l}\right]\sin\frac{\pi z}{l}dz, \\ I_3 &= \frac{2}{ml}\int_0^l f(z)\sin^2\frac{\pi z}{l}dz, \end{aligned}$$

and, in addition,

$$\frac{2\pi^2}{ml^3}\int_0^l G(z)\cos^2\frac{\pi z}{l}dz = -\frac{2\pi}{ml^2}\int_0^l \frac{d}{dz}\left[G(z)\cos\frac{\pi z}{l}\right]dz = 2\kappa\,.$$

For the approximate evaluation of integrals I_1, I_2, and I_3, it is noted that with a known degree of accuracy,

$$f(z) = \frac{m\pi^2}{4l^2}\left[z(l-z)+\frac{l^2}{\pi^2}\sin^2\frac{\pi z}{l}\right] \approx \frac{m\pi^2}{4}\left(\frac{1}{4}+\frac{1}{\pi^2}\right)\sin\frac{\pi z}{l}\,.$$

Integrating twice and using the boundary conditions $F(0)=F(l)=0$ leads to

$$F(z) = \frac{ml^2}{4}\left(\frac{1}{4}+\frac{1}{\pi^2}\right)\sin\frac{\pi z}{l}\,.$$

Then

$$I_1 = I_3 = \frac{2}{3}\pi\left(\frac{1}{4}+\frac{1}{\pi^2}\right) = 0.736\,.$$

$$I_2 = \frac{1}{2}I_1 = 0.368\,.$$

In addition (see § 14),

$$\kappa = \frac{\pi^4}{4l^2}\left(\frac{M_L}{ml}+0.27\right).$$

● **3.** Consider Eqs. (17.37) with the nonlinear functions

$$\begin{aligned}\psi_x &= I_1\Phi(U''\Phi+2U'\Phi'+U\Phi'')+2\kappa(U+a_y\Phi)[(U')^2+UU'']\,,\\ \psi_\varphi &= \frac{I_1}{r^2}[U+(a_y-\beta_y)\Phi](U''\Phi+2U'\Phi'+U\Phi'')\\ &\quad+2\kappa\left(\frac{a_y}{r^2}U+\Phi\right)[(U')^2+UU'']\,.\end{aligned} \tag{17.38}$$

The steady-state solutions within the limits of the principal regions of excitation will be sought in the form

$$U(t) = U_0\cos\frac{\theta t}{2}+\cdots\,,\qquad \Phi(t) = \Phi_0\cos\frac{\theta t}{2}+\cdots\,. \tag{17.39}$$

Substituting (17.39) into (17.38) and transforming leads to

$$\begin{aligned}\psi_x &= -\frac{\theta^2}{4}[\kappa U_0^2(U_0+a_y\Phi^0)+I_1U_0\Phi_0^2]\sin\frac{\theta t}{2}+\cdots\\ \psi_\varphi &= -\frac{\theta^2}{4}\left\{\kappa U_0^2\left(\frac{a_y}{r^2}U_0+\Phi_0\right)+\frac{I_1}{r^2}U_0\Phi_0[U_0+(a_y-\beta_y)\Phi_0]\sin\frac{\theta t}{2}+\cdots\right\}.\end{aligned} \tag{17.40}$$

(The dots denote terms containing higher harmonics.)

Substitution of expressions (17.39) and (17.40) into the differential equations (17.37) and comparison of coefficients of $\sin\theta t/2$ gives the following system of algebraic equations (using the notation of the preceding paragraph):

$$\begin{aligned} &[1-(\mu-\nu)]U_0-(a_y-e_y)(\mu-\nu)\Phi_0 \\ &\qquad\qquad -n^2(1+\kappa U_0^2)(U_0+a_y\Phi_0) = 0 \\ &-\frac{a_y-e_y}{r^2}\gamma(\mu-\nu)\,U_0+\left[1-\gamma(\mu-\nu)\left(1+\frac{2\beta_y e_y}{r^2}\right)\right]\Phi_0 \\ &\qquad\qquad -\gamma n^2(1+\kappa U_0^2)\left(\frac{a_y}{r^2}U_0+\Phi_0\right) = 0\,. \end{aligned} \tag{17.41}$$

The amplitudes U_0 and Φ_0 of steady-state vibrations are found by solving this system. To obtain clearer results, consider first the case where the influence of inertial load $\Delta q(z, t)$ can be neglected (limits of application for this case will be stated later). In place of (17.41) is obtained

$$\begin{aligned} &[1-(\mu-\nu)]U_0-(a_y-e_y)(\mu-\nu)\Phi_0 \\ &\qquad\qquad -n^2[(1+\kappa U_0^2)U_0+a_y\Phi_0)+I_1U_0\Phi_0^2] = 0\,, \\ &-\frac{a_y-e_y}{r^2}\gamma(\mu-\nu)U_0+\left[1-\gamma(\mu-\nu)\left(1+\frac{2\beta_y e_y}{r^2}\right)\right]\Phi_0 \\ &\qquad -\gamma n^2\Big\{(1+\kappa U_0^2)\left(\frac{a_y}{r^2}U_0+\Phi_0\right) \\ &\qquad\qquad +\frac{I_1}{r^2}U_0\Phi_0[U_0+(a_y-\beta_y)\Phi_0]\Big\} = 0\,. \end{aligned} \tag{17.42}$$

This system is satisfied for $U_0 = \Phi_0 = 0$, which corresponds to the absence of bending-torsional vibrations. To obtain conditions for the existence of nonzero solutions, the determinant made up of coefficients of U_0 and Φ_0 is equated to zero. The calculation of amplitudes reduces now to the solution of the equation containing only U_0:

$$\begin{vmatrix} 1-(\mu-\nu)-n^2(1+\kappa U_0^2) & -(a_y-e_y)(\mu-\nu)-n^2(1+\kappa U_0^2)a_y \\ -\frac{a_y-e_y}{r^2}\gamma(\mu-\nu)-\gamma n^2\left(1+\kappa U_0^2\right)\frac{a_y}{r^2} & 1-\gamma(\mu-\nu)\left(1+\frac{2\beta_y e_y}{r^2}\right)-\gamma n^2(1+\kappa U_0^2) \end{vmatrix} = 0.$$

Comparing this equation with the equation for boundary frequencies (17.24) we can see that it can be satisfied by setting

$$n^2(1+\kappa U_0^2) = n_*^2\,. \tag{17.43}$$

(n^* is the nondimensional upper boundary frequency). Hence a very simple formula is obtained[11]:

$$U_0 = \pm\frac{1}{\sqrt{\kappa}}\sqrt{\frac{\theta_*^2}{\theta^2}-1}\,. \tag{17.44}$$

Thus with the assumptions made, the amplitudes of bending vibrations can be determined by the same formula as in the case of plane vibrations of rods (§ 21). A graph showing the dependence of amplitudes on the frequencies is given in Figure 108. The dashes represent unstable solutions, which are obtained by setting

[11] See also the example in § 70.

$$U(t) = U_0 \sin \frac{\theta t}{2} + \cdots ,$$

$$\Phi(t) = \Phi_0 \sin \frac{\theta t}{2} + \cdots ,$$

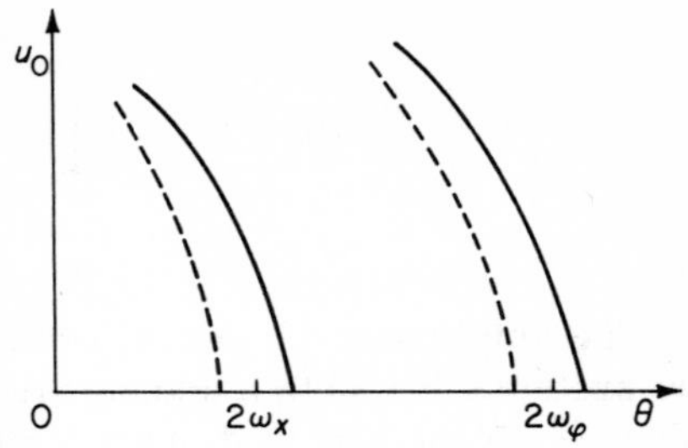

FIG. 108.

In order to explain how the amplitude changes with the angle of twist, we consider the second of Eqs. (17.42). For the case $e_y = 0$, we find

$$\Phi_0 = \frac{\mu - \nu + n^2(1 + \kappa U_0^2)}{1 - \gamma[\mu - \nu + n^2(1 + \kappa U_0^2)]} \frac{\gamma a_y U}{r^2}$$

or, if (17.43) is considered and also $n_*^2 \approx 1$, then

$$\Phi_0 \approx \frac{\gamma}{1 - \gamma} \frac{a_y U_0}{r^2} . \tag{17.45}$$

Consequently, for the region with the mainly bending vibrations, the torsional deformations increase as the center of bending moves away from the center of gravity and also as individual frequencies approach one another.

By using formula (17.45) we will attempt to evaluate the influence of inertial loading $\Delta q(z, t)$ on the amplitudes of bending vibrations. To accomplish this, the approximate value of Φ_0 from (17.45) is substituted into the first of Eqs. (17.41). Easily obtained for $e_y = 0$ is

$$U_0^2 = \frac{1}{n^2} \frac{1 - (\mu - \nu - n^2)(1 + c)}{\kappa(1 + c) + (I_1 c^2/r^2)} ,$$

where

$$c = \frac{\gamma}{1 - \gamma} \frac{a_y^2}{r^2} .$$

But from (17.25) it can be seen that for $c \ll 1$,

$$\frac{1}{1 + c} - (\mu - \nu) \approx n_*^2 .$$

Consequently,

$$U_0^2 = \frac{\dfrac{n_*^2}{n^2} - 1}{\kappa + \dfrac{I_1}{r^2} \dfrac{c^2}{1 + c}} .$$

This formula can also be represented in the form of (17.44) if κ is replaced by a quantity

$$\kappa_1 = \kappa\left(1 + \frac{I_1}{\kappa r^2} \frac{c^2}{1 + c}\right) . \tag{17.46}$$

Examination of formula (17.46) shows that the more pronounced are the inequalities $a_y \ll r$, $\gamma \ll 1$, $M \ll ml$, the smaller will be the influence of the inertial loading $\Delta q(z, t)$. In particular, for rods in which the center of bending is markedly removed from the center of gravity (for example, tube sections can be considered to be rods of this type), this nonlinear factor can be controlling.

Eighteen

DYNAMIC STABILITY OF CURVED RODS

§ 76. Elementary Problem

● 1. The differential equation for bending vibrations of a circular rod having a constant cross section and loaded by the uniformly distributed radial load, $q_0 + q_t\Phi(t)$, can be obtained from the equation of bending

$$\frac{EJ}{R^4}\left(\frac{d^5u}{d\varphi^5} + 2\frac{d^3u}{d\varphi^3} + \frac{du}{d\varphi}\right) = \frac{dq_r}{d\varphi} - q_\varphi\,, \tag{18.1}$$

by introducing in its right-hand side terms which take into account additional components of an external load formed during buckling, and components of internal forces. The longitudinal vibrations will be neglected.

The notation used will be as follows: R is the radius of the axis of the bar, u add v are the radial and tangential displacements of points on the axis of the rod, q_r and q_φ are the radial and tangential components of the external load, and φ is the central angle measured from some initial point.

Assuming that during vibration the vectors of the external load remain perpendicular to the axis of the bar and rotate together with the corresponding cross sections gives

$$q_r = (q_0 + \Phi q_t)\left[1 - \frac{1}{R}\left(\frac{\partial^2 u}{\partial\varphi^2} + u\right)\right] - m\frac{\partial^2 u}{\partial t^2}\,,$$

$$q_\varphi = -m\frac{\partial^2 v}{\partial t^2}\,.$$

Substitution in Eq. (18.1) gives

$$\frac{EJ}{R^4}\left(\frac{\partial^5 u}{\partial_\varphi^{\,5}} + 2\frac{\partial^3 u}{\partial\varphi^3} + \frac{\partial u}{\partial\varphi}\right) + \frac{q_0 + q_t\Phi(t)}{R}\left(\frac{\partial^3 u}{\partial\varphi^3} + \frac{\partial u}{\partial\varphi}\right)$$
$$+ m\left(\frac{\partial^3 u}{\partial\varphi\partial t^2} - \frac{\partial^2 v}{\partial t^2}\right) = 0\,. \tag{18.2}$$

One of the unknowns in Eq. (18.2) can be eliminated by making use of the differential equation for the longitudinal deformation

$$\frac{dv}{\partial\varphi} - u = \frac{NR}{EF}\,.$$

Thus if we assume that the axis of the arch is incompressible, then the following equation is obtained:

$$\frac{EJ}{R^4}\left(\frac{\partial^6 v}{\partial \varphi^6} + 2\frac{\partial^4 v}{\partial \varphi^4} + \frac{\partial^2 v}{\partial \varphi^2}\right) + \frac{q_0 + q_t\Phi(t)}{R}\left(\frac{\partial^4 v}{\partial \varphi^4} + \frac{\partial^2 v}{\partial \varphi^2}\right) + m\left(\frac{\partial^4 v}{\partial \varphi^2 \partial t^2} - \frac{\partial^2 v}{\partial t^2}\right) = 0 . \qquad (18.3)$$

●**2.** Let us first investigate the case of a closed circular ring (Fig. 109). It is assumed that there are no restrictions placed on the forms of vibrations except the conditions of periodicity

$$u(\varphi + 2\pi) = u(\varphi) ,$$
$$v(\varphi + 2\pi) = v(\varphi) .$$

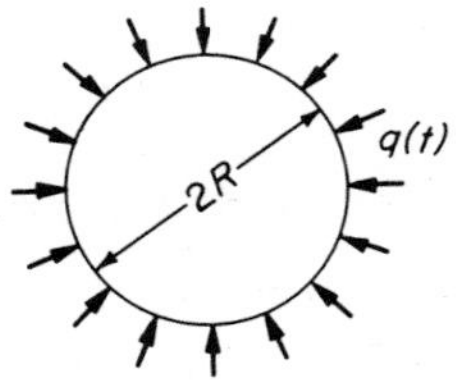

FIG. 109.

In this case the solution of Eq. (18.3) can be represented in the form

$$v_k(\varphi, t) = f_k(t) \sin k\varphi , \qquad (k = 2, 3, 4, \cdots) .$$

As a result of substitution, the following ordinary differential equation for functions $f_k(t)$ is obtained:

$$\frac{d^2 f_k}{dt^2} + \omega_k^2\left[1 - \frac{q_0 + q_t\Phi(t)}{q_k}\right] f_k = 0 , \qquad (k = 2, 3, 4, \cdots) , \qquad (18.4)$$

where the following notation is introduced for the natural frequencies, and critical loads:

$$\omega_k = \frac{k(k^2-1)}{R^2}\sqrt{\frac{EJ}{m(k^2+1)}} ,$$

$$q_k = \frac{EJ}{R^3}(k^2 - 1) .$$

Thus the problem of vibrations of a closed circular ring reduces to the special case of an independent single equation.[1]

In contrast to the case just considered, a double-hinged arch (Fig. 110) requires a system of differential equations which does not decompose into separate equations. In fact, in this case the eigenfunctions of the problem of free vibrations and the problem of static stability do not coincide.

Limiting ourselves to antisymmetric vibrations, we will seek the solution of Eq. (18.2) in the form of a series

$$u(\varphi, t) = \sum_{k=1}^{\infty} f_k(t) \sin n_k\varphi ,$$
$$v(\varphi, t) = \sum_{k=1}^{\infty} f_k(t) \frac{(-1)^k - \cos n_k\varphi}{n_k} , \qquad (18.5)$$

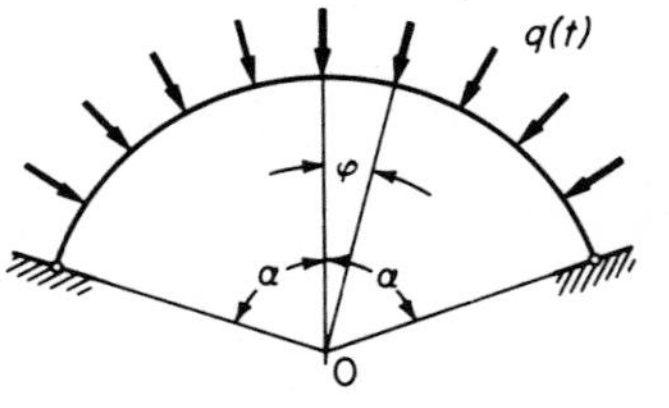

FIG. 110.

which satisfies the boundary conditions of the problem,

[1] Dzhanelidze and Radtsig [1]. In this work the bending-torsional vibrations of a ring are also investigated.

$$u(\alpha) = u(-\alpha) = v(\alpha) = v(-\alpha) = \frac{\partial^2 u(\alpha)}{\partial \varphi^2} = \frac{\partial^2 u(-\alpha)}{\partial \varphi^2} = 0\,,$$

and the condition of incompressibility. Here the notation $n_k = k\pi/\alpha$ is introduced.

To find the relationship between functions $f_k(t)$, the Galerkin method is used. Difficulties may arise in the choice of a condition of orthogonality (we have here two systems of eigenfunctions). In this case it is appropriate to regard the Galerkin method as a form of a principle of virtual displacements. Equation (18.3) expresses the condition that the sum of the *tangential* components of all the forces which act on an element of the arc is equal to zero. When this is considered the following condition of orthogonality results:

$$\int_{-\alpha}^{+\alpha} L(u, v, t)[(-1)^k - \cos n_k\varphi]d\varphi = 0, \qquad (k = 1, 2, 3, \cdots)\,.$$

Substitution gives

$$\frac{mR^4}{n_k^2(n_k^2 - 1)^2 EJ}\left[(n_k^2 + 3)\frac{d^2 f_k}{dt^2} + 2n_k \sum_{i=1}^{\infty} \frac{(-1)^{k+i}}{n_i}\frac{d^2 f_i}{dt^2}\right] + \left[1 - \frac{q_0 + q_t\Phi(t)}{q_k}\right] f_k = 0\,, \qquad (k = 1, 2, 3, \cdots)\,,$$

where q_k denotes the kth critical parameter,

$$q_k = \frac{(n_k^2 - 1)EJ}{R^3}\,.$$

The equations obtained written in matrix form,

$$\boldsymbol{C}\frac{d^2\boldsymbol{f}}{dt^2}[\boldsymbol{E} - q_0\boldsymbol{A} - q_t\Phi(t)\boldsymbol{B}]\boldsymbol{f} = \boldsymbol{0}\,,$$

coincide with Eqs. (12.18). In fact, for this case matrix $\boldsymbol{A}$ is a diagonal matrix

$$\boldsymbol{A} = \frac{R^3}{EJ}\begin{pmatrix} \frac{1}{n_1^2 - 1} & 0 & 0 & \cdot \\ 0 & \frac{1}{n_2^2 - 1} & 0 & \cdot \\ 0 & 0 & \frac{1}{n_3^2 - 1} & \cdot \\ \cdot & \cdot & \cdot & \cdot \end{pmatrix}$$

and matrix $\boldsymbol{C}$ has the form

$$\boldsymbol{C} = \frac{mR^4}{EJ}\begin{pmatrix} \frac{n_1^2 + 3}{n_1^2(n_1^2 - 1)^2} & -\frac{2}{n_1 n_2(n_1^2 - 1)^2} & \frac{2}{n_1 n_3(n_1^2 - 1)^2} & \cdot \\ -\frac{2}{n_1 n_2(n_2^2 - 1)^2} & \frac{n_2^2 + 3}{n_2^2(n_2^2 - 1)^2} & -\frac{2}{n_2 n_3(n_2^2 - 1)^2} & \cdot \\ -\frac{2}{n_3 n_1(n_3^2 - 1)^2} & -\frac{2}{n_3 n_2(n_3^2 - 1)} & \frac{n_3^2 + 3}{n_3^2(n_3^2 - 1)^2} & \cdot \\ \cdot & \cdot & \cdot & \cdot \end{pmatrix}.$$

This result does not seem unexpected, since the assumed fundamental functions (18.5) represent static buckling forms of an arch. From the equation

$$| \boldsymbol{E} - (q_0 \pm \tfrac{1}{2} q_t)\boldsymbol{A} - \tfrac{1}{4}\theta^2 \boldsymbol{C} | = 0$$

as a first approximation, the following formula for the boundary frequencies[2] is obtained:

$$\theta = \frac{2n_k(n_k^2 - 1)}{R^2} \sqrt{\frac{EJ}{m(n_k^2+3)} \left(1 - \frac{q_0 \pm \frac{1}{2} q_t}{q_k}\right)}, \qquad (18.6)$$
$$(k = 1, 2, 3, \cdots) .$$

It is evident that formula (18.6) can give the largest error for small values of q_0/q_k. To evaluate this error, the problem of free vibrations of an arch will be considered. Such consideration leads to the equation

$$| \boldsymbol{E} - \omega^2 \boldsymbol{C} | = 0 .$$

The first approximation gives

$$\tilde{\omega}_k = \frac{n_k(n_k^2 - 1)}{R^2} \sqrt{\frac{EJ}{m(n_k^2+3)}} . \qquad (18.7)$$

From the equation for the second approximation,

$$\begin{vmatrix} 1 - \dfrac{\omega^2}{\tilde{\omega}_1^2} & -\dfrac{\omega^2}{\tilde{\omega}_1^2(n_1^2+3)} \\ -\dfrac{4\omega^2}{\tilde{\omega}_2^2(n_2^2+3)} & 1 - \dfrac{\omega^2}{\tilde{\omega}_2^2} \end{vmatrix} = 0 ,$$

it is easily found that

$$\omega_1 \approx \tilde{\omega}_1 \sqrt{1 - \frac{\gamma}{1-\gamma} \frac{4}{(n_1^2+3)(n_2^2+3)}} ,$$
$$\omega_2 \approx \tilde{\omega}_2 \sqrt{1 + \frac{1}{1-\gamma} \frac{4}{(n_1^2+3)(n_2^2+3)}} , \qquad (\gamma = \tilde{\omega}_1^2/\tilde{\omega}_2^2) .$$

As can be seen from the formulas obtained, the correction of the second approximation is very small (for the lower frequency of a semicircular arch it constitutes only 0.2 percent).

§ 77. The Influence Functions for Deflections of Arches

●1. For a somewhat more extensive investigation of the dynamic stability of arches (consideration of an arbitrary form of axes, varying rigidity, etc.), it is expedient to use a method of integral equations. This permits obtaining a series of results under very general assumptions about the construction of the arch and the character of the external load.

The radial and tangential displacements of an arbitrary point on the arch (Fig. 111) can be expressed in terms of radial and tangential components of the external load in the following way:

[2] The first approximation was investigated by Malkina [1].

$$u(s) = \int K_{rr}(s, \sigma)q_r(\sigma)d\sigma + \int K_{r\varphi}(s, \sigma)q_\varphi(\sigma)d\sigma ,$$
$$v(s) = \int K_{\varphi r}(s, \sigma)q_r(\sigma)d\sigma + \int K_{\varphi\varphi}(s, \sigma)q_\varphi(\sigma)d\sigma . \tag{18.8}$$

In formulas (18.8), $K_{rr}(s, \sigma)$, $K_{r\varphi}(s, \sigma)$, $K_{\varphi r}(s, \sigma)$ and $K_{\varphi\varphi}(s, \sigma)$ are the corresponding influence functions; the first index denotes the direction of displacement sought, the second denotes the direction of the unit load. The integration extends over the whole length of the arch.

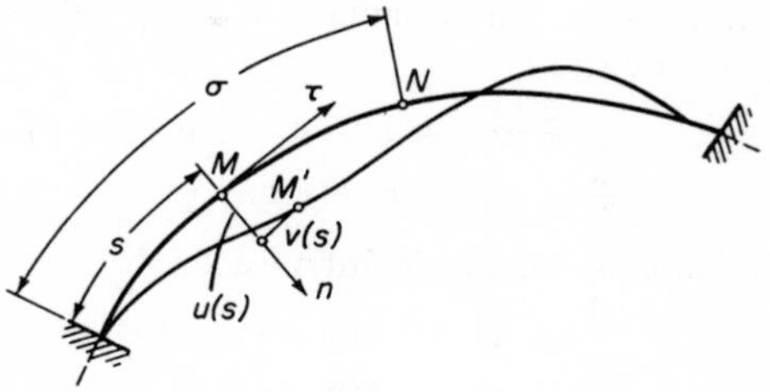

FIG. 111.

The expressions (18.8) can easily be generalized to the case where, in addition to the distributed load, concentrated forces are also applied. To include concentrated forces, it suffices to make use of the Stieltjes integral. Nevertheless, this will be confined to the case of distributed loads (distributed masses) in view of the fact that the generalization of further results is elementary.

The influence functions constitute an *influence tensor*[3]

$$\boldsymbol{K}(s, \sigma) = \begin{pmatrix} K_{rr}(s, \sigma) & K_{r\varphi}(s, \sigma) \\ K_{\varphi r}(t, \sigma) & K_{\varphi\varphi}(s, \sigma) \end{pmatrix} .$$

This tensor is symmetric since on the basis of the theorem on reciprocity of displacements we have

$$K_{rr}(s, \sigma) \equiv K_{rr}(\sigma, s) ,$$
$$K_{\varphi\varphi}(s, \sigma) \equiv K_{\varphi\varphi}(\sigma, s) ,$$
$$K_{r\varphi}(s, \sigma) \equiv K_{\varphi r}(\sigma, s) .$$

Furthermore, it is possible to express all the components of the influence tensor by one arbitrary component. Thus, if it is assumed that the axis of the arch is incompressible $\left(\frac{\partial v}{\partial s} - \frac{u}{r} = 0\right)$, then,

$$K_{r\varphi}(s, \sigma) = r(s) \frac{\partial K_{\varphi\varphi}(s, \sigma)}{\partial s} ,$$
$$K_{rr}(s, \sigma) = r(s)r(\sigma) \frac{\partial^2 K_{\varphi\varphi}(s, \sigma)}{\partial s \partial \sigma} .$$

In this way,

$$K(s, \sigma) = \begin{pmatrix} r(s)r(\sigma) \dfrac{\partial^2 K_{\varphi\varphi}(s, \sigma)}{\partial s \partial \sigma} & r(s) \dfrac{\partial K_{\varphi\varphi}(s, \sigma)}{\partial s} \\ r(\sigma) \dfrac{\partial K_{\varphi\varphi}(s, \sigma)}{\partial \sigma} & K_{\varphi\varphi}(s, \sigma) \end{pmatrix} .$$

[3] Or so-called *Green's tensor* (see § 59).

Let us clarify how the tensor $\boldsymbol{K}(s, \sigma)$ changes during transformation to other axes, let us say to axes x, y. The components of the load are transformed here in the following way (Fig. 112):

$$q_y = q_r \cos\varphi - q_\varphi \sin\varphi ,$$
$$q_x = q_r \sin\varphi + q_\varphi \cos\varphi .$$

An analogous transformation takes place for displacements.

$$\eta = u \cos\varphi - v \sin\varphi ,$$
$$\xi = u \sin\varphi + v \cos\varphi .$$

If a rotation tensor is introduced,

$$\boldsymbol{T} = \begin{pmatrix} \cos\varphi & -\sin\varphi \\ -\sin\varphi & \cos\varphi \end{pmatrix},$$

it can be easily proved with the help of (18.8) that

$$\boldsymbol{K}^*(s, \sigma) = \boldsymbol{T}^{-1}(s)\boldsymbol{K}(s, \sigma)\boldsymbol{T}(\sigma) .$$

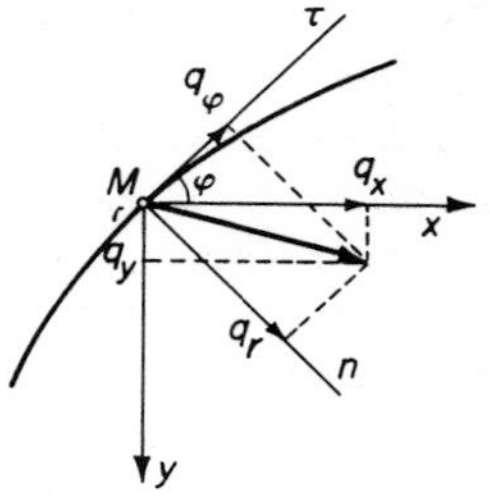

FIG. 112.

●2. As an example, consider the construction of an influence function $K_{yy}(x, \xi)$ for a double-hinged arch (Fig. 113). The use of a known formula gives

$$K_{yy}(x, \xi) = \int_0^l \frac{M(\zeta, \xi)M_0(\zeta, x)}{EJ(\zeta)\cos\varphi(\zeta)} d\zeta , \quad (18.9)$$

where $M_0(x, \xi)$ is the moment influence function for a beam and $M(x, \xi)$ is the moment influence function for the arch,

$$M(x, \xi) = M_0(x, \xi) - H(\xi)y(x) ,$$

in which $H(\xi)$ is the influence function for thrust:

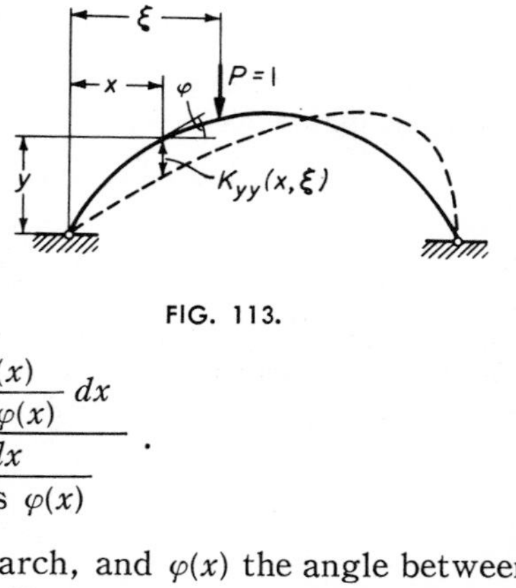

FIG. 113.

$$H(\xi) = \frac{\displaystyle\int_0^l \frac{M_0(x, \xi)y(x)}{EJ(x)\cos\varphi(x)} dx}{\displaystyle\int_0^l \frac{y^2(x)dx}{EJ(x)\cos\varphi(x)}} .$$

$y(x)$ denotes the ordinate of the axis of the arch, and $\varphi(x)$ the angle between the tangent to the axis and the horizontal. For practical calculations, it is more convenient to consider kernel $K_{yy}(x, \xi)$ as a limiting value of some degenerating kernel. Consequently, we will represent the moment influence function for a beam, in the form of a series, is

$$M_0(x, \xi) = \frac{2l}{\pi^2} \sum_{k=1}^{\infty} \frac{\sin\dfrac{k\pi x}{l} \sin\dfrac{k\pi\xi}{l}}{k^2} . \quad (18.10)$$

Making use of Eq. (18.10) we obtain the following expansion for the thrust influence function:

$$H(\xi) = \frac{2l}{\pi^2} \sum_{k=1}^{\infty} \frac{\lambda_k}{k^2 c} \sin \frac{k\pi\xi}{l},$$

where

$$\lambda_k = \int_0^l \frac{y(x) \sin \frac{k\pi x}{l}}{EJ(x) \cos \varphi} dx, \qquad c = \int_0^l \frac{y^2(x)dx}{EJ(x) \cos \varphi}.$$

For the deflection influence function $K_{yy}(x, \xi)$, we obtain[4]

$$K_{yy}(x, \xi) = \frac{4l^2}{\pi^4} \sum_{i=1}^{\infty} \sum_{k=1}^{\infty} \frac{\mu_{ik} - \frac{\lambda_i \lambda_k}{c}}{i^2 k^2} \sin \frac{i\pi x}{l} \sin \frac{k\pi\xi}{l}, \tag{18.11}$$

where the following notation is introduced:

$$\mu_{ik} = \int_0^l \frac{\sin \frac{i\pi x}{l} \sin \frac{k\pi x}{l}}{EJ(x) \cos \varphi} dx.$$

The symmetry of the influence functions is ensured by the fact that $\mu_{ik} \equiv \mu_{ki}$.

§ 78. The Integral Equations for Vibrations and for the Boundaries of Static and Dynamic Stability of Arches

● **1.** The vibrations of an arch subjected to an external periodic load

$$q_r(s, t) = [\alpha + \beta\Phi(t)]p_r(s),$$
$$q_\varphi(s, t) = [\alpha + \beta\Phi(t)]p_\varphi(s)$$

will now be investigated.

In regard to this load, it is assumed that it changes its direction during the vibrations, forming the initial angle with the curved axis of the arch. In this case, the additional bending moments which arise during the deviation of the arch axis from the initial position can be taken into account by introducing a load

$$\Delta q_r = -\frac{\partial}{\partial s}\left[N(s, t)\left(\frac{\partial u}{\partial s} + \frac{v}{r}\right)\right],$$
$$\Delta q_\varphi = 0.$$

Adding the inertia forces to the load gives

$$q_r(s, t) = [\alpha + \beta\Phi(t)]p_r(s) - \frac{\partial}{\partial s}\left[N(s)\left(\frac{\partial u}{\partial s} + \frac{v}{r}\right)\right] - m(s)\frac{\partial^2 u}{\partial t^2},$$
$$q_\varphi(s, t) = [\alpha + \beta\Phi(t)]p_\varphi(s) - m(s)\frac{\partial^2 v}{\partial t^2}.$$

The expressions obtained are substituted into (18.8). When the arch axis is assumed as the deflection curve produced by the load given above, then the

[4] Formula (18.11) is derived in the author's work [3].

following holds[5]:

$$\int K_{rr}(s,\sigma)p_r(\sigma)d\sigma + \int K_{r\varphi}(s,\sigma)p_\varphi(\sigma)d\sigma \equiv 0\,,$$

$$\int K_{\varphi r}(s,\sigma)p_r(\sigma)d\sigma + \int K_{\varphi\varphi}(s,\sigma)p_\varphi(\sigma)d\sigma \equiv 0\,,$$

and the following systems of homogeneous integro-differental equations are obtained:

$$\begin{aligned} u(s,t) &- \int N(\sigma,t)\frac{\partial K_{rr}(s,\sigma)}{\partial\sigma}\left[\frac{\partial u(\sigma,t)}{\partial\sigma} + \frac{v(\sigma,t)}{r(\sigma)}\right]d\sigma \\ &+ \int K_{rr}(s,\sigma)m(\sigma)\frac{\partial^2 u(\sigma,t)}{\partial t^2}\,d\sigma + \int K_{r\varphi}(s,\sigma)m(\sigma)\frac{\partial^2 v(\sigma,t)}{\partial t^2}\,d\sigma = 0\,. \\ v(s,t) &- \int N(\sigma,t)\frac{\partial K_{\varphi r}(s,\sigma)}{\partial\sigma}\left[\frac{\partial u(\sigma,t)}{\partial\sigma} + \frac{v(\sigma,t)}{r(\sigma)}\right]d\sigma \\ &+ \int K_{\varphi r}(s,\sigma)m(\sigma)\frac{\partial^2 u(\sigma,t)}{\partial t^2}\,d\sigma + \int K_{\varphi\varphi}(s,\sigma)m(\sigma)\frac{\partial^2 v(\sigma,t)}{\partial t^2}\,d\sigma = 0\,. \end{aligned} \tag{18.12}$$

Equations (18.12) are not linearly independent: it is easily seen that one can be obtained from the other by the differentiation under the integrals. However, for further derivation it is convenient to consider both equations simultaneously.

●**2.** As a special case of the integro-differential equations (18.12), consider the integral equations for the free vibrations of an arch:

$$\begin{aligned} u(s) - \omega^2\int m(\sigma)K_{rr}(s,\sigma)u(\sigma)d\sigma - \omega^2\int m(\sigma)K_{r\varphi}(s,\sigma)v(\sigma)d\sigma &= 0\,, \\ v(s) - \omega^2\int m(\sigma)K_{\varphi r}(s,\sigma)u(\sigma)d\sigma - \omega^2\int m(\sigma)K_{\varphi\varphi}(s,\sigma)v(\sigma)d\sigma &= 0\,. \end{aligned} \tag{18.13}$$

These equations can be combined into one equation

$$\psi(s) - \omega^2\int_{L_1+L_2} K(s,\sigma)\psi(\sigma)d\sigma = 0\,,$$

if one conditionally assumes that the region of integration consists of two regions L_1 and L_2, each of which coincides with the region of integration in (18.13). The eigenfunctions and the kernel of this new equation are given in the following manner:

$$\psi(s) = \begin{cases} \sqrt{m(s)}u(s)\,, & (s \in L_1)\,, \\ \sqrt{m(s)}v(s)\,, & (s \in L_2)\,; \end{cases}$$

$$K(s,\sigma) = \begin{cases} \sqrt{m(s)m(\sigma)}K_{rr}(s,\sigma)\,, & (s \in L_1\,,\ \sigma \in L_1)\,, \\ \sqrt{m(s)m(\sigma)}K_{r\varphi}(s,\sigma)\,, & (s \in L_1\,,\ \sigma \in L_2)\,, \\ \sqrt{m(s)m(\sigma)}K_{\varphi r}(s,\sigma)\,, & (s \in L_2\,,\ \sigma \in L_1)\,, \\ \sqrt{m(s)m(\sigma)}K_{\varphi\varphi}(s,\sigma)\,, & (s \in L_2\,,\ \sigma \in L_2)\,. \end{cases}$$

[5] It is assumed that the axis of the arch is incompressible; moreover the longitudinal vibrations are neglected.

Since the kernel $K(s, \sigma)$ formed in this way is symmetric, the eigenfunctions satisfy the conditions of orthogonality

$$\int_{L_1+L_2} \psi_i \psi_k ds = \delta_{ik} .$$

Returning to the initial equations gives

$$\int m u_i u_k ds + \int m v_i v_k ds = \delta_{ik} . \tag{18.14}$$

The condition (18.14) permits a simple physical interpretation. It means that during some mode of free vibrations the work of the inertia forces, on the displacements corresponding to the remaining vibration forms, is equal to zero.[6] The condition (18.14) differs from an analogous condition (12.21) by the presence of a term which takes into account the work of the tangential inertial forces.

Furthermore, from a consideration of the potential energy of deformation of the arch, it follows that the kernel $K(s, \sigma)$ is positive definite and thus satisfies the conditions of the Mercer theorem. Consequently, it can be expanded into an absolutely and uniformly convergent series in terms of its fundamental functions

$$K(s, \sigma) = \sum_{k=1}^{\infty} \frac{\psi_k(s)\psi_k(\sigma)}{\omega_k^{\,2}} .$$

If the initial kernels are used, then important formulas for future applications are obtained:

$$\begin{aligned} K_{rr}(s, \sigma) &= \sum_{k=1}^{\infty} \frac{u_k(s)u_k(\sigma)}{\omega_k^{\,2}} , \quad & K_{r\varphi}(s, \sigma) &= \sum_{k=1}^{\infty} \frac{u_k(s)v_k(\sigma)}{\omega_k^{\,2}} , \\ K_{\varphi r}(s, \sigma) &= \sum_{k=1}^{\infty} \frac{v_k(s)u_k(\sigma)}{\omega_k^{\,2}} , \quad & K_{\varphi\varphi}(s, \sigma) &= \sum_{k=1}^{\infty} \frac{v_k(s)v_k(\sigma)}{\omega_k^{\,2}} . \end{aligned} \tag{18.15}$$

These formulas make it possible to express the deflection influence functions in terms of eigenfunctions of the problem of free vibrations.

●**3.** We now discuss another special case, i.e., the equations of static stability:

$$\begin{aligned} u(s) - \alpha \int N_0(\sigma) \frac{\partial K_{rr}(s, \sigma)}{\partial \sigma} \left[\frac{du(\sigma)}{d\sigma} + \frac{v(\sigma)}{r(\sigma)} \right] d\sigma &= 0 , \\ v(s) - \alpha \int N_0(\sigma) \frac{\partial K_{\varphi r}(s, \sigma)}{\partial \sigma} \left[\frac{du(\sigma)}{d\sigma} + \frac{v(\sigma)}{r(\sigma)} \right] d\sigma &= 0 . \end{aligned} \tag{18.16}$$

Differentiating the first equation termwise with respect to s, dividing the second by $r(s)$, and combining the results gives the following integral equation:

$$\psi(s) - \alpha \int S(s, \sigma)\psi(\sigma) d\sigma = 0 . \tag{18.17}$$

[6] Of course, condition (18.14) can be obtained also directly from Eqs. (18.13) if two solutions, corresponding to different eigenvalues, are considered.

The unknown in Eq. (18.17) is the quantity $du/ds + v/r$ (angle of rotation of the tangent with respect to the axis of the arch), while the kernel has the form

$$S(s, \sigma) = N_0(\sigma)\left[\frac{\partial^2 K_{rr}(s, \sigma)}{\partial s \partial \sigma} + \frac{1}{r(s)}\frac{\partial K_{\varphi r}(s, \sigma)}{\partial \sigma}\right].$$

Generally speaking, the kernel $S(s, \sigma)$ is not symmetric. This result can easily be explained if one recalls that here a case in which the load rotates is being considered. Generally, the kernels of integral equations for such problems will not be symmetric and the operators for the differential equations will not be self-adjoint. As seen before (§ 72), the problem of the static stability may in such cases have complex eigenvalues. For a practical solution it is therefore more convenient to start not from the integral equation (18.17) but from the integro-differential equations (18.16).

Assume that the solution of a problem concerning the free vibrations of an arch is known, i.e., that the system of eigenfunctions $u_k(s)$ and $v_k(s)$ and the corresponding eigenvalues ω_k^2 are known. On the basis of formulas (18.15), the solution for the static stability problem can be sought in the form of a series

$$u(s) = \sum_{k=1}^{\infty} f_k u_k(s),$$

$$v(s) = \sum_{k=1}^{\infty} f_k v_k(s).$$

It is assumed that the eigenfunctions constitute an orthonormalized system

$$\int m u_k^2 ds + \int m v_k^2 ds = 1.$$

Substituting this series into the first of Eqs. (18.16) and using expansion (18.15) gives

$$\sum_{i=1}^{\infty} f_i u_i(s) - \alpha \sum_{i=1}^{\infty}\sum_{k=1}^{\infty} \frac{f_k}{\omega_i^2} u_i(s) \int N_0(\sigma) \frac{du_i}{d\sigma}\left(\frac{du_k}{d\sigma} + \frac{v_k}{r}\right) d\sigma = 0.$$

By equating the coefficients of $u_i(s)$, a system of linear homogeneous equation results:

$$f_i - \alpha \sum_{k=1}^{\infty} a_{ik} f_k = 0, \qquad (k = 1, 2, 3, \cdots),$$

where

$$a_{ik} = \frac{1}{\omega_i^2} \int N_0(\sigma) \frac{du_i}{d\sigma}\left(\frac{du_k}{d\sigma} + \frac{v_k}{r}\right) d\sigma. \tag{18.18}$$

The equation for critical parameters has the form

$$| \boldsymbol{E} - \alpha \boldsymbol{A} | = 0.$$

where $\boldsymbol{A}$ is a matrix composed of the coefficients of system (18.18).

●4. The solution of the integro-differential equations for the boundaries of dynamic stability are sought in an analogous manner. Assuming that

$$N(s, t) = \alpha N_0(s) + \beta\Phi(t) N_t(s) \; ,$$

leads to the solutions of Eqs. (18.12) in the form

$$u(s, t) = \sum_{k=1}^{\infty} f_k(t) u_k(s) \; ,$$

$$v(s, t) = \sum_{k=1}^{\infty} f_k(t) v_k(s) \; .$$

Substitution leads to the following system of ordinary differential equations with respect to functions $f_k(t)$:

$$\frac{d^2 f_k}{dt^2} + \omega_i^2 \left[f_i - \sum_{k=1}^{\infty} (\alpha a_{ik} + \beta\Phi(t) b_{ik}) f_k \right] = 0 \; .$$

$$(i = 1, 2, 3, \cdots), \tag{18.19}$$

where, in addition to (18.18), the following notation is introduced:

$$b_{ik} = \frac{1}{\omega_i^2} \int N_t(\sigma) \frac{du_i}{d\sigma} \left(\frac{du_k}{d\sigma} + \frac{v_k}{r} \right) d\sigma \; .$$

It is easily seen that the differential equations obtained differ from the equations of dynamic stability of straight rods (13.8) only in the method of calculation of coefficients.

The analogy with straight rods will become even more distinct if the case of relatively shallow arches (for which the influence of the tangential component of the load can be neglected) is considered. In this case, the integral equations for free vibrations and for the boundaries of static stability take the form

$$u(s) - \omega^2 \int m(\sigma) K_{rr}(s, \sigma) u(\sigma) d\sigma = 0 \; .$$

$$\frac{du(s)}{ds} - \alpha \int N_0(\sigma) \frac{\partial^2 K_{rr}(s, \sigma)}{\partial s \partial \sigma} \frac{du(\sigma)}{d\sigma} d\sigma = 0 \; .$$

Accordingly, formula (18.18) takes the form

$$a_{ik} = \frac{1}{\omega_i^2} \int N_0(\sigma) \frac{du_i}{d\sigma} \frac{du_k}{d\sigma} d\sigma \; .$$

The equations obtained differ from the corresponding equations in the theory of straight rods only in that the role of lateral deflections is here played by the radial displacements. For shallow arches, though, the radial displacement can be replaced, without any error, by the vertical displacement. In this way we come to the formulation of the "principle of stretching."[7]

●5. The case of a "following" load was considered above. For the case of a load which does not change direction, we obtain

[7] See for example Shtaerman [1].

$$\Delta q_r = -\frac{\partial}{\partial s}\left[N(s,t)\left(\frac{\partial u}{\partial s}+\frac{v}{r}\right)\right],$$

$$\Delta q_\varphi = -\frac{N(s,t)}{r}\left(\frac{\partial u}{\partial s}+\frac{v}{r}\right).$$

Without the detailed derivation, which is basically analogous to the previous one, it can be shown that in this case the kernel of the equation for the boundaries of static stability is

$$S(s,\sigma) = N_0(\sigma)\left[\frac{\partial^2 K_{rr}(s,\sigma)}{\partial s\partial\sigma}+\frac{1}{r(s)}\frac{\partial K_{\varphi r}(s,\sigma)}{\partial\sigma} + \frac{1}{r(\sigma)}\frac{\partial K_{r\varphi}(s,\sigma)}{\partial\sigma}+\frac{1}{r(s)r(\sigma)}K_{\varphi\varphi}(s,\sigma)\right],$$

and the matrix elements a_{ik} are determined by the formula

$$a_{ik} = \frac{1}{\omega_i^2}\int N_0(\sigma)\left(\frac{du_i}{d\sigma}+\frac{v_i}{r}\right)\left(\frac{du_k}{d\sigma}+\frac{v_k}{r}\right)d\sigma\,. \tag{18.20}$$

It is easily noted that the kernel $S(s,\sigma)$ is symmetric to within the "weighting function" $N_0(\sigma)$.

The equations derived above can be used to solve the problems of the dynamic stability of centrally compressed arches supportend in an arbitrary manner and with arbitrarily varying rigidity along their length. These equations can also be obtained from the general equations of Chapter Twelve. For such a derivation, one must introduce a grid of orthogonal coordinates which includes the axis of the arch.

The convariant differentiation along the axis of the arch is defined in the following way:

$$\nabla u = \frac{\partial u}{\partial\sigma}+\frac{v}{r},$$

$$\nabla v = \frac{\partial v}{\partial r}-\frac{u}{r}$$

(the radial displacement is considered positive if it is directed towards the center of curvature). Then, for example, formula (18.20) can be obtained from formula (13.37) if one takes into account that the given stress condition is one-dimensional and the buckling is described by two functions, u and v the rule for differentiation has already been given.

§ 79. The Dynamic Stability of Arches Loaded by Compression and Bending. Statement of Problem

When an arch is subjected to symmetric vibrational loads, symmetric forced vibrations arise (Fig. 114a) which take place with the frequency of the exciting force. Resonance occurs when the perturbation frequencies coincide with one of the natural frequencies that correspond to the symmetric forms of the vibrations. Besides the usual resonance, a parametric resonance can also take place; it can be particularly dangerous when it is associated with the formation of a new type of deformation, i.e., antisymmetric deformation (Fig. 114b). The problem of the dynamic stability of the symmetric form of vibrations of arches has been given in the author's works.[8]

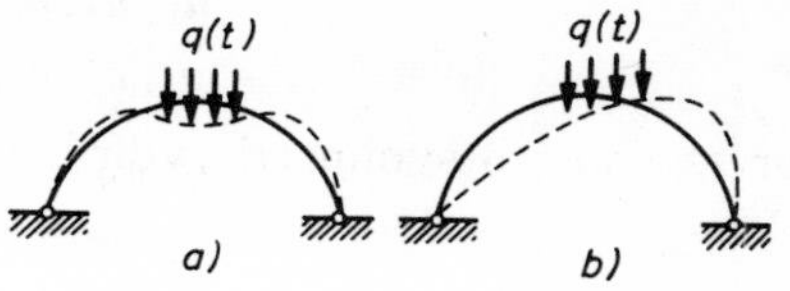

FIG. 114.

The investigation of the dynamic stability of an arch which is loaded by compression and bending is highly complicated by the fact that the initial condition corresponds to the symmetric form of motion of the arch. To simplify the problem, we assume that the loss of stability originates from the undeformed condition. This assumption introduces some errors into the final results. In investigating the corresponding statics problem, such an assumption is not justified because of large symmetrical deformations which precede the loss of stability. However, the loss of dynamic stability can occur at loads very much smaller in comparison with the critical (static) values and, accordingly, at small symmetric deformations (before buckling). It is sufficient to assume that the frequency of the symmetric vibrations occurs far from the resonance frequency.

The differential equations for the vibrations of an arch loaded by compression and bending,

$$\frac{d^2 f_i}{dt^2} + \omega_i^2 \left[f_i - \alpha \sum_{k=1}^{\infty} a_{ik} f_k - \beta \Phi(t) \sum_{k=1}^{\infty} b_{ik} f_k \right] = F_i(t) , \qquad (18.21)$$

$$(i = 1, 2, 3, \cdots) ,$$

differ from Eqs. (18.19) by the presence of additional terms on the right-hand side and by the method of calculating the coefficients a_{ik} and b_{ik}. The terms on the right-hand side are determined from formulas

$$F_i(t) = \int u_i(s) p_r(s, t) ds + \int v_i(s) p_\varphi(s, t) ds , \qquad (i = 1, 2, 3, \cdots) .$$

The coefficients a_{ik} and b_{ik} depend on the profile of the axis of the arch and on the pressure curve. It is difficult to obtain general expressions for these coefficients.

If the arch is symmetric, then the eigenfunctions for the problem of free vibrations separate into two groups. The first group

$$u_2 , u_4 , u_6 , \cdots , \quad u_{2j} , \cdots ,$$

$$v_2 , v_4 , v_6 , \cdots , \quad v_{2j} , \cdots$$

corresponds to antisymmetric vibrations

$$u_{2j-1}(-s) = -u_{2j-1}(s) ,$$

$$v_{2j-1}(-s) = v_{2j-1}(s)$$

(the starting point of arc s is taken on the axis of symmetry), while the second group of eigenfunctions

[8] Bolotin [4], [7].

$$u_1, u_3, u_5, \cdots, u_{2j-1}, \cdots,$$
$$v_1, v_3, v_5, \cdots, v_{2j-1}, \cdots$$

corresponds to symmetric vibrations

$$u_{2j}(-s) = u_{2j}(s),$$
$$v_{2j}(-s) = -v_{2j}(s).$$

If in accordance with the assumptions made, the mutual influence of symmetric and antisymmetric vibrations is neglected, then the system at differential equations (18.21) separates into two independent systems of differential equations.

Let the load acting on the arch be symmetric, i.e., let

$$q_r(-s,t) = q_r(s,t),$$
$$q_\varphi(-s,t) = -q_\varphi(s,t).$$

Then, obviously, one of these systems (which corresponds to the antisymmetric vibrations) is homogeneous,

$$\frac{d^2 f_i}{dt^2} + \omega_i^2\left[f_i - \alpha \sum_{k=1}^{\infty} a_{ik} f_k - \beta\Phi(t) \sum_{k=1}^{\infty} b_{ik} f_k\right] = 0, \qquad (18.22)$$
$$(i = 1, 2, 3, \cdots).$$

These are the usual equations of dynamic stability which were investigated earlier. They describe the behavior of antisymmetric perturbations with time. If the solutions of the system damp out, then the symmetric form of vibrations is stable. The solutions of the system of differential equations (18.22) which increase without bounds correspond to the case in which the symmetric form of the arch is dynamically unstable.

§ 80. Arch Hinged at the Ends[9]

As an example, a problem of the dynamic stability of a symmetric form of vibrations of a circular arch with hinged ends (Fig. 115) will now be considered. We will proceed from the differential equation

$$\frac{EJ}{R^4}\left(\frac{d^5u}{d\varphi^5} + 2\frac{\partial^3 u}{\partial\varphi^3} + \frac{du}{d\varphi}\right) = \frac{dq_r}{d\varphi} - q_\varphi, \qquad (18.23)$$

in which the notation of § 76 is retained.

To obtain the differential equations for the perturbed motion, it is necessary to introduce into Eq. (18.23) inertial forces and additional forces which arise during deflection of the axis of the arch from its initial position. Begin with a calculation of the latter forces, assuming, as was done in § 79, that the loss of dynamic stability originates from the undeformed condition of the arch. An estimate of the error arising in connection with this assumption will be given later.

Let the arch be subjected to a concentrated force applied at the crown, i.e.,

$$P(t) = P_0 + P_t \cos\theta t.$$

[9] This problem was solved in author's work [4], [7].

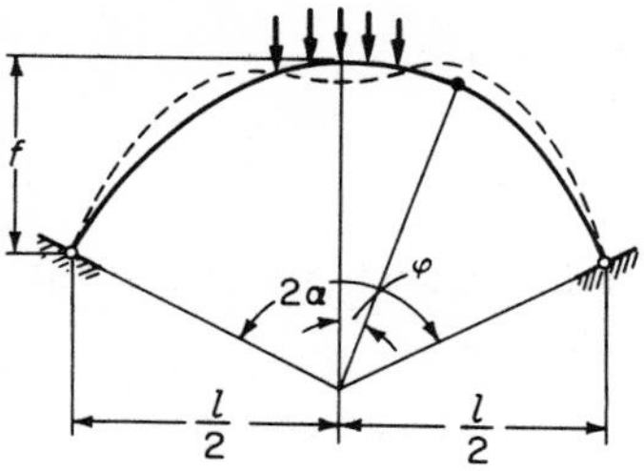

FIG 115.

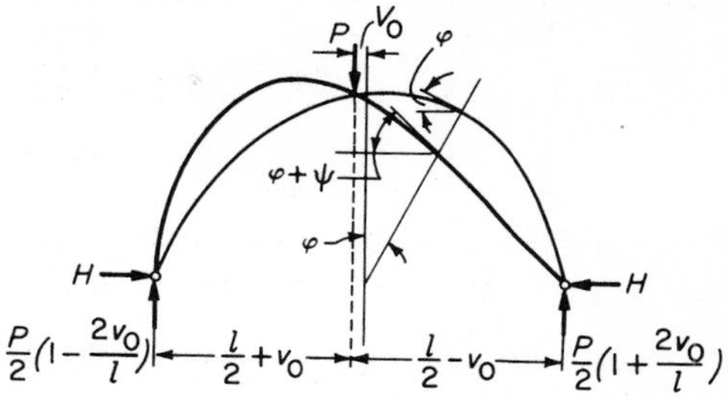

FIG. 116.

In this case it is possible to determine the additional loads Δq_φ and Δq_r on the basis of the following considerations. Denoting ψ as the increment of the angle of rotation of the arch cross sections due to bending (Fig. 116), and v_0 as the tangential displacement of the crown cross section (on the drawing $v_0 < 0$) gives the expression for the shear force:

$$Q = H \sin (\varphi + \psi) \mp \frac{1}{2} P\left(1 \pm \frac{2v_0}{l}\right) \cos (\varphi + \psi) .$$

Here, and also in the equations below, the upper sign is taken if $\varphi > 0$, the lower one if $\varphi < 0$. Variation of thrust appears as a small quantity of the second order and thus is not taken into account.

The increase in shear force, to within small quantities of the first order, is

$$\Delta Q = \frac{1}{2} \psi P(\lambda \cos \varphi \pm \sin \varphi) - \frac{Pv_0}{l} \cos \varphi , \tag{18.24}$$

with the notation

$$\lambda = \frac{2H}{P} .$$

From Kirchhoff's equations

$$\frac{dQ}{ds} + \frac{N}{R} + q_r = 0 ,$$

$$\frac{dN}{ds} - \frac{Q}{R} + q_\varphi = 0 ,$$

it follows that

$$\frac{\partial \Delta q_r}{\partial \varphi} - \Delta q_\varphi = - \frac{1}{R}\left(\frac{\partial^2 \Delta Q}{\partial \varphi^2} + \Delta Q\right) .$$

Substitution gives (for $\varphi > 0$)

$$\frac{\partial \Delta q_r}{\partial \varphi} - \Delta q_\varphi = - \frac{P}{2R}\left[\frac{\partial^2 \psi}{\partial \varphi^2} (\sin \varphi + \lambda \cos \varphi) + 2 \frac{\partial \psi}{\partial \varphi} (\cos \varphi - \lambda \sin \varphi)\right] . \tag{18.25}$$

Note that after substitution, the term which takes into account the variation of support reactions vanishes identically. For the left half of the arch

($\varphi < 0$) the following equation is obtained

$$\frac{\partial \Delta q_r}{\partial \varphi} - \Delta q_\varphi = -\frac{P}{2R}\left[\frac{\partial^2 \psi}{\partial \varphi^2}(\lambda \cos \varphi - \sin \varphi) - 2\frac{\partial \psi}{\partial \varphi}(\cos \varphi + \lambda \sin \varphi)\right]. \tag{18.26}$$

The expressions (18.25) and (18.26) remain valid everywhere except at the point of application of the concentrated load. In fact

$$\left.\frac{\partial \Delta Q}{\partial \varphi}\right|_{\varphi=+0} = \frac{1}{2}\psi_0 P, \qquad \left.\frac{\partial \Delta Q}{\partial \varphi}\right|_{\varphi=-0} = -\frac{1}{2}\psi_0 P,$$

where ψ_0 is the angle of rotation of the crown cross section. Thus,

$$\lim_{\varepsilon \to 0}\int_{-\varepsilon}^{+\varepsilon}\left(\frac{\partial \Delta q_r}{\partial \varphi} - \Delta q_\varphi\right)d\varphi = -\frac{\psi_0 P}{R}. \tag{18.27}$$

It is evident that a discontinuity occurs at the point $\varphi = 0$; it occurs because of the fact that the force P gives the projection in the direction tangent to the axis of the arch (Fig. 117a). If the force P turns together with the crown cross section remaining perpendicular to the axis of the arch (Fig. 117b), then expressions (18.25) and (18.26) are valid at all points on the arch.

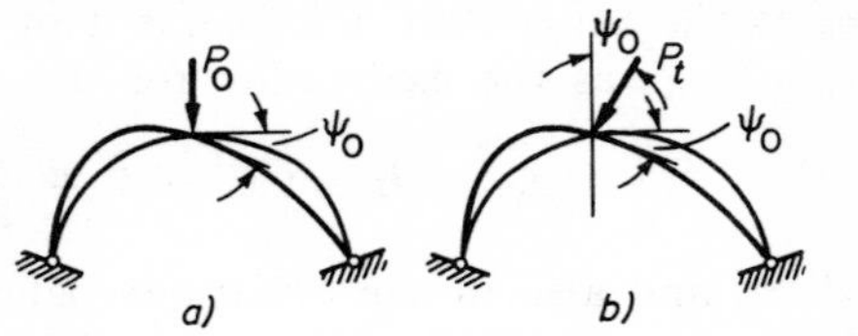

FIG. 117.

The increase of shear force for this case differs from (18.24) by the additional terms

$$\Delta Q^* = \frac{1}{2}\psi_0 P\left(\frac{2f}{l}\cos \varphi \mp \sin \varphi\right),$$

while the expression

$$\frac{\partial \Delta q_r^*}{\partial \varphi} - \Delta q_\varphi^* = -\frac{1}{R}\left(\frac{\partial^2 \Delta Q^*}{\partial \varphi^2} + \Delta Q^*\right)$$

vanishes identically at all points except $\varphi = 0$, where there is a discontinuity opposite to (18.27).

In practical problems the constant component P_0 does not usually change its direction (weight force), while the periodic component P_t rotates together with the corresponding cross section. This case will be examined. For $\varphi > 0$ it is

$$\frac{\partial \Delta q_r}{\partial \varphi} - \Delta q_\varphi = -\frac{P_0 + P_t \cos \theta t}{2R}\left[\frac{\partial^2 \psi}{\partial \varphi^2}(\sin \varphi + \lambda \cos \varphi) + 2\frac{\partial \psi}{\partial \varphi}(\cos \varphi - \lambda \sin \varphi)\right].$$

Respectively, for $\varphi < 0$ it is

$$\frac{\partial \Delta q_r}{\partial \varphi} - \Delta q_\varphi = -\frac{P_0 + P_t \cos \theta t}{2R}\left[\frac{\partial^2 \psi}{\partial \varphi^2}(\lambda \cos \varphi - \sin \varphi) - 2\frac{\partial \psi}{\partial \varphi}(\cos \varphi + \lambda \sin \varphi)\right].$$

Here

$$\lim_{\varepsilon \to 0} \int_{-\varepsilon}^{+\varepsilon} \left(\frac{\partial \Delta q_r}{\partial \varphi} - \Delta q_\varphi \right) d\varphi = - \frac{\psi_0 P_0}{R} .$$

● **2.** Introducing into Eq. (18.23) the additional load and the inertial forces gives

$$\frac{EJ}{R^4} \left(\frac{\partial^5 u}{\partial \varphi^5} + 2 \frac{\partial^3 u}{\partial \varphi^3} + \frac{du}{\partial \varphi} \right) + \frac{\partial}{\partial \varphi} \left(m \frac{\partial^2 u}{\partial t^2} \right) - m \frac{\partial^2 v}{dt^2} = \frac{\partial \Delta q_r}{\partial \varphi} - \Delta q_\varphi . \tag{18.28}$$

Here $m(\varphi)$ is the mass per unit length of the arch, which generally is a constant quantity.

An exact solution of Eq. (18.28) is difficult to obtain; consequently, an approximate solution will be sought, making use of the Galerkin method. Assume that the axis of the arch is incompressible and set

$$u(\varphi, t) = f(t) \sin \frac{\pi \varphi}{\alpha} ,$$

$$v(\varphi, t) = - \frac{\alpha}{\pi} f(t) \left(1 + \cos \frac{\pi \varphi}{\alpha} \right) ,$$

where $f(t)$ is still an unknown function of time. Substitution gives

$$\frac{EJ}{R^4} \frac{\pi}{\alpha} \left(\frac{\pi^2}{\alpha^2} - 1 \right)^2 f(t) I_1(\alpha) + \frac{\alpha}{\pi} \frac{d^2 f}{dt^2} I_2(\alpha) = I_3(\alpha) . \tag{18.29}$$

In the left-hand side of the above equation, we denote

$$I_1(\alpha) = \int_{-\alpha}^{+\alpha} \cos \frac{\pi \varphi}{\alpha} \left(1 + \cos \frac{\pi \varphi}{\alpha} \right) d\varphi = \alpha ,$$

$$I_2(\alpha) = \int_{-\alpha}^{+\alpha} m(\varphi) \left[\frac{\pi^2}{\alpha^2} \sin^2 \frac{\pi \varphi}{\alpha} + \left(1 + \cos \frac{\pi \varphi}{\alpha} \right)^2 \right] d\varphi = \alpha \left[\frac{4M}{R\alpha} + m \left(\frac{\pi^2}{\alpha^2} + 3 \right) \right] .$$

In calculating the second integral it was assumed that, in addition to the uniformly distributed mass m, the arch carries a concentrated mass M at the crown. Expressing angle ψ in terms of u and v and carrying out the calculations leads to

$$I_3(\alpha) = \int_{-\alpha}^{+\alpha} \left(\frac{\partial \Delta q_r}{\partial \varphi} - \Delta q_\varphi \right) \left(1 + \cos \frac{\pi \varphi}{\alpha} \right) d\varphi = \frac{\pi f(t)}{R^2 \alpha} (P_0 + P_t \cos \theta t) \left(\frac{\pi^2}{\alpha^2} - 1 \right) F(\alpha) - \frac{2\pi P_0 f(t)}{R^2 \alpha} \left(1 - \frac{2\alpha^2}{\pi^2} \right) ,$$

where

$$F(\alpha) = \frac{(1 - \cos \alpha + \lambda \sin \alpha) \left(\frac{2\pi^2}{\alpha^2} + 1 \right)}{\frac{4\pi^2}{\alpha^2} - 1} + \frac{1 - \cos \alpha - \lambda \sin \alpha}{\frac{\pi^2}{\alpha^2} - 1} . \tag{18.30}$$

Formula (18.30) contains the quantity

$$\lambda = \left(\int_0^\alpha xyd\varphi\right) \div \left(\int_0^\alpha y^2 d\varphi\right),$$

where x and y are the Cartesian coordinates of the axis of the arch. Evaluation of this gives

$$\lambda = \frac{4 \cos \alpha - 3 \cos 2\alpha - 2\alpha \sin 2\alpha - 1}{4\alpha + 2\alpha \cos 2\alpha - 3 \sin 2\alpha}.$$

For sufficiently shallow arches ($\alpha < \frac{1}{6}\pi$), an approximate formula $\lambda = (15/8)(\sin \alpha/\alpha^2)$ can be used.

These formulas are also valid for the case of the three-hinge arch, for which it is necessary to set $\lambda = \operatorname{ctg} \frac{1}{2}\alpha$.

Now the following notations are introduced:

$$\frac{\pi}{R^2 \alpha}\left(\frac{\pi^2}{\alpha^2} - 1\right)\sqrt{\frac{EJ}{\frac{4M}{R^\alpha} + m\left(\frac{\pi^2}{\alpha^2} + 3\right)}} = \omega, \tag{18.31}$$

$$\frac{EJ}{R^2} \frac{\left(\frac{\pi^2}{\alpha^2} - 1\right)\alpha}{F(\alpha) - \frac{2\left(1 - \frac{2\alpha^2}{\pi^2}\right)}{\frac{\pi^2}{\alpha^2} - 1}} = P_*,$$

$$\frac{EJ}{R^2}\left(\frac{\pi^2}{\alpha^2} - 1\right)\frac{\alpha}{F(\alpha)} = P_{t*}. \tag{18.32}$$

Formula (18.31) gives the expression for the lowest frequency of free antisymmetric vibrations of an arch, while formulas (18.32) give the expressions for the critical forces calculated under the assumption that the (static) buckling takes place at very small symmetric deformations. The case of the "following" load gives the lower value for the critical parameter, which could have been foreseen from physical considerations (Fig. 117).

Using the notation introduced Eq. (18.29) can be expressed in the form

$$\frac{d^2 f}{dt^2} + \omega^2\left(1 - \frac{P_0}{P_*} - \frac{P_t}{P_{t*}} \cos \theta t\right) f = 0. \tag{18.33}$$

This is the usual differential equation of the first approximation (Mathieu differential equation) which was considered in detail earlier.

●3. To estimate the influence of symmetric vibrations on dynamic stability the following method is used. The approximate equation for the symmetric forced vibrations is obtained by approximating the form of vibrations by some suitable function and applying a variational method. Let M_s be the mass of the arch reduced to the crown, $u_0(t)$ the vertical displacement of the crown, and ω_s the frequency of the fundamental tone of the symmetric vibrations. Then the symmetric vibrations can be described in the first approximation by the equation

$$u_0'' + \omega_s^2 u_0 = \frac{1}{M_s}(P_0 + P_t \cos \theta t),$$

whose steady-state solution obviously is

$$u_0 = \frac{1}{M_s \omega_s^2}\left(P_0 + \frac{P_t \cos \theta t}{1 - \dfrac{\theta^2}{\omega_s^2}}\right).$$

The influence of symmetric vibrations will be taken into account by introducing in place of a static load $P_0 + P_t \cos \theta t$ the dynamic load

$$P_0 + P_t \cos \theta t - M_s w'' = P_0 + \frac{P_t \cos \theta t}{1 - \dfrac{\theta^2}{\omega_s^2}}.$$

Equation (18.33) takes the form

$$f'' + \omega^2\left[1 - \frac{P_0}{P_*} - \frac{P_t \cos \theta t}{P_{t*}\left(1 - \dfrac{\theta^2}{\omega_s^2}\right)}\right] f = 0. \tag{18.34}$$

This method of analysis is closely related to the contents of Chapter Eight, where the influence of longitudinal vibrations on the dynamic stability of compressed rods was considered. Let us introduce the notations

$$\omega^2\left(1 - \frac{P_0}{P_*}\right) = \Omega^2,$$

$$\frac{P_t}{P_{t*}\left(1 - \dfrac{P_0}{P_*}\right)} = 2\mu, \tag{18.35}$$

$$\frac{\theta}{2\Omega} = n, \quad \frac{4\Omega^2}{\omega_s^2} = \beta.$$

Then the following equation is obtained, which agrees completely with § 30:

$$f'' + \Omega^2\left(1 - \frac{2\mu}{1 - \beta n^2} \cos \theta t\right) f = 0.$$

In accordance with (8.13), the boundaries of the principal regions of instability are determined from the formula

$$n_*^2 = \frac{1 + \beta \pm \sqrt{(1-\beta)^2 \mp 4\mu\beta}}{2\beta}. \tag{18.36}$$

Thus two principal regions of instability have been obtained. One of these belongs to the frequency 2Ω; the other corresponds to the resonance of symmetrically forced vibrations.

In contrast to the problems considered in Chapter Eight, here it is impossible to assume $\beta \ll 1$ because the natural frequencies Ω and ω_s can be quantities of the same order. A numerical example will be given in § 82 in connection with the discussion of experimental results.

§ 81. The Nonlinear Problem of the Dynamic Stability of Arches

●1. Let us now solve the problem just considered on a nonlinear basis. The antisymmetric deformation of an arch is accompanied by symmetric deformation measured by small quantities of the second order. The inertia forces and the elastic forces which arise during these displacements depend nonlinearly on the antisymmetric components. These nonlinear forces are the fundamental factors limiting the increase of amplitudes of antisymmetric vibrations.

Consider first the simplest case, where the entire mass of the arch is concentrated at the crown (Fig. 118). It is necessary, first of all, to calculate the vertical displacement of the crown associated with the antisymmetric deformation. Instead of determining the value of the symmetric component from geometric considerations, the following method will be used.

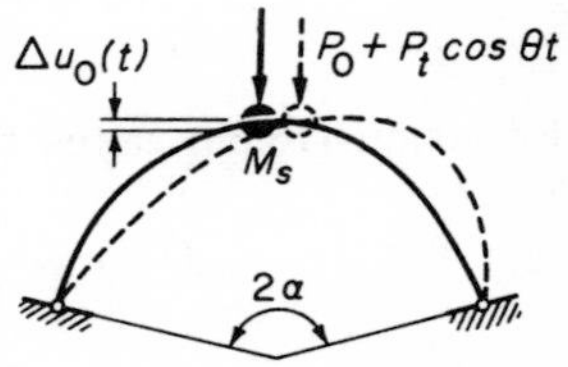

FIG. 118.

As is known, the critical values of a static load can be determined by equating its work on displacements during the loss of stability to the increase in energy of deformation. Denoting by Δu_0 the vertical component of displacement of the crown cross section, and by ΔU the increase in the energy of deformation during the loss of stability, gives

$$\Delta u_0 = \frac{\Delta U}{P_*}.$$

The increase in potential energy can be determined from the formula

$$\Delta U = \frac{EJ}{2R^3}\int_{-\alpha}^{+\alpha}\left(\frac{\partial^2 u}{\partial \varphi^2} + u\right)^2 d\varphi .$$

By setting

$$u(\varphi, t) = f(t) \sin \frac{\pi\varphi}{\alpha},$$

it is found that

$$\Delta U = \frac{EJ\alpha f^2(t)}{2R^3}\left(\frac{\pi^2}{\alpha^2} - 1\right)^2.$$

The critical static force was calculated in (18.32):

$$P_* = \frac{EJ}{R^2}\frac{\left(\frac{\pi^2}{\alpha^2} - 1\right)\alpha}{F(\alpha) - \frac{2\left(1 - \frac{2\alpha^2}{\pi^2}\right)}{\frac{\pi^2}{\alpha^2} - 1}}.$$

Substitution leads to

$$\Delta u_0 = \frac{f^2}{2R}\left(\frac{\pi^2}{\alpha^2} - 1\right)F_1(\alpha), \tag{18.37}$$

where

$$F_1(\alpha) = F(\alpha) - \frac{2\left(1 - \frac{2\alpha^2}{\pi^2}\right)}{\frac{\pi^2}{\alpha^2} - 1}.$$

Thus, as expected, the vertical displacement Δu_0 of the crown cross section is a small quantity of the second order in comparison to f.

The influence of nonlinear factors can be taken into account approximately by introducing a concentrated vertical force

$$\Delta P = -M_s \Delta u_0''.$$

Here M_s is the mass of the arch reduced to the crown cross section. If the force ΔP is added to the differential equation (18.33), the following is obtained:

$$f'' + \omega^2\left(1 - \frac{P_0}{P_*} - \frac{P_t}{P_{t*}} \cos \theta t - \frac{q}{q_*}\right) f = 0.$$

However, according to (18.37)

$$\Delta u_0'' = \frac{(f')^2 + f'' f}{R}\left(\frac{\pi^2}{\alpha^2} - 1\right) F_1(\alpha);$$

consequently, the differential equation takes the form

$$f'' + \omega^2\left(1 - \frac{P_0}{P_*} - \frac{P_t}{P_{t*}} \cos \theta t\right) f + 2\kappa f [(f')^2 + f'' f] = 0. \quad (18.38)$$

The coefficient of nonlinear inertia is

$$\kappa = \frac{M_s\left(\frac{\pi^2}{\alpha^2} - 1\right) F_1(\alpha)\omega^2}{2P_* R}. \quad (18.39)$$

Equation (18.38) coincides with the differential equation which has already been studied thoroughly (see § 19).

●2. The reduced mass M_s will now be calculated. For a three-hinge arch, the symmetric components of displacements can be approximated by the expressions

$$\Delta u(\varphi, t) = \Delta u_0(t)\left(1 - \frac{\varphi}{\alpha} - \frac{\pi}{4} \sin \frac{\pi\varphi}{\alpha}\right),$$
$$\Delta v(\varphi, t) = \Delta u_0(t)\left(\varphi - \frac{\varphi^2}{2\alpha} - \frac{\alpha}{2} \sin^2 \frac{\pi\varphi}{2\alpha}\right). \quad (\varphi > 0),$$

The second formula was obtained from the first using the condition of incompressibility $u - (\partial v/\partial \varphi) = 0$. It is easily proved that these expressions satisfy the geometric boundary conditions

$$\Delta u(0, t) = \Delta u_0(t),$$
$$\Delta u(\alpha, t) = \Delta v(0, t) = \Delta v(\alpha, t) = 0.$$

For the displacements Δu and Δv there arise the inertial loads

$$\Delta q_r = q\left(1 - \frac{\varphi}{\alpha} - \frac{\pi}{4} \sin \frac{\pi\varphi}{\alpha}\right),$$
$$\Delta q_\varphi = q\left(\varphi - \frac{\varphi^2}{2\alpha} - \frac{\alpha}{2} \sin^2 \frac{\pi\varphi}{2\alpha}\right). \qquad (18.40)$$

where the parameter q is equal to

$$q = -m\Delta u_0'' . \qquad (18.41)$$

Here m is the mass uniformly distributed along the length of the arch. Substitution of expressions (18.40) into the right-hand side of Eq. (18.28) and application of the Galerkin method gives zero (the work of symmetrical load on the antisymmetrical displacements). However, the load (18.40) must also enter into the left-side of the equation as a parameter related to the unknowns. The calculation of corresponding terms presents a considerably more difficult problem than the one described in § 80. The final result, nevertheless, can be written at once. Let q_* be the approximate (in the sense of the first approximation according to the Galerkin method) critical value of parameter q. The consideration of the parametric load (18.40) leads then to the equation

$$f'' + \omega^2\left(1 - \frac{P_0 - M_s\Delta u_0''}{P_*} - \frac{P_t}{P_{t*}} \cos \theta t\right) f = 0 .$$

or, after substitution of (18.41) and (18.37),

$$f'' + \omega^2\left(1 - \frac{P_0}{P_*} - \frac{P_t}{P_{t*}} \cos \theta t\right) f + 2\kappa_m f[(f')^2 + ff''] = 0 .$$

In contrast to Eq. (18.38), here

$$\kappa_m = \frac{m\left(\frac{\pi^2}{\alpha^2} - 1\right)F_1(\alpha)\omega^2}{2q_* R} . \qquad (18.42)$$

However, the difficulties have not yet been overcome because the critical value q_* is still unknown. To determine q_*, the following method is used.

It is known for the arch that the magnitude of the thrust at which the loss of static stability occurs due to symmetrical bending depends little on the form of loading. The shallower the arch, the more constant the critical thrust is maintained. One can set

$$q^*\bar{H}_q \approx P_*\bar{H}_p ,$$

where $\bar{H}_q$ and $\bar{H}_p$ are thrusts due to corresponding unit influences. Then formula (18.42) takes the form

$$\kappa_m = 2cmR\alpha \frac{\left(\frac{\pi^2}{\alpha^2} - 1\right) F_1(\alpha)\omega^2}{2P_* R} , \qquad (18.43)$$

where

$$c = \frac{\bar{H}_q}{2R\alpha\bar{H}_p} . \qquad (18.44)$$

Obviously, c is the coefficient for reducing the distributed mass to the crown cross section.

Proceed now to the calculation of the horizontal thrust force (Fig. 119). It can easily be verified that

$$fH_q = \frac{1}{2} V_q l - R^2 \int_0^\alpha [\Delta q_r \sin \varphi + \Delta q_\varphi (1 - \cos \varphi)] d\varphi ,$$

where V_q is the vertical component of the support reaction. Furthermore, taking into account that for the incompressible arch $(\partial \Delta q_r / \partial \varphi) - \Delta q_\varphi = 0$, and consequently

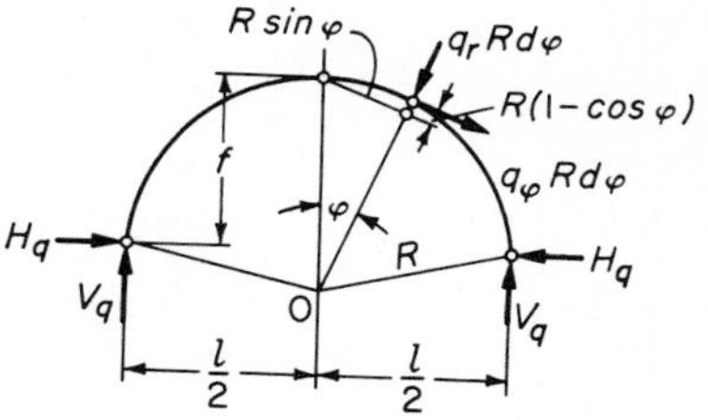

FIG. 119.

$$\int_0^\alpha (\Delta q_r \cos \varphi + \Delta q_\varphi \sin \varphi) d\varphi = 2\int_0^\alpha \Delta q_r \cos \varphi d\varphi ,$$

$$\int_0^\alpha (\Delta q_r \sin \varphi - \Delta q_\varphi \cos \varphi) d\varphi = 2\int_0^\alpha \Delta q_r \sin \varphi d\varphi ,$$

leads to

$$H_q = 2R \operatorname{ctg} \frac{\alpha}{2} \left[\int_0^\alpha \Delta q_r \left(\cos \varphi - \frac{\sin \varphi}{\sin \alpha} \right) d\varphi + \frac{1}{2 \sin \alpha} \int_0^\alpha \Delta q_\varphi d\varphi \right] .$$

Evaluating the integrals gives

$$H_q = 2qR\alpha \operatorname{ctg} \frac{\alpha}{2} \left[2 - \frac{\cos \alpha}{4} \left(4 + \frac{\pi^2}{(\pi^2/\alpha^2) - 1} \right) - \frac{\alpha}{\sin \alpha} \left(1 - \frac{\alpha^2}{24} \right) \right] .$$

On the other hand, the thrust force due to the concentrated load P applied at the crown is

$$H_p = \frac{1}{2} P \operatorname{ctg} \frac{\alpha}{2} .$$

Substituting the expressions obtained for $P = q = 1$ into formula (18.44) yields

$$c = \frac{2}{\alpha^2} \left[2 - \frac{\cos \alpha}{4} \left(4 + \frac{\pi^2}{(\pi^2/\alpha^2) - 1} \right) - \frac{\alpha}{\sin \alpha} \left(1 - \frac{\alpha^2}{24} \right) \right] . \qquad (18.45)$$

Function (18.45) is depicted in Figure 120. As can be seen from the graph, the coefficient c differs but slightly from $c = \frac{1}{2}$ as the central angle varies within wide limits. In other words, the influence of the distributed mass can be taken into account by introducting a concentrated mass $M_0 = mR\alpha$ at the crown.

At first glance, this result may appear trivial. But it should be remembered that the reduction principle is very complicated here (influence of nonlinear inertial forces on antisymmetric vibrations), and it would not have been justified to introduce arbitrary assumptions from the very beginning.

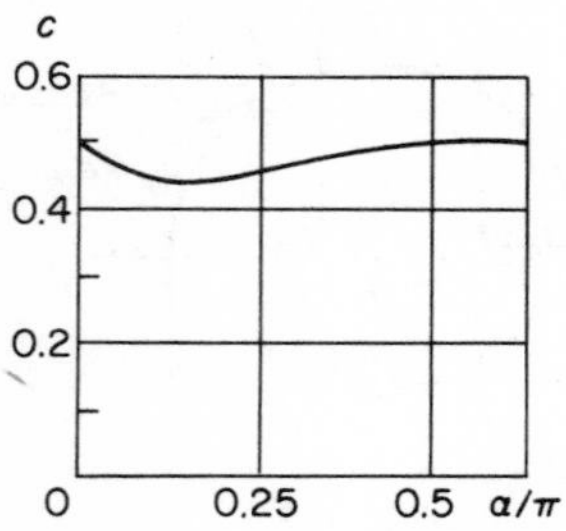

FIG. 120.

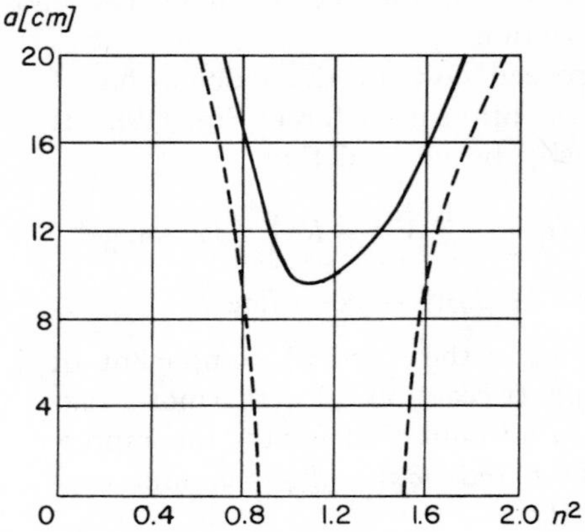

FIG. 121.

●**3.** Turn now to the determination of the steady-state amplitudes. As is known, for not too shallow double-hinged arches, the fundamental form of vibrations is antisymmetric. The natural frequencies of the symmetric and antisymmetric froms of vibrations are generally sufficiently close to each other; consequently, if the amplitudes of antisymmetric vibrations are to be determined, the influence of symmetric forms of vibrations must be taken into account.

The basic equations and the results which follow from them are generally analogous to those given in § 31. Let $u(t)$ be the vertical displacement of the crown due to symmetric vibrations. Then the total vertical displacement is

$$w = u + \frac{f^2}{2R}\left(\frac{\pi^2}{\alpha^2} - 1\right)F_1(\alpha) .$$

The vertical vibration equation has the form

$$M_s w'' = P_0 + P_t \cos \theta t - N ,$$

where N is the force transmitted to the arch. It is obvious that $N = ku$ (k is some constant). The second differential equation is

$$f'' + \omega^2\left(1 - \frac{N}{P_*}\right) f = 0 .$$

For simplicity it is assumed here that the force P_t does not change direction during vibrations. Further operations lead to formula (8.18):

$$a^2 = \frac{(1 - \beta n^2)(1 - n^2) \pm \mu}{\kappa n^2} , \tag{18.46}$$

where use has been made of the notation given by (18.35) and (18.39). The graph of resonance is shown in Figure 121. Discussion of results will be postponed to the next section.

§ 82. Experimental Results[10]

The experiments which involve the parametric excitation of antisymmetric vibrations of arches are of special interest. In fact, the possibility of such vibrations under the action of a symmetric load by no means is obvious by itself. This makes the results of experiments a particularly convincing proof of the validity of the theory.

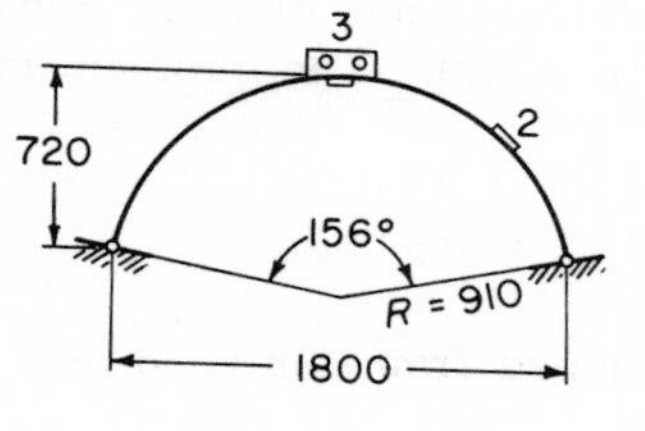

FIG. 122.

A double-hinged circular arch was loaded by a concentrated periodic force produced by a vibrator 3, placed at the crown (Fig. 122). The vibrations were recorded by a loop oscillograph with the help of strain-gages. Gage 1 was bonded at the crown, thus permitting the determination of amplitudes of symmetric vibrations; gage 2 was bonded near the quarter point of the span.

The following results were obtained from the oscillogram of the free damped vibrations. For the fundamental (antisymmetric) form of oscillations, the frequency and the decrement of damping were $\Omega = 24\ \text{sec}^{-1}$ and $\Delta = 0.031$, respectively. For the second (symmetric) form of oscillations, these values were $\omega_s = 55\ \text{sec}^{-1}$ and $\Delta_s = 0.055$.

No strongly expressed influence of inertial and other nonlinearties was detected: natural frequencies and decrements of damping appeared to be constant in a rather wide range of amplitudes.

At the frequency 2Ω, the vibration machine generated a force with amplitude $\bar{P}_t = 16.1$ kg, the constant component being $\bar{P}_0 = 26$ kg. The coefficient of excitation at the frequency 2Ω is

$$\bar{\mu} = \frac{\bar{P}_t}{2P_{t*}\left(1 - \frac{\bar{P}_0}{P_*}\right)} = 0.053\ .$$

The critical coefficient of excitation, according to (2.14), is

$$\mu_* = \frac{\Delta}{\pi} = 0.0099.$$

Since

$$\bar{\mu}/\mu_* = 5.35 \gg 1\ ,$$

the influence of damping on the boundaries of the principal region of instability can be neglected in the first approximation. Calculating first the boundaries of the instability region without taking into account the symmetric forced vibrations:

$$\theta_* \approx \frac{2\Omega}{\sqrt{1 \pm \bar{\mu}}}\ .$$

Substitution gives

$$46.7 \leq \theta \leq 49.3\ (\text{see}^{-1})\ .$$

[10] Bolotin [4], [7].

It is necessary to regard these results as a rough approximation. In fact, for the given arch the ratio is

$$\beta = \frac{4\Omega^2}{\omega_s^{\ 2}} = 0.762 \ ,$$

i.e., the order of magnitude of β is equal to 1. Formula (18.36) cannot be used directly, because under experimental conditions the amplitude of vibrational load and, consequently, the coefficients of excitation increase proportionally to the square of excitation frequency ($\mu = \bar{\mu}n^2$). The problem may be described by the equation (compare § 80)

$$f'' + \Omega^2\left(1 - \frac{2\bar{\mu}n^2}{1 - \beta n^2} \cos \theta t\right) f = 0 \ ,$$

whose principal regions of instability are determined from the condition

$$n^2 = 1 \pm \frac{\bar{\mu}n^2}{1 - \beta n^2} \ .$$

Thus, in place of formula (18.36),

$$n_*^{\ 2} = \frac{1 + \beta \pm \bar{\mu} \pm \sqrt{(1 + \beta \pm \bar{\mu})^2 - 4\beta}}{2\beta} \ . \tag{18.47}$$

The upper sign in front of the radical corresponds to the region of instability which lies near $n_*^{\ 2} = 1/\beta$, i.e., $\theta_* = \omega_s$; the lower sign corresponds to the region which is located near $n_*^{\ 2} = 1$ ($\theta_* = 2\Omega$). The distribution of the instability regions in the ($\bar{\mu}$, n^2) plane is represented in Figure 123.[11] As can be seen from the graph, both regions converge into one, even for very small values of $\bar{\mu}$. This value of $\bar{\mu}$ can easily be found by equating to zero the expression under the radical in (18. 47)

$$(1 + \beta \pm \bar{\mu})^2 - 4\beta = 0 \ ,$$

from which

$$\bar{\mu}_{**} = 1 + \beta - 2\sqrt{\beta} \ .$$

Calculations give $\bar{\mu}_{**} = 0.018$, which is substantialy smaller than the experimentally obtained value.

From formula (18.47) the boundaries for the region of instability can easily be found:

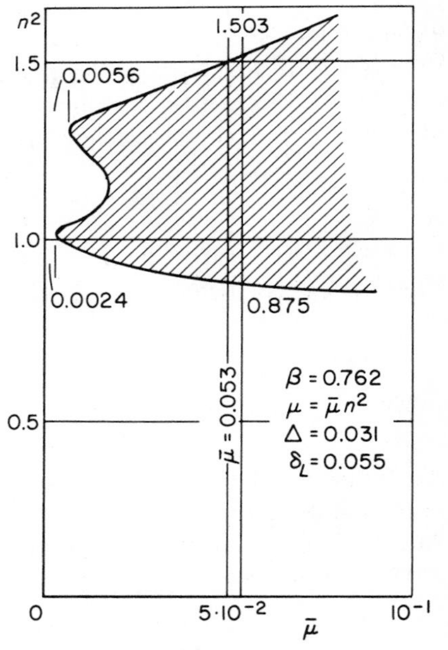

FIG. 123.

$$0.875 \leq n^2 \leq 1.503$$

[11] Here damping, as given by formula of § 29, was also considered.

or, converting to frequencies ($\theta = 2n\Omega$),

$$45.0 \leq \theta \leq 59.2 \text{ sec}^{-1} .$$

The lower critical frequency differs only slightly from that calculated previously; the upper critical frequency is now, naturally, substantially higher.

●**2.** The experiment itself, which gave good confirmation of the theoretical results, will now be described. Near the frequencies $\theta = 2\Omega$, intensive antisymmetric vibrations were obtained with half frequency.

A typical oscillogram, recorded by gage 2, is represented in Figure 124. The fundamental vibrations with large amplitude are parametrically excited vibrations. Besides the parametric vibrations, forced symmetric vibrations whose frequency coincides with that of the load frequency were also noted.

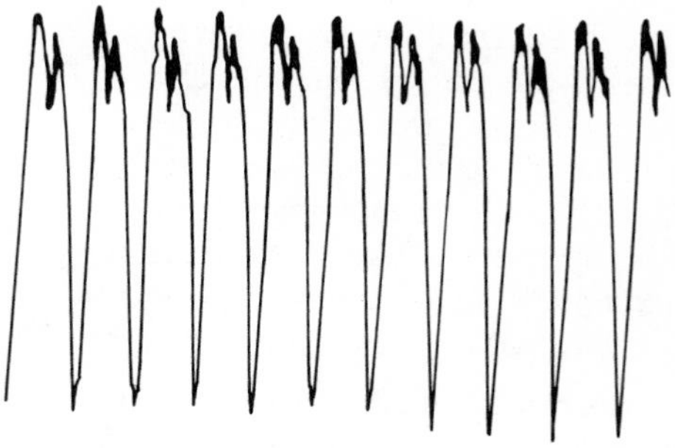

FIG. 124.

The lower boundary of the region of dynamic instability, as the theory predicted, lies near the frequency $\theta = 45 \text{ sec}^{-1}$. The upper boundary could not be determined since it lies near the resonance of symmetric vibrations ($\theta = 55 \text{ sec}^{-1}$). In general, with the approach to resonance, the picture of vibrations is more complex and difficult to understand. The increase of antisymmetric vibrations ceases suddenly, after which an increase of the symmetric form of vibrations begins.

One of the oscillograms is given in Figure 125. The left portion of the oscillogram represents a typical picture of the building up of ordinary forced vibrations; these are the harmonic vibrations which are modulated by a function $1 - e^{-\varepsilon t}$. Further on, the forced vibrations are displaced by parametric-

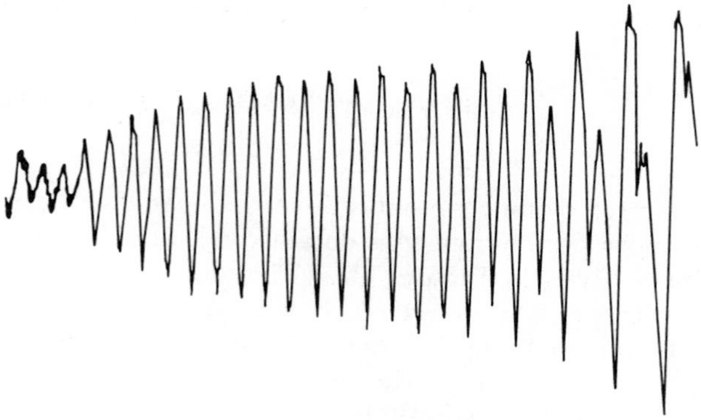

FIG. 125.

ally excited vibrations whose period is twice as large.

The dependence of the amplitudes of vibrations on the excitation frequency, as obtained from several experiments, is shown in Figure 126. The considerable scatter of the experimental points is explained by the complex and unsteady character of the vibrations. However, the graph clearly shows the decrease of the amplitudes approximately half-way between the two resonances and an increase of amplitude in the "overhang" of the vibrations towards the lower frequencies. The shape of the resonance curve is in complete agreement with the theory (§ 31).

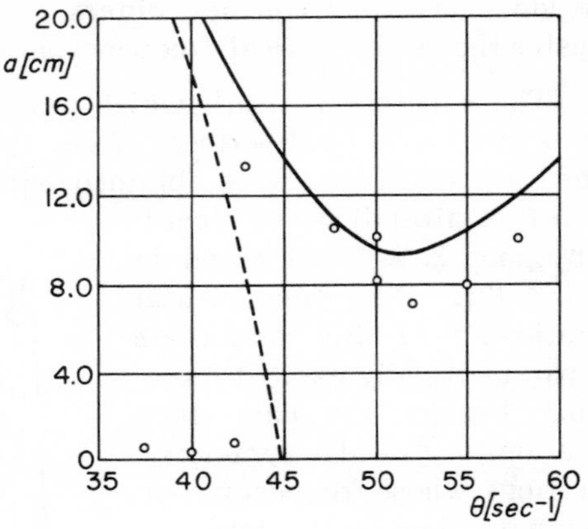

FIG. 126.

●**3.** Formula (18.46) will be used to compute the value of the steady-state amplitudes. Assuming in it $\mu = \bar{\mu} n^2$ leads to

$$a = \sqrt{\frac{(1 - \beta n^2)(1 - n^2) \pm \bar{\mu} n^2}{\kappa n^2}} .$$

From formula (18.43), the coefficient of nonlinear inertia is $\kappa = 5.4 \cdot 10^{-4}\, cm^{-2}$; which yields $n^2 = 0.875$ (lower boundary of the instability region) for $a = 13.7\, cm$. This value agrees in magnitude with the experimental value (Fig. 126).

A more rigorous theory can be constructed if the symmetric and antisymmetric vibrations are simultaneously considered on the basis of nonlinear differential equations. This theory would permit uncovering more minute effects than would the theories described above. The experiments described indicate the presence of these effects.

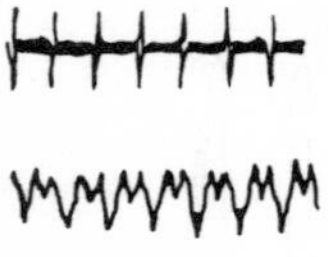

FIG. 127.

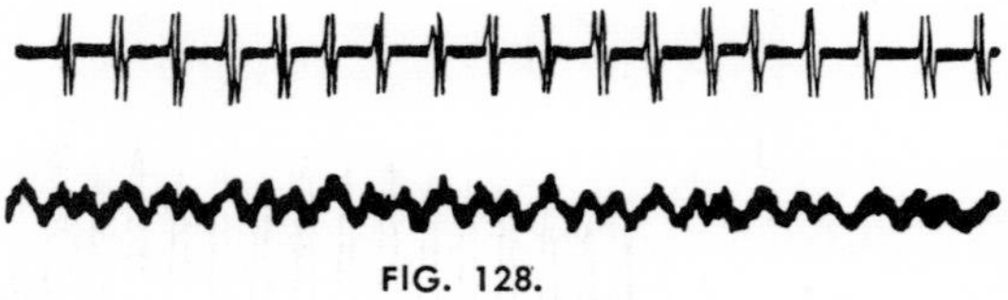

FIG. 128.

An oscillogram of symmetric vibrations obtained for a purely harmonic excitation (the upper oscillogram was obtained with the help of the procedure described in § 6) is given in Figure 127. The vibrations which occur with double frequency can clearly be seen on the oscillogram. Their formation can be explained by the influence of nonlinear (integral) terms. The interaction of the nonlinear terms of the second and third orders is shown in the oscillogram represented in Figure 128.

Nineteen

DYNAMIC STABILITY OF PLANE BENDING MODES

§ 83. Statement of the Problem. Pure Bending of a Narrow Rectangular Strip[1]

●**1.** A periodic load acting in the plane of largest rigidity of a beam excites vibrations which, in general, occur in the same plane. This load, however, appears as a parametric load with respect to the bending-torsional deformations from the plane of its action. In the static case, the consideration of small deviations from the principal plane of a beam leads to the problem of the static stability of a plane form of bending. Here we discuss the dynamic stability of a plane form of bending in the case of a vibrational load. The plane form of bending is assumed to be dynamically stable if small lateral perburbations are damped out with time. On the other hand, if the presence of small initial perturbations causes intensive bending-torsional vibrations out of the plane of greatest rigidity, then the plane form of bending is dynamically unstable.

Consider the problem involving the dynamic stability of a narrow rectangular strip loaded by periodic couples (Fig. 129) applied in the plane of largest rigidity.

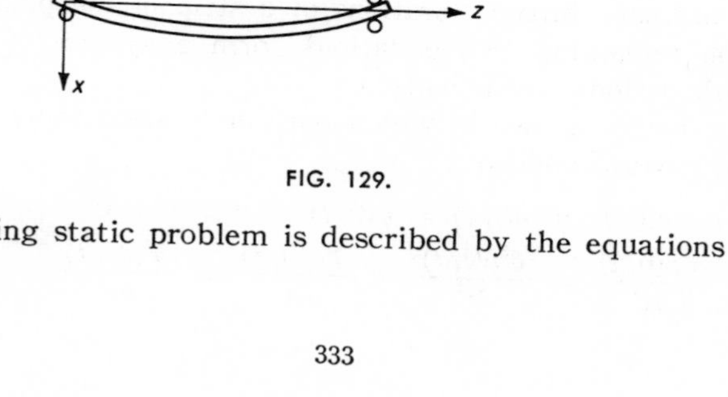

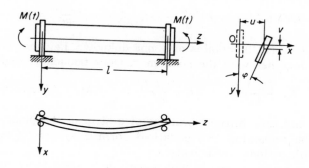

FIG. 129.

The corresponding static problem is described by the equations

[1] Bolotin [7].

$$
\begin{aligned}
EJ_x \frac{d^4 v}{dz^4} &= 0 , \\
EJ_y \frac{d^4 u}{dz^4} + M \frac{d^2 \varphi}{dz^2} &= 0 , \\
M \frac{d^2 u}{dz^2} - GJ_d \frac{d^2 \varphi}{dz^2} &= 0 ,
\end{aligned}
\tag{19.1}
$$

where u and v are deflections of the strip in the planes Oxz and Oyz, respectively, φ is the angle of twist, EJ_y and EJ_x are the bending rigidities of the cross section in the planes Oxz and Oyz, respectively, and GJ_d is the torsional rigidity.

Assuming that

$$
M = M_0 + M_t \cos \theta t ,
$$

we introduce into the right-hand side of Eqs. (19.1) additional terms which take into account the inertia forces,

$$
- m \frac{\partial^2 v}{\partial t^2} , \qquad - m \frac{\partial^2 u}{\partial t^2} , \qquad - m\rho^2 \frac{\partial^2 \varphi}{\partial t^2} .
$$

The symbol m denotes mass per unit length of the strip, and ρ denotes the polar radius of inertia.

It is assumed that inertial forces arising during the rotation of the cross sections of the strip with respect to its principal axes are small and can be neglected.

As a result, the following differential equations are obtained:

$$
\begin{aligned}
EJ_x \frac{\partial^4 v}{\partial z^4} + m \frac{\partial^2 v}{\partial t^2} &= 0 , \\
EJ_y \frac{\partial^4 u}{\partial z^4} + (M_0 + M_t \cos \theta t) \frac{\partial^2 \varphi}{\partial z^2} + m \frac{\partial^2 u}{\partial t^2} &= 0 , \\
(M_0 + M_t \cos \theta t) \frac{\partial^2 u}{\partial z^2} - GJ_d \frac{\partial^2 \varphi}{\partial z^2} + m\rho^2 \frac{\partial^2 \varphi}{\partial t^2} &= 0 .
\end{aligned}
\tag{19.2}
$$

The first of Eqs. (19.2) contains only one unknown, i.e., the vertical displacement $v(z, t)$; together with the nonhomogeneous boundary conditions

$$
EJ_x \frac{\partial^2 v(0, t)}{\partial z^2} = EJ_x \frac{\partial^2 v(l, t)}{\partial z^2} = - (M_0 + M_t \cos \theta t)
$$

describe the ordinary forced vibrations of a strip in the plane of its highest rigidity. The remaining two equations form a system of two differential equations with periodic coefficients.

We will consider a case in which both ends are simply supported (Fig. 129). The boundary conditions

$$
\begin{gathered}
u(0, t) = u(l, t) = \varphi(0, t) = \varphi(l, t) = 0 , \\
\frac{\partial^2 u(0, t)}{\partial z^2} = \frac{\partial^2 u(l, t)}{\partial z^2} = \frac{\partial^2 \varphi(0, t)}{\partial z^2} = \frac{\partial^2 \varphi(l, t)}{\partial z^2} = 0
\end{gathered}
$$

can be satisfied by taking the following expressions for $u(z, t)$ and $\varphi(z, t)$:

$$u(z, t) = \sum_{n=1}^{\infty} U_n(t) \sin \frac{n\pi z}{l},$$
$$\varphi(z, t) = \sum_{n=1}^{\infty} \Phi_n(t) \sin \frac{n\pi z}{l}. \tag{19.3}$$

Substitution into Eqs. (19.2) leads to the system of equations

$$\frac{d^2U_n}{dt^2} + \omega_{nx}^2\left[U_n - \frac{l^2\Phi_n}{n^2\pi^2EJ_y}(M_0 + M_t \cos \theta t)\right] = 0,$$
$$\frac{d^2\Phi_n}{dt^2} + \omega_{n\varphi}^2\left[\Phi_n - \frac{U_n}{GJ_d}(M_0 + M_t \cos \theta t)\right] = 0, \tag{19.4}$$
$$(n = 1, 2, 3, \cdots).$$

Here ω_{nx} and $\omega_{n\varphi}$ are the frequencies of bending and torsional vibrations of the unloaded beam,

$$\omega_{nx} = \frac{n^2\pi^2}{l^2}\sqrt{\frac{EJ_y}{m}}, \qquad \omega_{n\varphi} = \frac{n\pi}{\rho l}\sqrt{\frac{GJ_d}{m}}. \tag{19.5}$$

Hereafter, Eqs. (19.4) will be written in matrix form. For this purpose the following notations are introduced:

$$\boldsymbol{f}_n(t) = \begin{pmatrix} U_n(t) \\ \Phi_n(t) \end{pmatrix}, \quad \boldsymbol{A}_n = \begin{pmatrix} 0 & \dfrac{l^2}{n^2\pi^2EJ_y} \\ \dfrac{1}{GJ_d} & 0 \end{pmatrix}, \quad \boldsymbol{C}_n = \begin{pmatrix} \dfrac{1}{\omega_{nx}^2} & 0 \\ 0 & \dfrac{1}{\omega_{n\varphi}^2} \end{pmatrix}. \tag{19.6}$$

In what follows, the index n will be omitted. The system of differential equations (19.4) thus becomes

$$\boldsymbol{Cf}'' + [\boldsymbol{E} - (M_0 + M_t \cos \theta t)\,\boldsymbol{A}]\,\boldsymbol{f} = \boldsymbol{0}, \tag{19.7}$$

where $\boldsymbol{E}$ denotes the unit matrix.

•2. In this way the problem of the dynamic stability of the plane form of bending reduces to the investigation of a matrix equation of the type of (14.1). The basic results will now be formulated.

The regions of dynamic instability lie near the frequencies determined by the formula

$$\theta = \frac{2\Omega_p}{k}, \qquad (p = 1, 2;\ k = 1, 2, 3, \cdots), \tag{19.8}$$

where Ω_1 and Ω_2 are the roots of the equation

$$|\boldsymbol{E} - M_0\boldsymbol{A} - \Omega^2\boldsymbol{C}| = 0. \tag{19.9}$$

It is obvious that Ω_1 and Ω_2 represent the frequencies of free bending-torsional vibrations of a strip which is loaded by a constant component M_0 of the moment. As M_0 approaches zero, one of the frequencies reduces to ω_x and the other to ω_φ. The individual frequencies ω_x and ω_φ are not usually multiple. On the contrary, it follows from (19.5) that for $n = 1$ and $G \approx 0.4\,E$,

$$\gamma = \frac{\omega_x^2}{\omega_\varphi^2} \approx 0.55\frac{h^2}{l^2}\,. \tag{19.10}$$

In the case of a sufficiently long strip, $\omega_x \ll \omega_\varphi$; then the lower frequency of the combined system will correspond to bending-torsional vibrations in which bending deformations predominate, while the higher frequency will correspond to the vibrations with predominantly torsional character.

Thus, formula (19.8) leads to two series of regions of dynamic instability which correspond to the bending and to the torsion of a strip. In addition, the general theory (§ 60) indicates the possibility of a combination resonance. The necessary condition for its appearance has the form

$$\Omega_p \pm \Omega_q = k\theta\,, \qquad (p, q = 1, 2;\ k = 0, 1, 2, 3, \cdots)\,.$$

The loss of static stability (buckling) can be considered to be a particular case of the loss of dynamic stability for $\theta = 0$. Then the critical value of the load can be found from the equation

$$|\boldsymbol{E} - M\boldsymbol{A}| = 0\,,$$

or, in the expanded form,

$$\begin{vmatrix} 1 & -\dfrac{Ml^2}{n^2\pi^2EJ_y} \\ -\dfrac{M}{GJ_d} & 1 \end{vmatrix} = 0\,.$$

The solution of this equation leads to the well-known result:

$$M_* = \frac{n\pi}{l}\sqrt{EJ_yGJ_d}\,.$$

In proceeding now to a more exact calculation of the regions of instability, we use the results of §58. There an example in which matrices $\boldsymbol{A}$ and $\boldsymbol{C}$ were analogous in structure to matrices (19.6) was investigated. To obtain complete agreement, it is necessary to let

$$\alpha = M_0\,, \qquad \beta = M_t\,, \qquad a_{12} = \frac{l^2}{n^2\pi^2EJ_y}\,, \qquad a_{21} = \frac{1}{GJ_d}\,,$$

$$\omega_1 = \omega_{nx}\,, \qquad \omega_2 = \omega_{n\varphi}\,.$$

Then, using formulas (14.35), which hold for $\gamma \ll 1$, we obtain

$$\begin{aligned} \theta_* &\approx 2\omega_{nx}\sqrt{1 - \frac{(M_0 \pm \frac{1}{2}M_t)^2}{(1-\gamma)M_*^2}}\,, \\ \theta_* &\approx 2\omega_{n\varphi}\sqrt{1 + \frac{\gamma}{1-\gamma}\frac{(M_0 \pm \frac{1}{2}M_t)^2}{M_*^2}}\,. \end{aligned} \tag{19.11}$$

The first of formulas (19.11) corresponds to predominantly bending vibrations; the second corresponds to predominantly torsional vibrations.

The boundaries of the principal regions of instability can be determined more exactly from the equation

$$|\boldsymbol{E} - (M_0 \pm \tfrac{1}{2}M_t)\,\boldsymbol{A} - \tfrac{1}{4}\theta^2\boldsymbol{C}| = 0\,,$$

or, in the expanded form,

$$\begin{vmatrix} 1 - \dfrac{\theta^2}{4\omega_{nx}^2} & -\dfrac{(M_0 \pm \frac{1}{2}M_t)l^2}{n^2\pi^2 EJ_y} \\ -\dfrac{M_0 \pm \frac{1}{2}M_t}{GJ_d} & 1 - \dfrac{\theta^2}{4\omega_{n\varphi}^2} \end{vmatrix} = 0\,. \tag{19.12}$$

The boundaries of the instability regions of second order can be determined from formulas (14.37) and (14.38), the boundaries of the third region of instability from formulas (14.40), etc. The consideration of the width of the regions, mentioned in §58, remains of course valid also for the case under investigation. The widths of the first, second, and third regions of instability are of the orders of magnitude

$$\frac{\Delta\theta}{\omega_{nx}} \sim \frac{M_0 M_t}{M_*^2}\,, \qquad \frac{M_t^2}{M_*^2}\,, \qquad \frac{M_0^2 M_t^2}{M_*^4}\,,$$

respectively. The distribution of the regions of instability in the plane of parameters M_t/M_* and $\theta/2\Omega$ is shown in Figures 90 and 91.

§ 84. Generalization of the Results. The Case of an Arbitrary Vertical Load

●1. The results obtained above for a narrow strip of a rectangular cross section remain valid for rods of an arbitrary cross section, provided that the latter has two axes of symmetry.

The results so obtained can be easily extended to the case of non-zero warping rigidity. In considering problems involving vibrations of a thin-walled rod which has two axes of symmetry and is loaded by periodic couples we arrive at a system of two differential equations with respect to the lateral displacement $u(z, t)$ and the angle of twist $\varphi(z, t)$,

$$\begin{aligned} EJ_y\frac{\partial^4 u}{\partial z^4} + (M_0 + M_t\cos\theta t)\frac{\partial^2\varphi}{\partial z^2} + m\frac{\partial^2 u}{\partial t^2} &= 0\,, \\ (M_0 + M_t\cos\theta t)\frac{\partial^2 u}{\partial z^2} + EJ_\omega\frac{\partial^4\varphi}{\partial z^4} - GJ_d\frac{\partial^2\varphi}{\partial z^2} + m\rho^2\frac{\partial^2\varphi}{\partial t^2} &= 0\,. \end{aligned} \tag{19.13}$$

The first of Eqs. (19.13) coincides with the corresponding equation of system (19.2), while the second differs from the corresponding equation (19.2) by the presence of an additional term which vanishes for $EJ_\omega \to 0$.

Retaining the boundary conditions of the previous problem, we seek the solution in the form of series (19.3). By formal substitution we obtain a system of ordinary, differential equations with periodic coefficients:

$$U_n'' + \omega_{nx}^2\left[U_n - \frac{l^2\Phi_n}{n^2\pi^2EJ_y}(M_0 + M_t\cos\theta t)\right] = 0\,,$$
$$\Phi_n'' + \omega_{n\varphi}^2\left[\Phi_n - \frac{U_nl^2(M_0 + M_t\cos\theta t)}{GJ_dl^2 + n^2\pi^2EJ_\omega}\right] = 0\,, \tag{19.14}$$

where

$$\omega_{n\varphi} = \frac{n\pi}{\rho l}\sqrt{\frac{GJ_dl^2 + n^2\pi^2EJ_\omega}{ml^2}}\,. \tag{19.15}$$

Further derivations of §83 can obviously also be extended to differential equations (19.14). It is sufficient for this purpose to perform the following substitution in the appropriate formulas:

$$GJ_d \to GJ_d + \frac{n^2\pi^2}{l^2}EJ_\omega\,.$$

In particular, the equation for the critical frequencies remains valid:

$$\left(1 - \frac{\theta^2}{4\omega_{nx}^2}\right)\left(1 - \frac{\theta^2}{4\omega_{n\varphi}^2}\right) - \frac{(M_0 \pm \frac{1}{2}M_t)^2}{M_*^2} = 0\,,$$

where

$$M_* = \frac{n\pi}{l\rho}\sqrt{EJ_y\left(GJ_d + \frac{n^2\pi^2}{l^2}EJ_\omega\right)}\,.$$

● **2.** Let us proceed now to consider a more general case. The general differential equations for static stability of a plane form of bending of thin-walled rods were first obtained by Vlasov [1]. For the case where the cross section of a rod has one axis of symmetry and the external load acts in the plane of symmetry, these equations have the form

$$EJ_y\frac{d^4u}{dz^4} + \frac{d^2}{dz^2}(M\varphi) = 0\,,$$
$$EJ_\omega\frac{d^4\varphi}{dz^4} - \frac{d}{dz}\left[(2\beta_yM + GJ_d)\frac{d\varphi}{dz}\right] + q(e_y - a_y)\varphi + M\frac{d^2u}{dz^2} = 0\,. \tag{19.16}$$

In Eqs. (19.16) the following notation is used: $q(z)$ is the external transverse load per unit length, $M(z)$ is the bending moment due to the external load, e_y is the distance from the line of application of the transverse load to the center of gravity of the cross section (Fig. 130), a_y is the coordinate of the center of bending, and β_y is the geometric characteristic of the cross section, calculated from the formula

$$\beta_y = \frac{1}{2J_x}\int y^2(y^2 + x^2)\,dF - a_y\,.$$

The differential equations for the vibrations of a thin-walled rod which is subjected to a periodic load

$$q(z,t) = \lambda_0q_0(z) + \lambda_tq_t(z)\cos\theta t\,,$$

and, correspondingly, to a moment

$$M(z, t) = \lambda_0 M_0(z) + \lambda_t M_t(z) \cos \theta t ,$$

can be obtained from (19.16) by adding the inertia forces. Neglecting the influence of inertia forces that arise from the rotation of the cross sections of the beam with respect to the principal axis owing to their not remaining in the plane, we find that the inertia forces acting on the beam reduce to a distributed transverse load $-m[(\partial^2 u/\partial t^2) + \alpha_y(\partial^2\varphi/\partial t^2)]$ and a distributed moment $-m[\rho^2(\partial^2\varphi/\partial t^2) + \alpha_y(\partial^2 u/\partial t^2)]$. Here α_y is the distance from the center of inertia of each cross section to the center of bending, which, generally speaking, does not coincide with the coordinate of the center of bending a_y.

When the inertia forces are introduced into Eqs. (19.16), the following is obtained:

$$EJ_y\frac{\partial^4 u}{\partial z^4} + \frac{\partial^2}{\partial z^2}(M\varphi) + m\left(\frac{\partial^2 u}{\partial t^2} + \alpha_y\frac{\partial^2\varphi}{\partial t^2}\right) = 0 ,$$

$$EJ_\omega\frac{\partial^4\varphi}{\partial z^4} - \frac{\partial}{\partial z}\left[(2\beta_y M + GJ_d)\frac{\partial\varphi}{\partial z}\right] + q(e_y - a_y)\varphi \qquad (19.17)$$

$$+ M\frac{\partial^2 u}{\partial z^2} + m\left(\rho^2\frac{\partial^2\varphi}{\partial t^2} + \alpha_y\frac{\partial^2 u}{\partial t^2}\right) = 0 .$$

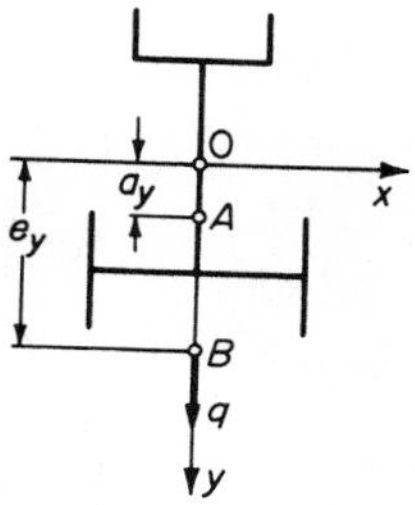

FIG. 130.

The coefficients of these differential equations depend on z; consequently, a complete separation of variables z and t is not possible even for the simplest boundary conditions. The problem considered in the preceding paragraph represents an exceptional case; for that problem the forms of free vibrations and the forms for the loss of static stability coincide.

●**3.** To find the solutions of system (19.17), variational methods will be used, approximating the forms of the vibrations by a suitable system of eigenfunctions. For example, in the case of a beam which is simply supported on the ends and loaded by an arbitrary periodic load, the solution of Eqs. (19.17) can be sought in the form of (19.3). It is possible also to investigate the problem in a more general form by letting

$$u(z, t) = \sum_{n=1}^{\infty} U_n(t)\chi_n(z), \qquad \varphi(z, t) = \sum_{n=1}^{\infty} \Phi_n(t)\psi_n(z) . \qquad (19.18)$$

Here two different systems of eigenfunctions are introduced with a provision that the boundary conditions for $u(z, t)$ and $\varphi(z, t)$ can be different. The solutions of the differential equations

$$EJ_y\frac{d^4\chi}{dz^4} - \kappa_y\chi = 0, \qquad EJ_\omega\frac{d^2\psi}{dz^4} - \kappa_\omega\psi = 0 ,$$

which satisfy the boundary conditions of the problem can be used as eigenfunctions. These are essentially the forms of the free vibrations of a rod which is appropriately supported at the ends (the so-called "beam" functions).

By using the Galerkin method, a system of ordinary differential equations with periodic coefficients is obtained:

$$\boldsymbol{F}\boldsymbol{f}'' + (\boldsymbol{R} - \lambda_0 \boldsymbol{S}_0 - \lambda_t \cos \theta t \boldsymbol{S}_t)\boldsymbol{f} = \boldsymbol{0} . \tag{19.19}$$

To within a second order matrix, the coefficients of this system are

$$\boldsymbol{F} = \begin{pmatrix} \int m\chi^2 dz & \int m a_y \chi\psi dz \\ \int m a_y \psi\chi dz & \int m\rho^2\psi^2 dz \end{pmatrix},$$

$$\boldsymbol{R} = \begin{pmatrix} \kappa_y \int \chi^2 dz & 0 \\ 0 & \kappa_\omega \int \psi^2 dz - GJ_d \int \psi \frac{d^2\psi}{dz^2} dz \end{pmatrix},$$

$$\boldsymbol{S}_0 = \begin{pmatrix} 0 & -\int \chi \frac{d^2}{dz^2}(M_0\psi)\, dz \\ -\int \psi M_0 \frac{d^2\chi}{dz^2} dz & 2\beta_y \int \psi \frac{d}{dz}\left(M_0 \frac{d\psi}{dz}\right) dz - (e_y - a_y)\int q_0\psi^2 dz \end{pmatrix}, \tag{19.20}$$

$$\boldsymbol{S}_t = \begin{pmatrix} 0 & -\int \chi \frac{d^2}{dz^2}(M_t\psi) dz \\ -\int \psi M_t \frac{d^2\chi}{dz^2} dz & 2\beta_y \int \psi \frac{d}{dz}\left(M_t \frac{d\psi}{dz}\right) dz - (e_y - a_y)\int q_t\psi^2 dz \end{pmatrix}.$$

Examples involving the application of Eq. (19.19) will be given below.

§ 85. Example

● **1.** Consider now a problem of the dynamic stability of a beam of a constant cross section, which is simply supported on the ends and loaded by a uniformly distributed periodic force:

$$q(t) = q_0 + q_t \cos \theta t .$$

Let the cross section of the beam be symmetric with respect to both axes; then $a_y = \beta_y = \alpha_y = 0$. In addition, let the load be applied at the height $e_y = -e$ (Fig. 131). Then, assuming

$$\chi(z) = \psi(z) = \frac{\sqrt{2}}{\sqrt{l}} \sin \frac{\pi z}{l}$$

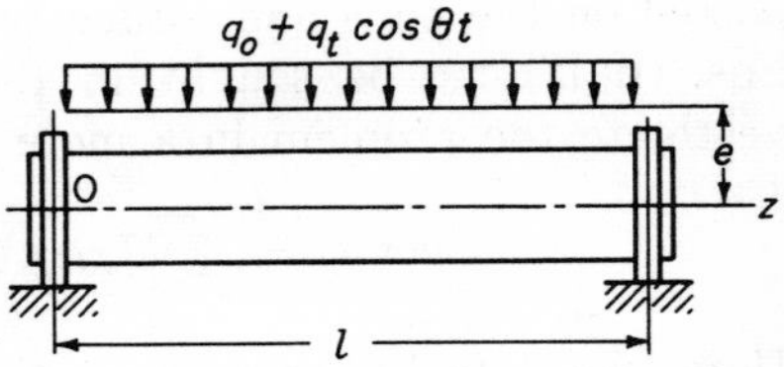

FIG. 131.

leads to

$$\boldsymbol{F} = m\begin{pmatrix} 1 & 0 \\ 0 & \rho^2 \end{pmatrix},$$

$$\boldsymbol{R} = \begin{pmatrix} EJ_y \frac{\pi^4}{l^4} & 0 \\ 0 & EJ_\omega \frac{\pi^4}{l^4} + GJ_d \frac{\pi^2}{l^2} \end{pmatrix}, \quad \boldsymbol{S} = \begin{pmatrix} 0 & \frac{1}{4}\left(\frac{\pi^2}{3} + 1\right) \\ \frac{1}{4}\left(\frac{\pi^2}{3} + 1\right) & 0 \end{pmatrix}.$$

In the first approximation, the boundaries of the principal regions of instability can be determined from the condition

$$|\boldsymbol{R} - (q_0 \pm \tfrac{1}{2}q_t)\,\boldsymbol{S} - \tfrac{1}{4}\theta^2\boldsymbol{F}| = 0\,,$$

or, in the expanded form,

$$\begin{vmatrix} 1 - \dfrac{\theta^2}{4\omega_x^2} & -\dfrac{(\frac{1}{3}\pi^2+1)(q_0 \pm \frac{1}{2}q_t)}{4EJ_y(\pi^4/l^4)} \\ -\dfrac{(\frac{1}{3}\pi^2+1)(q_0 \pm \frac{1}{2}q_t)}{4\left(EJ_\omega\dfrac{\pi^4}{l^4}+GJ_d\dfrac{\pi^2}{l^2}\right)} & 1 - \dfrac{\theta^2}{4\omega_\varphi^2} - \dfrac{(q_0 \pm \frac{1}{2}q_t)e}{EJ_\omega\dfrac{\pi^4}{l^4}+GJ_d\dfrac{\pi^2}{l^2}} \end{vmatrix} = 0\,.$$

Let $\gamma = \omega_x^2/\omega_\varphi^2$ be sufficiently small (or large) in comparison with unity. Then the following approximate formulas are obtained:

$$\begin{aligned} \theta_* &= 2\omega_x\sqrt{1 - \frac{(q_0 \pm \frac{1}{2}q_t)^2}{q_*^2\left(1-\gamma-2.93\,\varepsilon\,\dfrac{q_0 \pm \frac{1}{2}q_t}{q_*}\right)}}\,, \\ \theta_* &= 2\omega_\varphi\sqrt{1 - 2.93\,\varepsilon\frac{q_0 \pm \frac{1}{2}q_t}{q_*} + \frac{\gamma}{1-\gamma}\,\frac{(q_0 \pm \frac{1}{2}q_t)^2}{q_*^2}}\,, \end{aligned} \qquad (19.21)$$

where $\varepsilon = e\sqrt{\gamma}/\pi\rho$ is the relative eccentricity and q_* is the root of the equation

$$|\boldsymbol{E} - q\boldsymbol{S}| = 0\,,$$

determined for $e = 0$ (i.e., the load is applied at the center of gravity of the cross section). Calculations give

$$q_* = \frac{28.3}{l^3}\sqrt{EJ_y\left(EJ_\omega\frac{\pi^2}{l^2} + GJ_d\right)}\,,$$

which practically coincides with the exact expression.[2]

It is evident from formulas (19.21) that for $\gamma \ll 1$ even a relatively large eccentricity of load above the center of gravity of the cross section has a negligible influence on the magnitude of critical frequencies.

●**2.** The results obtained will be applied to the problem of the stability of the stiffener beams of suspension bridges. After the well-known disaster of the Tacoma Narrows Bridge (1940), a number of works on investigations of this problem were published. Two weeks after the disaster, an article[3] was published attempting to explain the collapse of the stiffener beam by the loss of its static stability due to the action of the aerodynamic moment. In the majority of later works, the problem of the aerodynamic stability of stiffener beams is treated on the basis of the flutter theory; this theory is used in approximately the same way as in the analysis of airplane wings. In many foreign works, the stiffener beam is considered to be a thin plate

[2] Timoshenko [1].

[3] Karman [1].

of infinite span. In this assumption, the fact is fully ignored that the aerodynamic characteristics of stiffener beams differ substantially from those of a flat plate.

The results of laboratory investigations[4] published subsequently shed new light on the problem of the aerodynamic stability of stiffener beams. Experiments in aerodynamic tunnels show that the excitation of vibrations in stiffener beams has little resemblance to the flutter phenomenon, at least to the flutter phenomena that take place in airplane wings. On the contrary, there are reasons to believe that these phenomena are similar in character to parametric resonance. Thus, it was noted that the excitation of vibrations observed at definite "resonance" velocity of the stream resumes again at approximately half the velocity (Fig. 132).

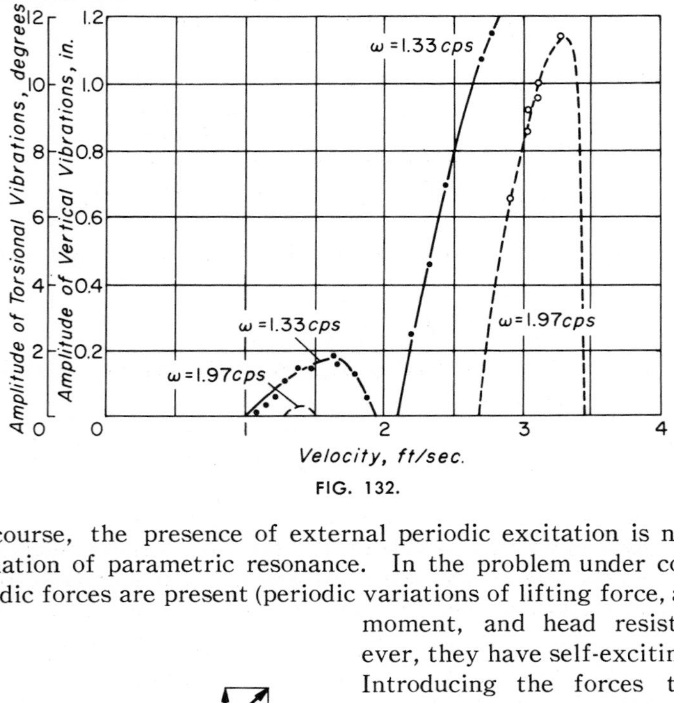

FIG. 132.

Of course, the presence of external periodic excitation is necessary for the formation of parametric resonance. In the problem under consideration, the periodic forces are present (periodic variations of lifting force, aerodynamic moment, and head resistance); however, they have self-exciting character. Introducing the forces that depend explicitly on time into the equations of the problem, we must keep in mind that these forces are equivalent only to a certain degree to the aerodynamic forces that do not explicitly depend on time.

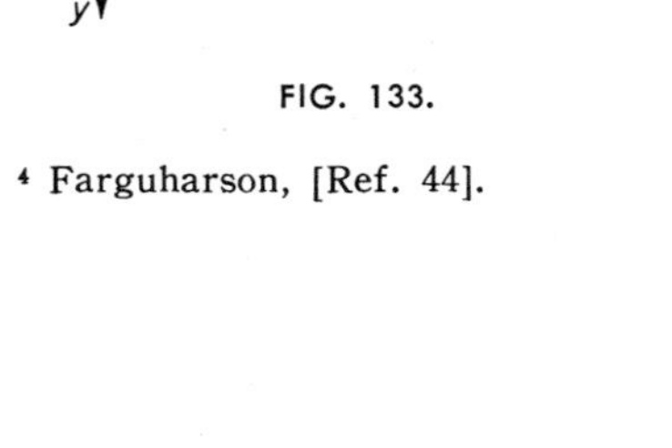

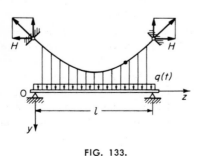

FIG. 133.

The first attempt to investigate the problem involving parametrically excited vibrations of a stiffener beam

[4] Farguharson, [Ref. 44].

of a suspension bridge was made by Gol'denblat [1]. The external forces that act on the beam lead to a distributed vertical load (Fig. 133):

$$q = q_0 + q_t \cos \theta t .$$

Neglecting the dynamic variation of thrust leads to an approximate equation for the vertical vibrations

$$EJ_x \frac{\partial^4 v}{\partial z^4} + H\left(1 + \frac{q_t}{q_0} \cos \theta t\right)\frac{\partial^2 v}{\partial z^2} + m\frac{\partial^2 v}{\partial t^2} = F(z, t) ,$$

where H is the thrust due to constant load and $F(z, t)$ is some function of time. Furthermore, assuming that

$$v(z, t) = f_k(t) \sin \frac{k\pi z}{l} , \qquad (k = 2, 3, 4, \cdots) ,$$

and neglecting the terms on the right-hand side of the equation leads to the Mathieu equation

$$f_k'' + \omega_{ky}^2(1 - 2\mu_k \cos \theta t) f_k = 0 , \qquad (k = 2, 3, 4, \cdots) . \qquad (19.22)$$

Here

$$\omega_{ky} = \frac{k^2\pi^2}{l^2}\sqrt{\frac{EJ_x}{m}\left(1 + \frac{Hl^2}{k^2\pi^2 EJ_x}\right)} ,$$

$$\mu_k = \frac{q_t}{2q_0}\frac{1}{1 + \dfrac{k^2\pi^2}{l^2}\dfrac{EJ_x}{H}} .$$

It follows from Eq. (19.22) that for frequencies of external loading which lie in the vicinity of $\theta = 2\omega_{ky}/n$ $(n = 1, 2, 3, \cdots)$, intensive vertical vibrations arise.

●**3.** It is known, however, that the Tacoma Narrows Bridge was destroyed because of bending-torsional vibrations that had a primarily torsional character before the collapse. To explain the origin of bending-torsional vibrations, it is sufficient to assume the presence of horizontal periodic forces.

Consider the problem involving the vibration of a stiffener beam subjected to a lateral periodic force (Fig. 134). To simplify the computations, assume that the cross section of the beam has two axes of symmetry and that the

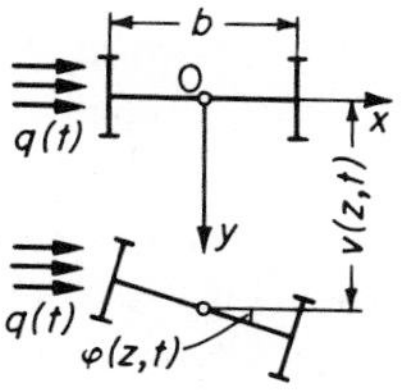

FIG. 134.

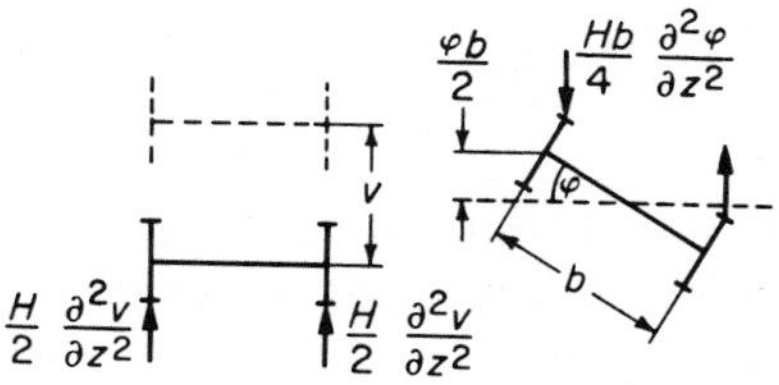

FIG. 135.

entire system is symmetrically supported. The differential equations for the problem can be obtained from equations (19.17) if terms which take into account the thrust H are introduced into them. The influence of the thrust during bending-torsional deformations is equivalent to the action of a distributed lateral load and a distributed moment.[5]

$$q_y = H\frac{\partial^2 v}{\partial z^2},$$

$$\mu = \tfrac{1}{4}Hb^2\frac{\partial^2 \varphi}{\partial z^2},$$

which can be determined from elementary considerations (Fig. 135). As a result, a system of equations is obtained

$$EJ_x\frac{\partial^4 v}{\partial z^4} + \frac{\partial^2}{\partial z^2}(M\varphi) - H\frac{\partial^2 v}{\partial z^2} + m\frac{\partial^2 v}{\partial t^2} = 0,$$

$$EJ_\omega\frac{\partial^4 \varphi}{\partial z^4} - (GJ_d + \tfrac{1}{4}Hb^2)\frac{\partial^2 \varphi}{\partial z^2} + M\frac{\partial^2 v}{\partial z^2} + \frac{qb}{2}\varphi + m\rho^2\frac{\partial^2 \varphi}{\partial t^2} = 0,$$

where

$$q = q_0 + q_t \cos\theta t,$$

$$M(z, t) = \frac{z(l - z)}{2}(q_0 + q_t \cos\theta t).$$

The fundamental (antisymmetric) form of vibrations will now be considered. Assuming that

$$v(z, t) = V(t)\sin\frac{2\pi z}{l},$$

$$\varphi(z, t) = \Phi(t)\sin\frac{2\pi z}{l},$$

and using the Galerkin method yields a system of equations of the same type as (19.19). To determine the boundary frequencies, the formulas of this section will be used, in which it is necessary to set

$$\omega_x = \frac{4\pi^2}{l^2}\sqrt{\frac{EJ_x}{m}\left(1 + \frac{Hl^2}{4\pi^2 EJ_x}\right)},$$

$$\omega_\varphi = \frac{2\pi}{l\rho\sqrt{m}}\sqrt{GJ_d + \tfrac{1}{4}Hb^2 + \frac{4\pi^2 EJ_\omega}{l^2}},$$

$$q_* = \frac{96\pi^3}{l^3(3 + \pi^2)}\sqrt{EJ_x\left(1 + \frac{Hl^2}{4\pi^2 EJ_x}\right)\left(GJ_d + \tfrac{1}{4}Hb^2 + \frac{4\pi^2 EJ_\omega}{l^2}\right)}.$$

The above considerations lead, therefore, to two series of boundary frequencies, one of which corresponds to primarily bending vibrations and the other to primarily torsional vibrations. In addition, a combined excitation is possible.

[5] Under the condition that the supports are closely spaced.

§ 86. The Influence of Load Behavior[1]

●**1.** Heretofore, it has been assumed that the periodic components $\lambda_t q_t$ of the load does not change direction during vibrations. However, in practical problems the exciter of vibrations turns together with the beam, so that vectors $\lambda_t q_t$ always remain in one of the principal planes (Fig. 136).

The additional transverse load and the torsional moment, which arise as a consequence of the rotation of the load, are

$$q_x = -\lambda_t q_t(z)\varphi(z, t)\cos\theta t,$$
$$\mu = \lambda_t q_t(z)(e_y - a_y)\varphi(z, t)\cos\theta t.$$

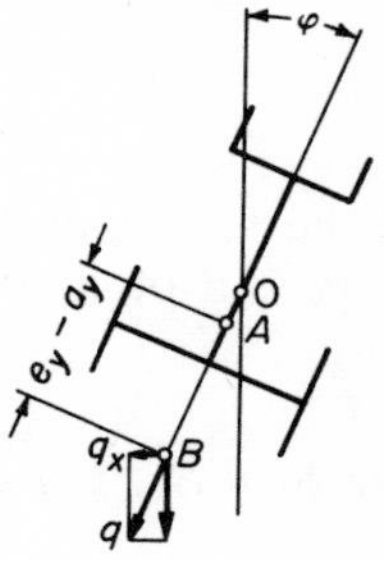

FIG. 136.

Introducing these terms into the right-hand sides of Eqs. (19.17) gives

$$EJ_y\frac{\partial^4 u}{\partial z^4} + \frac{\partial^2}{\partial z^2}(M\varphi) + m\left(\frac{\partial^2 u}{\partial t^2} + \alpha_y\frac{\partial^2\varphi}{\partial t^2}\right) = q_x(z, t),$$
$$EJ_\omega\frac{\partial^4\varphi}{\partial z^4} - \frac{\partial}{\partial z}\left[(2\beta_y M + GJ_d)\frac{\partial\varphi}{\partial z}\right] + q(e_y - a_y)\varphi + M\frac{\partial^2 u}{\partial z^2}$$
$$+ m\left(\rho^2\frac{\partial^2\varphi}{\partial t^2} + \alpha_y\frac{\partial^2 u}{\partial t^2}\right) = \mu(z, t).$$

Again, assuming that

$$u(z, t) = U(t)\chi(z), \qquad \varphi(z, t) = \Phi(t)\psi(z),$$

and applying the Galerkin method yields equations of the type (19.19). It is evident that matrices $\boldsymbol{F}$, $\boldsymbol{R}$, and $\boldsymbol{S}_0$ are determined, as before, according to (19.20). Matrix $\boldsymbol{S}_t$ assumes the form

$$\boldsymbol{S}_t = \begin{pmatrix} 0 & -\int\chi\frac{d^2}{dz^2}(M_t\psi)\,dz - \int q_t\chi\psi\,dz \\ -\int\psi M_t\frac{d^2\chi}{dz^2}dz & 2\beta_y\int\psi\frac{d}{dz}\left(M_t\frac{d\psi}{dz}\right)dz \end{pmatrix}. \tag{19.23}$$

●**2.** Assume that the beam is of constant cross section, is simply supported at both ends, and is loaded at the midpoint by a concentrated force $P_0 + P_t\cos\theta t$. In place of (19.19) there results

$$\boldsymbol{F}\boldsymbol{f}'' + (\boldsymbol{R} - P_0\boldsymbol{S}_0 - P_t\boldsymbol{S}_t\cos\theta t)\boldsymbol{f} = \boldsymbol{0},$$

where $\boldsymbol{F}$ and $\boldsymbol{R}$ are defined as in §85, and

$$\boldsymbol{S}_0 = \begin{pmatrix} 0 & \frac{1}{2l}\left(1 + \frac{\pi^2}{4}\right) \\ \frac{1}{2l}\left(1 + \frac{\pi^2}{4}\right) & 0 \end{pmatrix}.$$

[6] See Bolotin [7].

If the force P_t does not change direction during vibration, then $\boldsymbol{S}_t = \boldsymbol{S}_0$. In the case of the "following" force we have, according to (19.23),

$$\boldsymbol{S}_t = \begin{pmatrix} 0 & -\frac{1}{2l}\left(3 - \frac{\pi^2}{4}\right) \\ \frac{1}{2l}\left(1 + \frac{\pi^2}{4}\right) & 0 \end{pmatrix}.$$

In the first approximation, the boundaries of the principal regions of instability can be determined from the equation

$$|\boldsymbol{R} - P_0\boldsymbol{S}_0 \pm \tfrac{1}{2}P_t\boldsymbol{S}_t - \tfrac{1}{4}\theta^2\boldsymbol{F}| = 0 .$$

For $\boldsymbol{S}_t = \boldsymbol{S}_0$, the equation assumes the form

$$\begin{vmatrix} 1 - \frac{\theta^2}{4\omega_x^2} & -\frac{l^3(1 + \frac{1}{4}\pi^2)(P_0 \pm \frac{1}{2}P_t)}{2\pi^4 EJ_y} \\ -\frac{(1 + \frac{1}{4}\pi^2)(P_0 \pm \frac{1}{2}P_t)}{2\left(EJ_\omega\frac{\pi^4}{l^3} + GJ_d\frac{\pi^2}{l}\right)} & 1 - \frac{\theta^2}{4\omega_\varphi^2} \end{vmatrix} = 0 .$$

Correspondingly, for the case of a "following" force, this is

$$\begin{vmatrix} 1 - \frac{\theta^2}{4\omega_x^2} & -\frac{l^3(1 + \frac{1}{4}\pi^2)(P_0 \mp 0.075P_t)}{2\pi^4 EJ_y} \\ -\frac{(1 + \frac{1}{4}\pi^2)(P_0 \pm \frac{1}{2}P_t)}{2\left(EJ_\omega\frac{\pi^4}{l^3} + GJ_d\frac{\pi^2}{l}\right)} & 1 - \frac{\theta^2}{4\omega_\varphi^2} \end{vmatrix} = 0 .$$

Let $\gamma = \omega_x^2/\omega_\varphi^2$ be sufficiently small (or large) compared to unity. In this case the boundaries of the principal regions of instability can be determined from the approximate formulas

$$\begin{aligned} \theta_* &= 2\omega_x \sqrt{1 - \frac{(P_0 \pm \frac{1}{2}P_t)^2}{(1-\gamma)P_*^2}}\,, \\ \theta_* &= 2\omega_\varphi \sqrt{1 + \frac{\gamma}{1-\gamma}\frac{(P_0 \pm \frac{1}{2}P_t)^2}{P_*^2}}\,, \end{aligned} \tag{19.24}$$

Formulas (19.24) correspond to the case in which the load does not change its direction. P_* denotes the approximate expression for the critical force, which can be obtained from the equation

$$|\boldsymbol{R} - P\boldsymbol{S}_0| = 0$$

and which is

$$P_* = \frac{17.8}{l^2}\sqrt{EJ_y\left(GJ_d + \frac{\pi^2}{l^2}EJ_\omega\right)} . \tag{19.25}$$

For the case of a "following" loading

$$\theta_* = 2\omega_x \sqrt{1 - \frac{(P_0 \pm \frac{1}{2}P_t)(P_0 \mp 0.075\, P_t)}{(1-\gamma)P_*^2}},$$
$$\theta_* = 2\omega_\varphi \sqrt{1 + \frac{\gamma}{1-\gamma}\,\frac{(P_0 \pm \frac{1}{2}P_t)(P_0 \mp 0.075\, P_t)}{P_*^2}}, \tag{19.26}$$

where the notation (19.25) is retained. A comparison of the results calculated from formulas (19.24) and (19.26) is shown in Figure 137. It can be seen from the graph that as a result of load rotation, the width of the instability regions is decreased approximately by half.

The question of the influence of load behavior has been examined already twice, i.e., in connection with vibrations of compressed struts and in connection with antisymmetric vibrations of arches loaded by compression and bending. In the problem under consideration, this influence can be explained as follows. The external force that rotates together with the cross section of a beam can be decomposed into two components, one vertical and the other directed along axis Ox (Fig. 138). The horizontal component, being always directed opposite to the displacements, increases the static stability of the beam.

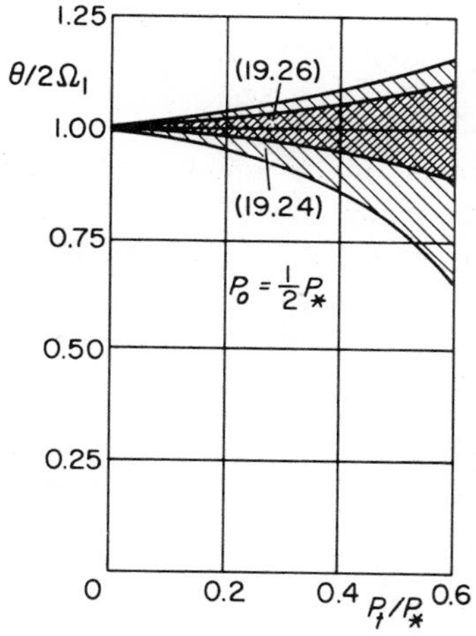

FIG. 137.

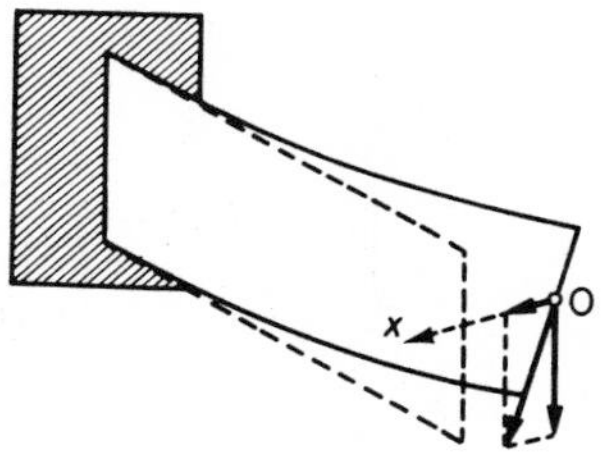

FIG. 138.

Consider also the corresponding statics problem. The equation for static stability is

$$|\boldsymbol{R} - P\boldsymbol{S}_t| = 0 \tag{19.27}$$

or, in the expanded form,

$$\begin{vmatrix} EJ_y\frac{\pi^4}{l^4} & \frac{P}{2l}\left(3 - \frac{\pi^2}{4}\right) \\ -\frac{1}{2l}\left(1 + \frac{\pi^2}{4}\right) & EJ_\omega\frac{\pi^4}{l^4} + GJ_d\frac{\pi^2}{l^2} \end{vmatrix} = 0 .$$

It can easily be seen that this equation does not have real roots, i.e., that under the action of the "following" force, loss of stability in the Euler sense is impossible.

●**3.** With the method developed here we can find an approximate solution to problems involving the stability of the plane form of bending of a beam loaded by a force that is constant in time but "following" with respect to time-dependent disturbances. The matrix variational equations for this problem are

$$\boldsymbol{F}\boldsymbol{f}'' + (\boldsymbol{R} - P\boldsymbol{S}_t)\boldsymbol{f} = \boldsymbol{0}\,,$$

from which, after substitution of

$$\boldsymbol{f} = \boldsymbol{a}e^{ipt}\,,$$

yields the characteristic equation

$$|\boldsymbol{R} - P\boldsymbol{S}_t - \rho^2\boldsymbol{F}| = 0\,.$$

The problem is reduced to finding the conditions under which this equation will not have complex roots with negative imaginary parts.

If this equation is applied to the problem investigated in (§86, ●2), we obtain

$$\begin{vmatrix} 1 - \dfrac{\rho^2}{\omega_x^2} & \dfrac{Pl^3(3 - \frac{1}{4}\pi^2)}{2\pi^4 EJ_y} \\ \dfrac{P(1 + \frac{1}{4}\pi^2)}{2\left(EJ_\omega \dfrac{\pi^4}{l^3} + GJ_d \dfrac{\pi^2}{l}\right)} & 1 - \dfrac{\rho^2}{\omega_\varphi^2} \end{vmatrix} = 0$$

or

$$\left(1 - \frac{\rho^2}{\omega_x^2}\right)\left(1 - \frac{\rho^2}{\omega_\varphi^2}\right) + \frac{P^2}{P_{**}^2} = 0\,,$$

where, for brevity, P_{**} denotes

$$P_{**} = \frac{45.61}{l^2}\sqrt{EJ_y\left(GJ_d + \frac{\pi^2}{l^2}EJ_\omega\right)}\,.$$

In addition, we denote

$$\rho^2/\omega_x^2 = \lambda\,, \qquad \omega_x^2/\omega_\varphi^2 = \gamma\,,$$

and obtain the equation

$$\lambda^2\gamma - (1 + \gamma)\lambda + 1 + \frac{P^2}{P_{**}^2} = 0\,,$$

whose roots are

$$\lambda_{1,2} = \frac{1}{2\gamma}\left[1 + \gamma \pm \sqrt{(1 - \gamma)^2 - 4\gamma\frac{P^2}{P_{**}^2}}\right].$$

As long as the expression under the radical is positive, both roots $\lambda_{1,2}$ are real and positive. Equating this expression to zero yields the critical value of the force P:

$$P_* = \frac{1-\gamma}{2\sqrt{\gamma}} P_{**} .$$

As the two frequencies approach one another, the critical force decreases; in the case of multiple frequencies ($\gamma = 1$), it is sufficient to have an arbitrarily small force for the excitation of bending-torsional vibrations. However, all the remarks made in §72, ●6 are applicable to the solution given here. If the same problem with damping taken into account is considered, then the critical force proves to be smaller; however, the qualitative character of the dependence remains the same. A detailed investigation of this question is beyond the scope of this book.

§ 87. Consideration of Nonlinear Terms

●1. The determination of nonlinear terms for three-dimensional deformations of a straight thin-walled rod was presented in §75. It is obvious that all considerations expressed there are valid for the present case. Here, as in §75, we will confine ourselves to consideration of nonlinear inertia terms. To within the quantities of the third order, the nonlinear inertia forces reduce to a distributed load (17.31):

$$\Delta q(z, t) = -(U''\Phi + 2U'\Phi' + U\Phi'')f(z) ,$$

a bending moment:

$$\Delta M(z, t) = -(U''\Phi + 2U'\Phi' + U\Phi'')F(z) ,$$

and an axial force (17.35):

$$\Delta N(z, t) = -[(U')^2 + UU''] G(z) .$$

Here $U(t)$ and $\Phi(t)$ are the coefficients in the expressions

$$u(z, t) = U(t)\chi(z) ,$$
$$\varphi(z, t) = \Phi(t)\psi(z) , \qquad (19.28)$$

where $f(z)$, $F(z)$ and $G(z)$ are certain functions that depend on the form of vibrations of a beam and on the distribution of the mass along its length.

If the additional nonlinear forces are considered, then the differential equations (19.17) take the form

$$EJ_y \frac{\partial^4 u}{\partial z^4} + \frac{\partial^2}{\partial z^2}[(M + \Delta M)\varphi] + \frac{\partial}{\partial z}\left[\Delta N\left(\frac{\partial u}{\partial z} + a_y \frac{\partial \varphi}{\partial z}\right)\right] + m\left(\frac{\partial^2 u}{\partial t^2} + \alpha_y \frac{\partial^2 \varphi}{\partial t^2}\right) = 0 ,$$

$$EJ_\omega \frac{\partial^4 \varphi}{\partial z^4} - \frac{\partial}{\partial z}\left\{[2\beta_y(M + \Delta M) + GJ_d]\frac{\partial \varphi}{\partial z}\right\} + (M + \Delta M)\frac{\partial^2 u}{\partial z^2}$$
$$+ (q + \Delta q)(e_y - a_y)\varphi + \frac{\partial}{\partial z}\left[\Delta N\left(r^2 \frac{\partial \varphi}{\partial z} + a_y \frac{\partial u}{\partial z}\right)\right] + m\left(\rho^2 \frac{\partial^2 \varphi}{\partial t^2} + \alpha_y \frac{\partial^2 u}{\partial t^2}\right) = 0 .$$

An approximate solution of these equations can be obtained on the basis of

(19.28) by using the Galerkin method. Let us investigate a particular case, i.e., a problem of the pure bending of a rectangular strip. Let $M = M_0 + M_t \cos\theta t$, $a_y = \alpha_y = \beta_y = e_y = EJ_\omega = 0$, and $\rho = r$. The equations for the problem are:

$$
\begin{aligned}
&EJ_y \frac{\partial^4 u}{\partial z^4} + (M_0 + M_t \cos\theta t)\frac{\partial^2 \varphi}{\partial z^2} + \frac{\partial^2}{\partial z^2}(\Delta M_\varphi) \\
&\qquad + \frac{\partial}{\partial z}\left(\Delta N \frac{\partial u}{\partial z}\right) + m\frac{\partial^2 u}{\partial t^2} = 0, \\
&(M_0 + M_t \cos\theta t)\frac{\partial^2 u}{\partial z^2} - GJ_d \frac{\partial^2 \varphi}{\partial z^2} + \Delta M \frac{\partial^2 u}{\partial z^2} \\
&\qquad + r^2 \frac{\partial}{\partial z}\left(\Delta N \frac{\partial \varphi}{\partial z}\right) + mr^2 \frac{\partial^2 \varphi}{\partial t^2} = 0.
\end{aligned}
\tag{19.29}
$$

Let the strip be simply supported at the ends. Then

$$
u(z, t) = U(t) \sin \frac{\pi z}{l}, \qquad \varphi(z, t) = \Phi(t) \sin \frac{\pi z}{l},
$$

represent an approximate solution of the problem (an exact solution for the linear formulation). Using the Galerkin method yields a system of ordinary differential equations

$$
\begin{aligned}
&\frac{d^2 U}{dt^2} + \omega_x^2\left[U - \frac{l^2 \Phi}{\pi^2 EJ_y}(M_0 + M_t \cos\theta t)\right] + \psi_x = 0, \\
&\frac{d^2 \Phi}{dt^2} + \omega_\varphi^2\left[\Phi - \frac{U}{GJ_d}(M_0 + M_t \cos\theta t)\right] + \psi_\varphi = 0.
\end{aligned}
\tag{19.30}
$$

Here ψ_x and ψ_φ denote the nonlinear functions of U and Φ and their derivatives:

$$
\begin{aligned}
\psi_x &= I_1 \Phi(U''\Phi + 2U'\Phi' + U\Phi'') + 2\kappa U[(U')^2 + UU''], \\
\psi_\varphi &= \frac{I_1 U}{r^2}(U''\Phi + 2U'\Phi' + U\Phi'') + 2\kappa\Phi[(U')^2 + UU''].
\end{aligned}
\tag{19.31}
$$

If it is assumed that one of the ends of the strip does not have displacements in the longitudinal direction and that the concentrated mass is absent on the other end, then (see §75)

$$
I_1 = 0.7360, \qquad \kappa l^2 = 6.57.
$$

● 2. A steady-state solution of the nonlinear system (19.30) is sought in the form

$$
\begin{aligned}
U(t) &= U_0 \sin \frac{\theta t}{2} + \cdots, \\
\Phi(t) &= \Phi_0 \sin \frac{\theta t}{2} + \cdots,
\end{aligned}
\tag{19.32}
$$

where the dots denote the higher harmonics. The second solution with period $4\pi/\theta$,

$$U(t) = U_0 \cos\frac{\theta t}{2} + \cdots ,$$

$$\Phi(t) = \Phi_0 \cos\frac{\theta t}{2} + \cdots ,$$

appears unstable for the case of nonlinear inertia, and it will not be used. Substituting (19.32) into expressions (19.31) for the nonlinear functions, we obtain after a number of transformations

$$\begin{aligned}\psi_x &= -\frac{\theta^2}{4} U_0(I_1\Phi_0^2 + \kappa U_0^2) \sin\frac{\theta t}{2} + \cdots ,\\ \psi_\varphi &= -\frac{\theta^2}{4}\Phi_0 U_0^2\left(\frac{I_1}{r^2} + \kappa\right) \sin\frac{\theta t}{2} + \cdots .\end{aligned} \tag{19.33}$$

Now substitute (19.32) and (19.33) into Eq. (19.30). By equating the coefficients of $\sin \theta t/2$, a system of algebraic equations is obtained for determining the amplitudes:

$$\begin{aligned}\left(1 - \frac{\theta^2}{4\omega_x^2}\right) U_0 - \frac{(M_0 - \frac{1}{2}M_t)l^2}{\pi^2 E J_y}\Phi_0 - \frac{\theta^2}{4\omega_\varphi^2} U_0(I_1\Phi_0^2 + \kappa U_0^2) &= 0 ,\\ -\frac{M_0 - \frac{1}{2}M_t}{GJ_d} U_0 + \left(1 - \frac{\theta^2}{4\omega_\varphi^2}\right)\Phi_0 - \frac{\theta^2}{4\omega_\varphi^2}\Phi_0 U_0^2\left(\frac{I_1}{r^2} + \kappa\right) &= 0 .\end{aligned} \tag{19.34}$$

Equations (19.34) are obviously satisfied for $U_0 = \Phi_0 = 0$. We now wish to determine the nontrivial solutions and consider the region of excitation lying near frequency $2\omega_x$. If the individual frequencies ω_x and ω_φ differ sufficiently from one another, then this region will be the region with principally bending vibrations. Assuming that $U_0 \gg \Phi_0 r$, we can neglect the nonlinear terms with $U_0\Phi_0^2$ and $\Phi_0 U_0^2$ in Eqs. (19.34). From the system obtained,

$$\begin{aligned}\left[1 - \frac{\theta^2}{4\omega_x^2}(1 + \kappa U_0^2)\right] U_0 - \frac{M_0 - \frac{1}{2}M_t}{\pi^2 E J_y} l^2 \Phi_0 &= 0 ,\\ -\frac{M_0 - \frac{1}{2}M_t}{GJ_d} U_0 + \left[1 - \frac{\theta^2}{4\omega_\varphi^2}(1 + \kappa U_0^2)\right]\Phi_0 &= 0 ,\end{aligned}$$

the amplitude U_0 can be easily determined.[7] In fact, this system will be considered a system of linear homogeneous equations in U_0 and Φ_0. The condition for its nontrivial solution is that the determinant of the coefficients of the unknowns must equal zero, i.e.,

$$\begin{vmatrix} 1 - \dfrac{\theta^2}{4\omega_x^2}(1 + \kappa U_0^2) & -\dfrac{M_0 - \frac{1}{2}M_t}{\pi^2 E J_y} l^2 \\ -\dfrac{M_0 - \frac{1}{2}M_t}{GJ_d} & 1 - \dfrac{\theta^2}{4\omega_\varphi^2}(1 + \kappa U_0^2) \end{vmatrix} = 0 . \tag{19.35}$$

Comparing Eqs. (19.35) and (19.12), it is found that

[7] See also the example in § 70.

$$\theta^2(1 + \kappa U_0^2) = \theta_*^2 ,$$

where θ_* is the boundary frequency corresponding to the upper boundary of the region of dynamic instability. Hence the following formula results:

$$U_0 = \frac{1}{\sqrt{\kappa}}\sqrt{\left(\frac{\theta_*}{\theta}\right)^2 - 1} , \tag{19.36}$$

which coincides in form with (17.44). To refine this formula we use the procedure employed in §75. First, let us establish the relationship between U_0 and Φ_0. The second of Eqs. (19.34) gives

$$\Phi_0 = \frac{M_0 - \frac{1}{2}M_t}{1 - \frac{\theta^2}{4\omega_\varphi^2}\left[1 + \left(\frac{I_1}{r^2} + \kappa\right) U_0^2\right]} \frac{U_0}{GJ_d} .$$

This formula can be simplified by setting $\theta = 2\omega_x$ and neglecting the nonlinear term which, as can be seen from (19.36), has the order $(\theta_*/\theta)^2 - 1$. Then

$$\Phi_0 \approx \frac{M_0 - \frac{1}{2}M_t}{GJ_d(1 - \gamma)} U_0 . \tag{19.37}$$

Now substitute (19.37) into the first of Eqs. (19.34):

$$\left[1 - \frac{\theta^2}{4\omega_x^2} - \frac{(M_0 - \frac{1}{2}M_t)^2}{M_*^2}\right] U_0 - \frac{\theta^2}{4\omega_x^2}\left[\kappa + \frac{(M_0 - \frac{1}{2}M_t)^2 I_1}{(GJ_d)^2(1-\gamma)^2}\right] U_0^3 = 0 .$$

Hence, together with the trivial solution $U_0 = 0$,

$$U_0 = \frac{1}{\sqrt{\kappa_1}}\sqrt{\left(\frac{\theta_*}{\theta}\right)^2 - 1} . \tag{19.38}$$

In contrast to formula (19.36), here

$$\kappa_1 = \kappa + \frac{(M_0 - \frac{1}{2}M_t)^2 I_1}{(GJ_d)^2(1-\gamma)^2} . \tag{19.39}$$

The second component in (19.39) will now be transformed. Recalling that

$$\gamma = \frac{\omega_x^2}{\omega_\varphi^2} = \frac{\pi^2 r^2}{l^2}\frac{EJ_y}{GJ_d} , \qquad \text{M}_* = \frac{\pi}{l}\sqrt{EJ_y GJ_d} ,$$

and combining these formulas leads to

$$(GJ_d)^2 = \frac{M_*^2}{\gamma} r^2 .$$

Then

$$\kappa_1 = \kappa + \frac{(M_0 - \frac{1}{2}M_t)^2}{M_*^2}\frac{\gamma I_1}{(1-\gamma)^2 r^2} . \tag{19.40}$$

For a rectangular strip, $I_1 = 0.736$, $\kappa = 6.57/l^2$, $\gamma = 0.55\, h^2/l^2 \ll 1$, and $r = 0.29h$. Substitution into Eq. (19.40) gives

$$\kappa_1 \approx \kappa\left[1 + \frac{(M_0 - \frac{1}{2}M_t)^2}{M_*^2}\right].$$

Thus for $M/M_* = 0.3$ the influence of the vertical inertial load on the amplitudes of the vibrations scarcely exceeds 4 percent.

§ 88. The Interaction of Forced and Parametrically Excited Vibrations

●1. The approximate solution derived above did not take into account the interaction of the forced vertical vibrations with the parametrically excited (bending-torsion) vibrations. For a section with two axes of symmetry, a simultaneous consideration of the two types of vibrations leads to the equations

$$\begin{aligned} EJ_x\frac{\partial^4 v}{\partial z^4} + \frac{\partial}{\partial z}\left(N_z\frac{\partial v}{\partial z}\right) + \frac{\partial^2}{\partial z^2}(M_y\varphi) + m\frac{\partial^2 v}{\partial t^2} &= q(z, t)\,, \\ EJ_y\frac{\partial^4 u}{\partial z^4} + \frac{\partial}{\partial z}\left(N_z\frac{\partial u}{\partial z}\right) + \frac{\partial^2}{\partial z^2}(M_x\varphi) + m\frac{\partial^2 u}{\partial t^2} &= 0\,, \\ EJ_\omega\frac{\partial^4 \varphi}{\partial z^4} - GJ_d\frac{\partial^2 \varphi}{\partial z^2} + M_x\frac{\partial^2 u}{\partial z^2} + M_y\frac{\partial^2 v}{\partial z^2} & \\ + r^2\left(N_z\frac{\partial \varphi}{\partial z}\right) + qe\varphi + mr^2\frac{\partial^2 \varphi}{\partial t^2} &= 0\,. \end{aligned} \tag{19.41}$$

Here

$$\begin{aligned} M_x &= EJ_x\frac{\partial^2 v}{\partial z^2}\,, \\ M_y &= EJ_y\left(\frac{\partial^2 u}{\partial z^2} + \frac{\partial^2 v}{\partial z^2}\varphi\right), \end{aligned} \tag{19.42}$$

and, if the longitudinal vibrations of the system are not taken into account,

$$N_z = -\frac{m}{2}\frac{\partial^2}{\partial t^2}\int_z^l\left[\left(\frac{\partial u}{\partial \zeta}\right)^2 + \left(\frac{\partial v}{\partial \zeta}\right)^2\right]d\zeta\,. \tag{19.43}$$

To clarify the distinguishing peculiarities of the problem, we will simplify its statement considerably. Assume that the weightless beam with bending rigidities $EJ_x \gg EJ_y$ and torsional rigidity GJ_d carries on its end a concentrated mass M with a moment of inertia MR^2 (Fig. 139). We let v and u denote the vertical and horizontal displacements of the end of the beam, respectively, and φ the angle of twist of the cross section.

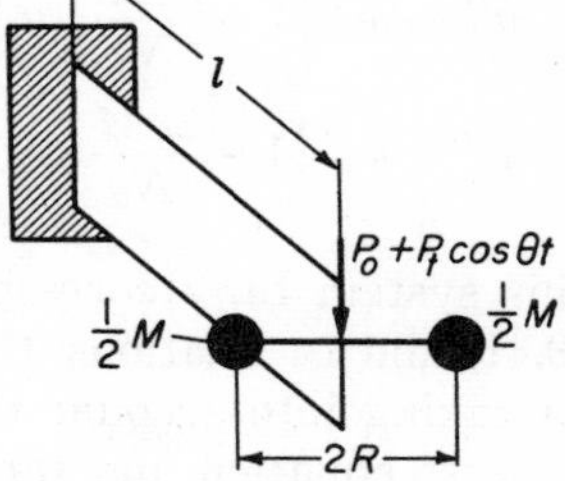

FIG. 139.

The individual frequencies will be introduced as

$$\omega_x^2 = \frac{3EJ_y}{Ml^3}\,, \quad \omega_y^2 = \frac{3EJ_x}{Ml^3}\,, \quad \omega_\varphi^2 = \frac{GJ_d}{MR^2 l}\,,$$

and the individual critical forces as

$$N_x = \frac{\pi^2 EJ_y}{l^2}, \qquad N_\varphi = \frac{GJ_d}{r^2}.$$

The equations for bending-torsional vibrations assume the form

$$\begin{aligned} u'' + \omega_x^2\left(1 - \frac{N}{N_x}\right)u - \omega_x^2\frac{Q}{a_{12}}\varphi &= 0, \\ \varphi'' + \omega_\varphi^2\left(1 - \frac{N}{N_\varphi}\right)\varphi - \omega_\varphi^2\frac{Q}{a_{21}}u &= 0, \end{aligned} \tag{19.44}$$

where N is the axial force, Q is the shear force at any cross section of the beam, and the product of the matrix elements $a_{12}a_{21} = P_*^2$ (P_* is the critical value of parameter Q). It is evident that for the given problem

$$Q = \frac{3EJ_x}{l^3}v, \qquad N = -Mw'', \tag{19.45}$$

where $w = k(u^2 + v^2)$ is the longitudinal displacement of the end of the beam, and k is a coefficient.

The third equation relating u, v, and φ can be obtained from a consideration of the vertical vibrations of the load:

$$Q = P_0 + P_t \cos\theta t - Mv_1''. \tag{19.46}$$

Here v_1 is the total vertical displacement, i.e., determined with bending-torsional deformations taken into account,

$$v_1 = v + k_1 u\varphi. \tag{19.47}$$

Coefficient k_1 is calculated from formula (17.27),

$$k_1 = \int_0^l \int_0^z u''(\zeta)\varphi(\zeta)dz\,d\zeta,$$

where $u(z)$ and $\varphi(z)$ are deflection forms of a beam which satisfy the condition $u(l) = \varphi(l) = 1$. Substituting (19.45) and (19.47) into (19.44) and (19.46) yields a system of equations:

$$\begin{aligned} v'' + \omega_y^2 v + k_1(u''\varphi + 2u'\varphi' u\varphi'') &= \frac{1}{M}(P_0 + P_t\cos\theta t), \\ u'' + \omega_x^2\left\{1 - \frac{2kM}{N_x}[(u')^2 + (v')^2 + uu'' + vv'']\right\}u - \frac{\omega_x^2\omega_y^2 M}{a_{12}}v\varphi &= 0, \\ \varphi'' + \omega_\varphi^2\left\{1 - \frac{2kM}{N_\varphi}[(u')^2 + (v')^2 + uu'' + vv'']\right\}\varphi - \frac{\omega_\varphi^2\omega_y^2 M}{a_{21}}uv &= 0. \end{aligned} \tag{19.48}$$

This system fully corresponds to the system of partial differential equations (19.41) and to relations (19.42) and (19.43). Equations (19.48) differ only in not taking into account the distributed mass of the beam. Omitting v'' in the first equation and terms with v' and v'' in the second and third equations, and eliminating v from the last two equations, gives a system which coincides with (19.30) to within the constant coefficients. The agreement becomes even more pronounced if we return to the previous notation:

$$\frac{kM\omega_x^2}{N_x} = \frac{R^2}{r^2}\frac{kM\omega_\varphi^2}{N_\varphi} = \kappa\,,$$

$$\frac{k_1M\omega_x^2}{a_{12}} = \frac{R^2k_1M\omega_\varphi^2}{a_{21}} = I_1\,.$$

●2. The following periodic solution will now be sought:

$$v = V_0 + V_t \cos\theta t + \cdots\,,$$

$$u = U\sin\frac{\theta t}{2} + \cdots\,, \qquad \varphi = \Phi\sin\frac{\theta t}{2} + \cdots\,, \tag{19.49}$$

(terms containing higher harmonics are left out). Expressions (19.49) are now substituted into (19.48). Equating the coefficients of I and $\cos\theta t$ in the first equation and the coefficients of $\sin\theta t/2$ in the other two gives a system of algebraic equations:

$$\omega_y^2 V_0 = \frac{P_0}{M}\,,$$

$$(\omega_y^2 - \theta^2)V_t + \frac{I_1\theta^2}{2}U\Phi = \frac{P_t}{M}\,,$$

$$(\omega_x^2 - \tfrac{1}{4}\theta^2)U - \tfrac{1}{4}\kappa\theta^2U^3 - \kappa\theta^2V_0V_tU - \frac{M\omega_y^2}{a_{12}}\omega_x^2\Phi(V_0 - \tfrac{1}{2}V_t) = 0\,,$$

$$(\omega_\varphi^2 - \tfrac{1}{4}\theta^2)\Phi - \tfrac{1}{4}\kappa\theta^2U^2\Phi - \kappa\theta^2\frac{r^2}{R^2}V_0V_t\Phi - \frac{M\omega_y^2\omega_\varphi^2U}{a_{21}}(V_0 - \tfrac{1}{2}V_t) = 0\,.$$

With the help of the first two equations, V_0 and V_t can easily be eliminated from the latter. Neglecting the terms of a still higher order gives

$$\left(1 - \frac{\theta^2}{4\omega_x^2}\right)U - \frac{1}{a_{12}}\left[P_0 - \frac{P_t}{2\left(1 - \dfrac{\theta^2}{\omega_y^2}\right)}\right]\Phi - \frac{\kappa\theta^2}{4\omega_x^2}U^3 - \frac{I_1\dfrac{\theta^2}{\omega_x^2}}{1 - \dfrac{\theta^2}{\omega_y^2}}U\Phi^2 = 0\,,$$

$$\left(1 - \frac{\theta^2}{4\omega_\varphi^2}\right)\Phi - \frac{1}{a_{21}}\left[P_0 - \frac{P_t}{2\left(1 - \dfrac{\theta^2}{\omega_y^2}\right)}\right]U - \frac{\kappa\theta^2r^2}{4\omega_\varphi^2R^2}U^2\Phi - \frac{I_1}{R^2}\frac{\dfrac{\theta^2}{\omega_\varphi^2}}{1 - \dfrac{\theta^2}{\omega_y^2}}U^2\Phi = 0\,.$$

Now we denote

$$\frac{\theta^2}{4\omega_x^2} = n^2\,, \qquad \frac{\theta^2}{4\omega_\varphi^2} = \frac{\omega_x^2}{\omega_\varphi^2}n^2 = \gamma n^2\,, \qquad \frac{\theta^2}{\omega_y^2} = \frac{4\omega_x^2}{\omega_y^2}n^2 = \beta n^2\,, \tag{19.50}$$

so that the system assumes the form

$$(1 - n^2)U + \frac{P_0 - \dfrac{1}{1 - \beta n^2}P_t}{a_{12}}\Phi - \kappa n^2U^3 - \frac{I_1n^2U\Phi^2}{1 - \beta n^2} = 0\,,$$

$$(1 - \gamma n^2)\Phi + \frac{P_0 - \dfrac{1}{1 - \beta n^2}P_t}{a_{21}}U - \kappa\gamma n^2\frac{r^2U^2}{R^2}\Phi - \frac{I_1\gamma n^2}{R^2}\frac{U^2\Phi}{1 - \beta n^2} = 0\,. \tag{19.51}$$

If the solution is sought in a form

$$v = V_0 + V_t \cos \theta t + \cdots ,$$

$$u = U \cos \frac{\theta t}{2} + \cdots , \qquad \varphi = \Phi \sin \frac{\theta t}{2} + \cdots ,$$

then the system of equations will differ from (19.51) only by the signs in front of $\frac{1}{2}P_t$. Both systems will be combined by writing $\pm$ in front of $\frac{1}{2}P_t$. In the case $\beta = 0$, $r = R$, the system of Eqs. (19.51) is transformed into (19.34).

● 3. Let us first consider a linear approximation:

$$(1 - n^2)U + \frac{P_0(1 - \beta n^2) \pm \frac{1}{2}P_t}{a_{12}(1 - \beta n^2)} \Phi = 0 ,$$

$$(1 - \gamma n^2)\Phi + \frac{P_0(1 - \beta n^2) \pm \frac{1}{2}P_t}{a_{21}(1 - \beta n^2)} U = 0 .$$

Equating the determinant of the coefficients of the system to zero gives equations for the critical frequencies:

$$\begin{vmatrix} 1 - n^2 & -\dfrac{P_0(1 - \beta n^2) \pm \frac{1}{2}P_t}{a_{12}(1 - \beta n^2)} \\ -\dfrac{P_0(1 - \beta n^2) \pm \frac{1}{2}P_t}{a_{21}(1 - \beta n^2)} & 1 - \gamma n^2 \end{vmatrix} = 0 ,$$

or, expanding the above,

$$(1 - n^2)(1 - \beta n^2)^2(1 - \gamma n^2) + \frac{[P_0(1 - \beta n^2) \pm \frac{1}{2}P_t]^2}{P_*^{\,2}} = 0 , \qquad (19.52)$$

where $P_*^{\,2} = a_{12}a_{21}$.

Equation (19.52) gives three regions of dynamic instability (near $n = 1$, $n = 1/\beta$, and $n = 1/\gamma$, i.e., recalling notation (19.50), near $\theta = 2\omega_x$, $\theta = 2\omega_\varphi$, and $\theta = \omega_y$). The character of the distribution of the regions is shown in Figure 140. If $\beta \ll 1$, then the influence of forced vibrations on the boundaries of the principal region ($n = 1$) is very small. An approximate formula can easily be obtained,

$$n_*^{\,2} \approx \frac{[P_0(1 - \beta) \pm \frac{1}{2}P_t]^2}{P_*^{\,2}(1 - \beta)^2(1 - \gamma)} .$$

Let us return now to the nonlinear equations (19.51). In the preceding section (§87), it was shown that the influence of additional vertical inertia forces on the amplitudes of vibrations remains insignificant under sufficiently wide conditions. This influence is taken into account in Eqs. (19.51) by the last terms. The significance of these terms increases as n^2 approaches $1/\beta$; consequently, the assumption that these terms are small is valid only for frequencies which are not near the resonance frequency of the forced vibrations. Assuming that $n^2 \ll 1/\beta$, an approximate equation is obtained from (19.51):

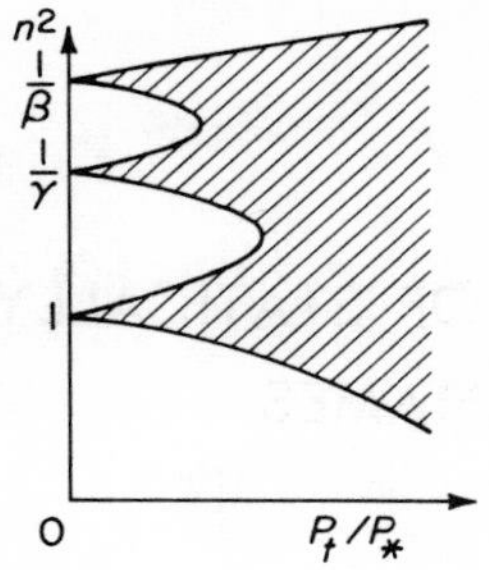

FIG. 140.

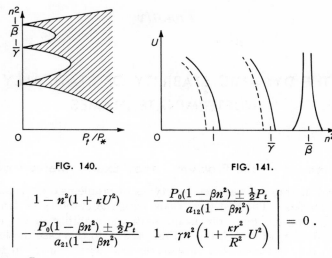

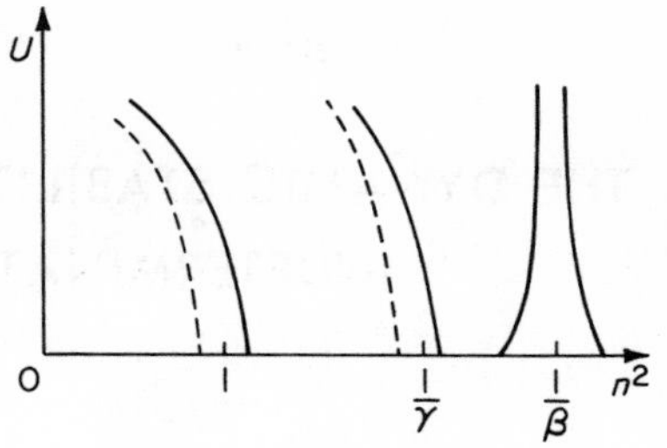

FIG. 141.

$$\begin{vmatrix} 1 - n^2(1 + \kappa U^2) & -\dfrac{P_0(1 - \beta n^2) \pm \frac{1}{2}P_t}{a_{12}(1 - \beta n^2)} \\ -\dfrac{P_0(1 - \beta n^2) \pm \frac{1}{2}P_t}{a_{21}(1 - \beta n^2)} & 1 - \gamma n^2\left(1 + \dfrac{\kappa r^2}{R^2} U^2\right) \end{vmatrix} = 0 .$$

Hence, for $r = R$,

$$(1 - n^2 x)(1 - \gamma n^2 x) = \frac{[P_0(1 - \beta n^2) \pm \frac{1}{2}P_t]^2}{P_*^{\,2}(1 - \beta n^2)^2} ,$$

where

$$x = 1 + \kappa U^2 .$$

A characteristic example of the variation of U is shown in Figure 141.

We note that the finite amplitudes for $n^2 = 1/\beta$ can be obtained if the vertical nonlinear inertia force is considered. If this is taken into account, then the resonance curve for $n^2 = 1$ acquires a slope in the direction of increasing frequencies (see Fig. 68).

Twenty

THE DYNAMIC STABILITY OF STATICALLY INDETERMINATE FRAMES

§ 89. Statement of the Problem. The "Exact" Method of Solution

●1. We will distinguish between two types of problems concerning the static stability of frames. The first type deals with the stability of frames loaded only at the joints, or, more precisely, with the stability of the undeformed state of equilibrium of such frames (Fig. 142 a). In this case the forces acting at the nodes play the role of a parametric load with respect to the bending deformations of the frame. To the second type belong problems of the stability of the symmetrical form of bending of symmetric and symmetrically loaded frames (Fig. 142 b). Here the external load is a parametric load with respect to the antisymmetric deformations.

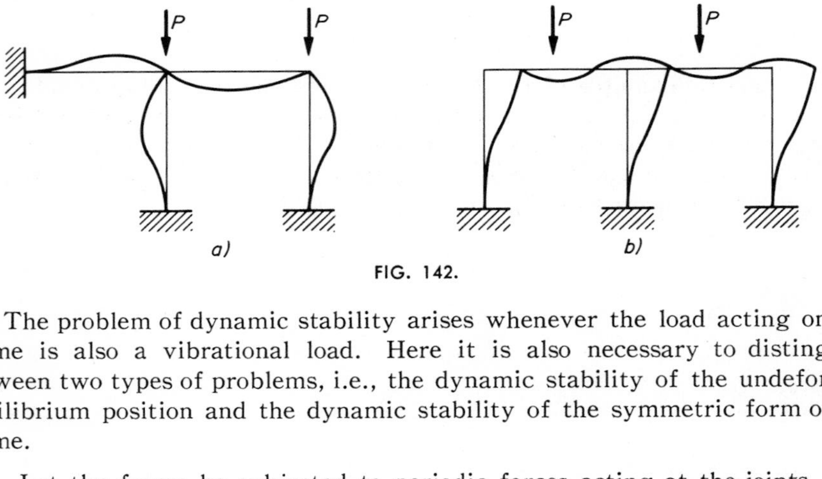

FIG. 142.

The problem of dynamic stability arises whenever the load acting on the frame is also a vibrational load. Here it is also necessary to distinguish between two types of problems, i.e., the dynamic stability of the undeformed equilibrium position and the dynamic stability of the symmetric form of the frame.

●2. Let the frame be subjected to periodic forces acting at the joints. Assume that the frequencies of all the forces are the same. The differential equations of motion for each rod in the frame have the form

$$EJ_i \frac{\partial^4 v_i}{\partial s^4} + (\alpha N_{0i} + \beta N_{ti} \cos \theta t) \frac{\partial^2 v_i}{\partial s^2} + m_i \frac{\partial^2 v_i}{\partial t^2} = 0\,, \quad (i = 1, 2, \cdots, p)\,, \qquad (20.1)$$

where the following notation is used: $v_i(s, t)$ is the transverse deflection of the ith rod, EJ_i and m_i are its rigidity and mass per unit length, respectively,

$\alpha N_{0i} + \beta N_{ti} \cos \theta t$ is the dynamic longitudinal force arising in the rod, and α and β are open parameters of the constant and periodic components of the external load. The total number of equations p is equal to the number of elements in the frame. The solutions of Eqs. (20.1) must satisfy geometric and dynamic boundary conditions.

It is essential that the problem be reduced to differential equations with periodic coefficients. As is well known, periodic solutions with periods $2\pi/\theta$ and $4\pi/\theta$ correspond to the boundaries of the instability regions for these equations. Let us consider one of the differential equations, (20.1) for convenience omitting the subscripts:

$$EJ\frac{\partial^4 v}{\partial s^4} + (\alpha N_0 + \beta N_t \cos \theta t)\frac{\partial^2 v}{\partial s^2} + m\frac{\partial^2 v}{\partial t^2} = 0 . \tag{20.2}$$

The periodic solution with period $4\pi/\theta$ is sought in the form of a series:

$$v(s,\ t) = \sum_{k=1,3,5}^{\infty} X_k(s) \sin \frac{k\theta t}{2}, \tag{20.3}$$

or

$$v(s,\ t) = \sum_{k=1\ 3\ 5}^{\infty} \Xi_k(s) \cos \frac{k\theta t}{2}. \tag{20.4}$$

In (20.3) and (20.4), $X_k(s)$ and $\Xi_k(s)$ are as yet unknown functions. If series (20.3) is substituted into Eq. (20.2), then the following system of equations is obtained:

$$\begin{gathered} EJ\frac{d^4 X_1}{ds^4} + (\alpha N_0 - \tfrac{1}{2}\beta N_t)\frac{d^2 X_1}{ds^2} - \tfrac{1}{4}m\theta^2 X_1 + \tfrac{1}{2}\beta N_t \frac{d^2 X_3}{ds^2} = 0 , \\ EJ\frac{d^4 X_k}{ds^4} + \alpha N_0 \frac{d^2 X_k}{ds^2} - \tfrac{1}{4}mk^2\theta^2 X_k + \tfrac{1}{4}\beta N_t \left(\frac{d^2 X_{k-2}}{ds^2} + \frac{d^2 X_{k+2}}{ds^2}\right) = 0 , \\ (k = 3,\ 5,\ \cdots) . \end{gathered} \tag{20.5}$$

Similarly, substituting series (20.4) leads to

$$\begin{gathered} EJ\frac{d^4 \Xi_1}{ds^4} + (\alpha N_0 + \tfrac{1}{2}\beta N_t)\frac{d^2 \Xi_1}{ds^2} - \tfrac{1}{4}m\theta^2 \Xi_1 + \tfrac{1}{2}\beta N_t \frac{d^2 \Xi_3}{ds^2} = 0 , \\ EJ\frac{d^4 \Xi_k}{ds^4} + \alpha N_0 \frac{d^2 \Xi_k}{ds^2} - \tfrac{1}{4}mk^2\theta^2 \Xi_k + \tfrac{1}{2}\beta N_t \left(\frac{d^2 \Xi_{k-2}}{ds^2} + \frac{d^2 \Xi_{k+2}}{ds^2}\right) = 0 \\ (k = 3,\ 5,\ \cdots) . \end{gathered} \tag{20.6}$$

In what follows it will be assumed that the number of terms in the series (20.3) and (20.4) is limited and equal to n. The general solution of system (20.5) has the form

$$X_i(s) = \sum_{k=1}^{4n} C_{ik}e^{\rho_k s}, \qquad (i = 1,\ 3,\ \cdots,\ 2n-1) ,$$

where C_{ik} are constants of integration and ρ_k are the roots of the characteristic equation

$$\begin{vmatrix} EJ\rho^4 + (\alpha N_0 - \tfrac{1}{2}\beta N_t)\rho^2 - \tfrac{1}{4}m\theta^2 & \tfrac{1}{2}\beta N_t \rho^2 & 0 & \cdots \\ \tfrac{1}{2}\beta N_t \rho^2 & EJ\rho^4 + \alpha N_0 \rho^2 - \tfrac{9}{4}m\theta^2 & \tfrac{1}{2}\beta N_t \rho^2 & \cdots \\ 0 & \tfrac{1}{2}\beta N_t \rho^2 & EJ\rho^4 + \alpha N_0 - \tfrac{25}{4}m\theta^2 & \cdots \\ \cdots & \cdots & \cdots & \cdots \end{vmatrix} = 0 . \tag{20.7}$$

The general solution of the system (20.6) has the form

$$\Xi_i(s) = \sum_{k=1}^{4n} D_{ik} e^{\sigma_i s}, \qquad (i = 1, 3, \cdots, 2n-1),$$

and the corresponding characteristic equation differs from (20.7) only by the sign in front of $\frac{1}{2}\beta$ in the first element of the main diagonal.

When Eq. (20.7) is solved, there remains the task of choosing the constants C_{ik} and D_{ik} in such a way as to satisfy the boundary conditions. For the determination of these constants, we have two systems of homogeneous linear equations. Equating the determinants of these systems to zero gives the desired equations for boundary frequencies. Here it is assumed that all calculations can be carried out in a general form with respect to the excitation frequency θ.

The calculations become somewhat simplified if we proceed according to the displacement method which is well known in structural mechanics. In such a case, the calculations are analogous to but considerably more complex than the calculations of vibrations and the static stability of frames by the displacement method.

If only the principal regions of dynamic instability are of interest, then in series (20.3) and (20.4) only the first terms need be retained:

$$v(s, t) = X(s) \sin \frac{\theta t}{2} \qquad \text{or} \qquad v(s, t) = \Xi(s) \cos \frac{\theta t}{2}.$$

Then the characteristic equation assumes the form

$$EJ\rho^4 + (\alpha N_0 \pm \tfrac{1}{2}\beta N_t)\rho^2 - \tfrac{1}{4}m\theta^2 = 0,$$

and determination of the boundary frequencies reduces to finding the natural frequencies for the frames that are loaded by external static load with parameters α, $\frac{1}{2}\beta$ and α, $-\frac{1}{2}\beta$.

●**3.** The method described can be called "exact" since the differential equations (20.1) are satisfied for every harmonic. The method, based on the expansion of the forms of vibrations in a series of "suitable" eigenfunctions, is designated, in contrast to the "exact" method, as an approximation method. As applied to frames, however, the efficiency of the second method is low. In a number of cases one can obtain the first two or three eigenfunctions by loading the frame in a definite, predetermined manner and constructing complete deformation diagrams. The energy method for determining the natural frequencies is based, in part, on such a procedure of assigning the coordinate functions. The calculations, however, are very difficult, particularly for multiple statically indeterminate frames, and are insufficiently reliable in view of the arbitrariness in the choice of acting forces.

In what follows, an approximate method for solving vibration and stability problems of frames is presented which, since it is based on an approximation of vibrational forms of the frame with the aid of certain functions, enables us to avoid the determination of displacements in the statically indeterminate system. Consider first the problem concerning the vibrations of frames; such a calculation is of special interest in itself independently of the stability problem.[1]

§ 90. An Approximation Method for Designing Frames for Vibrations

●1. To establish the means of designating the coordinates of the points s of the frame, we introduce a function $v(s)$ which denotes the displacement of each point in the direction perpendicular to the axis of a given element (the transverse deflection of the elements of the frame). The deformed state of the frame is determined if, in addition to function $v(s)$, the longitudinal displacement[2] u_j of each element of the frame is known.

Having chosen some suitable system of coordinate functions $\varphi_1(s)$, $\varphi_2(s)$, $\cdots$, $\varphi_n(s)$, we will seek expressions for the dynamic deflections of the frame in the form

$$v(s, t) = \sum_{k=1}^{n} z_k(t)\,\varphi_k(s)\,. \tag{20.8}$$

where $z_k(t)$ are the "generalized coordinates." Accordingly, the longitudinal displacement of the jth rod of the frame can be represented as

$$u_j(t) = \sum_{k=1}^{n} z_k(t)\,\chi_{jk}\,. \tag{20.9}$$

Here χ_{jk} is the displacement of the jth rod due to $z_k = 1$.

Let us now construct the Lagrange equations for the problem under consideration:

$$\frac{d}{dt}\left(\frac{\partial T}{\partial \dot{z}_j}\right) + \frac{\partial}{\partial z_i}(U - T) = Q_i\,, \qquad (i = 1,\, 2,\, \cdots,\, n)\,, \tag{20.10}$$

where T and U are the kinetic and potential energies of system, respectively, and Q_i are the generalized forces.

The kinetic energy of the frame can be determined from the formula

$$T = \tfrac{1}{2}\int m(s)\left(\sum_{k=1}^{n} \frac{dz_k}{dt}\,\varphi_k\right)^2 ds + \tfrac{1}{2}\sum_j M_j\left(\sum_{k=1}^{n} \frac{dz_k}{dt}\,\chi_{jk}\right)^2;$$

where $m(s)$ represents the mass per unit length of an element of the frame, and M_j represents the total mass of the jth element. Integration and summation extends over all rods of the frame.

The potential energy due to bending is

$$U = \tfrac{1}{2}\int EJ(s)\left(\sum_{k=1}^{n} z_k\frac{d^2\varphi_k}{ds^2}\right)^2 ds\,,$$

where EJ is the bending stiffness.

Finally, the work of the external load is

[1] Bolotin [12].

[2] We confine ourselves to the usual assumption that the longitudinal deformation of the rod is negligibly small.

$$V = \int q(s, t) \sum_{k=1}^{n} z_k \varphi_k(s)\, ds + \sum_j P_j \sum_{k=1}^{n} z_k \chi_{jk} .$$

Here $q(s, t)$ is a linear transverse load, and P_j is a projection of the resultant of all the forces acting on the jth element in the direction of its length.

Constructing a derivative $\partial V/\partial z_i$ gives the following expression for the generalized force:

$$Q_i = \int q(s, t)\, \varphi_i(s)\, ds + \sum_j P_j \chi_{ji} . \tag{20.11}$$

Substituting the expressions obtained into Eq. (20.10) gives

$$\sum_{k=1}^{n} \frac{d^2 z_k}{dt^2} \left[\int m(s)\, \varphi_i \varphi_k\, ds + \sum_j M_j \chi_{ji} \chi_{jk} \right] + \sum_{k=1}^{n} z_k \int EJ(s) \frac{d^2\varphi_i}{ds^2} \frac{d^2\varphi_k}{ds^2}\, ds = Q_i ,$$

$$(i = 1, 2, \cdots, n) .$$

In what follows these equations will be expressed as

$$\sum_{k=1}^{n} f_{ik} z_k'' + \sum_{k=1}^{n} r_{ik} z_k = Q_i , \qquad (i = 1, 2, \cdots, n) , \tag{20.12}$$

where, for brevity, the notation is introduced

$$\begin{aligned} f_{ik} &= \int m(s) \varphi_i \varphi_k\, ds + \sum_j M_j \chi_{ji} \chi_{jk} , \\ r_{ik} &= \int EJ(s) \frac{d^2\varphi_i}{ds^2} \frac{d^2\varphi_k}{ds^2}\, ds . \end{aligned} \tag{20.13}$$

The primes in (20.12) denote differentiation with respect to time.

Although in deriving Eqs. (20.12) the mass $m(s)$ and load $q(s, t)$ were considered to be distributed over the length, these equations are valid also for the case of concentrated masses (forces). It is necessary then to interpret the integrals in formulas (20.11) and (20.13) in the Stieltjes sense.

In the problem concerning free vibrations ($Q_i \equiv 0$), a substitution

$$z_k = Z_k \sin (\omega t + \lambda)$$

leads to the equation for natural frequencies

$$| \boldsymbol{F} - \omega^2 \boldsymbol{R} | = 0 . \tag{20.14}$$

Here $\boldsymbol{F}$ and $\boldsymbol{R}$ are matrices with elements f_{ik} and r_{ik}, respectively.

In the case of forced vibrations, one may assume, without restricting the generality of the results, that the frequencies for all forces are the same. The solution of a nonhomogeneous system

$$\sum_{k=1}^{n} f_{ik} z_k'' \sum_{k=1}^{n} r_{ik} z_k = \bar{Q}_i \cos \theta t , \qquad (i = 1, 2, \cdots, n) ,$$

has the form

$$z_k = Z_k \cos \theta t .$$

As a result, we arrive at a system of equations

$$\sum_{k=1}^{n} (r_{ik} - \theta^2 f_{ik}) Z_k = \bar{Q}_i , \qquad (i = 1, 2, \cdots, n) , \tag{20.15}$$

from which we can find the amplitudes Z_k of the forced vibrations.

●2. We proceed now to the fundamental question concerning the choice of coordinate (approximating) functions in the expressions (20.8) and (20.9).

As we have mentioned previously, the coordinate functions are ordinarily taken as static deflection forms of the frame due to the influence of certain forces. These forces are taken in such a way that the deflection forms sufficiently resemble the forms of free (or forced) vibrations of the frame. However, during the choice of the coordinate functions, the construction of the basic equations is preceded by many calculations which are required for the construction of complete deformation diagrams for statically indeterminate systems. The volume of the calculations increases rapidly with the increase in degree of the static (or kinematic) indeterminability of the frame; therefore the range of application of this method is almost limited to simpler problems.

The difficulties connected with the determination of displacements in a statically indeterminate system can be avoided if we take the deflection forms of elements of the frame as coordinate functions. Let n_0 be the number of unknowns in the solution of the problem by the displacement method (degree of kinematic indeterminateness). One can take the static buckling forms of the rods of the frame as the first n_0 coordinate functions. Then corresponding unit influence curves (Fig. 143) can be taken as the first eigenfunctions n_0. The remaining coordinate functions are chosen for $z_1 = z_2 = \cdots = z_{n_0} = 0$, their number being defined by a requirement concerning the exactness of calculations (Fig. 144).

Let us consider the first n_0 equations of the system (20.12), neglecting in it terms with $k > n_0$:

$$\sum_{k=1}^{n_0} f_{ik} z_k'' + \sum_{k=1}^{n_0} r_{ik} z_k = Q_i , \qquad (i = 1, 2, \cdots, n_0) . \tag{20.16}$$

Since

$$\frac{d^2\varphi_i}{ds^2} = \frac{\bar{M}_i}{EJ(s)} ,$$

where $\bar{M}_i$ is the bending moment due to the ith unit force, the coefficients r_{ik} can be represented in the form

$$r_{ik} = \int \frac{\bar{M}_i \bar{M}_k}{EJ(s)} ds .$$

In this way, coefficients r_{ik} for $i, k \leq n_0$ represent the usual unit reactions in the displacement method. Furthermore, on the basis of the reciprocity theorem,

$$\varphi_i(s) = - R_i(s) , \qquad (i = 1, 2, \cdots, n_0) ,$$

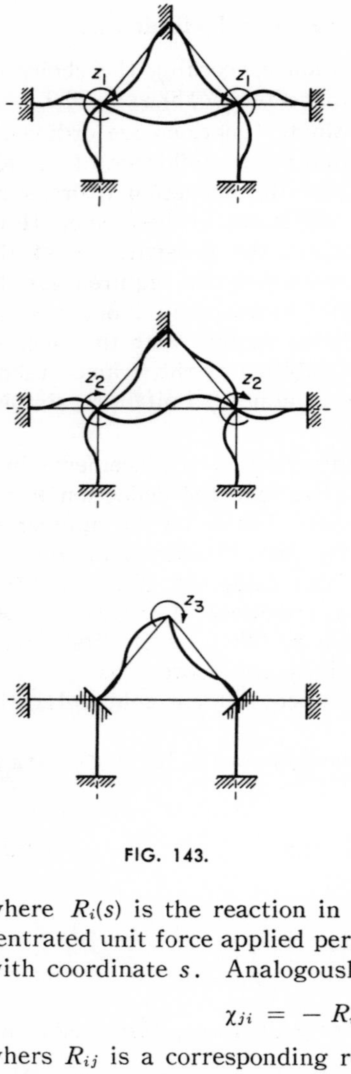

FIG. 143.

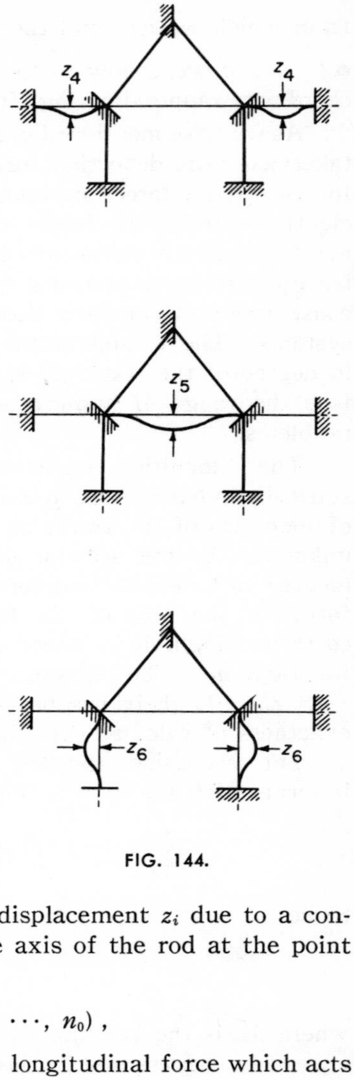

FIG. 144.

where $R_i(s)$ is the reaction in the direction of displacement z_i due to a concentrated unit force applied perpendicular to the axis of the rod at the point with coordinate s. Analogously,

$$\chi_{ji} = -R_{ij}, \qquad (i = 1, 2, \cdots, n_0),$$

whers R_{ij} is a corresponding reaction to a unit longitudinal force which acts on the jth bar.

Using these relations allows transforming the formula (20.13) for the coefficients f_{ik} to the following:

$$f_{ik} = -\int R_i(s)\, m(s)\, \varphi_k\, ds - \sum_j R_{ij} M_j \chi_{jk}.$$

In this way, the expressions of the type $f_{ik} z_k''$ $(i \leq n_0)$ represent the reactions to the inertia forces acting in the direction of the corresponding unknowns, which arise due to displacement z_k.

Finally, the generalized force (20.11) can be represented as

$$Q_i = -\int R_i(s)\, q(s, t)\, ds - \sum_j R_{ij}P_j, \qquad (i \le n_0).$$

Consequently, it can be interpreted as a generalized reaction load (with the opposite sign).

Thus, Eqs. (20.16) are essentially equations of the displacement method; it is assumed in constructing these equations that the forms of the dynamic deflections of the rods of the frame coincide with the forms of the static deflections due to corresponding loading. Therefore, for $n = n_0$ the equation for natural frequencies (20.14) and the equations for forced vibrations (20.15) are completely analogous to the equations of the "exact" method, which is also based on the deflection method. In contrast to the equations of the "exact" method, the former do not contain transcendental functions[3]. For $n > n_0$, Eqs. (20.12), (20.14), and (20.15) are no longer analogous to the equations of the "exact" method.

A few comments on the convergence of the method will now be made. The deformed state of a frame is fully defined if, in addition to all the unknowns $z_1, z_2, \cdots, z_{n_0}$ in the displacement method, the deflection of each rod is also given in the basic system of the displacement method. Thus, series (20.8) can be represented in the form

$$v(s, t) = \sum_{k=1}^{n_0} z_k(t)\varphi_k(s) + v_1(s, t).$$

Here $v_1(s, t)$ is the dynamic deflection of each rod in the fundamental system (i.e., rod fixed on both ends, or fixed on one end and simply supported on the other). For this system $\psi_1(s)\ \psi_2(s), \cdots, \psi_i(s), \cdots$ will be taken for the forms of free vibrations of the rod. As is well known, such a system is complete; therefore the arbitrary form of deflection $v_1(s, t)$ can be expanded into the uniformly and absolutely convergent series

$$v_1(s, t) = \sum_{i=1}^{\infty} z_{n_0+i}(t)\psi_i(s),$$

Consequently, if we take in the series (20.8), for $k \le n_0$., the static forms of deflection due to a unit deformation z_k as $\varphi_k(s)$, and for $k > n_0$ the forms of free vibrations of a rod in the fundamental system, we will obtain uniformly and absolutely converging series each time.

In the solution of practical problems, if we are concerned with the determination of the lowest natural frequencies or with the calculation of the lowest-frequency vibrational loading, we can limit ourselves to the "principal portion" of the series (20.8) for $n = n_0$. Peculiarities in the application of this method will be seen from further examples.

[3] These equations can also be obtained directly from the equations of the "exact" method by expanding the transcendental functions into a series and retaining first terms (see Kornoukhov, [1]).

●**3.** In constructing equations for natural frequencies, it is appropriate to consider each element of the determinant (20.14) as an expression for the reaction which results when the inertial forces are taken into account:

$$\tilde{r}_{ik} = r_{ik} - \omega^2 f_{ik}.$$

An analogous expression can also be taken for forced vibrations:

$$\tilde{r}_{ik} = r_{ik} - \theta^2 f_{ik}.$$

These quantities will be called *dynamic reactions*. As can be seen from (20.13), they are symmetric, i.e., $\tilde{r}_{ik} = \tilde{r}_{ki}$.

However, in calculating the dynamic reactions it is not always necessary to calculate integrals of the type (20.13). It is sufficient to determine these reactions for the simpler elements of the basic system (i.e., rods fixed on both ends, or fixed on one end and pinned on the other end). Further calculations reduce to a simpler summation of reactions in accordance with the usual procedure of the displacement method.

TABLE I.

Displacement	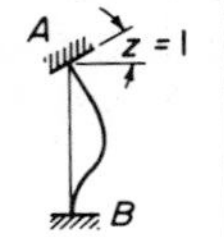	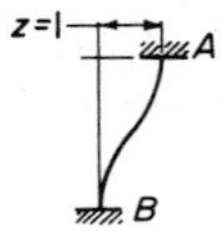	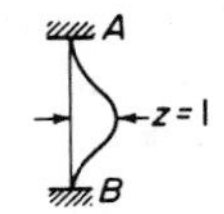		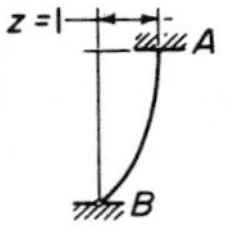	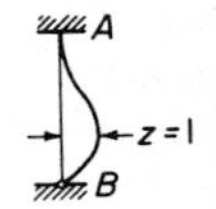
Moment	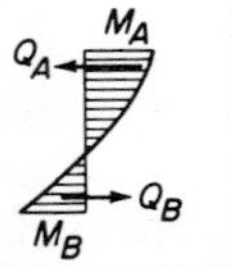	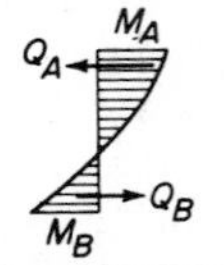	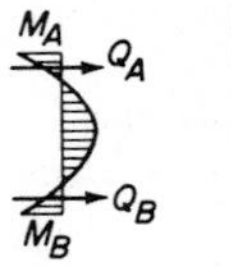	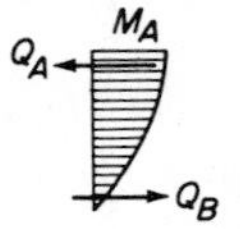	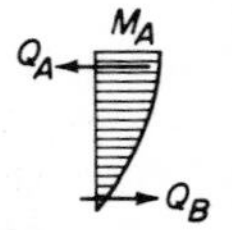	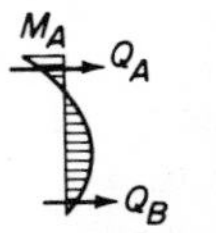
M_A	$\frac{4EJ}{l} - \frac{m\omega^2 l^3}{105}$	$\frac{6EJ}{l^2} - \frac{11m\omega^2 l^2}{210}$	$-\frac{2}{35}m\omega^2 l^2$	$\frac{3EJ}{l} - \frac{2m\omega^2 l^3}{105}$	$\frac{3EJ}{l^2} - \frac{3m\omega^2 l^2}{35}$	$-\frac{19}{210}m\omega^2 l^2$
M_B	$\frac{2EJ}{l} + \frac{m\omega^2 l^3}{140}$	$\frac{6EJ}{l^2} + \frac{13m\omega^2 l^2}{420}$	$-\frac{2}{35}m\omega^2 l^2$	0	0	0
Q_A	$\frac{6EJ}{l^2} - \frac{11m\omega^2 l^2}{210}$	$\frac{12EJ}{l^3} - \frac{13m\omega^2 l}{35}$	$-\frac{4}{15}m\omega^2 l$	$\frac{3EJ}{l^2} - \frac{3m\omega^2 l^2}{35}$	$\frac{3EJ}{l^3} - \frac{17m\omega^2 l}{35}$	$-\frac{5}{14}m\omega^2 l$
Q_B	$\frac{6EJ}{l^2} + \frac{13m\omega^2 l^2}{420}$	$\frac{12EJ}{l^3} + \frac{9m\omega^2 l}{70}$	$-\frac{4}{15}m\omega^2 l$	$\frac{3EJ}{l^2} + \frac{11m\omega^2 l^2}{280}$	$\frac{3EJ}{l^3} + \frac{39m\omega^2 l}{280}$	$-\frac{27}{70}m\omega^2 l$
$\tilde{r}_{ik}$	$-\frac{2}{35}m\omega^2 l^2$	$-\frac{4}{15}m\omega^2 l$	$\frac{1024EJ}{5l^3} - \frac{128m\omega^2 l}{315}$	$-\frac{19}{210}m\omega^2 l^2$	$-\frac{5}{14}m\omega^2 l$	$\frac{576EJ}{5l^3} - \frac{152m\omega^2 l}{315}$

The necessary data are given in Table I. For $i \leq n_0$, the deflection forms of rods resulting from a unit displacement are taken as the eigenfunctions $\varphi_i(s)$; and for $i > n_0$, the deflection forms resulting from uniformly distributed transverse loads are taken as the eigenfunctions. The mass and the rigidity along the length of each rod are assumed to be constant.

We will now illustrate the procedure for constructing the table by considering an example of a rod which is fixed on both ends. Giving one of the fixed ends a unit rotation and a unit displacement, we determine the static displacements in each case:

$$\varphi(x) = x - 2\frac{x^2}{l} + \frac{x^3}{l^2}, \qquad \psi(x) = 1 - \frac{3x^2}{l^2} + \frac{2x^3}{l^3}. \tag{20.17}$$

In accordance with formula (20.13), the bending moment at the upper fixed end, with inertia loading taken into account, is

$$M_A = EJ\int_0^l \left(\frac{d^2\varphi}{dx^2}\right)^2 dx - m\omega^2 \int_0^l \varphi^2\,dx\,.$$

Accordingly, for the lower fixed end

$$M_B = EJ\int_0^l \frac{d^2\varphi(x)}{dx^2}\,\frac{d^2\varphi(l-x)}{dx^2}\,dx - m\omega^2\int_0^l \varphi(x)\varphi(l-x)\,dx\,.$$

The shear force at the upper fixed end due to unit rotation is

$$Q_A = EJ\int_0^l \frac{d^2\varphi}{dx^2}\,\frac{d^2\psi}{dx^2}\,dx - m\omega^2\int_0^l \varphi\psi\,dx\,,$$

etc. Substituting (20.17) here, we can determine the reactions $\tilde{r}_{ik}$, which are given in Table I. It is necessary to calculate only the second integrals; the first terms are the known unit reactions r_{ik}.

●**4.** Let us consider a numerical example. We will determine the lowest frequency of free vibration of the frame shown in Figure 145. Since the lowest frequency is accompanied by an antisymmetric form of vibrations, the coordinate function is chosen as shown in Figure 146. To simplify the calculations, we have constructed unit load curves. With the aid of Table I, it is found that

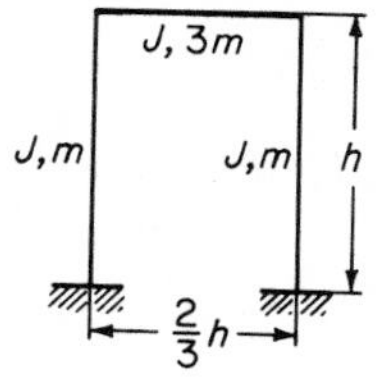

FIG. 145.

$$\tilde{r}_{11} = \frac{26EJ}{h} - \frac{4}{189}m\omega^2h^3.$$

$$\tilde{r}_{12} = \tilde{r}_{21} = -\frac{12EJ}{h^2} + \frac{11}{105}m\omega^2h^2, \qquad \tilde{r}_{22} = \frac{24EJ}{h^3} - \frac{96}{35}m\omega^2h\,.$$

The equation for the natural frequencies (20.14) assumes the form

$$\begin{vmatrix} 26 - 0.021\lambda & -12 + 0.105\lambda \\ -12 + 0.105\lambda & 24 - 2.750\lambda \end{vmatrix} = 0, \quad \text{where } \lambda = \frac{m\omega^2h^4}{EJ}.$$

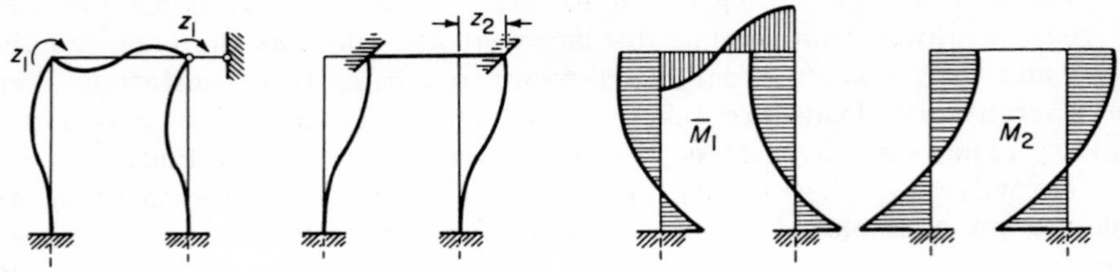

FIG. 146

Expanding the determinant, the following equation results:

$$0.051\,\lambda^2 + 17.73\,\lambda - 120 = 0\,,$$

whose smallest root is $\lambda = 6.90$. Consequently, the lowest natural frequency is

$$\omega = \frac{2.63}{h^2}\sqrt{\frac{EJ}{m}}\,,$$

which practically coincides with the exact expression[4].

However, any conclusion about a high degree of accuracy of the approximate method for $n = n_0$ would be premature. On the contrary, if the frame does not have linear displacement (or if vibrations without linear displacements are being investigated), then n_0 eigenfunctions are not sufficient for a satisfactory description of the deflections. This conclusion will be made obvious by the following example.

Let us determine the second natural frequency for the frame considered above (Fig. 145). The second frequency is accompanied by a symmetric form of vibrations. We will confine ourselves first to one generalized coordinate, i.e., to a symmetric rotation in the nodes (Fig. 147). The dynamic reaction is

$$\tilde{r}_{33} = \frac{14EJ}{h} - \frac{46}{945}\,m\omega^2 h^3\,.$$

Equating it to zero, we find that $\lambda = 288$ and that

$$\omega = \frac{17.00}{h^2}\sqrt{\frac{EJ}{m}}\,;$$

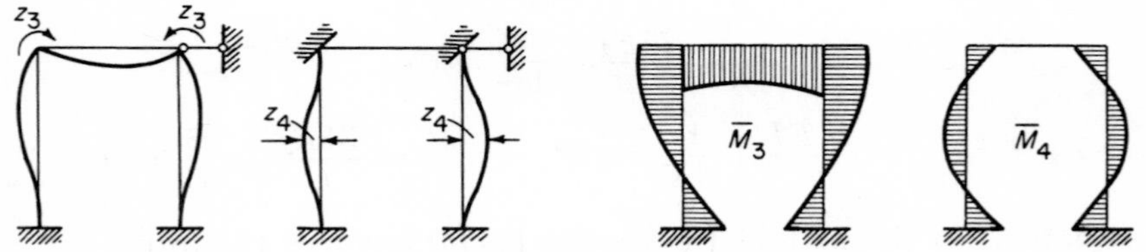

FIG. 147

[4] See Hohenemser and Prager [1].

this expression differs by 19 percent from the exact expression[5].

$$\omega = \frac{14.29}{h^2}\sqrt{\frac{EJ}{m}}\,.$$

The explanation for such a large difference is that the static deflection form is not very suitable for representing the symmetric form of vibrations of a frame.

Introducing a function ψ_1 (Fig. 147), we will take into account additional deflection of the columns. With the aid of Table I we find

$$\tilde{r}_{44} = \frac{2048}{5}\frac{EJ}{h^3} - \frac{256}{315}m\omega^2 h\,,$$

$$\tilde{r}_{34} = \tilde{r}_{43} = -\frac{4}{35}m\omega^2 h^2\,.$$

The solution of the equation

$$\begin{vmatrix} 14 - 0.049\,\lambda & -0.114\,\lambda \\ -0.114\,\lambda & 409.6 - 0.82\,\lambda \end{vmatrix} = 0$$

gives $\lambda = 222$, i.e.,

$$\omega = \frac{14.95}{h^2}\sqrt{\frac{EJ}{m}}\,.$$

The difference here is already reduced to 5 percent. If, in addition, the deformation of the crossbar is taken into account, the error will be reduced to 0.8 percent.

●5. Thus the approximate method is very effective in the case of frames in which the nodes undergo displacements, i.e., where the application of the usual methods requires a considerable amount of calculations.

The above example illustrates the approximate method. This method is also applicable to complex frames with elements having variable masses and rigidities along their length, etc. It stands to reason that in the latter case, Table I should be expanded[6].

§ 91. Calculation of The Static Stability of Frames

●1. We will now consider a frame subjected to static load acting at the nodes, which is given with reference to a still undetermined parameter α (Fig. 148). The longitudinal force arising in the elements of the frame will be denoted $\alpha N(s)$. As before, we will seek the solution of the problem in a form of series

$$v(s) = \sum_{k=1}^{n} z_k \varphi_k(s)\,, \tag{20.18}$$

where for $k \leq n_0$, $\varphi_k(s)$ are the deflection forms of

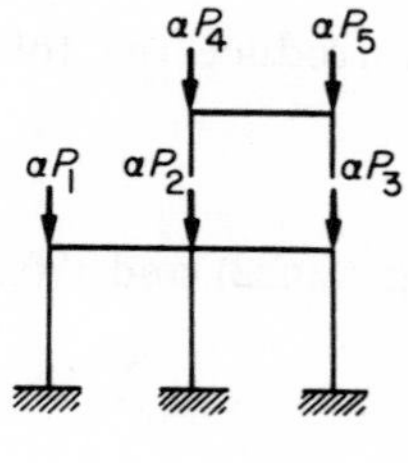

FIG. 148.

[5] See Hohenemser and Prager [1], p. 182.

[6] See Bolotin [12].

the frame due to unit influences in the displacement method, and for $k > n_0$ they are the forms of deflection in the fundamental system of the displacement method due to some definite transverse load; z_k are numbers which have to be determined. For the static case, the Lagrange equations (20.10) assume the form

$$\frac{\partial U}{\partial z_i} = Q_i \,, \qquad (i = 1, 2, 3, \cdots, n) \,,$$

or, expressing them in another form,

$$\sum_{k=1}^{n} z_k r_{ik} = Q_i \,, \qquad (i = 1, 2, 3, \cdots, n) \,, \tag{20.19}$$

where Q_i are generalized forces. Neglecting in formula (20.11) the secondary term (in stability problems they are, with few exceptions, unnecessary), gives

$$Q_i = \int_L q(s)\varphi_i(s)\, ds \,, \tag{20.20}$$

where $q(s)$ is the transverse load per unit length. With the help of shear force $Q(s)$, (20.20) can be represented in the form of the Stieltjes integral:

$$Q_i = \int_L \varphi_i(s)\, dQ(s) \,.$$

Integrating by parts yields

$$Q_i = -\int_L Q(s) \frac{d\varphi_i}{ds}\, ds \,. \tag{20.21}$$

The influence of the longitudinal forces on the bending deformation can be taken into account by introducing the shear force in formula (18.21):

$$Q(s) = -\alpha N(s) \frac{dv}{ds} \,.$$

Consequently,

$$Q_i = \alpha \int_L N(s) \frac{d\varphi_i}{ds} \frac{dv}{ds}\, ds = \alpha \sum_{k=1}^{n} z_k \int_L N(s) \frac{d\varphi_i}{ds} \frac{d\varphi_k}{ds}\, ds \,. \tag{20.22}$$

We introduce the following notation:

$$\int_L N(s) \frac{d\varphi_i}{ds} \frac{d\varphi_k}{ds}\, ds = s_{ik} \,. \tag{20.23}$$

Using (20.22) and (20.23), the system of equations (20.19) assumes the form

$$\sum_{k=1}^{n} (r_{ik} - \alpha s_{ik}) z_k = 0 \,, \qquad (i = 1, 2, 3, \cdots, n) \,. \tag{20.24}$$

As in the calculation of vibrations, the first n_0 equations can be interpreted as the equations of the displacement method; this analogy does not hold for the remaining equations. As can be seen from (20.23), the unit "reactions" found with consideration of the longitudinal force

$$\tilde{r}_{ik} = r_{ik} - \alpha s_{ik}$$

are symmetric. Equating to zero the determinant (20.24) yields an equation for the critical parameters:

$$| \boldsymbol{R} - \alpha \boldsymbol{S} | = 0 ,$$

where $\boldsymbol{S}$ is the matrix with elements s_{ik}. In the general case, it gives n roots of α_*, all of which are real. This property follows from the symmetry of matrices $\boldsymbol{R}$ and $\boldsymbol{S}$.

In the solution of practical problems, the first n_0 eigenfunctions are sufficient for representing the deformation of elements not loaded by longitudinal forces, and additional generalized coordinates must be introduced only for compressed bars.

Table II below contains the necessary data for calculating the unit reactions. The longitudinal force is assumed to be constant along the length of each rod. The use of the table is the same as for the calculation of vibrations. As for the peculiarities, they will be explained in numerical examples.

● 2. Let us determine the minimum

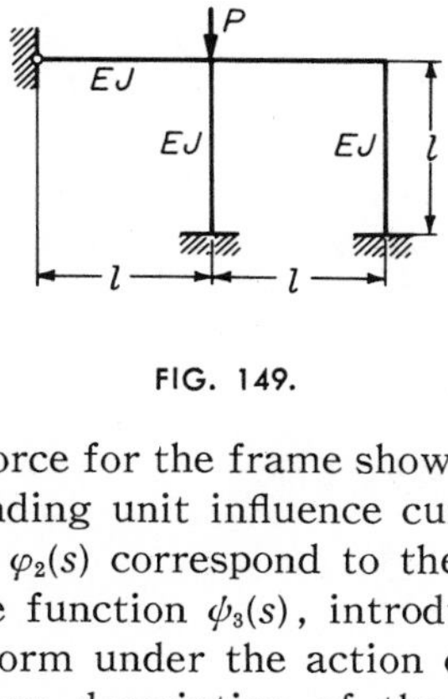

FIG. 149.

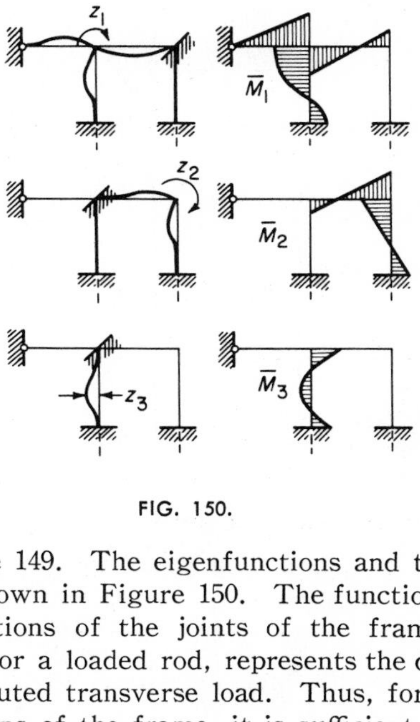

FIG. 150.

critical force for the frame shown in Figure 149. The eigenfunctions and the corresponding unit influence curves are shown in Figure 150. The functions $\varphi_1(s)$ and $\varphi_2(s)$ correspond to the unit rotations of the joints of the frame, while the function $\psi_3(s)$, introduced only for a loaded rod, represents the deflection form under the action of a distributed transverse load. Thus, for a satisfactory description of the deformations of the frame, it is sufficient to have three generalized coordinates.

With the aid of Table II, we determine the unit reactions:

$$\tilde{r}_{11} = 11\frac{EJ}{l} - \frac{2}{15}Pl , \qquad \tilde{r}_{22} = 8\frac{EJ}{l}$$

$$\tilde{r}_{33} = \frac{1024}{5}\frac{EJ}{l^3} - \frac{512}{105}\frac{P}{l}, \quad \tilde{r}_{12} = \tilde{r}_{21} = \frac{2EJ}{l} \tag{20.25}$$

$$\tilde{r}_{13} = \tilde{r}_{31} = \frac{8}{15}\frac{P}{l} , \qquad \tilde{r}_{23} = \tilde{r}_{32} = 0 .$$

TABLE II.

Displacements	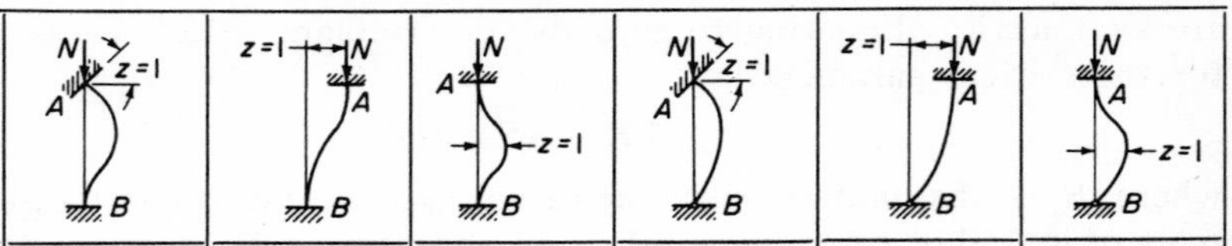					
Moments	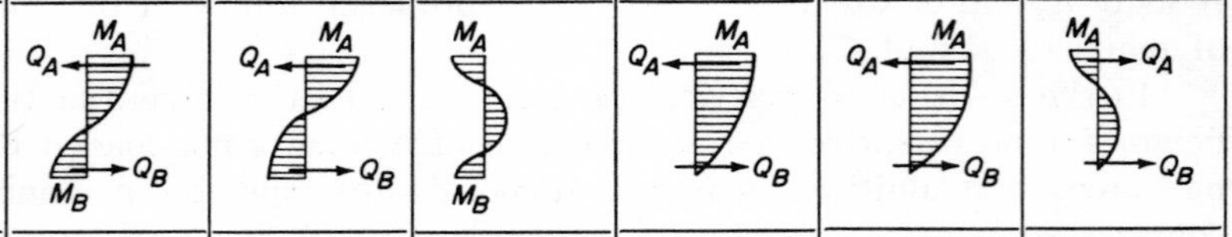					
M_A	$\frac{4EJ}{l}-\frac{2}{15}Nl$	$\frac{6EJ}{l^2}-\frac{1}{10}N$	$-\frac{8}{15}N$	$\frac{3EJ}{l}-\frac{1}{5}Nl$	$\frac{3EJ}{l^2}-\frac{1}{5}N$	$-\frac{4}{5}N$
M_B	$\frac{2EJ}{l}+\frac{1}{15}Nl$	$\frac{6EJ}{l^2}-\frac{1}{10}N$	$-\frac{8}{15}N$	0	0	0
Q_A	$\frac{6EJ}{l^2}-\frac{1}{10}N$	$\frac{12EJ}{l^3}-\frac{6}{5}\frac{N}{l}$	0	$\frac{3EJ}{l^2}-\frac{1}{5}N$	$\frac{3EJ}{l^3}-\frac{6}{5}\frac{N}{l}$	$-\frac{4}{5}\frac{N}{l}$
Q_B	$\frac{6EJ}{l^2}-\frac{1}{10}N$	$\frac{12EJ}{l^3}-\frac{6}{5}\frac{N}{l}$	0	$\frac{3EJ}{l^2}-\frac{1}{5}N$	$\frac{3EJ}{l^3}-\frac{6}{5}\frac{N}{l}$	$-\frac{4}{5}\frac{N}{l}$
$\tilde{r}_{ik}$	$-\frac{8}{15}N$	0	$\frac{1024EJ}{5l^3}-\frac{512}{105}\frac{N}{l}$	$-\frac{4}{5}N$	$-\frac{4}{5}\frac{N}{l}$	$\frac{576EJ}{5l^3}-\frac{192}{35}\frac{N}{l}$

The equation for static stability has the form

$$\begin{vmatrix} 11-0.133\,\alpha & 2 & 0.53\,\alpha \\ 2 & 8 & 0 \\ 0.53\,\alpha & 0 & 204.8-4.85\,\alpha \end{vmatrix} = 0\,,$$

where the following notation is used

$$\alpha = \frac{Pl^2}{EJ}\,.$$

For determining α_* we have the equation $2.909\,\alpha^2 - 627.2\,\alpha + 17220 = 0$, Whose minimum root is $\alpha_*=32.29$. Consequently,

$$P_* = 32.29\frac{EJ}{l^2}\,,$$

which differs from the exact solution[7] by 4 percent.

[7] See Smirnov [1], p. 197, from which the data for this example were taken.

● 3. If the joints of the frame have linear displacements, then the necessity of introducing the additional coordinates is eliminated as a rule. Thus the given method is most applicable to those types of frames whose solution is very difficult to obtain by the usual methods. We will illustrate this application in the example of the frame shown in Figure 151.

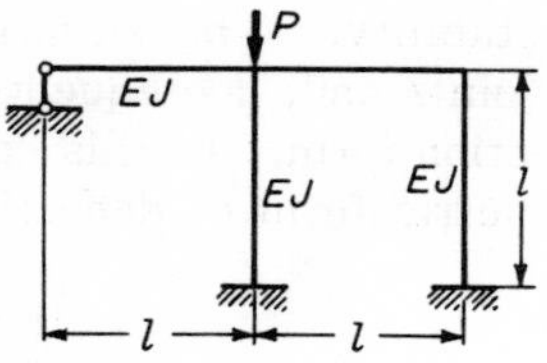

FIG. 151.

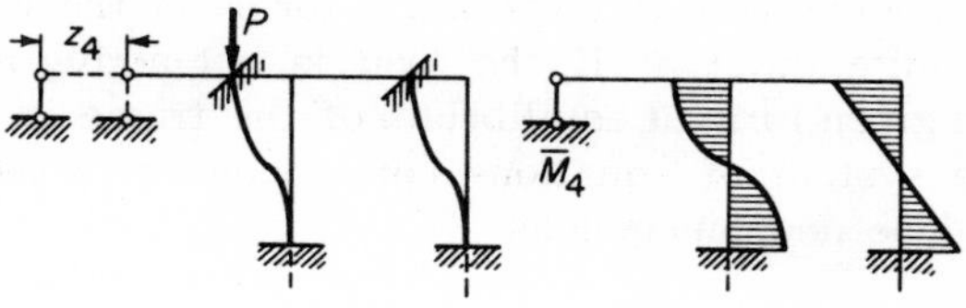

FIG. 152.

In addition to unit reactions (20.25), the consideration of linear displacements gives (Fig. 152):

$$\tilde{r}_{44} = \frac{24EJ}{l^3} - \frac{6}{5}\frac{P}{l}, \qquad \tilde{r}_{14} = \tilde{r}_{41} = \frac{6EJ}{l^2} - \frac{1}{10}P,$$

$$\tilde{r}_{24} = \tilde{r}_{42} = \frac{6EJ}{l^2}, \qquad \tilde{r}_{34} = \tilde{r}_{43} = 0.$$

We now construct the equation for static stability:

$$\begin{vmatrix} 11 - 0.133\,\alpha & 2 & 0.533\,\alpha & 6 - 0.1\,\alpha \\ 2 & 8 & 0 & 6 \\ 0.533\,\alpha & 0 & 204.8 - 4.87\,\alpha & 0 \\ 6 - 0.1\,\alpha & 6 & 0 & 24 - 1.2\,\alpha \end{vmatrix} = 0. \qquad (20.26)$$

where the previous notation for α is used.

We will limit ourselves to the coordinates z_1, z_2, and z_4; as will be seen below, consideration of these coordinates gives the necessary accuracy. Equation (20.26) takes the form

$$\begin{vmatrix} 11 - 0.133\,\alpha & 2 & 6 - 0.1\,\alpha \\ 2 & 8 & 6 \\ 6 - 0.1\,\alpha & 6 & 24 - 1.2\,\alpha \end{vmatrix} = 0.$$

Expansion of the determinant gives

$$1.20\,\alpha^2 - 114.3\,\alpha + 1476 = 0,$$

from which $\alpha_* = 15.41$, and hence

$$P_* = 15.41\,\frac{EJ}{l^2}.$$

If this problem were to be solved by the "exact" method, we would obtain

$$P_* = 15.1\,\frac{EJ}{l^2}.$$

Thus, the difference slightly exceeds 2 percent.

●**4.** The method described can be fully applied to the calculation of the stability of frames with symmetric deflection forms (Fig. 142b). In this case, Eqs. (20.24) break up into two groups, one containing symmetric and the other antisymmetric unknowns.

If the frame is loaded at the joints, then both systems are homogeneous. This homogeneity means that it is possible to state the problem for both symmetric and antisymmetric forms of the loss of stability. The situation is quite different if the load is not acting at the joints and, consequently, the given form of equilibrium of the frame is a deflection form. In this case the system of equations corresponding to the symmetric form of deflection will be nonhomogenous:

$$\sum_{k=1}^{n_1} (r_{ik} - \alpha s_{ik}) z_k = Q_i, \qquad (i = 1, 2, 3, \cdots, n_1), \tag{20.27}$$

where n_1 is the number of symmetric unknowns, and Q_i is calculated from the lateral deflection

$$Q_i = \int \varphi_i(s)\, dQ(s) + \sum_j P_j \chi_{ji}. \tag{20.28}$$

System (20.27), together with the right-hand side of Eq. (20.28), resolves the question concerning the longitudinal and transverse deflection of a symmetric frame loaded by compression and bending.

Let us now consider the antisymmetric group of equations. Because of symmetry, the external load acts orthogonally to the antisymmetric forms of deflection; thus all $Q_i \equiv 0 \; (n_1 < i \leq n)$. In this way, a homogeneous system of equations is obtained:

$$\sum_{k=n_1+1}^{n} (r_{ik} - \alpha s_{ik}) z_k = 0, \qquad (i = n_1 + 1, n_1 + 2, \cdots, n),$$

which answers the question on the stability of the symmetric form of equilibrium.

Here some discussion is necessary. In constructing Eqs. (20.24), it was assumed that the loss of stability originates from the initial unbent condition of the frame. As in the analysis of the stability of arches, here the undeformed form of equilibrium was perturbed. In fact large bending deformations precede the loss of stability of the bent frame in compression.

The discussion concerning bent frames in compression is also valid, to a certain degree, for frames with rods which undergo axial compression. In fact, the method described (as well as other methods for solving stability problems) does not take into account initial longitudinal deformations. If they are taken into account, the frame behaves as a bent system in compression from the beginning. Obviously, here the usual concept of stability problems must be replaced by others. The current accomplishments in this area (we have in mind the so-called "displacement solution" for frames, arches, etc.) are the first approaches to solving very interesting problems.

§ 92. Calculation of Dynamic Stability of Frames

● 1. The approximate methods described above permit a general approach to vibration problems and static stability problems and, consequently, also to problems of dynamic stability. Let the frame be loaded by an external load acting at the joints which causes longitudinal forces in the rods:

$$N(s, t) = (\alpha + \beta \cos \theta t) N_t(s) .$$

Assuming that

$$v(s, t) = \sum_{k=1}^{n} z_k(t)\varphi_k(s) ,$$

the Lagrange equations (20.10) for this problem. Calculations similar to those we can construct made above give

$$\sum_{k=1}^{n} f_{ik}z_k'' + \sum_{k=1}^{n} [r_{ik} - (\alpha + \beta \cos \theta t)s_{ik}] z_k = 0 , \qquad (i = 1, 2, 3, \cdots, n) ,$$

or in matrix form,

$$\boldsymbol{F}\boldsymbol{z}'' + [\boldsymbol{R} - (\alpha + \beta \cos \theta t) \boldsymbol{S}] \boldsymbol{z} = \boldsymbol{0} . \tag{20.29}$$

Here $\boldsymbol{z}$ is a vector with components $z_k(t)$. Particular cases of Eq. (20.29), i.e., equations of free vibrations and static stability, follow clearly from it. Less obvious is another particular case. Let the frame be subjected to static load $\alpha N(s)$. The equation of vibrations for such a frame has the form

$$\boldsymbol{F}\boldsymbol{z}'' + (\boldsymbol{R} - \alpha\boldsymbol{S}) \boldsymbol{z} = \boldsymbol{0} .$$

Substitution of

$$\boldsymbol{z} = \boldsymbol{Z} \sin (\Omega t + \delta) ,$$

where Ω is the natural frequency and δ is the phase of vibrations, gives

$$| \boldsymbol{R} - \alpha\boldsymbol{S} - \Omega^2\boldsymbol{F}) \boldsymbol{z} = \boldsymbol{0} .$$

Equating the determinant of homogeneous system to zero, gives the equation for the frequencies:

$$| \boldsymbol{R} - \alpha\boldsymbol{S} - \Omega^2\boldsymbol{E} | = \boldsymbol{0} . \tag{20.30}$$

Equation (20.30) permits us to determine the influence of the load at the joints on the natural frequencies of the frame. It is easily seen that the consideration of longitudinal forces does not complicate the determination of natural frequencies, whereas use of the known methods would have led to a multiple increase in computations.

Multiplying Eq. (20.29) from the left by $\boldsymbol{R}^{-1}$ and denoting $\boldsymbol{R}^{-1} \boldsymbol{F} = \boldsymbol{C}$, $\boldsymbol{R}^{-1}\boldsymbol{S} = \boldsymbol{A}$ we can reduce it to a usual form

$$\boldsymbol{C}\boldsymbol{z}'' + [\boldsymbol{E} - (\alpha + \beta \cos \theta t) \boldsymbol{A}] \boldsymbol{z} = \boldsymbol{0} .$$

Hence it follows directly that the derivation of the general theory can also be extended to dynamic stability problems of frames.

Tables I and II can be used for the practical calculation of matrix elements r_{ik}, f_{ik} and s_{ik}. For example, the coefficient f_{ik} represents the inertia term from Table I divided by ω^2.

●**2.** We will illustrate the application of Eq. (20.29) by an example (Fig. 153). Because of symmetry, the symmetrical and antisymmetric vibrations can be investigated separately. Let us begin with the latter. Using the results of the example from §90 gives the matrix

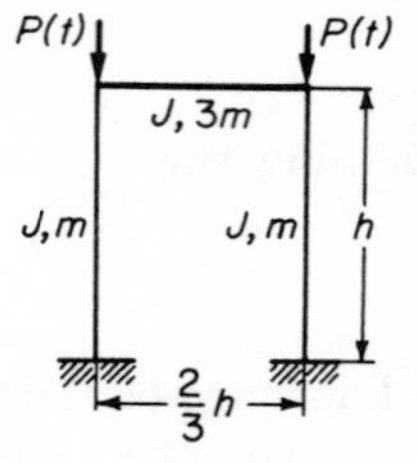

FIG. 153.

$$\boldsymbol{R} = \begin{pmatrix} \dfrac{26EJ}{h} & -\dfrac{12EJ}{h^2} \\ -\dfrac{12EJ}{h^2} & \dfrac{24EJ}{h^3} \end{pmatrix}.$$

Analogously.

$$\boldsymbol{F} = \begin{pmatrix} \dfrac{4}{189}mh^3 & -\dfrac{11}{105}mh^2 \\ -\dfrac{11}{105}mh^2 & \dfrac{96}{35}mh \end{pmatrix}.$$

Finally, Table II is used to construct matrix $\boldsymbol{S}$. The elements s_{ik} can be found by dividing the second component by N (force $P_0 + P_t \cos \theta t$ is considered as a parameter with respect to which the load is given). Then

$$\boldsymbol{S} = \begin{pmatrix} \dfrac{4}{15}h & \dfrac{1}{5} \\ \dfrac{1}{5} & \dfrac{12}{5h} \end{pmatrix}.$$

In the first approximation, the boundaries of the principal region of instability can be determined from the equation

$$|\boldsymbol{R} - (P_0 \pm \tfrac{1}{2}P_t)\boldsymbol{S} - \tfrac{1}{4}\theta^2\boldsymbol{F}| = 0.$$

In the expanded form, this can be expressed as

$$\begin{vmatrix} \dfrac{26EJ}{h} - (P_0 \pm \tfrac{1}{2}P_t)\tfrac{4}{15}h - \dfrac{mh^3\theta^2}{189} & -\dfrac{12EJ}{h^2} - (P_0 \pm \tfrac{1}{2}P_t)\tfrac{1}{5} + \tfrac{11}{420}mh^2\theta^2 \\ -\dfrac{12EJ}{h^2} - (P_0 \pm \tfrac{1}{2}P_t)\tfrac{1}{5} + \tfrac{11}{420}mh^2\theta^2 & \dfrac{24EJ}{h^3} - (P_0 \pm \tfrac{1}{2}P_t)\dfrac{12}{5h} - \tfrac{24}{35}mh\theta^2 \end{vmatrix} = 0. \tag{20.31}$$

For brevity the following nondimensional quantities are introduced:

$$\frac{mh^4\theta^2}{4EJ} = \lambda, \quad \frac{P_0h^2}{EJ} = \alpha, \quad \frac{P_th^2}{EJ} = \beta.$$

Equation (20.31) can then be expressed as

$$\begin{vmatrix} 26 - 0.267(\alpha \pm \tfrac{1}{2}\beta) - 0.213\lambda & -12 + 0.20(\alpha \pm \tfrac{1}{2}\beta) + 0.105\lambda \\ -12 + 0.20(\alpha \pm \tfrac{1}{2}\beta) + 0.105\lambda & 24 - 2.4(\alpha \pm \tfrac{1}{2}\beta) - 2.75\lambda \end{vmatrix} = 0. \tag{20.32}$$

The minimum critical force for the frame can be determined from (20.32) for $\lambda = \beta = 0$. Solving the equation gives:

$$P_* = 6.92 \frac{EJ}{h^2} .$$

Let $P_0 = 0.5\, P_*$ and $P_t = 0.1\, P_*$, Then $\alpha = 3.46$ and $\beta = 0.069$. Solving Eq. (20.32) shows two regions of instability. One lies in the interval $6.23 \leq \lambda \leq 6.51$, the other in the interval $1394 \ll \lambda \ll 1401$. On conversion to the excitation frequencies, this gives

$$\frac{5.0}{h^2}\sqrt{\frac{EJ}{m}} \leq \theta \leq \frac{5.1}{h^2}\sqrt{\frac{EJ}{m}}, \qquad \frac{74.8}{h^2}\sqrt{\frac{EJ}{m}} \leq \theta \leq \frac{74.9}{h^2}\sqrt{\frac{EJ}{m}} .$$

The symmetrical forms of vibrations can be calculated analogously. It is sufficient to take into account the first two symmetric deflection shapes. For the present, we will limit ourselves to the above consideration. In connection with the nonlinear theory, two other examples will be investigated below.

§ 93. Determination of the Amplitudes in the Resonance Case

●1. To illustrate the application of the nonlinear theory, a simple frame shown in Figure 154 will be investigated. Let us assume that at the joint there is a concentrated mass M with a moment of inertia Mr^2; the rods of the frame are considered to be weightless. The fundamental form of vibrations of such a frame is antisymmetric (Fig. 155a), If the flexibility of the rods is sufficiently large ($\lambda > 40$), then the longitudinal vibrations can be neglected. In considering the problem of estimating the order of amplitudes in the resonance case, we will limit ourselves to the first rough approximation ($n = n_0 = 1$). Using Tables I and II leads to the equation for the bending vibrations:

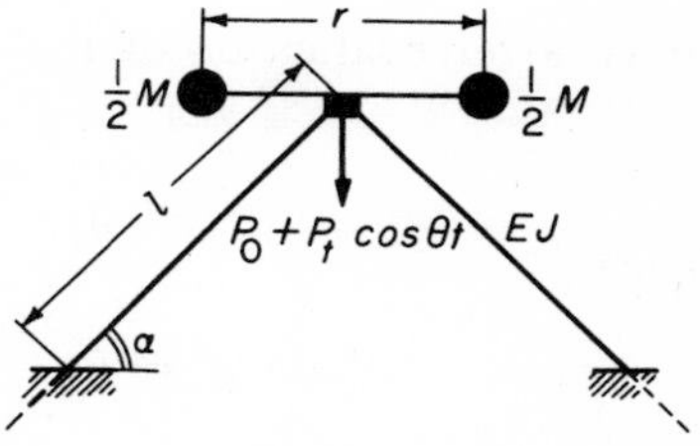

FIG. 154.

$$2\frac{4EJ}{l}z - 2\frac{2}{15}Nl + Mr^2 z'' = 0 ,$$

where N is the longitudinal force acting in each rod. Expressing the above equation in another form,

$$z'' + \omega^2\left(1 - \frac{N}{N_*}\right)z = 0 , \tag{20.33}$$

where
$$\omega^2 = \frac{8EJ}{Mr^2 l}, \qquad N_* = \frac{30EJ}{l^2} . \tag{20.34}$$

To determine the longitudinal force N, equilibrium forces at the joint will be considered:

$$2N \sin \alpha = P_0 + P_t \cos \theta t - Mw'' , \tag{20.35}$$

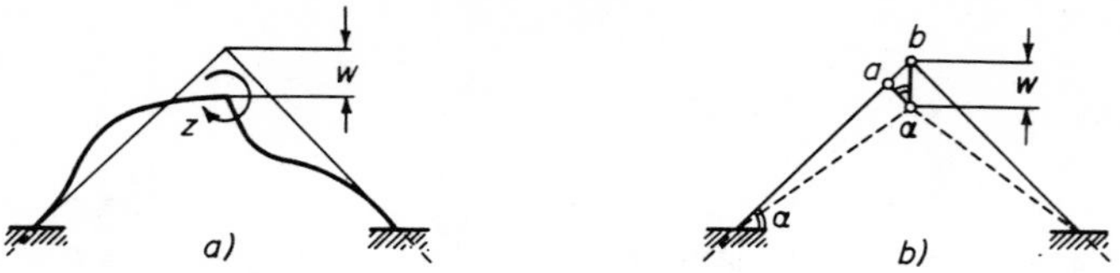

FIG. 155.

where w is the vertical displacement of the joint which can easily be found from a geometric consideration (Fig. 155b). In fact, $w = ab/\sin\alpha$, where ab is the difference between the arc length of the inclined rod and its projection,

$$ab = \tfrac{1}{2}\int_0^l \left(\frac{\partial v}{\partial x}\right)^2 dx\,.$$

Approximating the deflection form by a static deflection curve due to the rotation of the node through an angle z:

$$v(x) = z\left(x - \frac{2x^2}{l} + \frac{x^3}{l^2}\right),$$

yields, after evaluation of the integral,

$$w = \frac{z^2 l}{15\sin\alpha}\,.$$

Hence

$$2N\sin\alpha = P_0 + P_t\cos\theta t - \frac{2Ml}{15\sin\alpha}[(z')^2 + zz'']\,.$$

Substituting the expression for $N(t)$ into (20.34) yields

$$z'' + \omega^2\left(1 - \frac{P_0 + P_t\cos\theta t}{P_*}\right)z + \frac{2M\omega^2 l}{15P_*\sin\alpha}z[(z')^2 + zz''] = 0\,, \qquad (20.36)$$

where
$$P_* = \frac{60EJ\sin\alpha}{l^2}\,.$$

Furthermore, denoting

$$\frac{M\omega^2 l}{15P_*\sin\alpha} = \kappa\,, \qquad \omega^2\left(1 - \frac{P_0}{P_*}\right)\Omega^2, \qquad \frac{P_t}{2(P_* - P_0)} = \mu\,,$$

we can represent Eq. (20.36) in a familiar form:

$$z'' + \Omega^2(1 - 2\mu\cos\theta t)z + 2\kappa z[(z')^2 + zz''] = 0\,.$$

Let us estimate the order of magnitude of the possible amplitudes. In the case of the principal resonance,

$$a^2 \approx \frac{2\mu}{\kappa}\,.$$

Using (20.34) gives for κ

$$\kappa = \frac{2}{225}\frac{l^2}{r^2}\frac{1}{\sin^2\alpha}.$$

Consequently,

$$a \approx 10.6\frac{r\sin\alpha}{l}\sqrt{\frac{P_t}{P_* - P_0}}, \tag{20.37}$$

where amplitude a is given in radians. For example, let $P_t = 0.05\,P_*$, $P_0 = 0$, $r = 0.05\,l$, and $\alpha = 45°$. Then from formula (20.37) $a \approx 0.083$ radians, i.e., approximately 5°. It is noted here that the amplitude increases proportionally to the radius of gyration of the mass.

● **2.** The system with nonlinear inertia and nonlinear elasticity can be obtained by introducing the elastic coupling, as is shown in Figure 156. Let c be the spring coefficient. Then in place of (20.35) we have

$$2N\sin\alpha = P_0 + P_t\cos\theta t - Mw'' - cw,$$

where, as before.

$$w = \frac{z^2 l}{15\sin\alpha}.$$

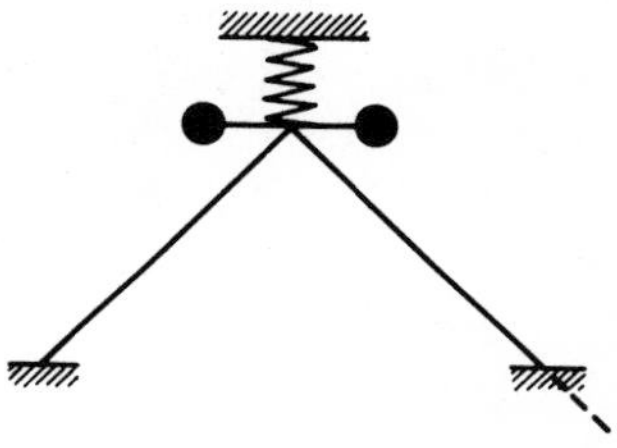

FIG. 156.

Eliminating from Eq. (20.33) the longitudinal force N gives

$$z'' + \Omega^2(1 - 2\mu\cos\theta t)z + 2\kappa z[(z')^2 + zz''] + \gamma z^3 = 0.$$

Here

$$\gamma = \frac{c\omega^2 l}{15P_*\sin\alpha}.$$

Taking into account formulas (20.34) gives

$$\gamma = \kappa\frac{c}{M} = \kappa\omega_0^{\;2},$$

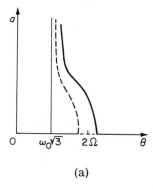

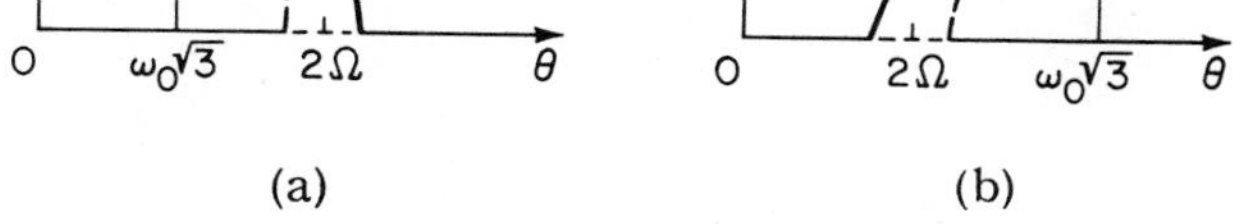

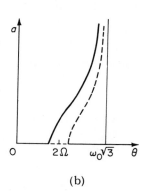

FIG. 157.

where ω_0 is the natural frequency of a system having "nonlinear elasticity and nonlinear inertia." The resonance curves will have the form as shown in Figure 157 (a) and (b), depending on which of the two relationships, $\omega_0\sqrt{3} \gtrless 2\Omega$, is satisfied.

● **3.** Let us investigate the frame shown in Figure 158. For an infinitely rigid crossbar, the vibrations of the frame can be described with the help of one coordinate, i. e., linear displacement z. Projecting all of the forces acting on the crossbar on the horizontal plane and using Table I and II yields

$$2z\left(\frac{12EJ}{l^3} - \frac{6}{5l}N\right) + Mz'' + \frac{13}{35}mlz'' = 0 .$$

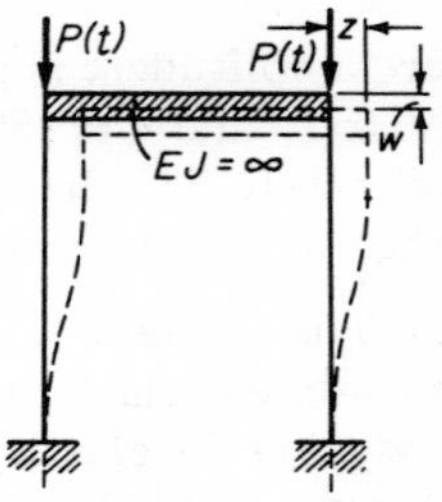

FIG. 158.

Here N denotes the longitudinal force in the column, M denotes the mass of the cross bar and ml denotes the mass of the column. The resulting equation can be expressed in the form (20.33), i.e.,

$$z'' + \omega^2\left(1 - \frac{N}{N_*}\right)z = 0 , \tag{20.38}$$

by letting

$$\omega^2 = \frac{24EJ}{(M + \frac{13}{35}ml)l^3} , \qquad N_* = \frac{10EJ}{l^2} .$$

To determine the dynamic longitudinal force, we will consider the vertical vibrations of the crossbar. We can easily obtain (neglecting the additional mass of the columns)

$$N = P_0 + P_t \cos \theta t - Mw'' , \tag{20.39}$$

where

$$w = \frac{1}{2}\int_0^l \left(\frac{\partial v}{\partial x}\right)^2 dx .$$

The deflection of the columns due to linear movement is

$$v(x) = \left(1 - \frac{3x^2}{l^2} + \frac{2x^3}{l^3}\right)z .$$

Evaluating the integral, we find that

$$w = \frac{6z^2}{5l} . \tag{20.40}$$

We substitute (20.39) and (20.40) into (20.38). As a result, the equation is obtained

$$z'' + \omega^2\left(1 - \frac{P_0 + P_t \cos \theta t}{P_*}\right)z + 2\kappa z[(z')^2 + zz''] = 0 ,$$

where

$$P_* = \frac{20EJ}{l^2} , \qquad \kappa = \frac{6M\omega^2}{5P_*l} .$$

Let us estimate the order of the amplitudes magnitude. It can easily be seen that

$$\kappa = \frac{12}{5l^2}\frac{M}{M + \frac{13}{35}ml} \approx \frac{12}{5l^2}\,.$$

From this follows the linear approximation for the amplitudes on the lower boundary of the principal region on instability

$$a \approx 1.55\, l \sqrt{\frac{P_t}{P_* - P_0}}\,.$$

For the case of $P_t = 0.05\, P_*$ and $P_0 = 0$, we obtain $a \approx 0.347\, l$. Consequently, in the resonance case the amplitudes can be very large. It is noted that damping has not been taken into account in this case.

Twenty-One

DYNAMIC STABILITY OF PLATES

§ 94. Equations for the Free Vibrations and Boundaries of Static Stability of Plates

● **1.** Let the middle surface of the plate coincide with the plane xOy and let the axis Oz be directed downward. As is well known, determination of the deflections $w(x, y)$ of the plate subjected to a transverse load $q(x, y)$ leads to the integration of the equation

$$\Delta\Delta w = \frac{q(x, y)}{D}. \tag{21.1}$$

Here $\Delta\Delta$ is the differential operator

$$\Delta\Delta = \frac{\partial^4}{\partial x^4} + 2\frac{\partial^4}{\partial x^2 \partial y^2} + \frac{\partial^4}{\partial y^4},$$

and D is flexural rigidity,

$$D = \frac{Eh^3}{12(1-\nu^2)}, \tag{21.2}$$

with h the plate thickness and ν Poisson's ratio.

We introduce the deflection influence function $K(x,y,\xi,\eta)$, i.e., an analytical function for the deflection of the plate at point x, y due to a unit load applied at a point ξ, η. The solution of Eq. (21.1) can be represented in the following form:

$$w(x, y) = \iint K(x, y, \xi, \eta)q(\xi, \eta)d\xi d\eta, \tag{21.3}$$

where the integration above and in what follows, extends over the entire middle surface of the plate.

We will investigate the problem of the transverse vibrations of a plate subjected to a load applied to its middle surface. This load is, obviously, a parametric load with respect to deflections $w(x, y)$. Let this load correspond to the stresses from the plane problem of the theory of elasticity $\sigma_x, \sigma_y, \tau_{xy}$. The effect of longitudinal forces and also inertia forces can be taken into account with the help of reduced loading;

$$q(x, y, t) = N_x\frac{\partial^2 w}{\partial x^2} + 2N_{xy}\frac{\partial^2 w}{\partial x \partial y} + N_y\frac{\partial^2 w}{\partial y^2} - m\frac{\partial^2 w}{\partial t^2},$$

where $N_x = h\sigma_x$, $N_y = h\sigma_y$, $N_{xy} = h\tau_{xy}$, and m is the mass of the plate per unit area. Forces N_x and N_y are considered positive if they produce tension. The differential equation for vibrations is

$$\Delta\Delta w = \frac{1}{D}\left(N_x \frac{\partial^2 w}{\partial x^2} + 2N_{xy}\frac{\partial^2 w}{\partial x \partial y} + N_y \frac{\partial^2 w}{\partial y^2} - m\frac{\partial^2 w}{\partial t^2}\right). \tag{21.4}$$

Equating (21.4) and (21.1) and making use of formula (21.3), we obtain an integro-differential equation

$$\begin{aligned} w(x, y, t) &+ m\iint K(x, y, \xi, \eta)\frac{\partial^2 w(\xi, \eta, t)}{\partial t^2}d\xi d\eta \\ &- \iint K(x, y, \xi, \eta)\Big[N_x(\xi, \eta, t)\frac{\partial^2 w(\xi, \eta, t)}{\partial \xi^2} \\ &+ 2N_{xy}(\xi, \eta, t)\frac{\partial^2 w(\xi, \eta, t)}{\partial \xi \partial \eta} + N_y(\xi, \eta, t)\frac{\partial^2 w(\xi, \eta, t)}{\partial \eta^2}\Big]d\xi d\eta = 0 . \end{aligned} \tag{21.5}$$

●**2.** Let us investigate certain particular cases of this equation. The integro-differential equation for the natural vibrations of a plate has the form

$$w(x, y, t) + m\iint K(x, y, \xi, \eta)\frac{\partial^2 w(\xi, \eta, t)}{dt^2}d\xi d\eta = 0 .$$

Assuming that

$$w(x, y, t) = \varphi(x, y)\sin(\omega t + \delta) ,$$

where ω is the frequency and δ is the phase of the free vibrations, we arrive, after cancellation of $\sin(\omega t + \delta)$, at the integral equation

$$\varphi(x, y) - \lambda\iint K(x, y, \xi, \eta)\varphi(\xi, \eta)d\xi d\eta = 0 . \tag{21.6}$$

Its eigenvalues are $\lambda_k = m\omega_k^2$, and the eigenfunctions $\varphi_k(x, y)$ are the forms of the free vibrations of the plate. These functions constitute a complete orthonormalized system in the sense that

$$\iint m\varphi_i\varphi_k dx = \delta_{ik} \tag{21.7}$$

(δ_{ik} is the Kronecker delta symbol) and that an arbitrary function $f(x, y)$ represented "sourcewise" with the help of a kernel $K(x, y, \xi, \eta)$,

$$f(x, y) = \iint K(x, y, \xi, \eta)F(\xi, \eta)d\xi d\eta ,$$

may be expanded into absolutely and uniformly converging series in terms of the functions $\varphi_k(x, y)$:

$$f(x, y) = \sum_{k=1}^{\infty} f_k\varphi_k(x, y) .$$

In particular, we have the bilinear expansion for the kernel

$$K(x, y, \xi, \eta) = \sum_{k=1}^{\infty}\frac{\varphi_k(x, y)\varphi_k(\xi, \eta)}{m\omega_k^2} . \tag{21.8}$$

●**3.** Let us now investigate another particular case of Eq. (21.5), i.e., the equation for the boundaries of static stability. Assuming that the parametric load is given to within the parameter α, and omitting inertia terms, we obtain

$$\psi(x, y) - \alpha\iint K(x, y, \xi, \eta)\Big[N_x(\xi, \eta)\frac{\partial^2\psi(\xi, \eta)}{\partial\xi^2} + 2N_{yx}(\xi, \eta)\frac{\partial^2\psi(\xi, \eta)}{\partial\xi\partial\eta} + N_y(\xi, \eta)\frac{\partial^2\psi(\xi, \eta)}{\partial\eta^2}\Big]d\xi d\eta = 0\,, \tag{21.9}$$

where $\psi(x, y)$ are the buckling modes of the plate.

We will now consider the transformation of the integral in Eq. (21.9). Let us assume, first of all, that on each portion of the contour *at least one* of three conditions is fulfilled;

$$\begin{aligned} &(1)\quad w = 0\,,\\ &(2)\quad \frac{\partial w}{\partial n} = 0\,.\\ &(3)\quad \begin{cases} N_x \cos(n, x) + N_{xy}\cos(n, y) = 0\,,\\ N_{yx}\cos(n, x) + N_y \cos(n, y) = 0\,,\end{cases}\end{aligned} \tag{21.10}$$

(n is normal to the contour). The meaning of the first two conditions is quite clear, while the last condition, consisting of two equations, expresses the absence of the external load on a portion of the contour. Together, conditions (21.10) reduce to a requirement that the load be absent on the portions of the contour which do not exclude deflections or rotations. In the majority of practical problems, conditions (21.10) are satisfied.

We use Green's formula

$$\iint\left(\frac{\partial u}{\partial\xi} + \frac{\partial v}{\partial\eta}\right)d\xi d\eta = \oint[u\cos(\xi, n) + v\sin(\eta, n)]ds\,,$$

where $u(\xi, \eta)$ and $v(\xi, \eta)$ are arbitrary functions[36] and the curvilinear integral is taken over the contour confining the region of integration included in the double integral. We assume that a third function $f(\xi, \eta)$ is given which together with its first derivatives, is continuous. Then on the basis of Green's formula it is easily shown that

$$\iint f\left(\frac{\partial u}{\partial\xi} + \frac{\partial v}{\partial\eta}\right)d\xi d\eta = -\iint\left(u\frac{\partial f}{\partial\xi} + v\frac{\partial f}{\partial\eta}\right)d\xi d\eta + \oint[fu\cos(\xi, n) + fv\cos(\eta, n)]ds\,. \tag{21.11}$$

Let us apply formula (21.11) to the integral entering in (21.9). First of all we transform the integral expression by constructing an identity

$$N_x\frac{\partial^2\psi}{\partial\xi^2} + 2N_{xy}\frac{\partial^2\psi}{\partial\xi\partial\eta} + N_y\frac{\partial^2\psi}{\partial\eta^2} = \frac{\partial}{\partial\xi}\left(N_x\frac{\partial\psi}{\partial\xi} + N_{xy}\frac{\partial\psi}{\partial\eta}\right) + \frac{\partial}{\partial\eta}\left(N_{yx}\frac{\partial\psi}{\partial\xi} + N_y\frac{\partial\psi}{\partial\eta}\right), \tag{21.12}$$

[36] For the assumptions under which this formula was obtained, see for example Lichtenstein [1].

resulting from the equilibrium equations

$$\begin{aligned} \frac{\partial N_x}{\partial \xi} + \frac{\partial N_{xy}}{\partial \eta} &= 0 , \\ \frac{\partial N_{yx}}{\partial \xi} + \frac{\partial N_y}{\partial \eta} &= 0 . \end{aligned} \tag{21.13}$$

For the case considered,

$$\begin{aligned} f(x, y, \xi, \eta) &= K(x, y, \xi, \eta) , \\ u(\xi, \eta) &= N_x \frac{\partial \psi}{\partial \xi} + N_{xy} \frac{\partial \psi}{\partial \eta} , \\ v(\xi, \eta) &= N_{yx} \frac{\partial \psi}{\partial \xi} + N_y \frac{\partial \psi}{\partial \eta} . \end{aligned}$$

Formula (21.11) with consideration of the edge conditions (21.10) gives

$$\begin{aligned} &\iint K\left(N_x \frac{\partial^2 \psi}{\partial \xi^2} + 2N_{xy} \frac{\partial^2 \psi}{\partial \xi \partial \eta} + N_y \frac{\partial^2 \psi}{\partial \eta^2}\right) d\xi d\eta \\ &\quad = - \iint \left[\left(N_x \frac{\partial \psi}{\partial \xi} + N_{xy} \frac{\partial \psi}{\partial \eta}\right) \frac{\partial K}{\partial \xi} + \left(N_{yx} \frac{\partial \psi}{\partial \xi} + N_y \frac{\partial \psi}{\partial \eta}\right) \frac{\partial K}{\partial \eta}\right] d\xi d\eta . \end{aligned}$$

But on the basis of (21.13),

$$\begin{aligned} N_x \frac{\partial \psi}{\partial \xi} + N_{xy} \frac{\partial \psi}{\partial \eta} &= \frac{\partial}{\partial \xi} (N_x \psi) + \frac{\partial}{\partial \eta} (N_{xy} \psi) , \\ N_{yx} \frac{\partial \psi}{\partial \xi} + N_y \frac{\partial \psi}{\partial \eta} &= \frac{\partial}{\partial \xi} (N_{xy} \psi) + \frac{\partial}{\partial \eta} (N_y \psi) . \end{aligned}$$

Again applying (21.11) and utilizing (21.10), we finally obtain

$$\begin{aligned} &\iint K\left(N_x \frac{\partial^2 \psi}{\partial \xi^2} + 2N_{xy} \frac{\partial^2 \psi}{\partial \xi \partial \eta} + N_y \frac{\partial^2 \psi}{\partial \eta^2}\right) d\xi d\eta \\ &\quad = \iint \left(N_x \frac{\partial^2 K}{\partial \xi^2} + 2N_{xy} \frac{\partial^2 K}{\partial \xi \partial \eta} + N_y \frac{\partial^2 K}{\partial \eta^2}\right) \psi d\xi d\eta . \end{aligned}$$

Thus Eq. (21.9) is transformed to an integral equation

$$\psi(x, y) - \alpha \iint S(x, y, \xi, \eta) \psi(\xi, \eta) d\xi d\eta = 0 \tag{21.14}$$

whose kernel has the form[37]

$$\begin{aligned} S(x, y, \xi, \eta) &= N_x(\xi, \eta) \frac{\partial^2 K(x, y, \xi, \eta)}{\partial \xi^2} + 2N_{xy} \frac{\partial^2 K(x, y, \xi, \eta)}{\partial \xi \partial \eta} \\ &\quad + N_y(\xi, \eta) \frac{\partial^2 K(x, y, \xi, \eta)}{\partial \eta^2} . \end{aligned} \tag{21.15}$$

The integral equation for the boundaries of static stability can be obtained in another way. We differentiate Eq. (21.9) twice with respect to x and

[37] The more general equation free from restrictions (21.10) was obtained in § 53 directly from equations of the nonlinear theory of elasticity. (See also Gurevich [1].

multiply the result by $N_x(x, y)$; further, we differentiate with respect to x and y and multiply the result by $2N_{xy}(x, y)$, and finally, differentiate twice with respect to y and multiply by $N_y(x, y)$. The operations mentioned are justified since all the derivatives do exist. Combining the equations obtained we arrive at the integral equation for the kernel, which is transposed with respect to (21.15):

$$\chi(x, y) - \alpha\iint S(\xi, \eta, x, y)\chi(\xi, \eta)d\xi d\eta = 0 . \tag{21.16}$$

Here $\chi(x, y)$ is the reduced transverse load, i.e.,

$$\chi(x, y) = N_x \frac{\partial^2 w}{\partial x^2} + 2N_{xy}\frac{\partial^2 w}{\partial x \partial y} + N_y \frac{\partial^2 w}{\partial y^2} .$$

The eigenfunctions of Eqs. (21.14) and (21.16) are orthogonal to each other:

$$\iint \varphi_i \chi_k dx\, dy = 0 , \qquad (i \neq k) . \tag{21.17}$$

The condition (21.17) is interpreted in the same way as the analogous condition in the problems on the static stability of rods.

§ 95. Derivation of Differential Equations for the Boundaries of the Dynamic Stability of Plates

● 1. We seek the solution of Eq. (21.5) in the form of a series

$$w(x, y, t) = \sum_{k=1}^{\infty} f_k(t)\varphi_k(x, y) , \tag{21.18}$$

where $\varphi_k(x, y)$ are the eigenfunctions for the free vibration problem and $f_k(t)$ are time functions which must be determined. The convergence of series (21.18) follows from a well-known theorem in the theory of linear integral equations.

Let us substitute (21.18) in Eq. (21.5). Taking into account that

$$\iint K(x, y, \xi, \eta)\varphi_i(\xi, \eta)d\xi d\eta = \frac{\varphi_i(x, y)}{m\omega_i^2} ,$$

and using the expansion

$$\iint K(x, y, \xi, \eta)\Big[N_x(\xi, \eta, t)\frac{\partial^2\varphi_k(\xi, \eta)}{\partial \xi^2} + 2N_{xy}(\xi, \eta, t)\frac{\partial^2\varphi_k(\xi, \eta)}{\partial \xi \partial \eta}$$
$$+ N_y(\xi, \eta, t)\frac{\partial^2\varphi_k(\xi, \eta)}{\partial \eta^2}\Big]d\xi d\eta = \sum_{i=1}^{\infty} F_{ik}(t)\varphi_i(x, y) ,$$

we arrive at a system of differential equations for the coefficients of series (21.18):

$$f_i'' + \omega_i^2\Big[f_i - \sum_{k=1}^{\infty} F_{ik}(t)f_k\Big] = 0 , \qquad (i = 1, 2, 3, \cdots) . \tag{21.19}$$

Functions $F_{ik}(t)$ are defined by the formula

$$F_{ik}(t) = \frac{1}{m\omega_i^2}\iint \varphi_i\left(N_x \frac{\partial^2 \varphi_k}{\partial x^2} + 2N_{xy}\frac{\partial^2 \varphi_k}{\partial x \partial y} + N_y \frac{\partial^2 \varphi_k}{\partial y^2}\right)dxdy\,,$$

where the primes denote differentiation with respect to time.

We will now examine the case in which a periodic load acts on the plate. Neglecting logitudinal inertia forces in the linear approximation, we can express the forces through the quasi-static stresses of the plane problem

$$\begin{aligned} N_x(x, y, t) &= \alpha N_x(x, y) + \beta\Phi(t)N_{xt}(x, y)\,, \\ N_{xy}(x, y, t) &= \alpha N_{xy}(x, y) + \beta\Phi(t)N_{xyt}(x, y)\,, \\ N_y(x, y, t) &= \alpha N_y(x, y) + \beta\Phi(t)N_{yt}(x, y)\,. \end{aligned}$$

Here α and β are still unknown parameters in the constant and periodic components of the load, respectively. In place of Eq. (21.19), we obtain

$$f_i'' + \omega_i^2\left[f_i - \alpha\sum_{k=1}^{\infty} a_{ik} f_k - \beta\Phi(t)\sum_{k=1}^{\infty} b_{ik} f_k\right] = 0\,, \qquad (i = 1, 2, 3, \cdots)\,, \tag{21.20}$$

where

$$\begin{aligned} a_{ik} &= \frac{1}{m\omega_i^2}\iint \varphi_i\left(N_x \frac{\partial^2 \varphi_k}{\partial x^2} + 2N_{xy}\frac{\partial^2 \varphi_k}{\partial x \partial y} + N_y \frac{\partial^2 \varphi_k}{\partial y^2}\right)dxdy\,, \\ b_{ik} &= \frac{1}{m\omega_i^2}\iint \varphi_i\left(N_{xt} \frac{\partial^2 \varphi_k}{\partial x^2} + 2N_{xyt}\frac{\partial^2 \varphi_k}{\partial x \partial y} + N_{yt} \frac{\partial^2 \varphi_k}{\partial y^2}\right)dxdy\,. \end{aligned} \tag{21.21}$$

The matrices $\boldsymbol{A}$ and $\boldsymbol{B}$ with elements a_{ik} and b_{ik} and a diagonal matrix $\boldsymbol{C}$ with elements $c_{ik} = \delta_{ik}/\omega_i^2$ are introduced. Representing by $\boldsymbol{f}$ the matrix column of functions $f_i(t)$, we express the system of Eqs. (21.20) in a matrix form:

$$\boldsymbol{C}\boldsymbol{f}'' + [\boldsymbol{E} - \alpha\boldsymbol{A} - \beta\Phi(t)\boldsymbol{B}]\boldsymbol{f} = \boldsymbol{0}\,. \tag{21.22}$$

●**2.** We will show that Eqs. (21.20) can be represented in a canonical form

$$\frac{dp_i}{dt} = -\frac{\partial H}{\partial q_i}\,, \qquad \frac{dq}{dt} = \frac{\partial H}{\partial p_i}\,, \qquad (i = 1, 2, 3, \cdots)\,,$$

and that the general theory stated in Chapter Fourteen is applicable to them.

Rewriting the matrix equation (21.22) in the form

$$\boldsymbol{f}'' + \boldsymbol{C}^{-1}[\boldsymbol{E} - \alpha\boldsymbol{A} - \beta\Phi(t)\boldsymbol{B}]\boldsymbol{f} = \boldsymbol{0}\,,$$

we will prove that matrices $\boldsymbol{C}^{-1}\boldsymbol{A}$ and $\boldsymbol{C}^{-1}\boldsymbol{B}$ are symmetric matrices. Consider, for example, matrix $\boldsymbol{C}^{-1}\boldsymbol{A}$. Its elements are

$$\{\boldsymbol{C}^{-1}\boldsymbol{A}\}_{ik} = \iint \varphi_i\left(N_x \frac{\partial^2 \varphi_k}{\partial x^2} + 2N_{xy}\frac{\partial^2 \varphi_k}{\partial x \partial y} + N_y \frac{\partial^2 \varphi_k}{\partial y^2}\right)dxdy\,.$$

Applying formula (21.11) twice to the integral and using the boundary conditions (21.10), as was done in § 94 for an analogous integral, we obtain

$$\begin{aligned} &\iint \varphi_i\left(N_x \frac{\partial^2 \varphi_k}{\partial x^2} + 2N_{xy}\frac{\partial^2 \varphi_k}{\partial x \partial y} + N_y \frac{\partial^2 \varphi_k}{\partial y^2}\right)dxdy \\ &\qquad = \iint \varphi_k\left(N_x \frac{\partial^2 \varphi_i}{\partial x^2} + 2N_{xy}\frac{\partial^2 \varphi_i}{\partial x \partial y} + N_y \frac{\partial^2 \varphi_i}{\partial y^2}\right)dxdy\,. \end{aligned}$$

Further proof is analogous to that presented in § 57.

§ 96. Simple Cases of Integration

The characteristic equations

$$|\boldsymbol{E} - \alpha \boldsymbol{A}| = 0 , \quad |\boldsymbol{E} - \beta \boldsymbol{B}| = 0 \tag{21.23}$$

give the solutions for problems of the static stability of a plate subjected to the action of a load with parameters α and β, respectively. Also it is obvious that the frequencies of the transverse vibrations of the plate satisfy the equation

$$|\boldsymbol{E} - \omega^2 \boldsymbol{C}| = 0 .$$

We will now consider the matrix equation (21.22). The case in which all the matrices entering into the differential equation are of diagonal form was called in § 49 a special case of individual independent equations. In the present case the unknown functions in the system of equations (21.20) separate, and also, on the basis of (21.23), the equations for the boundaries of dynamic stability assume the form

$$f_k'' + \omega_k^2\left(1 - \frac{\alpha}{\alpha_k} - \frac{\beta}{\beta_k}\Phi(t)\right)f_k = 0 , \quad (k = 1, 2, 3, \cdots) , \tag{21.24}$$

where α_k and β_k are the critical parameters. Let us establish the conditions under which the problem of the dynamic stability of plates reduces to equations of the same type as (21.24). For the matrix $\boldsymbol{A}$ to be diagonal, it is necessary and sufficient that the following condition be satisfied for $i \neq k$:

$$\iint \varphi_i\left(N_x \frac{\partial^2 \varphi_k}{\partial x^2} + 2N_{xy}\frac{\partial^2 \varphi_k}{\partial x \partial y} + N_y \frac{\partial^2 \varphi_k}{\partial y^2}\right)dxdy = 0 , \quad (k = 1, 2, 3, \cdots) . \tag{21.25}$$

Using the condition of orthogonality (21.7) and the completeness of eigenfunctions we obtain

$$N_x \frac{\partial^2 \varphi_k}{\partial x^2} + 2N_{xy}\frac{\partial^2 \varphi_k}{\partial x \partial y} + N_y \frac{\partial^2 \varphi_k}{\partial y^2} = c_k \varphi_k \quad (k = 1, 2, 3, \cdots) , \tag{21.26}$$

where c_k are arbitrary constants. Let us set

$$N_x = \frac{\partial^2 \Phi}{\partial y^2} , \qquad N_y = \frac{\partial^2 \Phi}{\partial x^2} , \qquad N_{xy} = -\frac{\partial^2 \Phi}{\partial x \partial y}$$

where Φ is the Airy stress function.

Relationship (21.26) can now be expressed in the form

$$\frac{\partial^2 \Phi}{\partial y^2}\frac{\partial^2 \varphi_k}{\partial x^2} - 2\frac{\partial^2 \Phi}{\partial x \partial y}\frac{\partial^2 \varphi_k}{\partial x \partial y} + \frac{\partial^2 \Phi}{\partial x^2}\frac{\partial^2 \varphi_k}{\partial y^2} = c_k \varphi_k , \quad (k = 1, 2, 3, \cdots) .$$

The results obtained, as in the problem on the dynamic stability of rods, can be interpreted as requiring that the eigenfunctions of static stability and free vibrations coincide. Actually, condition (21.25), expressed in terms of the function φ coincides with the orthogonality condition (21.17) for the eigenfunctions of static stability. Furthermore, substituting in the integral equation (21.6) the expression for φ found from formula (21.26), we obtain

$$\varphi_k(x, y) - \frac{\lambda}{c_k}\iint K(x, y, \xi, \eta)\Big[N_x(\xi, \eta)\frac{\partial^2\varphi_k(\xi, \eta)}{\partial\xi^2} + 2N_{xy}(\xi, \eta)\frac{\partial^2\varphi_k(\xi, \eta)}{\partial\xi\partial\eta} + N_y(\xi, \eta)\frac{\partial^2\varphi_k(\xi, \eta)}{\partial\eta^2}\Big]d\xi d\eta = 0 .$$

From this, it follows that the eigenfunctions of the free vibration problem must satisfy the equation (21.9) for the boundaries of static stability. But both systems are complete; hence, they are in agreement with one another.

●2. As an example of problems that lead to single differential equations of the type (21.24), we consider a problem on the dynamic stability of a rectangular plate simply supported on its edges and compressed by uniformly distributed forces along its edges (Fig. 159):

$$\begin{aligned} N_x(x, y, t) &= -(N_x + N_{xt}\cos\theta t) , \\ N_y(x, y, t) &= -(N_y + N_{yt}\cos\theta t) , \\ N_{xy} &= 0 . \end{aligned} \qquad (21.27)$$

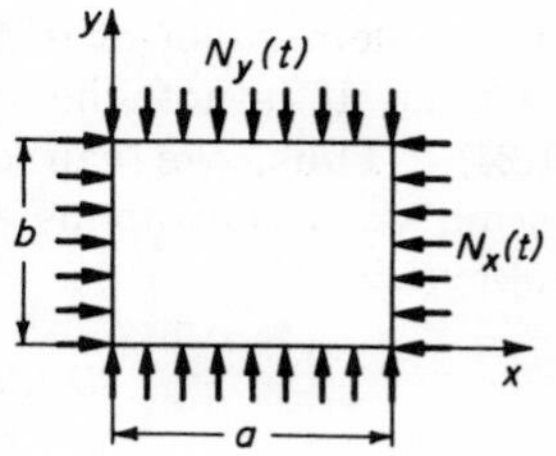

FIG. 159.

The equation for natural vibrations

$$\Delta\Delta w + \frac{m}{D}\frac{\partial^2 w}{\partial t^2} = 0$$

is satisfied if we substitute

$$w(x, y, t) = \sin\frac{i\pi x}{a}\sin\frac{k\pi y}{b}\sin(\omega t + \delta)$$
$$(i, k = 1, 2, 3, \cdots) .$$

The eigenfunctions for the free vibrations are

$$\varphi_{ik}(x, y) = \sin\frac{i\pi x}{a}\sin\frac{k\pi y}{b}$$

or, after compliance with the condition of normalization (21.7),

$$\varphi_{ik}(x, y) = \frac{2}{\sqrt{abm}}\sin\frac{i\pi x}{a}\sin\frac{k\pi y}{b} . \qquad (21.28)$$

The free vibration frequencies of the unloaded plate are

$$\omega_{ik} = \pi^2\Big(\frac{i^2}{a^2} + \frac{k^2}{b^2}\Big)\sqrt{\frac{D}{m}} . \qquad (21.29)$$

The eigenfunctions and the natural frequencies are written with a double index, which corresponds to the number of half waves in the direction of axes Ox and Oy.

The equation for the boundaries of static stability

$$\Delta\Delta w + \frac{1}{D}\left(N_x \frac{\partial^2 w}{\partial x^2} + N_y \frac{\partial^2 w}{\partial y^2}\right) = 0$$

is satisfied by functions (21.28); for the critical values of the load parameters, we obtain the relationship

$$\frac{i^2 N_x}{a^2} + \frac{k^2 N_y}{b^2} = \left(\frac{i^2}{a^2} + \frac{k^2}{b^2}\right)^2 \pi^2 D . \tag{21.30}$$

For the case where the plate is uniformly compressed in one direction only ($N_x = 0$), we obtain

$$f''_{ik} + \omega_{ik}^2\left(1 - \frac{N_y + N_{yt}\cos\theta t}{N_{ik}}\right) f_{ik} = 0 , \qquad (i, k = 1, 2, 3, \cdots) \tag{21.31}$$

where

$$N_{ik} = \frac{k^2 \pi^2 D}{b^2}\left[1 + \left(\frac{ib}{ka}\right)^2\right]^2 . \tag{21.32}$$

The problem under consideration has been investigated in a number of works.[38] However, it is not the only problem which leads to equations of the type (21.24). Thus, we can obtain analogous equations for a rectangular plate resting on a continuous elastic foundation. The differential equation for this problem is

$$D\Delta\Delta w + kw + N_y \frac{\partial^2 w}{\partial y^2} + m \frac{\partial^2 w}{\partial t^2} = 0 ,$$

where k is the foundation coefficient, and it also is satisfied by functions (21.28)

● **3.** For certain other problems, an approximate solution can be obtained by using Galerkin's method and approximating the forms of vibrations with the help of some suitable function that satisfies the boundary conditions. The use of this method will be demonstrated by the example of a circular plate clamped along its edges.[39]

We assume that the plate with a radius R is compressed by a radial load $q = q_0 + q_t \cos\theta t$ (Fig. 160). Using polar coordinates r, φ, we can express Eq. (21.4) in the form

$$D\Delta\Delta w = -m \frac{\partial^2 w}{\partial t^2} + N_r \frac{\partial^2 w}{\partial r^2} + N_\varphi\left(\frac{1}{r^2}\frac{\partial^2 w}{\partial \varphi^2} + \frac{1}{r}\frac{\partial w}{\partial r}\right), \tag{21.33}$$

where

$$\Delta = \frac{\partial^2}{\partial r^2} + \frac{1}{r}\frac{\partial}{\partial r} + \frac{1}{r^2}\frac{\partial^2}{\partial \varphi^2} ,$$

$$N_r = N_\varphi = -(q_0 + q_t \cos\theta t) .$$

[38] Bodner [1] and Chelomei [1].

[39] Bodner [1].

Consider the case of a plate clamped along the entire edge:

$$w(R) = \frac{\partial w(R)}{\partial r} = 0 .$$

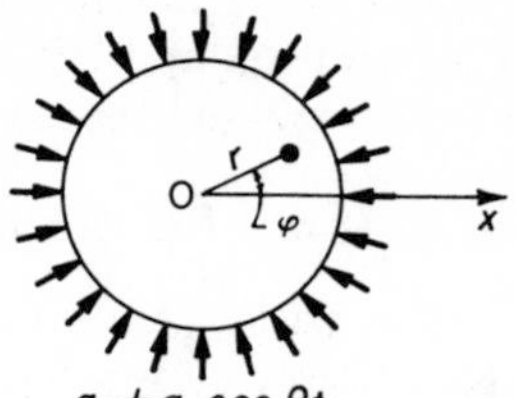

FIG. 160.

The equation for free vibrations,

$$D\Delta\Delta\psi - m\omega^2\psi = 0 ,$$

and the boundary conditions are satisfied if we let[40]

$$\psi(r, \varphi) = [I_n(kR)J_n(kr) - J_n(kR)I_n(kr)] \cos n\varphi .$$

Here $n = 1, 2, 3, \cdots$; $J_n(x)$ and $I_n(x)$ are Bessel functions of the nth order with real and purely imaginary arguments; and k are the roots of the characteristic equation

$$\begin{vmatrix} J_n(kR) & I_n(kR) \\ J_n'(kR) & I_n'(kR) \end{vmatrix} = 0 .$$

The natural vibration frequencies are

$$\omega = k^2 \sqrt{\frac{D}{m}} .$$

We seek the solution of the problem in the form

$$w(r, \varphi, t) = f(t)\psi(r, \varphi) . \tag{21.34}$$

Substitution of Eq. (21.34) into the differential equation (21.33) does not satisfy the latter, because in the given case the free vibration forms and the buckling modes do not coincide. Let us employ Galerkin's variational method. For this purpose we multiply the result of substitution by $\psi(r, \varphi)rdrd\varphi$ and integrate over the whole surface of the plate. Thus for $f(t)$, we obtain the equation

$$\frac{d^2f}{dt^2} + \omega^2\left(1 - \frac{q_0 + q_t \cos \theta t}{q_*}\right)f = 0 ,$$

were q_* is an approximate (in the sense of Galerkin's method) critical value of the load

$$q_* = - \frac{\int_0^R \int_0^{2\pi} \psi^2(r, \varphi)\, r\, dr\, d\varphi}{\int_0^R \int_0^{2\pi} \Delta\psi(r, \varphi)\psi\, r\, dr\, d\varphi} m\omega^2 .$$

One can easily verify that the following is true:

$$\Delta[J_n(kr) \cos n\varphi] = k^2 J_n(kr) \cos n\varphi ,$$
$$\Delta[I_n(kr) \cos n\varphi] = - k^2 I_n(kr) \cos n\varphi .$$

Consequently,

$$\Delta\psi(r, \varphi) = - k^2 [I_n(kR)J_n(kr) + J_n(kR)I_n(kr)] \cos n\varphi ,$$

[40] See, for example, Kuzmin [1].

and the evaluation of integrals in formulas for q_* simplifies. An analogous method can be applied to other forms of support, to problems on vibrations of annular plates, etc.[41]

§ 97. Some Particular Problems[42]

● **1.** We will now investigate the problem of the dynamic stability of a rectangular plate supported along its edges and subjected to the action of periodic longitudinal force

$$N_x(y, t) = (N_0 + N_t \cos \theta t)\left(\frac{ny}{b} - 1\right).$$

The case $n = 0$ corresponds to uniform compression, while the case $n = 2$ corresponds to pure bending (Fig. 161).

The eigenfunctions have the form (21.28). According to formulas (21.21), the elements of matrix $\boldsymbol{A}$ are

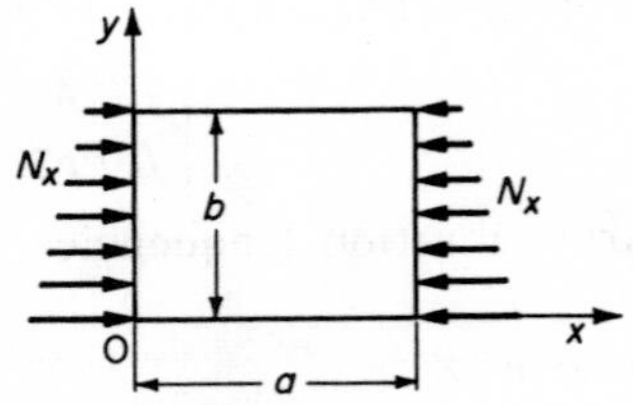

FIG. 161.

$$a_{ik,pq} = -\frac{4\pi^2 p^2}{a^3 bm\omega_{ik}^2} \times \int_0^a\int_0^b \left(\frac{ny}{b} - 1\right) \sin\frac{i\pi x}{a} \sin\frac{k\pi y}{b} \sin\frac{p\pi x}{a} \sin\frac{q\pi y}{b}\, dxdy .$$

Evaluation of the above integral gives

$$a_{ik,pq} = \begin{cases} 0 & \text{for } i \neq p, \\ \dfrac{i^2}{\pi^2 a}\dfrac{1 - \dfrac{n}{2}}{\left(\dfrac{i^2}{a^2} + \dfrac{k^2}{b^2}\right)^2 D} & \text{for } k = q, i = p, \\ -\dfrac{8p^2 n}{\pi^4 a^2\left(\dfrac{i^2}{a^2} + \dfrac{k^2}{b^2}\right)^2 D}\dfrac{kq}{(k^2 - q^2)^2} & \text{for } i = p, \text{ if } k \pm q \text{ is odd}, \\ 0 & \text{for } i = p, \text{ if } k \pm q \text{ is even}. \end{cases}$$

For the determination of the principal regions of instability, we make use of the equation for the first approximation

$$|\,\boldsymbol{E} - (N_0 \pm \tfrac{1}{2} N_t)\boldsymbol{A} - \tfrac{1}{4}\theta^2 \boldsymbol{C}\,| = 0 . \tag{21.35}$$

Equating the diagonal elements of the determinant (21.35) to zero, we obtain

$$\theta_* \approx 2\omega_{ik}\sqrt{1 - \frac{\left(N_0 \pm \dfrac{1}{2} N_t\right)\left(1 - \dfrac{n}{2}\right)}{\left(\dfrac{i^2}{a^2} + \dfrac{k^2}{b^2}\right)^2 D}\frac{i^2}{\pi a^2}} . \tag{21.36}$$

[41] Bodner [1]. [42] Bolotin [10].

Formula (21.36) gives satisfactory results for $n = 0$ (pure compression):

$$\theta_* \approx 2\omega_{ik}\sqrt{1 - \frac{N_0 \pm \frac{1}{2}N_t}{N_{ik}}}\,.$$

With increasing n the error in formula (21.36) increases and, in particular, for $n = 2$ (pure bending), this formula leads to regions of instability which degenerate into lines. This means that for sufficiently large n it is necessary to consider approximations. This need is evident also from the error which results when the equation for the boundaries of static stability is constructed on the basis of the same assumptions:

$$|\boldsymbol{E} - N\boldsymbol{A}| = 0\,.$$

If we now consider only the diagonal terms we obtain the formula

$$N_{ik} = \frac{\left(\frac{i^2}{a^2} + \frac{k^2}{b^2}\right)^2}{1 - \frac{n}{2}} \frac{\pi^2 a^2 D}{i^2}\,,$$

which gives accurate results for $n = 0$; however, for $n > 1$ the accuracy for the first approximation becomes insufficient.[43]

● **2.** It is obvious that, for the problem under consideration, matrix $\boldsymbol{A}$ is quasi-diagonal:

$$\boldsymbol{A} = \begin{pmatrix} \boxed{\boldsymbol{A}_1} & & & \\ & \boxed{\boldsymbol{A}_2} & & \\ & & \ddots & \\ & & & \boxed{\boldsymbol{A}_n} \end{pmatrix}.$$

Each quasi-diagonal element (element matrix) contains only those elements $a_{ik,pq}$ which have the same index k, p:

$$\boldsymbol{A}_k = \begin{pmatrix} a_{k1,k1} & a_{k1,k2} & a_{k1,k3} & \cdots \\ a_{k2,k1} & a_{k2,k2} & a_{k2,k3} & \cdots \\ a_{k3,k1} & a_{k3,k2} & a_{k3,k3} & \cdots \\ \cdots & \cdots & \cdots & \cdots \end{pmatrix}.$$

Consequently, the differential equations for the boundaries of dynamic stability separate into independent groups. Thus the kth group describes the vibrations that occur with the deflection in the direction of axis Ox with k half waves:

$$\boldsymbol{C}_k \boldsymbol{f}_k'' + [\boldsymbol{E} - (N_0 + N_t \cos\theta t)\boldsymbol{A}_k]\boldsymbol{f}_k = 0\,, \qquad (k = 1, 2, 3, \cdots)\,.$$

Consider one of such groups, omitting for simplicity the subscript k. For the case of pure bending, matrix $\boldsymbol{A}$ has the form

[43] See for example, Timoshenko [2].

$$A = \begin{pmatrix} \boxed{\begin{matrix} 0 & a_{12} \\ a_{21} & 0 \end{matrix}} & \begin{matrix} 0 & a_{14} & \cdots \\ a_{23} & 0 & \cdots \end{matrix} \\ \begin{matrix} 0 & a_{32} \\ a_{41} & 0 \end{matrix} & \begin{matrix} 0 & a_{34} & \cdots \\ a_{43} & 0 & \cdots \end{matrix} \\ \cdots & \cdots \end{pmatrix}.$$

Retaining in Eqs. (21.35) the second order matrix, we obtain the equation

$$\begin{vmatrix} \omega_1{}^2 - \frac{1}{4}\theta^2 & -(N_0 \pm \frac{1}{2}N_t)a_{12} \\ -(N_0 \pm \frac{1}{2}N_t)a_{21} & \omega_2{}^2 - \frac{1}{4}\theta^2 \end{vmatrix} = 0 .$$

Its solution gives the following formula for determining the boundaries of the principal regions of instability:

$$\theta_* = \frac{2\omega_1}{\sqrt{\gamma}} \sqrt{1 + \gamma \pm \sqrt{(1-\gamma)^2 + 4\gamma \frac{(N_0 \pm \frac{1}{2}N_t)^2}{N_*{}^2}}}, \tag{21.37}$$

where N_* is an approximate value for the critical parameter

$$N_* = \frac{9\pi^4 a^2 D}{32k^2}\left(\frac{k^2}{a^2} + \frac{1}{b^2}\right)\left(\frac{k^2}{a^2} + \frac{4}{b^2}\right),$$

and γ is the ratio of the squares of the individual frequencies

$$\gamma = \frac{\omega_1{}^2}{\omega_2{}^2} = \left(\frac{1 + \dfrac{a^2}{k^2 b^2}}{1 + \dfrac{4a^2}{k^2 b^2}}\right)^2.$$

If $\gamma \ll 1$, then formula (21.37) can be written in a simpler form:

$$\theta_* \approx 2\omega_1 \sqrt{1 - \frac{(N_0 \pm \frac{1}{2}N_t)^2}{(1-\gamma)N_*^2}},$$

or

$$\theta_* \approx 2\omega_2 \sqrt{1 + \frac{\gamma}{1-\gamma}\frac{(N_0 \pm \frac{1}{2}N_t)^2}{N_*^2}}.$$

For further refinement, the results of § 58 can be applied to the framed second-order matrix. If the shape of the plate differs slightly from a square ($a/b < 1.5$), such an approximation gives sufficient accuracy. In the case of long plates, it is necessary to take a matrix of a higher order. Thus, retaining in Eqs. (21.35) the third-order matrix we obtain

$$\begin{vmatrix} 1 - \dfrac{1}{4}\dfrac{\theta^2}{\omega_1{}^2} & -\left(N_0 \pm \dfrac{1}{2}N_t\right)a_{12} & 0 \\ -\left(N_0 \pm \dfrac{1}{2}N_t\right)a_{21} & 1 - \dfrac{1}{4}\dfrac{\theta^2}{\omega_2{}^2} & -\left(N_0 \mp \dfrac{1}{2}N_t\right)a_{23} \\ 0 & -\left(N_0 \pm \dfrac{1}{2}N_t\right)a_{32} & 1 - \dfrac{1}{4}\dfrac{\theta^2}{\omega_3^2} \end{vmatrix} = 0 .$$

Assuming that $\gamma_2 = \omega_1{}^2/\omega_2{}^2 \ll 1$ and $\gamma_3 = \omega_1{}^2/\omega_3{}^2 \ll 1$, we obtain the formula

$$\theta_* \approx 2\omega_1 \sqrt{1 - \frac{1}{1-\gamma_2}\left(\frac{a_{23}a_{32}}{1-\gamma_3} + a_{12}a_{21}\right)\left(N_0 \pm \frac{1}{2}N_t\right)^2}.$$

● **3.** Let us investigate the problem of the dynamic stability of a simply supported rectangular plate subjected to shear stresses (Fig. 162). The elements of matrix $\boldsymbol{A}$ are determined from the formula

$$a_{ik,pq} = \frac{8pq}{\pi^2 a^2 b^2 D\left(\frac{i^2}{a^2} + \frac{k^2}{b^2}\right)^2} \times \int_0^a \int_0^b \sin\frac{i\pi x}{a} \sin\frac{k\pi y}{b} \cos\frac{p\pi x}{a} \cos\frac{q\pi y}{b}\, dxdy .$$

Evaluating the integral, we find that

$$a_{ik,pq} = \begin{cases} \dfrac{32}{\pi^4 abD\left(\frac{i^2}{a^2} + \frac{k^2}{b^2}\right)^2} \dfrac{pqik}{(i^2 - p^2)(k^2 - q^2)}, & \text{if } i \pm p \text{ and } k \pm q \text{ are odd,} \\ 0, & \text{if } i \pm p \text{ or } k \pm q \text{ are even.} \end{cases}$$

The structure of matrix $\boldsymbol{A}$ is such that with proper numbering of rows it becomes quasi-diagonal:

$$\boldsymbol{A} = \begin{pmatrix} \boxed{\boldsymbol{A}_1} & \\ & \boxed{\boldsymbol{A}_2} \end{pmatrix}.$$

Matrix $\boldsymbol{A}_1$ contains only the elements $a_{ik,pq}$ for which $i \pm k$ and $p \pm q$ are even numbers; matrix $\boldsymbol{A}_2$ contains only the elements for which $i \pm k$ and $p \pm q$ are odd numbers. Therefore, the basic differential system of the problem separates into two independent systems. We will consider the system which contains the minimum natural frequency

$$\omega_{11} = \pi^2\left(\frac{1}{a^2} + \frac{1}{b^2}\right)\sqrt{\frac{D}{m}} .$$

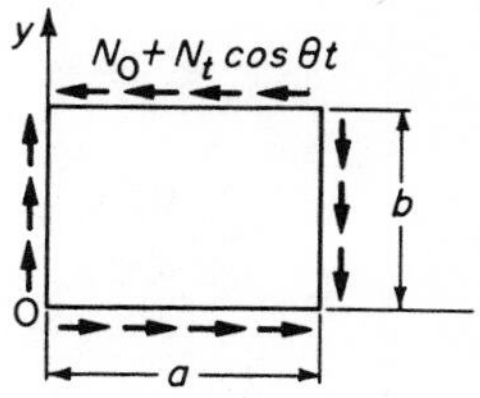

FIG. 162.

The vector $\boldsymbol{f}(t)$ will be constructed in the following form:

$$\boldsymbol{f}(t) = (f_{11}(t), f_{22}(t), f_{13}(t), f_{31}(t), f_{33}(t)) .$$

Matrix $\boldsymbol{A}$ has the form

$$\boldsymbol{A} = \begin{pmatrix} 0 & a_{11,22} & 0 & 0 & 0 \\ a_{22,11} & 0 & a_{22,13} & a_{22,31} & a_{22,33} \\ 0 & a_{13,22} & 0 & 0 & 0 \\ 0 & a_{31,22} & 0 & 0 & 0 \\ 0 & a_{33,22} & 0 & 0 & 0 \end{pmatrix}.$$

To within matrices of the second order, matrix $\boldsymbol{A}$ coincides with the matrices of the previous example and of the example in § 58. In particular, we can make use of formula (21.37) if we assume that

$$N_* = \frac{9\pi^4 abD}{32}\left(\frac{1}{a^2} + \frac{1}{b^2}\right)^2, \qquad \gamma = \frac{1}{16}.$$

§ 98. Application of Variational Methods

●**1.** The solution of particular problems does not entail any difficulties if the eigenfunctions for the free problem vibration and the stresses for plane problems are known. If the free forms of vibration are unknown, then for the coordinate functions we can take an arbitrary system of functions which satisfy the boundary conditions and which are suitable for representing the buckling forms of a plate:

$$w(x, y, t) \approx \sum_{k=1}^{n} f_k(t)\psi_k(x, y) . \tag{21.38}$$

For example, the products of appropriate "beam" functions can be taken as the coordinate functions.

We begin with the differential equation

$$D\Delta\Delta w = -m\frac{\partial^2 w}{\partial t^2} + N_x\frac{\partial^2 w}{\partial x^2} + 2N_{xy}\frac{\partial^2 w}{\partial x\partial y} + N_y\frac{\partial^2 w}{\partial y^2} .$$

Substituting in it series (21.38) and applying Galerkin's variational method, we obtain a system of ordinary differential equations

$$\boldsymbol{F}\boldsymbol{f}'' + (\boldsymbol{R} - \alpha\boldsymbol{P} - \beta\boldsymbol{Q}\cos\theta t)\boldsymbol{f} = \boldsymbol{0},$$

where

$$\begin{aligned}
\{\boldsymbol{F}\}_{ik} &= \iint m\psi_i\psi_k dxdy ,\\
\{\boldsymbol{R}\}_{ik} &= D\iint \psi_i\Delta\Delta\psi_k dxdy ,\\
\{\boldsymbol{P}\}_{ik} &= \iint \psi_i\left(N_x\frac{\partial^2\psi_k}{\partial x^2} + 2N_{xy}\frac{\partial^2\psi_k}{\partial x\partial y} + N_y\frac{\partial^2\psi_k}{\partial y^2}\right)dxdy ,\\
\{\boldsymbol{Q}\}_{ik} &= \iint \psi_i\left(N_{xt}\frac{\partial^2\psi_k}{\partial x^2} + 2N_{xyt}\frac{\partial^2\psi_k}{\partial x\partial y} + N_{yt}\frac{\partial^2\psi_k}{\partial y^2}\right)dxdy .
\end{aligned} \tag{21.39}$$

Difficulties can be encountered also in the determination of stresses of the plane problem and in the evaluation of integrals (21.39) as well when these stresses are known but are expressed in a complex form. As an example, one can investigate the dynamic stability of a plate subjected to the action of concentrated periodic forces (Fig. 163). These difficulties can, however, be overcome if the double integral in the expressions for $\{\boldsymbol{P}\}_{ik}$ and $\{\boldsymbol{Q}\}_{ik}$ is transformed to an integral along the contour. Otherwise these results are easier to obtain by reverting to The Lagrange equations.

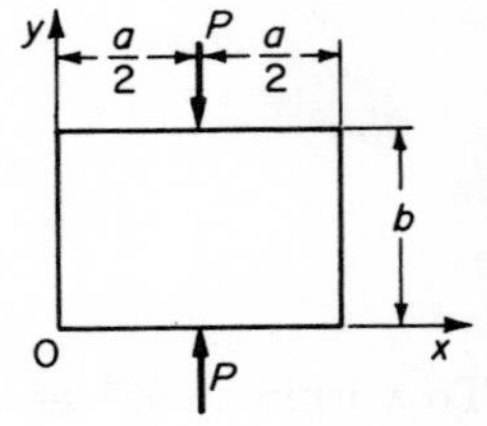

FIG. 163.

●**2.** The application of the Lagrange equations will be shown on the example problem illustrated in Figure 163.

For the case of a plate simply supported along the contour, we can take the coefficients of the series

$$w(x, y, t) = \sum_{i=1}^{\infty} \sum_{k=1}^{\infty} q_{ik}(t) \sin \frac{i\pi x}{a} \sin \frac{k\pi y}{b}$$

as the generalized coordinates.

The potential energy of deformation due to bending is calculated from the formula

$$U = \frac{1}{2} D\int_0^a \int_0^b \left\{\left(\frac{\partial^2 w}{\partial x^2} + \frac{\partial^2 w}{\partial y^2}\right)^2 - 2(1-\nu)\left[\frac{\partial^2 w}{\partial x^2}\frac{\partial^2 w}{\partial y^2} - \left(\frac{\partial^2 w}{\partial x \partial y}\right)^2\right]\right\} dxdy .$$

Evaluation gives

$$U = \frac{\pi^4 D}{8ab} \sum_{i=1}^{\infty} \sum_{k=1}^{\infty} \left(\frac{i^2}{a^2} + \frac{k^2}{b^2}\right)^2 q_{ik}^2 .$$

The work due to external forces is

$$V = \frac{1}{2}(P_0 + P_t \cos \theta t)\int_0^b \left(\frac{\partial w((a/2), y)}{\partial y}\right)^2 dy .$$

After substitution we obtain

$$V = \frac{\pi^2}{4b}(P_0 + P_t \cos \theta t) \qquad \sum_{k=1}^{\infty} \left(\sum_{i=1,3,5}^{\infty} (-1)^{(i-1)/2} q_{ik}(t)\right)^2 .$$

The kinetic energy for bending vibrations is calculated from the formula

$$T = \frac{1}{2} m\int_0^a \int_0^b \left(\frac{\partial w}{\partial t}\right)^2 dxdy .$$

Evaluation gives

$$T = \frac{mab}{8} \sum_{i=1}^{\infty} \sum_{k=1}^{\infty} \left(\frac{dq_{ik}}{dt}\right)^2 .$$

After substitution of the expressions obtained into the Lagrange equations

$$\frac{d}{dt}\left(\frac{\partial T}{\partial \dot{q}_{ik}}\right) - \frac{\partial}{\partial q_{ik}}(T - U) = \frac{\partial V}{\partial q_{ik}}, \qquad (i, k = 1, 2, 3, \cdots),$$

a system of ordinary differential equations is obtained:

$$q_{ik}'' + \frac{\pi^4 D}{m}\left(\frac{i^2}{a^2} + \frac{k^2}{b^2}\right)^2 q_{ik} - \frac{2\pi^2 k(-1)^{(i-1)/2}(P_0 + P_t \cos \theta t)}{mab^2} \sum_{p=1,3,5}^{\infty} (-1)^{(p-1)/2} q_{ik} = 0 ,$$

$$(i = 1, 3, 5, \cdots), \qquad (k = 1, 2, 3, \cdots),$$

$$q_{ik}'' + \frac{\pi^4 D}{m}\left(\frac{i^2}{a^2} + \frac{k^2}{b^2}\right)^2 q_{ik} = 0 ,$$

$$(i = 2, 4, 6, \cdots), \qquad (k = 1, 2, 3, \cdots) .$$

In matrix notation, this system assumes the form

$$\boldsymbol{C}\boldsymbol{f}'' + [\boldsymbol{E} - (P_0 + P_t \cos \theta t)\boldsymbol{A}]\boldsymbol{f} = \boldsymbol{0} ,$$

where $\boldsymbol{f}(t)$ is a vector with components $q_{ik}(t)$, and the elements of matrix $\boldsymbol{A}$ are calculated by the formula

$$a_{ik,pq} = \begin{cases} \dfrac{2k(-1)^{(p-1)/2}(-1)^{(i-1)/2}}{\pi^2 ab^2 D\left(\dfrac{i^2}{a^2} + \dfrac{k^2}{b^2}\right)^2} & \text{if } i \text{ and } p \text{ are odd, and } k = q, \\ 0 , & \text{if } i \text{ or } p \text{ are even or } k \neq q . \end{cases}$$

Further solution does not present any difficulties.

§ 99. Statement of the Nonlinear Problem. The Fundamental Equations[44]

●1. As in the problem on the vibrations of rods, we can consider three groups of nonlinear factors: nonlinear inertia, nonlinear damping, and nonlinear elasticity.

The first two factors are determined in a manner analogous to that of the investigation of the dynamic stability of rods. Thus the terms associated with the general designation " nonlinear inertia " include the additional inertia forces which arise during longitudinal displacement u and v; in fact, the latter are coupled nonlinearly with the deflection of the plate, w. The terms characterizing nonlinear damping can be determined by considering resistance forces in the longitudinal direction which arise at the fixed support of the plate. These forces in the first approximation are proportional to the velocities $\partial u/\partial t$ and $\partial v/\partial t$. Moreover, we may also assume here that the " nonlinear damping " takes into account any variation of the damping coefficient which depends on the amplitude. Thus we are not bound by any concrete expression for the nonlinear functions.

Let as now consider the third nonlinear factor—nonlinear elasticity. Under the general designation of "nonlinear elasticity" those terms of nonlinear functions which contain no derivatives of displacements with respect to time are included. In the problem on the dynamic stability of rods, consideration of exact expressions for curvature leads to nonlinear terms of this type. In the problem on the dynamic stability of plates, it is necessary to take into account a new factor, i.e., the influence of stretching of the middle surface.

As is well known, the elementary bending theory of plates is based on the assumption that the middle plane does not undergo any axial deformation during bending. This assumption is realized only in a particular case in which the deflection surface is a developable surface. In a general case, the bending of the plate is accompanied by stretching of the middle surface; the additional stresses arising in connection with this will be more significant as the plate deflection gets larger in comparison to the plate thickness.

[44] Bolotin [9].

Consideration of stretching of the middle surface leads to nonlinear differential equations, because stretching introduces components of finite deformations into the corresponding equations. Thus, the well-known equations for the bending of plates in the case of finite (but not too large) deflections have the form

$$\begin{aligned} \Delta\Delta w &= \frac{h}{D}\left(\frac{q}{h} + \frac{\partial^2\Phi}{\partial y^2}\frac{\partial^2 w}{\partial x^2} - 2\frac{\partial^2\Phi}{\partial x\partial y}\frac{\partial^2 w}{\partial x\partial y} + \frac{\partial^2\Phi}{\partial x^2}\frac{\partial^2 w}{\partial y^2}\right), \\ \Delta\Delta\Phi &= \boldsymbol{E}\left[\left(\frac{\partial^2 w}{\partial x\partial y}\right)^2 - \frac{\partial^2 w}{\partial x^2}\frac{\partial^2 w}{\partial y^2}\right], \end{aligned} \tag{21.40}$$

where $\Phi(x, y)$ is the Airy stress function. It can be easily seen that if one of the unknowns is eliminated from Eqs. (21.40), for example $\Phi(x, y)$, an equation containing nonlinear terms of the third order is obtained. These terms define the nonlinear elasticity of the system.

In contrast to straight rods, the role of nonlinear elasticity in the problems on dynamic stability of plates is very significant. This can be forseen by comparing the behavior of axially compressed rods and plates in the post-critical stage. The critical load for a rod is practically the ultimate load, the plate fixed on all edges, however, can support a load which exceeds the critical value tenfold.

The equations for dynamic problems can be obtained from (21.40) if the inertia forces are introduced in them. The vibration loading, given on the boundary, is taken into account in the boundary conditions. The solution of the resulting nonlinear system is very difficult. An approximate method of solution which permits one to obtain the results in a closed form is presented below.

●2. In what follows, the deflections of the plate are considered to be finite, even though sufficiently small, so that the angles of rotation of elements of the plate can be neglected in comparison with unity. The Von Kármán's equations (21.40) were constructed on the basis of such an assumption.

During the deflection of the plate, the forces forming in the middle plane are

$$\begin{aligned} N_x &= \frac{Eh}{1-\nu^2}(\varepsilon_{xx} + \nu\varepsilon_{yy}), \\ N_y &= \frac{Eh}{1-\nu^2}(\varepsilon_{yy} + \nu\varepsilon_{xx}), \\ N_{xy} &= \frac{Eh}{2(1+\nu)}\varepsilon_{xy}, \end{aligned} \tag{21.41}$$

where $\varepsilon_{xx}, \varepsilon_{yy}, \varepsilon_{xy}$ are the components of finite deformations:

$$\begin{gathered} \varepsilon_{xx} = \frac{\partial u}{\partial x} + \frac{1}{2}\left(\frac{\partial w}{\partial x}\right)^2, \\ \varepsilon_{yy} = \frac{\partial v}{\partial y} + \frac{1}{2}\left(\frac{\partial w}{\partial y}\right)^2, \qquad \varepsilon_{xy} = \frac{\partial u}{\partial y} + \frac{\partial v}{\partial x} + \frac{\partial w}{\partial x}\frac{\partial w}{\partial y}. \end{gathered} \tag{21.42}$$

Combining Eqs. (21.41) and (21.42) and substituting into the equations of motion

$$\frac{\partial N_x}{\partial x} + \frac{\partial N_{xy}}{\partial y} - m\frac{\partial^2 u}{\partial t^2} = 0\,,$$
$$\frac{\partial N_{yx}}{\partial x} + \frac{\partial N_y}{\partial y} - m\frac{\partial^2 v}{\partial t^2} = 0\,,$$

gives a system of equations which relates u, v, and w:

$$\begin{aligned}
&\frac{\partial^2 u}{\partial x^2} + \frac{1-\nu}{2}\frac{\partial^2 u}{\partial y^2} + \frac{1+\nu}{2}\frac{\partial^2 v}{\partial x \partial y} + \frac{\partial w}{\partial x}\left(\frac{\partial^2 w}{\partial x^2} + \frac{1-\nu}{2}\frac{\partial^2 w}{\partial y^2}\right) \\
&\quad + \frac{1+\nu}{2}\frac{\partial^2 w}{\partial x \partial y}\frac{\partial w}{\partial y} - \frac{m(1-\nu^2)}{Eh}\frac{\partial^2 u}{\partial t^2} = 0\,, \\
&\frac{\partial^2 v}{\partial y^2} + \frac{1-\nu}{2}\frac{\partial^2 v}{\partial x^2} + \frac{1+\nu}{2}\frac{\partial^2 u}{\partial x \partial y} + \frac{\partial w}{\partial y}\left(\frac{\partial^2 w}{\partial y^2} + \frac{1-\nu}{2}\frac{\partial^2 w}{\partial x^2}\right) \\
&\quad + \frac{1+\nu}{2}\frac{\partial^2 w}{\partial x \partial y}\frac{\partial w}{\partial x} - \frac{m(1-\nu^2)}{Eh}\frac{\partial^2 v}{\partial t^2} = 0\,.
\end{aligned} \tag{21.43}$$

The third equation completing this system of equations is (21.4).

In order to find an approximate solution of the problem, let us assume the deflection form of the plate during vibration as

$$w(x, y, t) = f(t)\psi(x, y)\,. \tag{21.44}$$

In Eq. (21.44), $\psi(x, y)$ denotes a function satisfying the boundary conditions for w (for example, the form of the free vibrations of the plate), and $f(t)$ denotes the unknown time function. Substitution leads to the following nonhomogeneous equations[45]:

$$\begin{aligned}
&\frac{\partial^2 u}{\partial x^2} + \frac{1-\nu}{2}\frac{\partial^2 u}{\partial y^2} + \frac{\partial^2 v}{\partial x \partial y}\frac{1+\nu}{2} - \frac{m(1-\nu^2)}{Eh}\frac{\partial^2 u}{\partial t^2} + F_x(x, y, t) = 0\,, \\
&\frac{\partial^2 v}{\partial y^2} + \frac{1-\nu}{2}\frac{\partial^2 v}{\partial x^2} + \frac{\partial^2 u}{\partial x \partial y}\frac{1-\nu}{2} - \frac{m(1-\nu^2)}{Eh}\frac{\partial^2 v}{\partial t^2} + F_y(x, y, t) = 0\,,
\end{aligned} \tag{21.45}$$

where

$$\begin{aligned}
F_x &= f^2(t)\left[\frac{\partial \psi}{\partial x}\left(\frac{\partial^2 \psi}{\partial x^2} + \frac{1-\nu}{2}\frac{\partial^2 \psi}{\partial y^2}\right) + \frac{1+\nu}{2}\frac{\partial^2 \psi}{\partial x \partial y}\frac{\partial \psi}{\partial y}\right], \\
F_y &= f^2(t)\left[\frac{\partial \psi}{\partial y}\left(\frac{\partial^2 \psi}{\partial y^2} + \frac{1-\nu}{2}\frac{\partial^2 \psi}{\partial x^2}\right) + \frac{1-\nu}{2}\frac{\partial^2 \psi}{\partial x \partial y}\frac{\partial \psi}{\partial x}\right].
\end{aligned} \tag{21.46}$$

Equations (21.45) can be solved independently from Eq. (21.4).

●**3.** Let us investigate the problem of vibrations of a rectangular plate which is simply supported along the edges and subjected to the action of longitudinal periodic forces (Fig. 159). We will investigate the resonance with respect to the principal form of the vibrations and will seek the solution in the form:

[45] These are essentially Lamé equations for the plane stress condition.

$$w(x, y, t) = f(t) \sin \frac{\pi x}{a} \sin \frac{\pi y}{b} . \tag{21.47}$$

As was shown in § 96, the expression (21.47) gives an accurate solution for the linear problem of a plate subjected to the action of a uniformly distributed axial load (for $i = k = 1$).

Substituting (21.47) in (21.46) gives

$$\begin{aligned} F_x &= -\frac{\pi^3 f^2}{4a} \sin \frac{2\pi x}{a} \left[\frac{1}{a^2} - \frac{\nu}{b^2} - \left(\frac{1}{a^2} + \frac{1}{b^2} \right) \cos \frac{2\pi y}{b} \right], \\ F_y &= -\frac{\pi^3 f^2}{4b} \sin \frac{2\pi y}{b} \left[\frac{1}{b^2} - \frac{\nu}{a^2} - \left(\frac{1}{a^2} + \frac{1}{b^2} \right) \cos \frac{2\pi x}{a} \right]. \end{aligned} \tag{21.48}$$

Solution of Eqs. (21.45) for the case (21.48) can be easily obtained if the terms which take into account longitudinal inertia forces are neglected. The influence of the discarded terms will obviously be small as long as the frequency of the transverse vibrations of the plate is small in comparison with the frequency of the vibrations in its own plane. Quantitative evaluation of the error and also methods for obtaining a more accurate solution are given below. The solution of the differential equation system (21.45) has the form

$$\begin{aligned} u(x, y, t) &= A_x \sin \frac{2\pi x}{a} + C_x \sin \frac{2\pi x}{a} \cos \frac{2\pi y}{b} + u_0(x, y, t) , \\ v(x, y, t) &= A_y \sin \frac{2\pi y}{b} + C_y \sin \frac{2\pi y}{b} \cos \frac{2\pi x}{a} + v_0(x, y, t) . \end{aligned}$$

Here A_x, A_y, C_x, C_y are coefficients while $u_0(x, y, t)$, and $v_0(x, y, t)$ are solutions of a homogeneous system

$$\begin{aligned} \frac{\partial^2 u}{\partial x^2} + \frac{1-\nu}{2} \frac{\partial^2 u}{\partial y^2} + \frac{1+\nu}{2} \frac{\partial^2 v}{\partial x \partial y} &= 0 , \\ \frac{\partial^2 v}{\partial y^2} + \frac{1-\nu}{2} \frac{\partial^2 v}{\partial x^2} + \frac{1+\nu}{2} \frac{\partial^2 u}{\partial x \partial y} &= 0 , \end{aligned}$$

chosen in such a way as to satisfy the boundary conditions. It is readily apparent that

$$\begin{aligned} A_x &= -\frac{\pi f^2 a}{16} \left(\frac{1}{a^2} - \frac{\nu}{b^2} \right), \\ A_y &= -\frac{\pi f^2 b}{16} \left(\frac{1}{b^2} - \frac{\nu}{a^2} \right). \end{aligned}$$

The coefficients C_x, C_y can be determined from a system of equations:

$$\begin{aligned} C_x \left(\frac{1}{a^2} + \frac{1-\nu}{2b^2} \right) + C_y \frac{1+\nu}{2ab} &= \frac{\pi f^2}{16a} \left(\frac{1}{a^2} + \frac{1}{b^2} \right), \\ C_x \frac{1+\nu}{2ab} + C_y \left(\frac{1}{b^2} + \frac{1-\nu}{2a^2} \right) &= \frac{\pi f^2}{16b} \left(\frac{1}{a^2} + \frac{1}{b^2} \right). \end{aligned} \tag{21.49}$$

By direct substitution one can verify that the expressions

$$C_x = \frac{\pi f^2}{16a}, \qquad C_y = \frac{\pi f^2}{16b}$$

satisfy system (21.49). Thus,

$$u(x, y, t) = \frac{\pi f^2}{16a} \sin \frac{2\pi x}{a} \left(\cos \frac{2\pi y}{b} - 1 + \frac{\nu a^2}{b^2} \right) + u_0(x, y, t),$$

$$v(x, y, t) = \frac{\pi f^2}{16b} \sin \frac{2\pi y}{b} \left(\cos \frac{2\pi x}{a} - 1 + \frac{\nu b^2}{a^2} \right) + v_0(x, y, t).$$

For the determination of middle plane forces, we obtain, according to Eqs. (21.41) and (21.42), the following:

$$\begin{aligned} N_x &= \frac{Eh}{1-\nu^2} \frac{\pi^2 f^2}{8a^2} \left[1 + \frac{\nu a^2}{b^2} - (1-\nu^2) \cos \frac{2\pi y}{b} \right] + N_x^0, \\ N_y &= \frac{Eh}{1-\nu^2} \frac{\pi^2 f^2}{8b^2} \left[1 + \frac{\nu b^2}{a^2} - (1-\nu^2) \cos \frac{2\pi x}{a} \right] + N_y^0, \\ N_{xy} &= N_{xy}^0, \end{aligned} \tag{21.50}$$

where the following notation is introduced:

$$\begin{aligned} N_x^0 &= \frac{Eh}{1-\nu^2} \left(\frac{\partial u_0}{\partial x} + \nu \frac{\partial v_0}{\partial y} \right), \\ N_y^0 &= \frac{Eh}{1-\nu^2} \left(\frac{\partial v_0}{\partial y} + \nu \frac{\partial u_0}{\partial x} \right), \\ N_{xy}^0 &= \frac{Eh}{2(1+\nu)} \left(\frac{\partial u_0}{\partial y} + \frac{\partial v_0}{\partial x} \right). \end{aligned}$$

§ 100. Two Nonlinear Problems[46]

Let a plate be compressed in the direction of the Oy axis by a load $N(t) = N_0 + N_t \cos \theta t$ transmitted through an absolutely rigid loading beam; in other words, the edge of the plate $y = b$ remains straight during vibrations (Fig. 164). Let the supports on the remaining contour be such that, on the edges $x = 0$ and $x = a$, horizontal displacements are impossible ($u = 0$); along the edge $y = 0$, the vertical displacement is equal to zero ($v = 0$).

These boundary conditions can be satisfied by letting

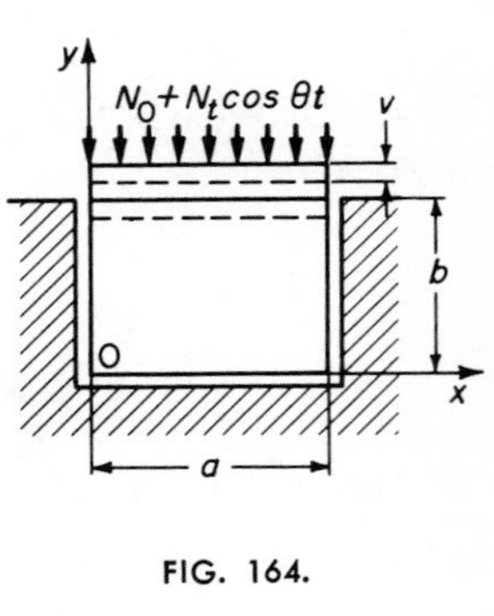

FIG. 164.

$$u_0(x, y, t) = 0,$$

$$v_0(x, y, t) = -\varphi(t) y \frac{1-\nu^2}{Eh},$$

where $\varphi(t)$ is a function of time which must be determined. The function $\varphi(t)$ can be found from the condition of equilibrium on the edge $y = b$:

[46] Bolotin [9].

$$\int_0^a N_y dx = -(N_0 + N_t \cos \theta t)a .$$

Since according to Eqs. (21.50),

$$N_y = \frac{Eh}{1-\nu^2}\frac{\pi^2 f^2}{8b^2}\left[1 + \frac{\nu b^2}{a^2} - (1-\nu^2)\cos\frac{2\pi x}{a}\right] - \varphi(t) ,$$

we obtain

$$\varphi(t) = N_0 + N_t \cos \theta t + \frac{Eh}{1-\nu^2}\frac{\pi^2 f^2}{8b^2}\left(1 + \frac{\nu b^2}{a^2}\right).$$

Finally, the forces in the middle plane are:

$$\begin{aligned} N_x &= \frac{\pi^2 f^2 Eh}{8a^2}\left(1 - \cos\frac{2\pi y}{b}\right) - \nu(N_0 + N_t \cos \theta t) , \\ N_y &= \frac{\pi^2 f^2 Eh}{8b^2} \cos\frac{2\pi x}{a} - (N_0 + N_t \cos \theta t) , \\ N_{xy} &= 0 . \end{aligned} \qquad (21.51)$$

Let as now consider the differential equation (21.4) for the transverse vibrations

$$D\Delta\Delta w = N_x \frac{\partial^2 w}{\partial x^2} + 2N_{xy}\frac{\partial^2 w}{\partial x \partial y} + N_y \frac{\partial^2 w}{\partial y^2} - m\frac{\partial^2 w}{\partial t^2} .$$

Assuming in it that

$$w(x, y, t) = f(t) \sin\frac{\pi x}{a} \sin\frac{\pi y}{b}$$

and utilizing the Galerkin variational method, we obtain

$$\begin{aligned} f'' + \omega^2 f + \frac{4\pi^2 f}{abm}\int_0^a\int_0^b \Bigg[\left(\frac{N_x}{a^2} + \frac{N_y}{b^2}\right) \sin^2\frac{\pi x}{a} \sin^2\frac{\pi y}{b} \\ + \frac{N_{xy}}{2ab}\sin\frac{2\pi x}{a}\sin\frac{2\pi y}{b}\Bigg]dxdy = 0 , \end{aligned} \qquad (21.52)$$

where ω is the minimum frequency of transverse vibrations of the plate,

$$\omega = \pi^2\left(\frac{1}{a^2} + \frac{1}{b^2}\right)\sqrt{\frac{D}{m}} ,$$

and the primes, as before, denote differentiation with respect to time. Substituting (21.51) into (21.52) and evaluating the integrals, we find that

$$f'' + \omega^2 f - \frac{\pi^2 f}{m}\left(\frac{\nu}{a^2} + \frac{1}{b^2}\right)(N_0 + N_t \cos \theta t) + \frac{\pi^4 Ehf^3}{16m}\left(\frac{3}{a^4} + \frac{1}{b^4}\right) = 0 .$$

Let us introduce the notation

$$N_* = \frac{\pi^2\left(\frac{1}{a^2} + \frac{1}{b^2}\right)^2 D}{\frac{\nu}{a^2} + \frac{1}{b^2}} ,$$

where the quantity N_* represents, as is evident from (21.30), the critical parameter of a longitudinal static load of the form $N_x = -\nu N_0$, $N_y = -N_0$, $N_{xy} = 0$ (we recall that edges $x = 0$ and $x = a$ were assumed to have no displacement; this assumption gives rise to the forces N_x). We further denote

$$\frac{\pi^4 Eh}{16m}\left(\frac{3}{a^4} + \frac{1}{b^4}\right) = \frac{3(1-\nu^2)}{4h^2}\frac{3 + \frac{a^4}{b^4}}{\left(1 + \frac{a^2}{b^2}\right)^2}\omega^2 = \gamma\,. \tag{21.53}$$

Thus the resulting differential equation can be expressed in the following form:

$$f'' + \omega^2\left(1 - \frac{N_0 + N_t \cos\theta t}{N_*}\right) f + \gamma f^3 = 0\,. \tag{21.54}$$

Equation (21.54), for $i = k = 1$, differs from Eq. (21.31) by the presence of the last nonlinear term which takes into account the axial deformation of the middle surface.

● **2.** Let us consider a particular case of Eq. (21.54), namely, the equation of static stability, which is obtained by letting $N = \text{const.}$ and neglecting the inertia terms:

$$\omega^2\left(1 - \frac{N}{N_*}\right) f + \gamma f^3 = 0\,.$$

Here f is the deflection at the center of the plate determined by the formula

$$f = \frac{\omega}{\sqrt{\gamma}}\sqrt{\frac{N}{N_*} - 1} \tag{21.55}$$

or

$$f = \frac{2h\left(1 + \frac{a^2}{b^2}\right)}{\sqrt{3(1-\nu^2)\left(3 + \frac{a^4}{b^4}\right)}}\sqrt{\frac{N}{N_*} - 1}\,.$$

Formula (21.55) gives real values for f only if $N \geq N_*$ (post-critical stage).

As an example, consider the case of a square plate with $a = b$, and $\nu = 0.3$. Formula (21.53) gives $\gamma \approx 0.75(\omega^2/h^2)$, and thus

$$f \approx 1.21\,h\sqrt{\frac{N}{N_*} - 1}\,.$$

Timoshenko [2] solved an analogous problem by the energy method and obtained the formula

$$f \approx 0.845\,h\sqrt{\frac{N}{N_*} - 1}\,.$$

The difference in deflections is about 50 percent and must be attributed to certain differences in the boundary conditions[47] and also to the peculiarity of the energy method which results in deformation values which are too low.

Another particular case of Eq. (21.54) is the equation for the natural frequencies

$$f'' + \omega^2 f + \gamma f^3 = 0 . \tag{21.56}$$

For the nonlinear frequency $\bar{\omega}$ we obtain, according to (4.21),

$$\bar{\omega} = \omega \sqrt{1 + \frac{3}{4}\frac{\gamma}{\omega^2} a^2} .$$

Thus, the natural frequency increases with increasing amplitude. In the example analyzed above at the amplitude of vibrations $a = h$, the natural frequency $\bar{\omega}$ exceeds the natural frequency calculated from linear theory by 25 percent.

●3. We will now consider a case with somewhat different boundary conditions. We assume that the vertical edges of the plate can displace while remaining straight (Fig. 165).

The boundary conditions can be satisfied by:

$$\begin{aligned} u_0(x, y, t) &= (a - 2x)\varphi_x(t)\frac{1 - \nu^2}{Eh} , \\ v_0(x, y, t) &= -y\varphi_y(t)\frac{1 - \nu^2}{Eh} , \end{aligned} \tag{21.57}$$

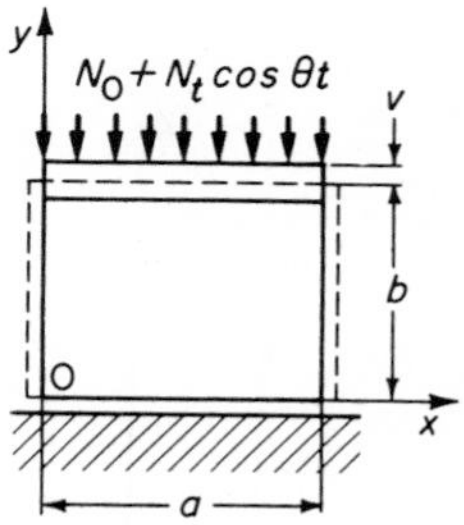

FIG. 165.

where $\varphi_x(t)$ and $\varphi_y(t)$ are unknown functions of time. For their determination, we have the conditions

$$\begin{aligned} \int_0^a N_y(x, b)dx &= -(N_0 + N_t \cos \theta t)a , \\ \int_0^b N_x(0, y)dy &= \int_0^b N_x(a, y)dy = 0 , \end{aligned} \tag{21.58}$$

the second of which states that the sum of the normal forces, acting along the edges $x = 0$ and $x = a$, is equal to zero. Using (21.50), (21.57), and (21.58) we find that

$$\begin{aligned} \varphi_x(t) &= \frac{Eh}{1 - \nu^2}\frac{\pi^2 f^2}{16a^2} - \frac{\nu}{2(1 - \nu^2)}(N_0 + N_t \cos \theta t) , \\ \varphi_y(t) &= \frac{Eh}{1 - \nu^2}\frac{\pi^2 f^2}{8b^2} + \frac{1}{1 - \nu^2}(N_0 + N_t \cos \theta t) . \end{aligned}$$

For the determination of longitudinal forces, we obtain the following expressions:

$$\begin{aligned} N_x &= -\frac{\pi^2 f^2 Eh}{8a^2}\cos\frac{2\pi y}{b} , \\ N_y &= -\left(\frac{\pi^2 f^2 Eh}{8b^2}\cos\frac{2\pi x}{a} + N_0 + N_t \cos \theta t\right) . \end{aligned} \tag{21.59}$$

[47] In the problem considered by Timoshenko, displacements along edges $x = 0$ and $x = a$ were also equal to zero. The boundary conditions considered here are obviously not so rigorous.

Substituting Eqs. (21.59) into (21.52) and evaluating the integrals, we again obtain an equation of the type (21.54):

$$f'' + \omega^2\left(1 - \frac{N_0 + N_t \cos \theta t}{N_*}\right) f + \gamma f^3 = 0\,,$$

where

$$N_* = \frac{\pi^2 D}{b^2}\left(1 + \frac{b^2}{a^2}\right)^2,$$

$$\gamma = \frac{\pi^4 Eh}{16m}\left(\frac{1}{a^4} + \frac{1}{b^4}\right) = \frac{3\omega^2(1-\nu^2)}{4h^2}\,\frac{1 + \frac{a^4}{b^4}}{\left(1 + \frac{a^2}{b^2}\right)^2}\,.$$

For a square plate with $\nu = 0.3$, we find that

$$\gamma \approx 0.341\,\frac{\omega^2}{h^2}\,,$$

from which, by formula (21.55),

$$f \approx 1.71\,h\sqrt{\frac{N}{N_*} - 1}\,.$$

For an analogous problem Timoshenko obtained

$$f = 1.11\,h\sqrt{\frac{N}{N_*} - 1}\,;$$

here the difference is also about 50 percent. It can be explained as in the previous case.

It is also possible to investigate other particular problems. Under the assumptions made above, the investigation of these problems leads to an equation of the type (21.54), where ω is the natural frequency and N_* is the critical load parameter. If the problem of static deflections of the plate in the post-critical stage is solved in some way, then the necessity of determining the coefficient γ is eliminated. In fact, the known approximate formulas for the deflection of a plate in the post-critical stage have the same structure:

$$f = kh\sqrt{\frac{N}{N_*} - 1}\,.$$

If the coefficient k is known, we can easily determine the coefficient of the nonlinear elasticity

$$\gamma = \frac{\omega^2}{k^2 h^2}\,.$$

For example, for a circular plate clamped along the edge and loaded by a radial compressive load q, we have the formula[48]

[48] Grigolyuk [1].

$$f = 2.14\,h\sqrt{\left(\frac{q}{q_*} - 1\right)\frac{1}{1-\nu^2}}\,.$$

Hence,

$$\gamma = \frac{\omega^2(1-\nu^2)}{4.58h^2}\,.$$

● **4.** Introducing the free vibration frequency of a plate loaded by a constant component of axial force as

$$\Omega = \omega\sqrt{1 - \frac{N_0}{N_*}}$$

and with the coefficient of excitation

$$\mu = \frac{N_t}{2(N_* - N_0)}\,,$$

we can rewrite Eq. (21.54) in the form

$$f'' + \Omega^2(1 - 2\mu\cos\theta t)f + \gamma f^3 = 0\,. \tag{21.60}$$

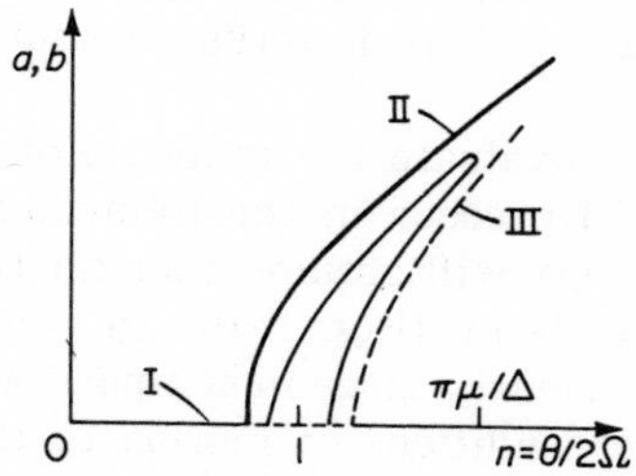

FIG. 166.

In the harmonic approximation, the steady-state solution will be

$$f(t) = a\sin\frac{\theta t}{2} + b\cos\frac{\theta t}{2}\,. \tag{21.61}$$

As was shown in § 20, three solutions of this form exist:

$$\begin{aligned} &\text{I.}\quad a = b = 0\,,\\ &\text{II.}\quad a = \frac{2\Omega}{\sqrt{3\gamma}}\sqrt{\frac{\theta^2}{4\Omega^2} - 1 + \mu}\,,\quad b = 0\,,\\ &\text{III.}\quad a = 0\,,\quad b = \frac{2\Omega}{\sqrt{3\gamma}}\sqrt{\frac{\theta^2}{4\Omega^2} - 1 - \mu}\,. \end{aligned} \tag{21.62}$$

The first of these solutions corresponds, obviously, to the plane form of the plate; the other two correspond to steady-state bending vibrations. These solutions are represented in Figure 166. As is apparent from the diagram, solution III is unstable. The "overhang" of the vibrations takes place in the direction of higher frequencies. Adding to Eq. (21.60) the damping term we obtain

$$f'' + 2\varepsilon f' + \Omega^2(1 - 2\mu\cos\theta t)f + \gamma f^3 = 0\,.$$

As before, we seek the periodic solutions of the same form as (21.61). The nontrivial solutions can be expressed by the formula

$$A = \frac{2\Omega}{\sqrt{3\gamma}}\sqrt{n^2 - 1 \pm \sqrt{\mu^2 - \frac{n^2\Delta^2}{\pi^2}}}\,,$$

where

$$A^2 = a^2 + b^2\,,\quad n = \frac{\theta}{2\Omega}\,,\quad \text{and}\quad \Delta = \frac{2\pi\varepsilon}{\Omega}\,.$$

As is evident from the formula obtained that in the presence of damping, the "overhang" of the vibrations is possible only for a frequency that does not exceed $n = (\pi\mu/\Delta)$ (see Figure 166 where the solution with damping taken into account is shown by thin lines).

§ 101. Consideration of Longitudinal Inertia Forces[49]

● **1.** Thus far inertia forces arising from displacements of the plate in its own plane have not been taken into account. In other words, the plane form of equilibrium of the plate rather than the plane form of motion was perturbed. The problem has been treated in this way in the majority of previously published works without, however, the necessary reservations being made.

To evaluate the influence of the vibrations of the plate in its own plane, we will proceed in the following way. Neglecting inertia forces of the plate itself, we will assume that all the "longitudinal" mass is concentrated in the loading beam (Fig. 164). In other words, it will be assumed that the beam is sufficiently large in comparison with the mass of the plate. Consideration of the conditions of motion of the beam gives

$$\int_0^a N_y(x, b)dx = -\left(N_0 + N_t \cos \theta t + m_0 \frac{d^2 V}{dt^2}\right)a , \tag{21.63}$$

where m_0 is the mass of the beam per unit length and $V(t) = v(b, t)$. As before, the beam is assumed to be absolutely rigid. The geometrical boundary conditions for the first particular problem of § 100 will be satisfied if we assume

$$u_0(x, y, t) = 0 , \qquad v_0(x, y, t) = -\varphi(t)y \frac{1-\nu^2}{Eh} ,$$

where $\varphi(t)$ is an unknown function. Then

$$\begin{aligned} N_x &= \frac{Eh}{1-\nu^2} \frac{\pi^2 f^2}{8a^2} \left[1 + \frac{\nu a^2}{b^2} - (1-\nu^2) \cos \frac{2\pi y}{b}\right] - \nu\varphi(t) , \\ N_y &= \frac{Eh}{1-\nu^2} \frac{\pi^2 f^2}{8b^2} \left[1 + \frac{\nu b^2}{a^2} - (1-\nu^2) \cos \frac{2\pi x}{a}\right] - \varphi(t) , \\ N_{xy} &= 0 . \end{aligned} \tag{21.64}$$

Substituting the second of formulas (21.64) into (21.63) gives an equation connecting $f(t)$ and $\varphi(t)$:

$$\frac{1}{\omega_0^2} \varphi'' + \varphi = N_0 + N_t \cos \theta t + \frac{\pi^2 f^2 Eh}{8(1-\nu^2)} \left(\frac{\nu}{a^2} + \frac{1}{b^2}\right) .$$

Here

$$\omega_0 = \sqrt{\frac{Eh}{m_0 b(1-\nu^2)}}$$

is the free vibration frequency of the plate in its own plane, calculated on the assumption that the entire mass is concentrated on the edge $y = b$.

[49] Bolotin [9].

To obtain the second equation, we start from (21.52):

$$f'' + \omega^2 f + \frac{4\pi^2 f}{abm}\int_0^a\int_0^b\left[\left(\frac{N_x}{a^2}+\frac{N_y}{b^2}\right)\sin^2\frac{\pi x}{a}\sin^2\frac{\pi y}{b} + \frac{N_{xy}}{2ab}\sin\frac{2\pi x}{a}\sin\frac{2\pi y}{b}\right]dxdy = 0\,,$$

where this time we substitute expressions (21.64). Evaluating the integrals we find that

$$f'' + \omega^2 f + \frac{\pi^4 f^3 Eh}{8m(1-\nu^2)}\left(\frac{3-\nu^2}{2a^4}+\frac{3-\nu^2}{2b^4}+\frac{2\nu}{a^2b^2}\right) - \frac{\pi^2 f\varphi}{m}\left(\frac{\nu}{a^2}+\frac{1}{b^2}\right) = 0\,.$$

● **2.** The problem then reduces to the solution of a system of nonlinear equations:

$$\frac{1}{\omega_0^2}\varphi'' + \varphi = N_0 + N_t\cos\theta t + \frac{\pi^2 f^2 Eh}{8(1-\nu^2)}\left(\frac{\nu}{a^2}+\frac{1}{b^2}\right),$$
$$f'' + \omega^2 f + \lambda f^3 - \kappa f\varphi = 0\,. \qquad (21.65)$$

In the second equation, for brevity, we have denoted

$$\lambda = \frac{\pi^4 Eh}{8m(1-\nu^2)}\left(\frac{3-\nu^2}{2a^4}+\frac{3-\nu^2}{2b^4}+\frac{2\nu}{a^2b^2}\right),$$
$$\kappa = \frac{\pi^2}{m}\left(\frac{\nu}{a^2}+\frac{1}{b^2}\right).$$

As before, we will assume

$$f(t) = f_0\cos\frac{\theta t}{2}\,. \qquad (21.66)$$

As is evident from Eqs. (21.65),

$$\varphi(t) = \varphi_0 + \varphi_1\cos\theta t\,, \qquad (21.67)$$

where φ_0 and φ_1 are unknown constants. Substituting Eqs. (21.66) and (21.67) into the first of Eqs. (21.65) and comparing the constant terms on the left- and right-hand sides of the equation, we obtain

$$\varphi_0 = N_0 + \frac{\pi^2 f_0^2 Eh}{16(1-\nu^2)}\left(\frac{\nu}{a^2}+\frac{1}{b^2}\right). \qquad (21.68)$$

Comparing the coefficients of $\cos\theta t$ gives

$$\varphi_1 = \alpha N_t + \frac{\alpha\pi^2 f_0^2 Eh}{16(1-\nu^2)}\left(\frac{\nu}{a^2}+\frac{1}{b^2}\right), \qquad (21.69)$$

where

$$\alpha = \frac{1}{1-\dfrac{\theta^2}{\omega_0^2}}\,.$$

Finally, Eqs. (21.66) and (21.67) are substituted into the second of Eqs. (21.65). Ultilizing the relationships

$$\cos^3 \frac{\theta t}{2} = \frac{3}{4} \cos \frac{\theta t}{2} + \frac{1}{4} \cos \frac{3\theta t}{2},$$

$$\cos \frac{\theta t}{2} \cos \theta t = \frac{1}{2} \cos \frac{\theta t}{2} + \frac{1}{2} \cos \frac{3\theta t}{2},$$

we obtain after comparing the coefficients of $\cos \theta t/2$,

$$\left(\omega^2 - \frac{\theta^2}{4}\right) f_0 + \frac{3}{4} \lambda f_0^3 - \kappa f_0 \left(\varphi_0 + \frac{1}{2} \varphi_1\right) = 0 . \tag{21.70}$$

Substitution of (21.68) and (21.69) into (21.70) gives

$$\left[\omega^2 - \frac{\theta^2}{4} - \kappa \left(N_0 + \frac{1}{2} \alpha N_t\right)\right] f_0$$
$$+ \left[\frac{3}{4} \lambda - \frac{\pi^2 \kappa Eh}{16(1-\nu^2)} \left(\frac{\nu}{a^2} + \frac{1}{b^2}\right)\left(1 + \frac{1}{2} \alpha\right)\right] f_0^3 = 0 .$$

Aside from the trivial solution, which has an obvious physical meaning, the equation has the roots

$$f_0^2 = \frac{\dfrac{\theta^2}{4} - \omega^2 + \kappa\left(N_0 + \dfrac{1}{2} \alpha N_t\right)}{\dfrac{3}{4} \lambda - \dfrac{\pi^2 \kappa Eh}{16(1-\nu^2)} \left(\dfrac{\nu}{a^2} + \dfrac{1}{b^2}\right)\left(1 + \dfrac{1}{2} \alpha\right)} . \tag{21.71}$$

Recalling the notation used in § 100, we can write

$$\kappa = \frac{\pi^2}{m} \left(\frac{\nu}{a^2} + \frac{1}{b^2}\right) = \frac{\omega^2}{N_*}.$$

On the other hand,

$$\omega^2\left(1 - \frac{N_0}{N_*}\right) = \Omega^2 , \qquad \frac{N_t}{2N_*\left(1 - \dfrac{N_0}{N_*}\right)} = \mu ,$$

as a result of which the numerator of formula (21.71) assumes the form

$$\frac{\theta^2}{4} - \Omega^2(1 - \alpha\mu) .$$

We now focus our attention on the transformation of the denominator writing it in the following form:

$$\frac{3}{4} \lambda - \frac{\pi^2 \kappa Eh}{16(1-\nu^2)} \left(\frac{\nu}{a^2} + \frac{1}{b^2}\right)\left(1 - \frac{\alpha}{2}\right) = \frac{3}{4} \gamma(\alpha) ,$$

where

$$\gamma(\alpha) = \frac{\pi^4 Eh}{8m(1-\nu^2)} \left(\frac{3-\nu^2}{2a^4} + \frac{3-\nu^2}{2b^4} + \frac{2\nu}{a^2 b^2}\right)$$
$$- \frac{\pi^2 \kappa Eh}{12(1-\nu^2)} \left(\frac{\nu}{a^2} + \frac{1}{b^2}\right)\left(1 + \frac{\alpha}{2}\right).$$

It can be easily verified that

$$\frac{\pi^4 Eh}{8m(1-\nu^2)}\left(\frac{3-\nu^2}{2a^4}+\frac{3-\nu^2}{2b^4}+\frac{2\nu}{a^2b^2}\right)-\frac{\pi^2\kappa Eh}{8(1-\nu^2)}\left(\frac{\nu}{a^2}+\frac{1}{b^2}\right)=\gamma\,.$$

Consequently,

$$\gamma(\alpha) = \gamma[1-c(\alpha-1)]\,,$$

where

$$c = \frac{2}{3}\,\frac{\left(1+\dfrac{\nu b^2}{a^2}\right)^2}{1+\dfrac{3b^4}{a^4}}\,.$$

Finally,

$$f_0 = \pm\frac{2\Omega}{\sqrt{3\gamma}}\sqrt{\frac{\dfrac{\theta^2}{4\Omega^2}-1+\alpha\mu}{1-c(\alpha-1)}}\,. \tag{21.72}$$

Above we have examined solutions of the type (21.66). The solution

$$f(t) = f_0\sin\frac{\theta t}{2}$$

corresponds to unstable vibrations, i.e., those which have no physical meaning. If the longitudinal inertia forces predominate, this solution may be stable.

Assuming, as before, that

$$\varphi(t) = \varphi_0+\varphi_1\cos\theta t\,,$$

we find that

$$\varphi_0 = N_0+\frac{\pi^2 f_0^2 Eh}{16(1-\nu^2)}\left(\frac{\nu}{a^2}+\frac{1}{b^2}\right),$$

$$\varphi_1 = \alpha N_t-\frac{\alpha\pi^2 f_0^2 Eh}{16(1-\nu^2)}\left(\frac{\nu}{a^2}+\frac{1}{b^2}\right).$$

In place of Eq. (21.70), we obtain

$$\left(\omega^2-\frac{\theta^2}{4}\right)f_0+\frac{3}{4}\lambda f_0^3-\kappa f_0\left(\varphi_0-\frac{1}{2}\varphi_1\right) = 0\,.$$

Omitting the calculations, we can express the final result as

$$f_0 = \pm\frac{2\Omega}{\sqrt{3\gamma}}\sqrt{\frac{\dfrac{\theta^2}{4\Omega^2}-1-\alpha\mu}{1-c(\alpha-1)}}\,.$$

● **3.** If the mass of the beam approaches zero, then $\omega_0\to\infty$ and $\alpha\to 1$. In this limiting case, formula (21.72) coincides with the corresponding formula (21.62). Let us now consider the case of the finite frequency ω_0. We denote

$$\frac{\theta^2}{4\Omega^2} = n^2\,,\qquad \frac{4\Omega^2}{\omega_0^2} = \beta\,;$$

then

$$\alpha = \frac{1}{1 - \beta n^2},$$

and the expression under the radical can be written as

$$\Phi_+(n^2) = \frac{(n^2 - 1)(1 - \beta n^2) + \mu}{1 - \beta n^2(1 + c)}.$$

We also introduce a function

$$\Phi_-(n^2) = \frac{(n^2 - 1)(1 - \beta n^2) - \mu}{1 - \beta n^2(1 + c)}.$$

An example for the functions $\Phi_+(n^2)$ and $\Phi_-(n^2)$ is shown in Figure 167. We find the zeros of the function which, as will be shown later, define the limits of the regions of instability for the trivial solution from the condition

$$(n^2 - 1)(1 - \beta n^2) \pm \mu = 0,$$

from which

$$n^2 = \frac{1 + \beta \pm \sqrt{(1 - \beta)^2 \pm 4\beta\mu}}{2\beta}. \tag{21.73}$$

Let us denote the zeros in the increasing order n_1, n_2, n_3, n_4. It is easily seen that $n_1^2 < 1 < n_2^2$, i.e., the first region of instability lies near $n^2 = 1$ (principal parametric resonance). Furthermore, $n_3^2 < 1/\beta < n_4^2$, which means that the second region corresponds to the resonance with respect to the "longitudinal" frequency ω_0. Both functions have a discontinuity in the neighborhood of

$$n_\infty^2 = \frac{1}{\beta(1 + c)}.$$

The variation of steady-state amplitudes is shown in Figure 168. As before, the dotted lines represent the unstable solutions. The thin lines represent solutions (21.62) in which the mass of the beam is not considered.

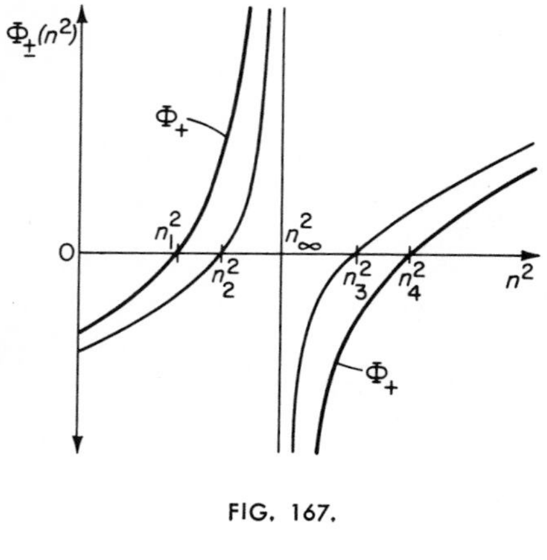

FIG. 167.

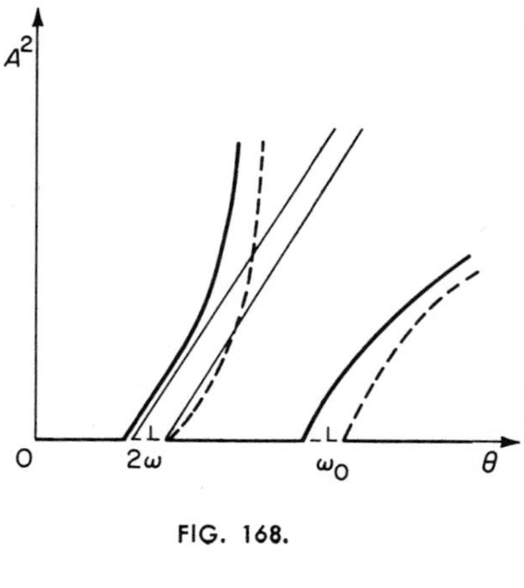

FIG. 168.

We wish to investigate the behavior of the system as the excitation frequency is gradually increased. As long as $n < n_1$, there exists a unique solution, and it is stable—this is the plane form of the vibrations of a plate. At $n = n_1$ there occurs a branching out of the forms of motion; the trivial solution is unstable from n_1 to n_2. For $n > n_2$, three solutions exist, one of which (the middle one) is unstable. It forms the boundary of stability of the vibrations. The steady-state transverse vibrations which arise in the interval (n_1, n_2) may form an "overhang" toward the increasing frequencies. The upper frequency boundary of the transverse vibrations depends on the disturbances acting on the system (fluctuation of the frequency or phase of the perturbation load, etc.). If the disturbances are sufficiently large, the system may enter the region of the trivial solution; then a sudden break of transverse vibrations will occur. On the other hand, a sufficiently strong impulse (in the right phase) which the system receives in the interval (n_2, n_∞) can transfer it from a condition of the plane state of motion into the state of steady-state transverse vibrations. In general, the depth of the overhang is limited by the frequency n_∞ or, if we take damping into account, by a slightly smaller frequency.

The trivial solution is stable up to the frequency n_3, beyond which the second resonance begins. This frequency had not been discovered, either in the framework of the usual linear theory or in the approximate investigations of nonlinear problems. Figure 169 shows the distribution of the regions of instability of the trivial solutions in the n^2, μ plane. The thin unbroken lines are the boundaries of the principal region of instability, calculated on the basis of conventional theory.

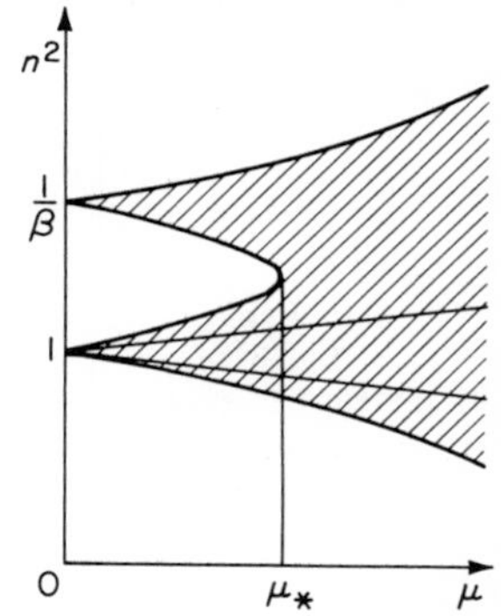

FIG. 169.

Additional regions are not shown (compare with Figure 5). An analogous phenomenon was encountered in the problems on the dynamic stability of straight rods in which the effect of longitudinal inertial forces was considered (Chapter Eight).

As can be seen from formula (21.73), the influence of the mass of the beam is very important for $\beta \sim 1$, i.e., for $\omega_0 \sim 2\Omega$. In this case, both resonance frequencies approach each other, and for sufficiently large $\mu (\mu > \mu_*)$ they generally coincide. It is obvious from (19.73) that

$$\mu_* = \frac{(1-\beta)^2}{4\beta}.$$

Note that the graphs in Figures 167 and 168 were constructed under the assumption that $\mu < \mu_*$. The variation of functions $\Phi_+(n^2)$ and $\Phi_-(n^2)$ and amplitudes for $\mu > \mu_*$ are given in Figures 170 and 171.

Let us now give the estimate for $\beta = 4\Omega^2/\omega_0^2$. If the plate is compressed then

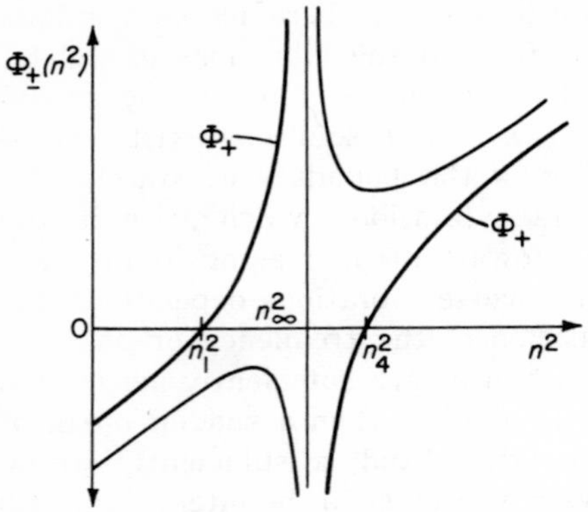

FIG. 170.

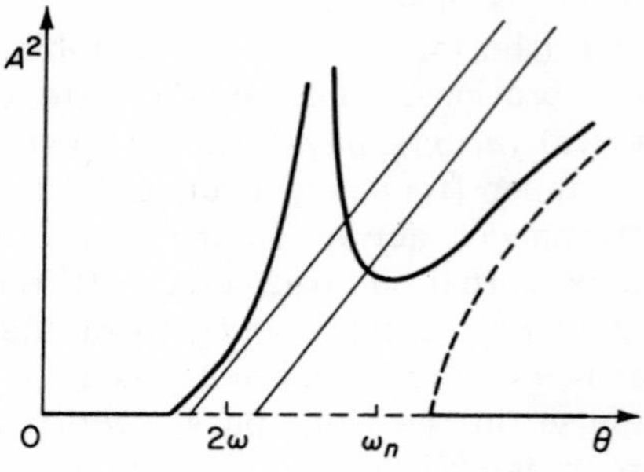

FIG. 171.

$$\Omega^2 \leq \omega^2 = \frac{\pi^4 D}{m}\left(\frac{1}{a^2} + \frac{1}{b^2}\right)^2 .$$

On the other hand,

$$\omega_0^{\ 2} = \frac{Eh}{m_0 b(1 - \nu^2)} .$$

Thus

$$\beta \leq \frac{\pi^4 m_0 bh^2}{3m}\left(\frac{1}{a^2} + \frac{1}{b^2}\right)^2$$

or, noting that $mab = M$, $m_0 a = M_0$,

$$\beta \leq \frac{\pi^4 M_0}{3M}\left(\frac{h}{a}\right)^2\left(\frac{a}{b} + \frac{b}{a}\right)^2 .$$

This means that β decreases with a decrease of the mass of the loading beam and the thickness of the plate. Let $a = b$, and $h = 0.01a$. Then

$$\beta \leq \frac{M_0}{75M} .$$

If $M_0 = 10M$, then $\beta \approx 0.13$ and the influence of longitudinal forces on the amplitudes is small for $\theta = 2\Omega$. Thus, on the upper boundary of the instability region ($n = n_2$), the third of formulas (21.62) gives

$$A = \frac{2\Omega}{\sqrt{3}}\sqrt{\frac{2\mu}{1-\mu}} . \qquad (21.74)$$

Correspondingly, from formula (21.72) we obtain

$$A = \frac{2\Omega}{\sqrt{3}\gamma}\sqrt{\frac{2\alpha\mu}{1 - c(\alpha - 1)}} . \qquad (21.75)$$

If $a = b$, and $\nu = 0.25$, then $c \approx 0.261$. Furthermore, from formula (21.73), for $\mu = 0.1$ we find that $n_2^{\,2} = 1.12$ and, consequently,

$$\alpha = \frac{1}{1 - \beta n^2} = 1.16\,.$$

The radical in formula (21.74) is

$$\sqrt{\frac{2\mu}{1-\mu}} = 0.472\,,$$

while the one in formula (21.75) is

$$\sqrt{\frac{2\alpha\mu}{1-c(\alpha-1)}} = 0.491\,.$$

The difference in amplitudes is about 4 percent. Consequently, the refined theory is applicable to sufficiently thick plates and heavy edge beams.

● **4.** In conclusion, an estimate will be given for the magnitudes of the resonance amplitudes. According to formula (21.53),

$$\gamma = \frac{3(1-\nu^2)\omega^2}{4h^2}\,\frac{3 + \dfrac{a^4}{b^4}}{\left(1 + \dfrac{a^2}{b^2}\right)^2}\,.$$

If we neglect the constant component of load N_0, then $\omega^2 = \Omega^2$, from which

$$\frac{4\Omega^2}{3\gamma} = \frac{16h^2}{9(1-\nu^2)}\,\frac{\left(1 + \dfrac{a^2}{b^2}\right)^2}{3 + \dfrac{a^4}{b^4}} \approx 1.95h^2$$

(for $a = b$ and $\nu = 0.3$). From formula (21.74),

$$A \approx 1.40h\sqrt{\frac{2\mu}{1-\mu}}\,.$$

Using the values given in the previous example, we find that $A = 0.63h$.

Calculating now the normal stresses due to bending,

$$\sigma_x = \frac{Eh}{2(1-\nu^2)}\left(\frac{\partial^2 w}{\partial x^2} + \nu\frac{\partial^2 w}{\partial y^2}\right).$$

In the center of the plate,

$$|\,\sigma_x\,| = \frac{\pi^2 EhA}{2(1-\nu^2)}\left(\frac{1}{a^2} + \frac{\nu}{b^2}\right).$$

The calculation gives

$$\sigma_x \sim 0.7\frac{Ah}{a^2}E\,.$$

For $h = 0.01a$ and $E = 2.1 \times 10^6\ \text{kg/cm}^2$, we obtain $\sigma_x \sim 928\ \text{kg/cm}^2$. These stresses are not very large if we consider that in the problem investigated the amplitude of the longitudinal force is $N_t \sim 0.2N_*$. In practice, considerably smaller amplitudes are usually encountered; for such amplitudes the influence of damping must be considered. To the stresses that were obtained, it is necessary to add the stresses uniformly distributed across the thickness of the plate. These must be calculated taking into account the deformation of the middle surface.

Twenty-Two

DYNAMIC STABILITY OF SHELLS

§ 102. Statement of the Problem

● 1. The deformed state of a shell is characterized by the displacements of its points lying on the middle plane. Let α and β be curvilinear orthogonal coordinates of the middle surface chosen in such a way that the lines $\alpha =$ const. and $\beta =$ const. represent the lines of principal curvatures of the middle plane. The deformed state is defined when the tangential displacements $u(\alpha, \beta)$ and $v(\alpha, \beta)$ of points along the lines of principal curvatures and the normal displacement $w(\alpha, \beta)$ are known.

We shall investigate the behavior of the shell under the action of an external surface load that changes with time according to the periodic law

$$X_0(\alpha, \beta, t), \qquad Y_0(\alpha, \beta, t), \qquad Z_0(\alpha, \beta, t). \tag{22.1}$$

Let the load (22.1) be such that it causes a membrane state of stress in the shell. For certain relations between parameters, this state can be shown to be dynamically unstable. In the membrane state, let the displacements of points in the middle plane be equal to u_0, v_0, and w_0.

Transition to a condition with bending gives us the displacements

$$\begin{aligned} u &= u_0 + \bar{u}, \\ v &= v_0 + \bar{v}, \\ w &= w_0 + \bar{w}, \end{aligned} \tag{22.2}$$

Displacements u, v, and w satisfy the equations of the bending theory:[50]

$$\begin{aligned} L_{11}(u) + L_{12}(v) + L_{13}(w) + \frac{1-\nu^2}{Eh} X &= 0, \\ L_{21}(u) + L_{22}(v) + L_{23}(w) + \frac{1-\nu^2}{Eh} Y &= 0, \\ L_{31}(u) + L_{32}(v) + L_{33}(w) + \frac{1-\nu^2}{Eh} Z &= 0, \end{aligned} \tag{22.3}$$

where $L_{11}, L_{12}, \cdots, L_{33}$ are linear differential operators referred to the lines of principal curvatures, h is the thickness of the shell, and $X, Y, Z,$ are the components of the surface load. This latter load is composed of the assigned external loading (22.1), inertia forces, and additional reduced loading (ΔX,

50 Vlasov [2].

ΔY, ΔZ, etc.) formed during the deflection of the middle surface from the initial membrane state i.e.,

$$X = X_0 + \Delta X - m\frac{\partial^2 u}{\partial t^2},$$
$$Y = Y_0 + \Delta Y - m\frac{\partial^2 v}{\partial t^2}, \tag{22.4}$$
$$Z = Z_0 + \Delta Z - m\frac{\partial^2 w}{\partial t^2}.$$

Here m is the mass of the shell per unit area of the middle surface.

Substituting (22.2) and (22.4) into Eqs. (22.3) and taking into account that the unperturbed parameters are related by the equations

$$L_{11}(u_0) + L_{12}(v_0) + L_{13}(w_0) + \frac{1-\nu^2}{Eh}\left(X_0 - m\frac{\partial^2 u_0}{\partial t^2}\right) = 0,$$
$$L_{21}(u_0) + L_{22}(v_0) + L_{23}(w_0) + \frac{1-\nu^2}{Eh}\left(Y_0 - m\frac{\partial^2 v_0}{\partial t^2}\right) = 0,$$
$$L_{31}(u_0) + L_{32}(v_0) + L_{33}(w_0) + \frac{1-\nu^2}{Eh}\left(Z_0 - m\frac{\partial^2 w_0}{\partial t^2}\right) = 0,$$

we obtain the "variational equations"

$$L_{11}(\bar{u}) + L_{12}(\bar{v}) + L_{13}(\bar{w}) + \frac{1-\nu^2}{Eh}\left(\Delta X - m\frac{\partial^2 \bar{u}}{\partial t^2}\right) = 0,$$
$$L_{21}(\bar{u}) + L_{22}(\bar{v}) + L_{23}(\bar{w}) + \frac{1-\nu^2}{Eh}\left(\Delta Y - m\frac{\partial^2 \bar{v}}{\partial t^2}\right) = 0, \tag{22.5}$$
$$L_{31}(\bar{u}) + L_{32}(\bar{v}) + L_{33}(\bar{w}) + \frac{1-\nu^2}{Eh}\left(\Delta Z - m\frac{\partial^2 \bar{w}}{\partial t^2}\right) = 0.$$

Further on we omit the bars over the displacements $\bar{u}$, $\bar{v}$, and $\bar{w}$.

●**2.** We proceed now to the determination of components of the reduced loads ΔX, ΔY, and ΔZ. It is assumed that the membrane state is characterized by the normal forces $N_1(\alpha, \beta, t)$ and $N_2(\alpha, \beta, t)$, which will be regarded as positive if they cause compression. Neglecting the inertia forces in the membrane state, we can calculate the internal forces from the equations of membrane theory[51]

$$\frac{\partial}{\partial \alpha}(BN_1) - N_2\frac{\partial B}{\partial \alpha} = ABX_0,$$
$$\frac{\partial}{\partial \beta}(AN_2) - N_1\frac{\partial A}{\partial \beta} = ABY_0, \tag{22.6}$$
$$k_1 N_1 + k_2 N_2 = Z_0.$$

Here A and B are coefficients of the first quadratic form of the middle surface referred to the lines of principal curvatures as in

[51] Vlasov [2].

$$ds^2 = A^2 d\alpha^2 + B^2 d\beta^2, \tag{22.7}$$

and k_1 and k_2 are the principal curvatures. Equations (22.6) express the equilibrium of an element of a shell having an area $AB\,d\alpha\,d\beta$. The first two equations require that the sum of the projections of all the forces in the direction tangent to, lines $\alpha = \text{const.}$ the $\beta = \text{const.}$ is equal to zero, while the last equation expresses equality to zero of the normal component.

Let ε_1 and ε_2 be the relative longitudinal elongations, and κ_1 and κ_2 be the increases of the principal curvatures due to bending deformation. Then the first quadratic form (22.7) becomes

$$ds^2 = A^2(1+\varepsilon_1)^2\,d\alpha^2 + B^2(1+\varepsilon_2)^2 d\beta^2;$$

consequently, in place of A and B, it is necessary to substitute $A(1+\varepsilon_1)$ and $B(1+\varepsilon_2)$ in Eq. (22.6). In addition, in the latter equation it is necessary to replace k_1 by $k_1 + \kappa_1$, and k_2 by $k_2 + \kappa_2$. Equations (22.6) in this case are not identically satisfied; obviously, in place of X_0, Y_0, and Z_0, it is necessary to take here $X_0 + \Delta X$, $Y_0 + \Delta Y$, and $Z_0 + \Delta Z$, where ΔX, ΔY, and ΔZ are the components of the additional (reduced) load. Thus,

$$\frac{\partial}{\partial\alpha}[B(1+\varepsilon_1)N_1] - N_2\frac{\partial}{\partial\alpha}[B(1+\varepsilon_2)] = AB(1+\varepsilon_1)(1+\varepsilon_2)(X_0 + \Delta X),$$

$$\frac{\partial}{\partial\beta}[A(1+\varepsilon_1)N_2] - N_1\frac{\partial}{\partial\beta}[A(1+\varepsilon_1)] = AB(1+\varepsilon_1)(1+\varepsilon_2)(Y_0 + \Delta Y),$$

$$(k_1+\kappa_1)N_1 + (k_2+\kappa_2)N_2 = Z_0 + \Delta Z.$$

Taking into account Eq. (22.6) and neglecting the second-order quantities (i.e., products of the type $\varepsilon_1\varepsilon_2$, $\varepsilon_1\Delta X$, etc.), we obtain the following formulas:

$$\begin{aligned}
\Delta X &= \frac{1}{AB}\left[\frac{\partial}{\partial\alpha}(\varepsilon_2 BN_1) - N_2\frac{\partial}{\partial\alpha}(\varepsilon_2 B)\right] - X_0(\varepsilon_1+\varepsilon_2),\\
\Delta Y &= \frac{1}{AB}\left[\frac{\partial}{\partial\beta}(\varepsilon_1 AN_2) - N_1\frac{\partial}{\partial\beta}(\varepsilon_1 A)\right] - Y_0(\varepsilon_1+\varepsilon_2),\\
\Delta Z &= N_1\kappa_1 + N_2\kappa_2.
\end{aligned} \tag{22.8}$$

In formulas (22.8), in place of ε_1, ε_2, κ_1, and κ_2, it is necessary to substitute the expressions

$$\begin{aligned}
\varepsilon_1 &= \frac{1}{A}\frac{\partial u}{\partial\alpha} + \frac{1}{AB}\frac{\partial A}{\partial\beta}v + k_1 w,\\
\varepsilon_2 &= \frac{1}{AB}\frac{\partial B}{\partial\alpha}u + \frac{1}{B}\frac{\partial v}{\partial\beta} + k_2 w,\\
\kappa_1 &= \frac{\partial k_1}{\partial\alpha}\frac{u}{A} + \frac{\partial k_1}{\partial\beta}\frac{v}{B} - k_1^2 w - \frac{1}{A}\frac{\partial}{\partial\alpha}\left(\frac{1}{A}\frac{\partial w}{\partial\alpha}\right) - \frac{1}{AB^2}\frac{\partial A}{\partial\beta}\frac{\partial w}{\partial\beta},\\
\kappa_2 &= \frac{\partial k_2}{\partial\alpha}\frac{u}{A} + \frac{\partial k_2}{\partial\beta}\frac{v}{B} - k_2^2 w - \frac{1}{B}\frac{\partial}{\partial\beta}\left(\frac{1}{B}\frac{\partial w}{\partial\beta}\right) - \frac{1}{A^2B}\frac{\partial B}{\partial\alpha}\frac{\partial w}{\partial\alpha}.
\end{aligned} \tag{22.9}$$

Thus, the terms in Eqs. (22.5) containing ΔX, ΔY, and ΔZ are linear with respect to internal forces N_1, N_2, and also with respect to the displacements

u, v, and w and their derivatives. In the case where the external load is periodic, the forces N_1, N_2 are also periodic functions of time; in this case, system (22.5) has periodic coefficients. Assuming that

$$u(\alpha, \beta, t) = \sum u_k(t)\varphi_k(\alpha, \beta) ,$$
$$v(\alpha, \beta, t) = \sum v_k(t)\psi_k(\alpha, \beta) ,$$
$$w(\alpha, \beta, t) = \sum w_k(t)\chi_k(\alpha, \beta) ,$$

where the eigenfunctions satisfy the corresponding boundary conditions, and substituting in (22.5), we can reduce the problem to a system of ordinary differential equations with periodic coefficients. Further investigation does not entail any difficulties.

§ 103. Case of an Extremely Shallow Shell

● 1. Let us assume that in the plan view the shell has the form of a rectangle with sides a and b and, moreover, that the rise of the shell f is relatively small in comparison with the sides of the rectangle (Fig. 172). The last assumption reduces for practical purposes to a requirement that $f \leq \frac{1}{5}a$, where a is the smallest side of the rectangle. Let x, y be the Cartesian coordinates of a point on the horizontal plane. The square of the length of a line element is

$$ds^2 = dx^2 + dy^2 , \qquad (22.10)$$

i.e., for the coefficients of the first quadratic form on a plane we have $A = B = 1$. For a shallow shell, the first quadratic form of the middle surface can be taken in the form (22.10) with sufficient accuracy. Furthermore, we assume that the principal curvatures of the middle plane in the directions of axes Ox and Oy are

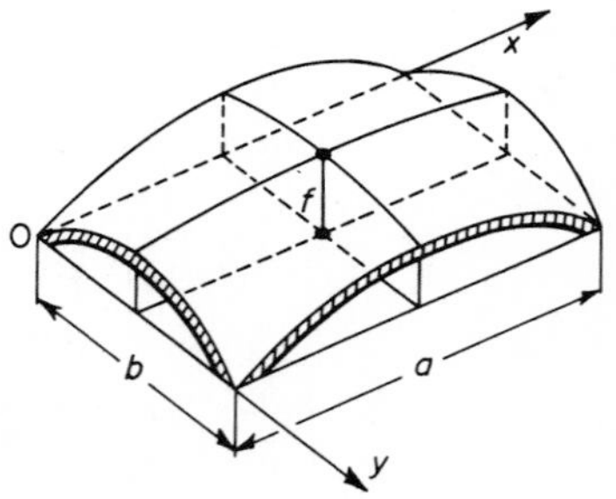

FIG. 172.

$$k_1 = \text{const} , \qquad k_2 = \text{const} . \qquad (22.11)$$

Finally, for the case of a shallow shell, the tangential components of the load can be neglected, so that $X = Y = 0$. Under these assumptions, the general equations of shells (22.3) can be reduced to one *solvable* equation.

$$\nabla^2\nabla^2\nabla^2\nabla^2 F = \frac{12(1-\nu^2)}{h^2}\nabla_k^2\nabla_k^2 F - \frac{Z}{D} = 0 . \qquad (22.12)$$

Here ∇^2 and ∇_k^2 are differential operators of the second order,

$$\nabla^2 = \frac{\partial^2}{\partial x^2} + \frac{\partial^2}{\partial y^2} ,$$

$$\nabla_k^2 = k_2\frac{\partial^2}{\partial x^2} + k_1\frac{\partial^2}{\partial y^2} ,$$

and D is the flexural stiffness of the shell:

$$D = \frac{Eh^3}{12(1-\nu^2)} \,.$$

The function $F(x, y)$ is related to the normal displacement $w(x, y)$ by the formula

$$w = \nabla^2\nabla^2 F \,.$$

The increase of principal curvatures due to the bending is determined from formulas (22.9):

$$\kappa_1 = -k_1^2 w - \frac{\partial^2 w}{\partial x^2} \approx -\frac{\partial^2 w}{\partial x^2} \,,$$

$$\kappa_2 = -k_2^2 w - \frac{\partial^2 w}{\partial y^2} \approx -\frac{\partial^2 w}{\partial y^2} \,,$$

Hence the reduced normal load is

$$\Delta Z = -\left(N_1 \frac{\partial^2}{\partial x^2} + N_2 \frac{\partial}{\partial y^2}\right)\nabla^2\nabla^2 F \,,$$

and the equation for the perturbed motion assumes the form

$$\nabla^2\nabla^2\nabla^2\nabla^2 F + \frac{12(1-\nu^2)}{h^2}\nabla_k^2\nabla_k^2 F + \frac{1}{D}\left(N_1\frac{\partial^2}{\partial x^2} + N_2\frac{\partial^2}{\partial y^2} + m\frac{\partial^2}{\partial t^2}\right)\nabla^2\nabla^2 F = 0 \,. \tag{22.14}$$

Equation (22.14) was formulated first by Vlasov [2].

●2. Assume that the shell is simply supported on all four sides. In this case the function $F(x, y, t)$ must be chosen in such a way that

$$F = \frac{\partial^2 F}{\partial x^2} = \frac{\partial^4 F}{\partial x^4} = \frac{\partial^6 F}{\partial x^6} = 0 \quad \text{at } x = 0 \text{ and } x = a \,.$$

$$F = \frac{\partial^2 F}{d y^2} = \frac{\partial^4 F}{\partial y^4} = \frac{\partial^6 F}{\partial y^6} = 0 \quad \text{at } y = 0 \text{ and } y = b \,.$$

The boundary conditions will be satisfied if we let

$$F(x, y, t) = f_{ik}(t)\sin\frac{i\pi x}{a}\sin\frac{k\pi y}{b}\,, \qquad (i, k = 1, 2, 3, \cdots) \,. \tag{22.15}$$

Here $f_{ik}(t)$ are unknown functions of time. Substituting (22.15) in (22.14), we obtain the ordinary differential equation

$$\frac{d^2 f_{ik}}{dt^2} + \omega_{ik}^2\left(1 - \frac{N_1}{N_{1*}} - \frac{N_2}{N_{2*}}\right) f_{ik} = 0 \,, \qquad (i, k = 1, 2, 3, \cdots) \,, \tag{22.16}$$

where

$$\omega_{ik}^2 = \frac{D}{m(n_i^2 + m_k^2)^2}\left[(n_i^2 + m_k^2)^4 + \frac{12(1-\nu^2)}{h^2}(k_2 n_i^2 + k_1 m_k^2)^2\right] ,$$

$$N_{1*} = \frac{D n_i^2 (n_i^2 + m_k^2)^2}{\left[(n_i^2 + m_k^2)^4 + \frac{12(1-\nu^2)}{h^2}(k_2 n_i^2 + k_1 m_k^2)^2\right]} \,, \tag{22.17}$$

$$N_{2*} = \frac{D m_k^2 (n_i^2 + m_k^2)^2}{\left[(n_i^2 + m_k^2)^4 + \frac{12(1-\nu^2)}{h^2}(k_2 n_i^2 + k_1 m_k^2)^2\right]} \,, \qquad n_i = \frac{i\pi}{a} \,, \qquad m_k = \frac{k\pi}{b} \,.$$

In this way, the problem is reduced to the "special" case of an independent single equation. Assuming, in particular,

$$N_1 = N_{10} + N_{1t} \cos \theta t ,$$
$$N_2 = N_{20} + N_{2t} \cos \theta t ,$$

we obtain the Mathieu equation.[52]

§ 104. Dynamic Stability of A Circular Cylindrical Shell

●1. Assume that the circular cylindrical shell of radius R and a thickness h is loaded by a uniformly distributed radial load $q_0 + q_t \cos \theta t$, and, in addition, compressed by a longitudinal force $P_0 + P_t \cos \theta t$. We select the coordinate system as shown in Figure 173; that is, we introduce a nondimensional longitudinal coordinate $\alpha = z/R$. We denote the displacements in the longitudinal direction by u, the circumferential displacements by v, and, finally, the radial displacements by w.

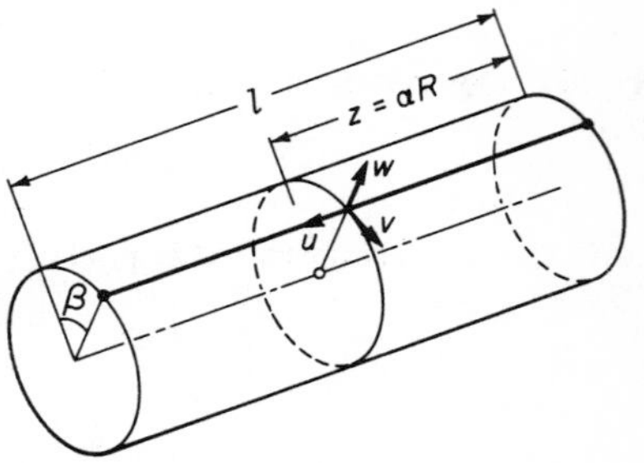

FIG. 173.

For a cylindrical shell, it is necessary to let.[53]

$$L_{11} = \frac{\partial^2}{\partial \alpha^2} + \frac{1-\nu}{2}\frac{\partial^2}{\partial \beta^2}, \qquad L_{22} = \frac{\partial^2}{\partial \beta^2} + \frac{1-\nu}{2}\frac{\partial^2}{\partial \alpha^2},$$
$$L_{33} = c^2\nabla^2\nabla^2 ,$$
$$L_{12} = L_{21} = \frac{1+\nu}{2}\frac{\partial^2}{\partial \alpha\, \partial \beta}, \qquad L_{13} = L_{31} = \nu\frac{\partial}{\partial \alpha}, \tag{22.18}$$
$$L_{23} = L_{32} = \frac{\partial}{\partial \beta},$$

when the engineering bending theory approximation is used. Here

$$c^2 = \frac{h^2}{12R^2},$$
$$\nabla^2 = \frac{\partial^2}{\partial \alpha^2} + \frac{\partial}{\partial \beta^2}, \qquad \nabla^2\nabla^2 = \frac{\partial^4}{\partial \alpha^4} + 2\frac{\partial^4}{\partial \alpha^2 \partial \beta^2} + \frac{\partial^4}{\partial \beta^4}. \tag{22.19}$$

Let us now calculate the components of the reduced load ΔX, ΔY, ΔZ. The internal forces corresponding to the initial membrane state are

$$N_1 = \frac{1}{2\pi R}(P_0 + P_t \cos \theta t),$$
$$N_2 = R(q_0 + q_t \cos \theta t). \tag{22.20}$$

[52] Oniashvili [1].

[53] For the preservation of symmetry of matrix L_{ik}, the sign before the last term in the third equation should be reversed (See Vlasov [2].)

Furthermore, taking into account that in this case $A = B = R$, $k_1 = 0$, $k_2 = 1/R$, we find with the help of formulas (22.9) that

$$\varepsilon_1 = \frac{1}{R}\frac{\partial u}{\partial \alpha}, \qquad \varepsilon_2 = \frac{1}{R}\left(\frac{\partial v}{\partial \beta} + w\right),$$
$$\kappa_1 = -\frac{1}{R^2}\frac{\partial^2 w}{\partial \alpha^2} \qquad \kappa_2 = -\frac{1}{R^2}\left(\frac{\partial^2 w}{\partial \beta^2} + w\right).$$

Hence, according to formulas (22.8),

$$\begin{aligned} \Delta X &= \frac{N_1 - N_2}{R^2}\frac{\partial}{\partial \alpha}\left(\frac{\partial v}{\partial \beta} + w\right), \\ \Delta Y &= \frac{N_1 - N_2}{R^2}\frac{\partial^2 u}{\partial \alpha\,\partial \beta}, \\ \Delta Z &= -\frac{1}{R^2}\left[N_1\frac{\partial^2 w}{\partial \alpha^2} + N_2\left(\frac{\partial^2 w}{\partial \beta^2} + w\right)\right]. \end{aligned} \tag{22.21}$$

In this way, the variational equations (22.5) take the form

$$\begin{aligned} &\frac{\partial^2 u}{\partial \alpha^2} + \frac{1-\nu}{2}\frac{\partial^2 u}{\partial \beta^2} + \frac{1+\nu}{2}\frac{\partial^2 v}{\partial \alpha\,\partial \beta} + \nu\frac{\partial w}{\partial \alpha} \\ &\qquad + \frac{1-\nu^2}{Eh}\left[\frac{N_1 - N_2}{R^2}\frac{\partial}{\partial \alpha}\left(\frac{\partial v}{\partial \beta} + w\right) - m\frac{\partial^2 u}{\partial t^2}\right] = 0, \\ &\frac{1+\nu}{2}\frac{\partial^2 u}{\partial \alpha\,\partial \beta} + \frac{\partial^2 v}{\partial \beta^2} + \frac{1-\nu}{2}\frac{\partial^2 v}{\partial \alpha^2} + \frac{\partial w}{\partial \beta} \\ &\qquad - \frac{1-\nu^2}{Eh}\left[\frac{N_1 - N_2}{R^2}\frac{\partial^2 u}{\partial \alpha\,\partial \beta} + m\frac{\partial^2 v}{\partial t^2}\right] = 0, \\ &\nu\frac{\partial u}{\partial \alpha} + \frac{\partial v}{\partial \beta} + c^2\nabla^2\nabla^2 w + \frac{1-\nu^2}{Eh}\left\{\frac{1}{R^2}\left[N_1\frac{\partial^2 w}{\partial \alpha^2} + N_2\left(\frac{\partial^2 w}{\partial \beta^2} + w\right)\right] + m\frac{\partial^2 w}{\partial t^2}\right\} = 0. \end{aligned} \tag{22.22}$$

● **2.** The solution of system (22.22) is sought in the form

$$\begin{aligned} u &= U \cos n\alpha \cos k\beta, \\ v &= V \sin n\alpha \sin k\beta, \\ w &= W \sin n\alpha \cos k\beta, \end{aligned} \tag{22.23}$$

where U, V, and W are functions of time,

$$n = \frac{i\pi R}{l}, \tag{22.24}$$

and i and k are positive integers. Here i denotes the number of half waves in the meridional direction (i is the length of the shell), and k gives the number of half waves in the circumferential direction. Solution in the form (22.23) corresponds to the case where, at the edges of the shell ($z = 0$, $z = l$), the radial and also the circumferential displacements vanish. The longitudinal displacement, is not equal to zero.

By a direct substitution it can be verified that Eqs. (22.22) are identically satisfied if the functions $U(t)$, $V(t)$, and $W(t)$ are determined from the system of ordinary differential equations

$$
\begin{aligned}
&\frac{m(1-\nu^2)}{Eh}\frac{d^2U}{dt^2}+\left(n^2+\frac{1-\nu}{2}k^2\right)U-\frac{1+\nu}{2}nkV-\nu nW\\
&\qquad\qquad -\frac{1-\nu^2}{Eh}\frac{N_1-N_2}{R^2}n(kV+W)=0,\\
&\frac{m(1-\nu^2)}{Eh}\frac{d^2V}{dt^2}-\frac{1+\nu}{2}nkU+\left(k^2+\frac{1-\nu}{2}n^2\right)V+kW\\
&\qquad\qquad +\frac{1-\nu^2}{Eh}\frac{N_1-N_2}{R^2}nkU=0,\\
&\frac{m(1-\nu^2)}{Eh}\frac{d^2W}{dt^2}-\nu nU+kV+c^2(n^2+k^2)^2W\\
&\qquad\qquad -\frac{1-\nu^2}{Eh}\frac{W}{R^2}[N_1n^2+N_2(k^2-1)]=0.
\end{aligned}
\tag{22.25}
$$

The system of equations (22.25) can be expressed in matrix form

$$
m\frac{d^2\boldsymbol{f}}{dt^2}+(\boldsymbol{R}-N_1\boldsymbol{S}_1-N_2\boldsymbol{S}_2)\boldsymbol{f}=\boldsymbol{0},
$$

where $\boldsymbol{f}$ is a vector with components U, V, and W, and

$$
\boldsymbol{R}=\frac{Eh}{1-\nu^2}\begin{pmatrix} n^2+\frac{1-\nu}{2}k^2 & -\frac{1+\nu}{2}nk & -\nu n\\ -\frac{1+\nu}{2}nk & k^2+\frac{1-\nu}{2}n^2 & k\\ -\nu n & k & c^2(n^2+k^2)^2\end{pmatrix},
$$

$$
\boldsymbol{S}_1=\frac{1}{R^2}\begin{pmatrix} 0 & nk & n\\ -nk & 0 & 0\\ 0 & 0 & n^2\end{pmatrix},
$$

$$
\boldsymbol{S}_2=\frac{1}{R^2}\begin{pmatrix} 0 & -nk & n\\ nk & 0 & 0\\ 0 & 0 & k^2-1\end{pmatrix}.
$$

The free vibration frequencies of an unloaded shell are determined from the equation:

$$
|\boldsymbol{R}-\omega^2\boldsymbol{E}|=0,
$$

while the critical parameters of the longitudinal compressive load and the radial load are determined from the equations

$$
\left|\boldsymbol{R}-\frac{P}{2\pi R}\boldsymbol{S}_1\right|=0 \quad\text{and}\quad |\boldsymbol{R}-qR\boldsymbol{S}_2|=0.
$$

The problem of dynamic stability leads, in the first approximation, to the equation

$$
\left|\boldsymbol{R}-\frac{1}{2\pi R}(P_0\pm\tfrac{1}{2}P_t)\boldsymbol{S}_1-(q_0\pm\tfrac{1}{2}q_t)R\boldsymbol{S}_2-\tfrac{1}{4}\theta^2\boldsymbol{E}\right|=0. \tag{22.26}
$$

●**3.** If the effect of the tangential inertia forces and of the tangential components of the reduced loads is ignored, then the vibration of circular cylindrical shells can be represented by a single equation. In the general case of a nonshallow cylindrical shell, this equation has the form[54]

$$(\nabla^2 + 1)^2\nabla^2\nabla^2 F - (1-\nu)\frac{\partial^2}{\partial\alpha^2}\left(\frac{\partial^2}{\partial\alpha^2} - \frac{\partial^2}{\partial\beta^2}\right)\nabla^2 F + \frac{1-\nu^2}{c^2}\frac{\partial^4 F}{\partial\alpha^4} - \frac{R^4}{D}Z = 0 .$$

Here $$w = \nabla^2\nabla^2 F . \tag{22.27}$$

Utilizing (22.27) and the last of Eqs. (22.21), we obtain

$$(\nabla^2 + 1)^2\nabla^2\nabla^2 F - (1-\nu)\frac{\partial^2}{\partial\alpha^2}\left(\frac{\partial^2}{\partial\alpha^2} - \frac{\partial^2}{\partial\beta^2}\right)\nabla^2 F + \frac{1-\nu^2}{c^2}\frac{\partial^4 F}{\partial\alpha^4}$$
$$+ \frac{mR^4}{D}\frac{\partial^2}{\partial t^2}\nabla^2\nabla^2 F + \frac{R^2}{D}\left[N_1\frac{\partial^2}{\partial\alpha^2} + N_2\left(\frac{\partial^2}{\partial\beta^2} + 1\right)\right]\nabla^2\nabla^2 F = 0 . \tag{22.28}$$

Let λ be the length of the half wave in the meridional (or circumferential) direction. Then the first term in Eq. (22.28) is on the order $(R/\lambda)^8$, the second term of the order $(R/\lambda)^6$ and the third term on the order $R^6/\lambda^4 h^2$. If the length of the half wave is small in comparison with the radius, then the secondary terms in Eq. (22.28) can be neglected. Excluding, on the basis of analogous considerations, certain other small terms we obtain

$$\nabla^2\nabla^2\nabla^2\nabla^2 F + \frac{1-\nu^2}{c^2}\frac{\partial^4 F}{\partial\alpha^4} + \frac{R^4}{D}\left(\frac{N_1}{R^2}\frac{\partial^2}{\partial\alpha^2} + \frac{N_2}{R^2}\frac{\partial^2}{\partial\beta^2} + m\frac{\partial^2}{\partial t^2}\right)\nabla^2\nabla^2 F = 0 . \tag{22.29}$$

This equation fully corresponds to Eq. (22.14) for shallow shells.

Let us return now to the general equation (22.28). Assuming that

$$F(\alpha, \beta, t) = f(t)\sin n\alpha \cos k\beta ,$$

which corresponds to case (22.23), we obtain the ordinary differential equation

$$\frac{mR^4}{D}\frac{\partial^2 f}{\partial t^2} + g(n, k) f - \frac{R^2}{D}[N_1 n^2 + N_2(k^2 - 1)] f = 0 , \tag{22.30}$$

where

$$g(n, k) = \frac{(n^2 + k^2 + 1)^2(n^2 + k^2)^2 + (1-\nu)n^2(n^4 - k^4) + \dfrac{1-\nu^2}{c^2}n^4}{(n^2 + k^2)^2} .$$

The following notation is introduced:

$$\frac{Dg(n, k)}{mR^4} = \omega^2, \qquad \frac{Dg(n, k)}{n^2R^2} = N_{1*} , \qquad \frac{Dg(n, k)}{(k^2 - 1)R^2} = N_{2*}.$$

Equation (22.30) can now be written in the form

$$\frac{d^2 f}{dt^2} + \omega^2\left(1 - \frac{P}{P_*} - \frac{q}{q_*}\right) f = 0 , \tag{22.31}$$

where $P_* = 2\pi R N_{1*}$, $q_* = N_{2*}/R$.

Thus the problem is reduced to a known equation.

[54] Vlasov [2].

4. The results of the preceding paragraph can easily be generalized to the case of an orthotropic cylindrical shell. Let E_1, E_2, and ν_1, ν_2 be the moduli of elasticity and Poisson's ratios in directions $\alpha = \text{const.}$ and $\beta = \text{const.}$, respectively, and let G be the shear modulus. Furthermore, let us introduce the following differential operators:

$$\nabla_0^2 = E_0\frac{\partial^2}{\partial\alpha^2} + E_2\frac{\partial^2}{\partial\beta^2},$$

$$\nabla_1^4 = E_1\frac{\partial^4}{\partial\alpha^4} + E_4\frac{\partial^4}{\partial\alpha^2\partial\beta^2} + E_2\frac{\partial^4}{\partial\beta^4},$$

$$\nabla_2^4 = E_1\frac{\partial^4}{\partial\alpha^4} + E_3\frac{\partial^4}{\partial\alpha^2\partial\beta^2} + E_2\frac{\partial^4}{\partial\beta^4},$$

where

$$E_0 = 2G(1-\nu_1\nu_2) + E_2\nu_1,$$

$$E_3 = 4G(1-\nu_1\nu_2) + E_1\nu_2 + E_2\nu_1,$$

$$E_4 = \frac{E_1 E_2}{G} - E_1\nu_2 - E_2\nu_1.$$

The equation, analogous to (22.29), for an orthotropic shell will assume the form

$$\nabla_1^4\nabla_2^4 F + \frac{E_1E_2(1-\nu_1\nu_2)}{c^2}\frac{\partial^4 F}{\partial\alpha^4} + \frac{1-\nu_1\nu_2}{c^2 h}\left(N_1\frac{\partial^2}{\partial\alpha^2} + N_2\frac{\partial^2}{\partial\beta^2} + mR^2\frac{\partial^2}{\partial t^2}\right)\nabla_1^4 F = 0,$$

where F is a function which is related to the radial deflection by the relationship

$$w = \nabla_0^2\nabla_0^2 F.$$

Further transformation leads to Eq. (22.31), whose coefficients can be determined without any difficulty for the case of a simply supported shell.[55]

§ 105. The Dynamic Stability of A Spherical Shell[56]

1. We will investigate the vibrations of a spherical shell subjected to a radial load uniformly distributed over the surface,

$$Z_0 = -(q_0 + q_t \cos\theta t). \tag{22.32}$$

[55] Markov [1].

[56] The nonlinear investigation of the dynamic stability of spherical shells can be found in Bolotin [18].

Let h be the thickness of the shell and R be the radius to its middle surface. As orthogonal coordinates defining the position of points on the sphere, we assume geographical coordinates ψ, β (in Figure 174, ψ is the angle of latitude and β is the angle of longitude). The displacements of points lying in the middle plane in the directions $\psi = \text{const.}$ and $\beta = \text{const.}$ are denoted by u and v, respectively, while the radial displacement (positive in the direction of the outward normal) is denoted by w. If the external load acting on the shell consists of radial load Z, then, as is well known,[57] the system of equations for a spherical shell can be reduced to a single equation

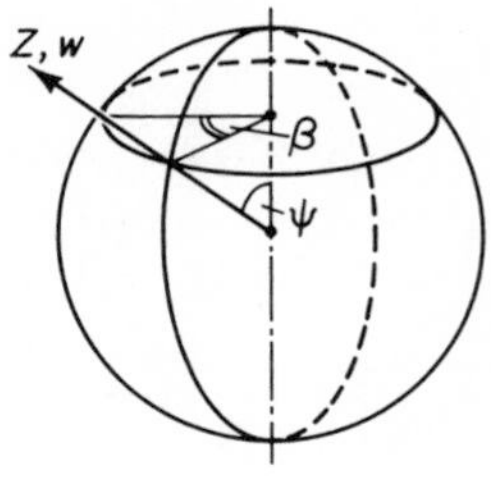

FIG. 174.

$$[c^2(\nabla^2 + 1)^2 + 1](\nabla^2 + 2)w = \frac{R^2 Z}{Eh}(\nabla^2 + 1 - \nu) . \qquad (22.33)$$

Here ∇^2 is the Laplace operator for the sphere,

$$\nabla^2 = \frac{1}{\sin\psi}\left[\frac{\partial}{\partial\psi}\left(\sin\psi\frac{\partial}{\partial\psi}\right) + \frac{1}{\sin^2\psi}\frac{\partial^2}{\partial\beta^2}\right], \qquad (22.34)$$

and

$$c^2 = \frac{h^2}{12R^2(1-\nu^2)} .$$

In the membrane state, the internal shell forces reduce to compressive forces

$$N_1 = N_2 = \tfrac{1}{2}R(q_0 + q_t \cos\theta t) .$$

For the determination of the additional curvatures κ_1, and κ_2, we make use of formulas (22.9). For the case of a spherical shell,

$$k_1 = k_2 = \frac{1}{R} ,$$

$$A = R , \qquad B = R\sin\psi ,$$

and formulas (22.9) assume the form

$$\kappa_1 = -\frac{1}{R^2}\left(w + \frac{\partial^2 w}{\partial\psi^2}\right) ,$$

$$\kappa_2 = -\frac{1}{R^2}\left(w - \frac{1}{\sin^2\psi}\frac{\partial^2 w}{\partial\beta^2} - \operatorname{ctg}\psi\frac{\partial w}{\partial\psi}\right) .$$

But, in accordance with (22.8), the additional reduced load formed during the deflection of the shell is

$$\Delta Z = \tfrac{1}{2}R(q_0 + q_t\cos\theta t)(\kappa_1 + \kappa_2) ,$$

from which

$$\Delta Z = -\frac{1}{2R}(q_0 + q_t\cos\theta t)(\nabla^2 + 2)w . \qquad (22.35)$$

[57] Vlasov [2].

The components ΔX and ΔY are obviously equal to zero.

Besides the external load (22.32) and the reduced load (22.35), the shell is also under the action of inertia forces

$$-m\frac{\partial^2 u}{\partial t^2}, \qquad -m\frac{\partial^2 v}{\partial t^2}, \qquad -m\frac{\partial^2 w}{\partial t^2}.$$

Neglecting, in accordance with the engineering shell theory, the tangential components of inertia forces, we find that the forces acting on the shell reduce to a radial load

$$Z = -(q_0 + q_t \cos \theta t) - \frac{q}{2R}(q_0 + q_t \cos \theta t)(\nabla^2 + 2)w - m\frac{\partial^2 w}{\partial t^2}.$$

The first term corresponds to the uniform radial compression of the shell, and can be neglected if $w(\psi, \beta, t)$ is understood to be the deviation from the unperturbed membrane state. The differential equation (22.33) then assumes the form

$$[c^2(\nabla^2+1)^2+1](\nabla^2+2)w + \frac{(q_0 + q_t \cos \theta t)R}{2Eh}(\nabla^2 + 1 - \nu)(\nabla^2+2)w$$
$$+ \frac{mR^2}{Eh}(\nabla^2+1-\nu)\frac{\partial^2 w}{\partial t^2} = 0. \tag{22.36}$$

●**2.** Determination of a general solution of Eq. (22.36) is difficult. Consequently, we will limit ourselves to a class of solutions having, as will be seen later, definite practical interest. We will seek the solution of Eq. (22.36) in the form

$$w(\psi, \beta, t) = f(t)F(\psi, \beta), \tag{22.37}$$

where $f(t)$ is an unknown function of time and $F(\psi, \beta)$ are the solutions of the differential equation

$$\nabla^2 F + \lambda F = 0 \tag{22.28}$$

satisfying boundary conditions for w (i.e., conditions of continuity and single-valuedness on the sphere). Substitution in (22.36) gives, after cancellation of $F(\psi, \beta)$,

$$[c^2(\lambda-1)^2+1](\lambda-2)f - \frac{(q_0 + q_t \cos \theta t)R}{2Eh}(\lambda - 1 + \nu)(\lambda-2)f$$
$$+ \frac{mR^2}{Eh}(\lambda-1+\nu)\frac{d^2 f}{dt^2} = 0.$$

Let us now introduce the following notation:

$$\frac{Eh}{mR^2}\frac{\lambda-2}{\lambda-1+\nu}[c^2(\lambda-1)^2+1] = \omega^2,$$
$$\frac{2Eh}{R(\lambda-1+\nu)}[c^2(\lambda-1)^2+1] = q_*. \tag{22.39}$$

The final equation then has the form

$$\frac{d^2f}{dt^2} + \omega^2\left(1 - \frac{q_0 + q_t \cos \theta t}{q_*}\right)f = 0 . \tag{22.40}$$

This is a known equation for a special case of an independent single equation; moreover, the problem is reduced to it exactly if one disregards the assumption made above about the tangential inertia forces. Formulas (22.39) give the natural frequencies and critical forces which depend on the still unknown parameter λ. However, one important practical problem can be solved even without knowing λ. The boundaries for the principal regions of instability can be found according to known approximate formulas. In particular, the lower boundary is

$$\theta_*{}^2 = 4\omega^2\left(1 - \frac{q_0 + \frac{1}{2}q_t}{q_*}\right).$$

For practical purposes it is interesting to know the envelope for the lower boundaries of the instability regions. We assume that the parameter λ can take on arbitrary real positive values, in other words, that Eq. (22.38) has a continuous spectrum of eigenvalues. Analogous statements were encountered in Chapter Nine while investigating the stability of infinite beams on a continuous elastic foundation. For a bounded region such as a sphere, the spectrum of eigenvalues is discrete. Yet in the vicinity of values of λ which are of interest to us, the spectrum of Eq. (22.38) nevertheless is sufficiently "dense" so that the error resulting from the assumptions made is insignificant. This case will be explained below in detail.

Hereinafter we will denote

$$\theta_*{}^2 = \frac{4Eh}{mR^2} g(\lambda) ,$$

where

$$g(\lambda) = (\lambda - 2)\left[\frac{c^2(\lambda - 1)^2 + 1}{\lambda - 1 + \nu} - \frac{(q_0 + \frac{1}{2}q_t)R}{2Eh}\right]. \tag{22.41}$$

For the determination of the envelope, let $dg/d\lambda = 0$; in this way we obtain an equation for λ. For a sufficiently large value of λ, i.e., $\lambda \gg 1$, we obtain

$$g(\lambda) \approx c^2\lambda^2 + 1 - \frac{(q_0 + \frac{1}{2}q_t)R\lambda}{2Eh} ,$$

from which the root of the equation $dg/d\lambda = 0$ is

$$\lambda_* = \frac{(q_0 + \frac{1}{2}q_t)R}{4Ehc^2} , \tag{22.42}$$

and consequently,

$$\theta_*{}^2 = \frac{4Eh}{mR^2}\left[1 - \frac{(q_0 + \frac{1}{2}q_t)^2 R}{16E^2h^2c^2}\right]. \tag{22.43}$$

Introducing the notation

$$\frac{4Ehc}{R} = q_{**}, \qquad \frac{Eh}{mR^2} = \omega_0{}^2,$$

formula (22.43) then assumes the form (Fig. 175)

$$\theta_*^{\,2} = 4\omega_0^{\,2}\left[1 - \frac{(q_0 + \frac{1}{2}q_t)^2}{q_{**}^2}\right]. \tag{22.44}$$

It is readily apparent that q_{**} represents an approximate (in the sense of the assumptions made) value of the minimum critical load. In fact, remembering that

$$c^2 = \frac{h^2}{12R^2(1-\nu^2)},$$

we obtain the well-known formula

$$q_{**} = \frac{2Eh^2}{R^2}\frac{1}{\sqrt{3(1-\nu^2)}}.$$

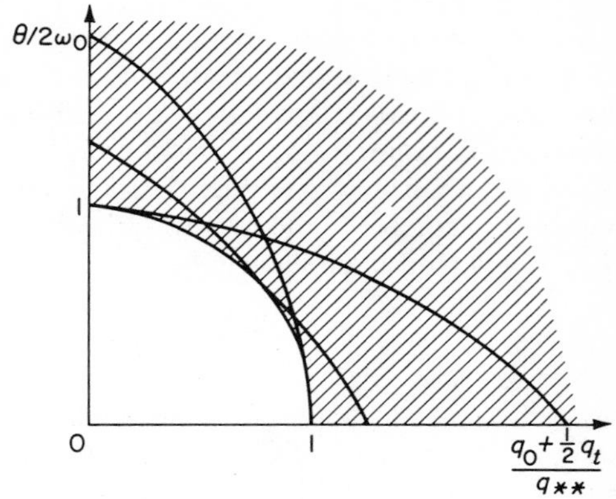

FIG. 175.

●**3.** We return to the question concerning the determination of parameter λ in the general case. By introducing polar coordinates, Eq. (22.38) assumes the form

$$\frac{1}{\sin\psi}\left[\frac{\partial}{\partial\psi}\left(\sin\psi\frac{\partial F}{\partial\psi}\right)\right] + \frac{1}{\sin^2\psi}\frac{\partial^2 F}{\partial\beta^2} + \lambda F = 0, \tag{22.45}$$

and leads, as is well known,[58] to spherical functions.

The solution of Eq. (22.45) is sought in the form

$$F(\psi, \beta) = P(\psi)\begin{matrix}\sin k\beta \\ \cos k\beta\end{matrix}.$$

The condition for uniqueness of $F(\psi, \beta)$ on the sphere requires that k be a positive integer ($k = 0, 1, 2, \cdots$). Substitution in Eq. (22.45) gives

$$\frac{1}{\sin\psi}\left[\frac{d}{\partial\psi}\left(\sin\psi\frac{\partial P}{\partial\psi}\right)\right] + \left(\lambda - \frac{k^2}{\sin^2\psi}\right)P = 0, \qquad (k = 0, 1, 2, \cdots).$$

Taking $x = \cos\psi$, the equation is reduced to the form

$$\frac{d}{dx}\left[(1-x^2)\frac{dP}{dx}\right] + \left(\lambda - \frac{k^2}{1-x^2}\right)P = 0, \qquad (k = 0, 1, 2, \cdots). \tag{22.46}$$

This is a well-known equation for the associated Legendre polynomials. Equation (22.46) has the eigenvalues

$$\lambda_n = n(n+1), \qquad (n = 0, 1, 2, \cdots). \tag{22.47}$$

To each eigenvalue there correspond $n+1$ eigenfunctions

[58] Smirnov [1].

$$P_n^{(k)}(x) = (1 - x^2)^{k/2} \frac{d^k}{dx^k} P_n(x) , \qquad (k = 0, 1, 2, \cdots, n) ,$$

where
$$P_n(x) = \frac{1}{2^n n!} \frac{d^n}{dx^n} [(x^2 - 1)^n] .$$

For the differential equation (22.45), we obtain a system of solutions:

$$\begin{aligned} k &= 0 , & F_0(\psi, \beta) &= P_n(\cos \psi) , \\ k &= 1 , & F_{-1}(\psi, \beta) &= P_n^{(1)}(\cos \psi) \sin \beta , \\ & & F_1(\psi, \beta) &= P_n^{(1)}(\cos \psi) \cos \beta \\ & & \cdots & \\ k &= n , & F_{-n}(\psi, \beta) &= P_n^{(n)}(\cos \psi) \sin n\beta , \\ & & F_n(\psi, \beta) &= P_n^{(n)}(\cos \psi) \cos n\beta . \end{aligned}$$

As is well known, the Legendre polynomials $P_n(x)$ have in the interval $(-1, +1)$ i.e., in the interval $0 < \psi < \pi$, exactly n zeros. Correspondingly, the associated functions $P_n^{(k)}(x)$ $(k = 0, 1, 2, \cdots, n)$ have $(n\text{-}k)$ zeros.

Because $\sin k\beta$ and $\cos k\beta$ become zero on $2k$ meridians, and $P_n^{(k)}(x)$, on $n\text{-}k$ latitudes, then the total surface of the sphere decomposes into zones inside of which the function $F(\psi, \beta)$ has a constant sign. Thus, the number λ defines the forms of vibration and, in particular, the length of "half waves" in the meridional and latitudinal directions. The shorter are the half waves, the larger is the parameter λ. For large eigenvalues the difference between the two adjacent eigenvalues is small in comparison with their magnitudes; thus the assumption about the continuous variation of λ is justified.

● **4.** In conclusion, a numerical example will be considered. Let the shell be subjected to the action of the external pressure $q_0 = 10$ atm, $q_t = 1.0$ atm. Furthermore, let $R = 4.0$ m, $h = 20$ mm, $\gamma = 0.0078$ kg/cm³, and $\nu = 0.3$. The critical pressure and the frequency ω_0 are

$$q_{**} = \frac{2 \times 2.1 \times 10^6 \times 2^2}{400^2} \frac{1}{\sqrt{3(1 - 0.3^2)}} = 64.7 \quad \text{kg/cm}^2 ,$$

$$\omega_0 = \frac{1}{400} \sqrt{\frac{2.1 \times 10^6 \times 2}{0.0078 \times 2}} = 41.0 \quad \text{sec}^{-1} .$$

The smallest critical frequency is found from formula (22.44)

$$\theta_* = 2 \times 41.0 \sqrt{1 - \frac{(10 + 0.5)^2}{64.7^2}} = 75.3 \quad \text{sec}^{-1} .$$

Let us evaluate now the length of half wave during the loss of dynamic stability. From formula (22.42)

$$\lambda_* = \frac{q_0 + \frac{1}{2} q_t}{q_{**}} \times \frac{2R\sqrt{3(1 - \nu)}}{h} \approx \frac{3q}{q_{**}} \frac{R}{h} .$$

Consequently, for the case investigated, $\lambda_* \approx 100$ and, from (22.47), $n \approx 10$. Thus, during the vibration the length of one zone is approximately, one-tenth of the length of the circumference.[59]

[59] Some results concerning the nonlinear problem were obtained by Bolotin [18].

REFERENCES

Ambartsumian, S. A., and A. A. Khachatrian
[1] "On the Stability and Vibrations of Anisotropic Plates," *Izv. Akad. Nauk SSSR, Otd. Tekhn. Nauk, Mekhan. i Mashinostr. 1,* 113-122 (1960).

Andronov, A. A., A. A. Witt and S. E. Khaikin
[1] *Vibration Theory* (Teoriia kolebanii), (Fizmatgiz, Moscow, 1959), 2nd ed.

Andronov, A. A., and M. A. Leontovich
[1] "On the Vibrations of Systems with Periodically Varying Parameters," *Zh. Russk. Fiz.-Khim. Obshch. 59,* 429-443 (1927).

Artem'ev, N. A.
[1] "Une méthode pour déterminer les exposants caractéristiques et son application à deux problèmes de la méchanique céleste," *Izv. Akad. Nauk SSSR, Ser. Mat. 8,* 61-100 (1944). (French summary.)

Beck, M.
[1] "Die Knicklast des einseitig eingespannten, tangential gedrückten Stabes," *Z. angew. Math. Phys. 3,* 225-228; Erratum 476-477 (1952).

Beilin, E. A.
[1] "On the Bending-Torsion Form of Vibrations and on the Loss of Stability of Curved Arches," *Sb. Nauchn. Tr. Leningr. Inzh. Stroit. Inst. 29,* 71-86 (1958).

Beilin, E. A., and G. U. Dzhanelidze
[1] "Survey of Work on the Dynamic Stability of Elastic Systems," *Prikl. Mat. i Mekhan. 16* (5), 635-648 (1952). (Available in English as ASTIA No. AD-264148.)

Beliaev, N. M.
[1] "Stability of Prismatic Rods Subjected to Variable Longitudinal Forces," Collection of Papers: Engineering Constructions and Structural Mechanics (Inzhenernye sooruzheniia i stroitel'naia mekhanika), (Put', Leningrad, 1924), pp. 149-167.

Benz, G.
[1] "Die mechanische Bedeutung des instabilen Zweiges der Frequenz-Amplituden-Kurve bei parametererregten Schwingungen, *Z. angew. Mat. Mechan. 36,* 273-274 (1956).

Bernstein, S. A.
[1] *The Foundations of the Dynamics of Structures* (Osnovy dinamiki sooruzhenii), (Stroiizdat, Moscow, 1947).

Biezeno, C. B., and R. Grammel
[1] *Engineering Dynamics,* (D. Van Nostrand Co., New York, 1954), Vol. I-IV.

Bodner, V. A.
[1] "The Stability of Plates Subjected to Longitudinal Periodic Forces," *Prikl. Mat. i Mekhan.* (N. S.) *2,* 87-104 (1938).

Bogoliubov, N. N. (see N. M. Krylov)

Bogoliubov, N. N. and Iu. A. Mitropol'skii

[1] *Asymptotic Methods in the Theory of Nonlinear Vibrations* (Asimtoticheskie metody v teorii nelineinykh kolebanii), (Gostekhizdat, Moscow, 1955) 2nd ed.

Bolotin, V. V.

[1] "Stresses in Bridges Subjected to Traveling Loads," *Tr. Mosk. Inst. Inzh. Transp. 74*, 269-296 (1950).

[2] "On the Transverse Vibrations of Rods Excited by Periodic Longitudinal Forces," Collection of Papers: *Transverse Vibrations and Critical Velocities* (Poperechnye kolebaniia i kriticheskie skorosti), 1, 46-77 (Akademiia Nauk SSSR, Moscow, 1951).

[3] "Interaction of Arches and their Superstructures," *Tr. Mosk. Inst. Inzh. Transp. 76*, 32-42 (1952).

[4] "Parametrically Excited Vibrations of Elastic Arches," *Dokl. Akad. Nauk SSSR 83*, 537-539 (1952).

[5] "On the Parametric Excitation of Transverse Vibrations," Collection of Papers: *Transverse Vibrations and Critical Velocities* (Poperechnye kolebaniia i kriticheskie skorosti), 2, 5-44 (Akademiia Nauk SSSR, Moscow, 1953).

[6] "Determination of the Amplitudes of Transverse Vibrations Excited by Longitudinal Forces," Collection of Papers: *Transverse Vibrations and Critical Velocities,* (Poperchnye kolebaniia i kriticheskie skorosti) *2*, 45-64, (Akademiia Nauk SSSR, Moscow, 1953).

[7] "Dynamic Stability of Plane Bending Forms," *Inzh. Sb. 14*, 109-122 (1953).

[8] "Parametric Excitation of Axisymmetric Vibrations of Elastic Arches," *Inzh. Sb. 15*, 83-88 (1953).

[9] "Certain Nonlinear Problems of the Dynamic Stability of Plates," *Izv. Akad Nauk SSSR, Otd. Tekhn. Nauk 10*, 47-59 (1954).

[10] "A note on the paper by Bondar': Dynamic Stability and Vibrations of Hingeless Parabolic Arches," *Inzh. Sb. 18*, 214-215 (1954).

[11] "On the Bending Vibrations of Beams Whose Cross Sections have Different Principal Stiffnesses," *Inzh. Sb. 19*, 37-54 (1954).

[12] "Approximate Methods for Vibration Analysis of Frames," *Tr. Mosk. Energ. Inst. 17*, 7-22 (1955).

[13] "On Errors in Certain Papers on Dynamic Stability," *Izv. Akad. Nauk SSSR, Otd. Tekhn. Nauk 11*, 144-147 (1955).

[14] "On the Interaction of Forces and Excited Vibrations," *Izv. Akad. Nauk SSSR, Otdel. Tekhn. Nauk 11*, 3-15 (1956).

[15] *Some Problems on the Theory of Elastic Stability*, Tr. 3. Mat. Vsesoiuzn. Kongr. (Akademiia Nauk SSSR, Moscow, 1956), Vol. 1, p. 200.

[16] "Problems on the General Theory of Elastic Stability," *Prikl. Mat. i Mekhan. 20*, 561-577 (1956).

]17] "Nonlinear Vibrations of Beams with Post-critical Rotational Speeds," Collection of Papers: *Problems on the Stability in Machine Construction* (Problemy prochnosti v machinostroenii) *1*, 25-63 (Akademiia Nauk SSSR, Moscow, 1958).

[18] "Stability of a Thin-Walled Spherical Shell Subjected to a Periodic Pressure," Collection of Papers: *Design for Stability* (Raschety na prochnost') *2*, 284-289 (Mashgiz, Moscow, 1958).

[19] "Investigation of the Vibrations of Beams with Different Principal Bending Stiffnesses," Collection of Papers: *Design for Stability* (Raschety na prochnost') *2*, 302-312 (Mashgiz, Moscow, 1958).

[20] "On the Vibrations and the Stability of Bars subjected to Nonconservative Forces," Collection of Papers: *Vibrations in Turbines* (Kolebaniia v turbomashinakh)

23-42 (Akademiia Nauk SSSR, Moscow, 1959).
[21] "On the Mechanical Model Which Describes the Interaction of Parametrically Excited and Forced Vibrations," *Tr. Mosk. Energ. Inst.* *32*, 54-66 (1959).

Bondarenko, G. V.
[1] *The Hill Differential Equation and its Uses in Engineering Vibration Problems* (Uravnenie Khilla i ego primenenie v oblasti technicheskikh kolebanii), (Akademiia Nauk SSSR, Moscow, 1936).

Brachkovski, B. Z.
[1] "On the Dynamic Stability of Elastic Systems," *Prikl. Mat. i Mekhan.* (N.S.) *6*, 87-88 (1942).

Bublik, B. M. and V. I. Merkulov
[1] "On the Dynamic Stability of a Thin Elastic Shell Filled with a Liquid," *Prikl. Mat. i Mekhan.* *24*, 941-947 (1960).

Bulgakov, B. V.
[1] *Vibrations* (Kolebaniia), (Gostekhizdat, Moscow, 1954).

Burnashev, I. A.
[1] "On the Dynamic Stability of the Plane Bending Form of a Beam," *Dokl. Akad. Nauk Uzb. SSR*, *3*, 7-12 (1954).

Chelomei, V. N.
[1] *The Dynamic Stability of Elements of Aircraft Structures*, (Dinamicheskaiia ustoichivost' elementov aviatsionnykh konstruktsii), (Aeroflot, Moscow, 1939).

Chetaev, N. G.
[1] *The Stability of Motion*, (Pergamon Press, New York, 1961), (translated from the Russian).

Collar, A. P. (see Duncan, R. A.)

Davidenkov, N. N.
[1] "On the Dissipation of Energy in Vibrations," *Zh. Tekh. Fiz.* *8* (6), 483-499 (1938).

Deineko, K. S. and M. Ia. Leonov
[1] "A Dynamic Method for the Investigation of the Stability of a Compressed Bar," *Prikl. Mat. i Mekhan.* *19*, 738-744 (1955).

den Hartog, J. P.
[1] Mechanical Vibrations (McGraw-Hill Book Co., Inc., New York, 1956) 4th ed.

Dimentberg, F. M.
[1] "The Transverse Vibrations of a Rotating Beam whose Cross-sections have Different Principal Moments of Inertia", Second Collection of Papers: *Transverse Vibrations and Critical Velocities* (Poperechnye kolebaniia i kriticheskie skorosti) 65-106 (Akademiia Nauk SSSR, Moscow 1953).

Duncan, W. J. (see Frazer, R. A.)

Dzhanelidze, G. U. (see also Beilin, E. A.)
[1] "Theorems on the Separation of Variables in Problems of the Dynamic Stability of Rods," *Tr. Leningr. Inst. Inzh. Vodn. Transp.* *20*, 193-198 (1953).

Dzhanelidze, G. U. and M. A. Radtsig
[1] "Dynamic Stability of Rings Subjected to Normal Periodic Forces," *Prikel. Mat. i Mekhan.* *4* (N. S.), (5-6), 55-60 (1940).

Einaudi, R.
[1] "Sulle Configurazioni di Equilibrio Instabile di una Piastra Sollecitata da Sforzi Tangenziali Pulsanti," *Atti Accad. Gioenia 1,* Memoria XX, 1-5 (1935-1936).

Epishev, L. V.
[1] "Vibrations of Gyroscopic Systems Under External Periodic Influences," *Nauchn. Dokl. Vysshei Shkoly, Ser. Mashinostr. i Priborostr. 1,* 200-210 (1958).

Euler, L.
[1] *Methodus inveniendi lineas curvas maximi minimive proprietate gaudentes, sive solutio problematis isoperimetrici latissimo sensu accepti. Additamentum I. De Curvis elastics.* (Lausanne and Geneva, 1744.)

Farquharson, F. B.
[1] "Rigidity and Aerodynamic Stability of Suspension Bridges," *Proc. Am. Soc. Civil Eng.*, 1003-1012 (1944).

Federhofer, Karl
[1] "Die durch pulsierende Axialkräfte gedrückte Kreiszylindershale," *Oesterr. Akad, Wiss., Math. Naturw. Kl. 163,* 41-54 (1954).

Federkov, G. V.
[1] "On the Damping of the Free Vibrations of Systems with Many Degrees of Freedom," *Tr. Mosk. Inst. Inzh. Transp. 76,* 135-140 (1952).

Fedos'ev, V. I.
[1] *Selected Problems and Questions of Strength of Material,* (Gostekhizdat, Moscow, 1953).

Feshback, H. (see Morse, P. M.)

Frazer, R. A., W. J. Duncan and A. R. Collar
[1] *Elementary Matrices,* (The Macmillan Co., New York, 1947).

Glivenko, V. I.
[1] *The Stieltjes Integral* (Integral Stil't'esa), (ONTI, Moscow, 1936).

Gol'denblat, I. I.
[1] *Contemporary Problems of Vibrations and Stability of Engineering Structures* (Sovremennye problemy kolebanii i ustoichivosti inhzenernykh sooruzhenii), (Stroiizdat, Moscow, 1947)

Grammel, R. (see Biezeno C. B.)

Grigoliuk, E. I.
[1] "On the Question of the Behavior of a Circular Plate After a Loss of Stability," *Vestn. Inzh. i Tekhn. 3,* 103-106 (1949).

Gurevich, S. G.
[1] "On the Stability of a Plane State of Stesss," *Uch. Zap. Leningr. Gos. Univ. 8,* 137-152 (1939).

Hohenmser, K., and W. Prager
[1] *Dynamik der Stabwerke,* (Springer, Berlin, 1933).

Inglis, G. E.
[1] *A Mathematical Treatise on Vibrations in Railway Bridges,* (Oxford University Press, Cambridge, 1934).

Ivovich, V. A.

[1] "On the Forced Pseudo-Harmonic Vibrations of Elastically Supported Bars," *Dokl. Akad. Nauk SSSR 119*, 42-45 (1958).

[2] "On the Sub-Harmonic Vibrations of Bars with Nonlinear Inertia," *Dokl. Akad Nauk SSSR 119*, 237-240 (1958).

[3] "On the Nonlinear Bending Vibrations of Bars," *Nauchn. Dokl. Vysshei Shkoly, Ser. Mashinostr. i Priborostr. 1*, 96-102 (1958).

[4] "Certain Nonlinear Problems of the Vibrations of Bars," Collection of Papers: Problems on the Stability in Machine Construction (Problemy prochnostyi v machinostroenii) *5*, 47-69 (1959).

Kappus, R.

[1] "Zur Elastizitätstheorie endlisher Verschiebungen," *Z. angew. Mat. Mechan. 19*, (I.) 271-285; (II) 344-361 (1939).

Karman, Th.

[1] "Aerodynamic Stability of Suspension Bridges," *Eng. News-Record 125*, 670 (1940).

Khaikin, S. E. (see Andronov, A. A.)

Khalilov, Z. I.

[1] "The Dynamic Stability of a Plate Under the Action of Periodic Longitudinal Forces," *Tr. Azerb. Gos. Univ., Ser. Mar. 1*, 28-32 (1942).

Khachatrian, A. A. (see Ambartsumian)

Kochin, N. E.

[1] "On the Torsional Vibrations of Crankshafts," *Prikl. Mat. i Mekhan, 2* (1), 3-28 (1934).

Kolsky, H.

[1] *Stress Waves in Solids*, (Dover Publications, Inc. New York, 1943).

Komarov, D. M.

[1] "The Calculation and Construction of a Coupling with Bent Rods," Collection of Papers: *Problems in the Design and Construction of Machine Details* (Vaprossy rashcheta i konstr. detal. mashin) 168-229, (Akademiya Nauk SSSR, Moscow, 1942)

Kornoukhov, N. M.

[1] *Strength and Stability of Rod Systems* (Prochnost' i ustoichivost' sterzhnevykh sistem) (Stroiizdat, Moscow, 1949).

Krein, M. G.

[1] "On Loaded Integral Equations Whose Distribution Functions are Not Monotonic," Collection of Papers Commemorating Academician Grave (Sbornik pamiati Akad. Grave), (GTTI, Moscow, 1940).

Krylov, N. M. and N. N. Bogoliubov

[1] "Calculations of the Vibrations of Frame Construction With the Consideration of Normal Forces and With the Help of the Methods of Nonlinear Mechanics," Collection of Papers: *Investigation of Vibration of Structures* (Issledovanie kolebanii knnstruksii), (ONTI Kharkov/Kiev, 1935), pp. 5-24.

[2] "An Investigation of the Appearance of Resonance of the Transverse Vibrations of Rods Due to the Action of Normal Periodic Forces on an End," Collection of Papers: *Investigation of Vibrations of Structures* (Issledovanie kolebanii konstruktsii), (ONTI Karkov/Kiev, 1935) pp. 25-42.

Kucharski, W.
[1] "Beiträge zur Theorie der durch gleichförmigen schub beanspruchten Platte," *Ing.-Arch. 18,* Part I. 385-393; Part II. 394-408 (1950).

Kuzmin, R. O.
[1] *Bessel Functions* (Besselevy funktssi), (ONTI, Moscow, 1935).

Lanczos, C.
[1] *Variational Principles of Mechanics,* (University of Toronto Press, Toronto, 1949).

Lazarev, V. A.
[1] "On Heteroparametric Excitation," *Zh. Tekhn. Fiz. 4,* 30-48 (1934).

Leonov, M. J. (see Deineko, K. S.)

Leontovich, M. A. (see Andronov, A. A.)

Liapunov, A. M.
[1] "Problème général de la stabilité du movement," *Ann. Fac. Sci. Univ. Toulouse* (2) *9,* 204-474 (1907); reprinted in the *Ann. Math. Studies 17,* (Univ. Press, Princeton, 1949).

Lichtenstein, L.
[1] *Grundlagen der Hydromecnhanik,* (Springer, Berlin, 1929).

Lovitt, W. V.
[1] *Linear Integral Equations,* (Dover Publcations, Inc., New York, 1950).

Lubkin, S. and J. J. Stoker
[1] "Stability of Columns and Strings Under Periodically Varying Forces," *Quart. Appl. Math. 1,* 215-236 (1943).

Lunts, E. V.
[1] "Damping of Torsional Vibrations," *Prikl. Mat. i Mekhan.* (N. S), *1,* 331-370 (1938). (English summary).

Makushin, V. M.
[1] "The Dynamic Stability of the Deformed State of Elastic Rods," *Tr. Mosk. Vissh Tekhn. Uchilishcha,* 61-84 (1947).

Malkin, I. G.
[1] Methods of Liapunov and Poincaré in the Theory of Nonlinear Vibrations (Metody Liapunova i Puankare v teorii nelineinykh kolebanii), (Gostekhizdat, Leningrad/Moscow, 1949).
[2] *Theory of Stability of Motion,* U.S.A.E.C., Tech. info. Service (translated from the Russian).

Malkina, R. L.
[1] "Stability of Curved Arches Subjected to Longitudinal Periodic Forces," *Inzh. Sb. 14,* 123-130 (1953).

Mal'tsev, A. I.
[1] *Fundamentals of Linear Algebra,* (O snovy lineinoi algebry), (Gostekizdat Moscow, 1948).

Mandel'shtam, L. I. and N. D. Papaleksi
[1] "On the Establishment of Vibrations According to a Resonance of the *n*th Form," *Zh. Eksper. i Teor. Fiz. 4*, 67-77 (1934).
[2] "Systems with Periodic Coefficients with many degrees of Freedom and Small Non-Linearities," *Zh. Eksper. i Teor. Fiz. 15*, 605-612 (1945).

Marguerre, K.
[1] "Über die Behandlung von Stabilitätsproblemen mit Hilfe der energetischen Methode," *Z. angew. Mat. Mechan. 18*, 57-73 (1938).
[2] "Über die Anwendung der energetischen Methode auf Stabilitätsproblems," *Jahrb. d. dt. Luftfahrtforschung, I*, 443-443 (1938).

Markov, A. N.
[1] "The Dynamic Stability of Anisotropic Cylindrical Shells," *Prikl. Mat. i Mekhan, 13*, 145-150 (1949). (English translation, TM-43, Douglas Aircraft Company, Santa Monica, California, March 17, 1961.)

McLachlan, N. W.
[1] *Theory and Application of Mathieu Functions*, (Oxford University Press, New York, 1947).

Meixner, J. and F. W. Schäfke
[1] *Mathieusche Funktionen und Sphäroidfunktionen mit Anwendungen auf physikalische und techniche Probleme*, (Springer-Verlag, Berlin, 1954).

Merkulov, V. I. (see Bublik, B. M.)

Mettler, E.
[1] "Biegeschwingungen eines Stabes unter pulsierendre Axiallast," *Mitt. Forsch.-Anst. GHH-Konzern 8*, 1-12 (1940).
[2] "Biegeschwingungen eines Stabes mit kleiner Vorkrümmung, exzentrisch angreifender publsierender Axiallast und statischer Querbelastung," *Forshungshefte aus d. Geb. d. Stahlbaues 4*, 1-23 (1941).
[3] "Über die Stabilität erzwungener Schwingungen elastischer Körper," *Ing.-Arch. 13*, 97-103 (1942).
[4] "Eine Theorie der Stabilität der elastischen Bewegung," *Ing.-Arch. 16*, 135-146 (1947).
[5] "Allgemine Theorie der Stabilität erzwungener Schwingungen elastischer Körper," *Ing.-Arch. 17*, 418-449 (1949).
[6] "Zum Problem der Stabilität erzwunger Schwingungen elastischer Körper," *Z. angew. Mat. Mechan. 31*, 263-264 (1951).
[7] "Zum Problem der nichtlinearen Schwingen elastischer Körper," *Publ. Sci. T'ech. Min. Air Paris 281*, 77-96 (1953).
[8] "Nichtlineare Schwingungen und Kinetische Instabilitäten bei Saiten und Stäben," *Ing.-Arch. 23*, 354-364. (1955).
[9] "Erzwungene Nichtlineare Schwingungen elastischer Körper," Ninth International Congress of Applied Mechanics, Vol. V, 5-26, Brussels (1957).

Mettler, E. and F. Weidenhammer
[1] "Der axial pulsierend belastete Stab mit Endmasse," *Z. angew. Mat. Mekhan. 36*, 284-287 (1956).
[2] "Kinetisches Durchschlagen des schwach gekrümmten Stabes," *Ing.-Arch. 29*, 301-(1960).

Michal, A. D.
[1] *Matrix and Tensor Calculus*, (John Wiley and Sons, Inc., New York, 1947).

Mitropl'skii, Iu. A. (see Bogoliubov, N. N.)

Morse, P. M. and H. Feshbach
[1] *Methods of Theoretical Physics,* (McGraw-Hill Book Co., Inc., New York, 1953).

Mournaghan, F.
[1] *Finite Deformation of an Elastic Solid,* (New York 1951).

Naumov, K. A.
[1] The Stability of Prismatic Rods Allowing for Damping," *Tr. Mosk, Inst. Inzh. Transp. 69,* 132-141 (1946).

Nemytskii, V. V. and V. V. Stepanov
[1] *Qualitative Theory of Differential Equations,* Princeton Mathematics Services, (Princeton University Press, Princeton, N. J. 1960).

Nikolai, E. L.
[1] "On Euler's Works on the Theory of Transverse Bending," *Uch. Zap. Leningr. Gos. Univ. Ser. Mat. 8,* 5-19 (1939), (English summary).
[2] *Works on Mechanics* (Trudy po mekhanike), (Gostekhizdat, Moscow, 1955).

Novozhilov, V. V.
[1] *Foundations of the Nonlinear Theory of Elasticity* (Graylock Press, Rochester, N. Y., 1953), (translated from the Russian).

Nudel' man, Ya. L.
[1] *Methods for the Determination of the Natural Frequencies and the Critical Forces for Bar Systems* (Methody opredeleniya sobstevennykh chastot i kritichestikh sil dlya sterzhnevykh sistem), (Gostekhizdat, Moscow, 1949).

Oniashvili, O. D.
[1] "On the Dynamic Stability of Shallow Shells," *Soobshch. Akad. Nauk Gruz. SSR 9,* 169-175 (1950).
[2] *Certain Dynamic Problems of the Theory of Shells,* (M. D. Friedman, Inc., West Newton, Mass., 1951), (translated from the Russian).

Panovko, Ya. G.
[1] "On the Calculation of Hysteresis Losses in Problems of the Applied Theory of Elastic Vibrations," *Zh. Tekhn. Fiz. 23,* 486-497 (1953).

Papaleksi, N. D. (see Mandel'shtam, L. I.)

Pflüger, A.
[1] *Stabilitätsprobleme der Elastostatik,* (Springer-Verlag, Berlin/Göttingen/Heidelberg, 1950).

Pipes, L. A.
[1] *Matrix Methods for Engineering,* (Prentice-Hall, Inc., New York, 1963).

Pisarenko, G. S.
[1] "Forced Transverse Vibrations of Clamped Cantilevers Allowing for Hysteresis Losses," *Inzh. Sb., 5,* 108-132 (1948).

Piszczek, K.
[1] "Longitudinal and Transverse Vibrations of a Rod Subjected to an Axial Pulsating Force, Taking Nonlnear Members into Consideration (I)," *Arch. Mechan. Stosovanei 7,* 345-362 (1955), (Polish with English and Russian summaries).

[2] "Dynamic Stability of the Plane Form of Bending with various Boundary Conditions," *Rozpravy Inzh. 4*, 175-225 (1956), (Polish with English and Russian summaries).

[3] "Influence of Geometrical and Dynamical Constraints on Resonance Regions in the Problem of the Dynamic Stability of a Thin-Walled Bar with Open Cross-Sections," *Rozpravy Inzh. 5*, 207-227 (1957), (Polish with English and Russian summaries).

[4] "The Influence of Curvature of an Originally Curved Bar on the Resonance Regions of the Plane Form of Bending," *Arch. Mech. Stosovanei 9*, 155-189 (1957), (Polish with English and Russian summaries).

[5] "Parametric Combination Resonance (of the Second Kind) in Nonlinear Systems," *Rozpravy Inzh. 8*, 211-229 (1960), (Polish with English summary).

Poincaré, H.

[1] Les méthodes nouvelles de la mécanique céleste, (Gauthier-Villars, Paris, 1892-1899).

Pozniak, E. L.

[1] "Forced and Parametrically Excited Vibrations of a Steel Core in a Magnetic Field," *Nauchn. Dokl. Vysshei Shkoly, Ser. Elektromekhan. i Avtomatika 2*, 49-60 (1959).

Prager, W. (see Hohenemser, K.)

Pratusevich, Ya. A.

[1] *Variational Methods in Structural Mechanics* (Variatsionnye metody v stroitel'noi mekhanike), (Gostekhizdat, Moscow, 1948).

Privalov, I. I.

[1] *Integral Equations* (Integral'nye uravneniia), (ONTI, Moscow, 1937).

Radtsig, M. A. (see Dzhanelidze, G. Yu.)

Rayleigh, John William Strutt (Lord)

[1] *The Theory of Sound*, (The Macmillian Co., Ltd., London, 1926), 2nd ed.

Reckling, K. A.

[1] "Die Stabilität erzwungener harmonisher Schwingungen gerader I-Träger im Verband eines Tragwerkes," *Ing.-Arch. 20*, 137-162 (1952).

[2] "Die dünne Kreisplatte mit pulsierender Randbelastung in ihrer Mittelebene als Stabilitätsproblem," *Ing.-Arch. 21*. 141-147 (1953).

[3] "Die Stabilität erzwungener Schwingungen von Stäben und Trägern nach Rechunung and Versuch," *Schiffstechnik 3*, 135-140 (1955/1956).

Riesz, F. and B. Sz.-Nagg

[1] Vorlesungen über Funktionalanalysis (Deutscher Verlag der Wissenschaften, Berlin, 1956), (translated from French).

Rzhanitsyn, A. R.

[1] *The Stability of Equilibrium of Elastic Systems*, (Ustolchivost' ravnovesiia uprugikh sistem), (Gostekhizdat, Moscow, 1955).

Salion, V. E.

[1] "The Dynamic Stability in Plane Bending of an I-Beam," *Dokl Akad. Nauk Ukr. SSR, 5*, 375-381 (1950).

[2] "Dynamic Stability in Plane Bending," *Dokl. Akad. Nauk SSSR 78*, 873-875, (1951).

[3] "The Dynamic Stability of a Curved Arch Under the Action of Periodic moments (Non-Plane Deformations)," Collection of Papers: *Problems of Stability and*

Strength (Issledovaniia po voprosam ustoichivosti i prochnosti), (Akademiia Nauk Ukr. SSR, Kiev, 1956), pp. 123-127.

Schäfke, F. W. (see Meixner, J.)

Sezawa K. (see Utida, I.)

Shtaerman, I. Ya.
[1] "The General Theory of the Stability of Arches" Collection of Papers: *Stability of Arches* (Stiikos't arok), (Akademiia Nauk Ukr. SSR, Kiev, 1936).

Smirnov, A. F.
[1] *The Static and Dynamic Stability of Structures,* (Staticheskaia i dinamicheskaia ustoichivost' sooruzhenii), (Transzheldorizdat, Moscow, 1947).
[2] *Stability and Vibrations of Structures* (Ustoichivost' i Kolebaniia sooruzhenii), (Transzheldorizdat, Moscow, 1958).

Smirnov, V. I.
[1] Lehrgang der höheren Mathematik, Teil III_1, 2 Aufl., (Deutsche-Verlag der Wisserschaften, Berlin 1960), (Translated from the Russian).
[2] Lehrgang der höherer Mathematik, Teil III_2, 3 Aufl., (Deutscher-Verlag der Wisserschaften, Berlin, 1961), (Translated from the Russian).
[3] Lehrgang der höheren Mathemaik, Teil IV, 2 Aufl., Deutsher Uerlag der Wisserschafter, Berlin 1961 (Translated from The Russian).

Sobolev, V. A.
[1] "The Dynamic Stability of Deformation of a Strip in Excentric Compression and Pure Bending," *Inzh. Sb. 19,* 65-72 (1954).

Sorokin, E. S.
[1] The Dynamics of Floors in Multistoried Buildings (Dinamika mezhduetazhnykh perekrytii), (Storiizdat, Moscow-Leningrad, 1941).

Stepanov, V. V. (see Nemytskii, V. V.)

Stoker, J. J.
[1] *Nonlinear Vibrations in Mechanical and Electrical Systems,* (Interscience Publishers, Inc., New York, 1950). (See also Lubkin, S.)

Strutt, M. J. O.
[1] *Lamesche, Mathieusche und verwandte Funktionen in Physik und Technik,* (Springer, Berlin, 1932).

Sz.-Nagg, B. (see Riesz, F.)

Teodorchik, K. F.
[1] *Self-Exciting Systems* (Avtokolebatel'nye Sistemy), (Gostekhizdat, Moscow-Leningrad, 1952), 3rd ed.

Timoshenko, S. P.
[1] *Vibrations Problems in Engineering,* (D. Van Nostrand Company, Inc. Princeton, New Jersey, 1955), 3rd ed.
[2] *Theory of Elastic Stability,* (McGraw-Hill, New York, 1936).

Trefftz, E.
[1] "Allgemeine Theorie der Knickung des geraden Stabes," *Z. angew, Mat. Mechan. 3,* 272-275 (1923).

[3] "Resonanzlösungen inhomogener Mathieuscher Systeme," *Z. angew. Mat. Mechan.* *32*, 154–156 (1952).

[4] "Biegeschwingungen des Stages mit nichtlinearem Elastizitätsgesetz," *Z. angew. Mat. Mechan.* *32*, 265–266 (1952).

[5] "Drehschwingungen in Kreuzgelenkwellen," *Ing.-Arch.* *23*, 189–197 (1955).

[6] "Rheolineare Drehschwingungen in Kolbenmotoren," *Ing.-Arch.* *23*, 262–269 (1955).

[7] "Das Stabilitätsverhalten der nichtilinearen Biegeschwingungen des axial pulsierend belasten Stabes," *Ing.-Arch.* *24*, 53–68 (1956).

[8] "Stabquerschwingungen schwach vorgekrümmter Stäbe mit pulsierender Axiallast," *Z. angew. Mat. Mechan.* *36*, 235–238 (1956). (See also Mettler, E.)

Tricomi, F. G.,

[1] *Integral Equations*, (Interscience Publisher Inc., New York, 1957).

Utida, I., and K. Sezawa

[1] "Dynamical Stability of a Column Under Periodic Longitudinal Forces," *Rep. Aeronaut. Res. Inst., Tokyo Imp. Univ.* *15*, 139–183 (1940).

Vlasov, V. S.

[1] *Thin-Walled Elastic Beams* (National Science Foundation OTS 61-11400, Washington, D.C., 1961), (translated from the Russian).

[2] Allgemeine Schalentheorie und ihre Anwendung in der Technik, (Akademie-Verlag, Berlin, 1958), (translated from the Russian).

Wang, C. T.

[1] *Applied Elasticity*, (McGraw-Hill Book Co., Inc., New York, 1953).

Watson, G. N. (see Whittaker, E. T.)

Weidenhammer, F.

[1] "Der eingespannte, axial-pulsierend belastete Stab als Stabilitätsproblem," *Ing.-Arch.* *19*, 162–191 (1951).

[2] "Nichtlineare Biegeschwingungen des axial-pulsierend belasteten Stabes," *Ing.-Arch.* *20*, 315–330 (1952).

Weingarten V. I.

[1] "Experimental Investigation of the Dynamic Stability of a Rod," TDR-269 (4560-40)-3, Aerospace Corporaton, EL Segundo, California (February 28, 1964).

Whittaker, E. T. and G. N. Watson

[1] *A Course of Modern Analysis*, (University Press, Cambridge, 1952), 4th ed.

Witt, A. A. (see Andronov, A. A.)

Yakubovich, V. A.

[1] "Remarks on Some Works on Systems of Linear Differential Equations with Periodic Coefficients," *Prikl. Mat. i Mekhan.* *21*, 707–713 (1957).

[2] "On the Dynamic Stability of Elastic Systems," *Dokl. Akad. Nauk SSSR* *121*, 602–605 (1958).

[3] "The Method of a Small Parameter for Canonical Systems with Periodic Coefficients," *Prikl. Mat. i Mekhan.* *23*, 15–35, (1959).

Yao, J. C.

[1] "Dynamic Stability of Cylindrical Shells Under Static and Periodic Axial and Radial Loads." *AIAA Journal* *1*, 2316–2320 (1963).

Ziegler, H.

[1] "Die Stabilitatskriterien der Elastomechanik," *Ing.-Arch.* *20*, 49–56 (1952).

Zurmühl, R.
[1] *Matrizen* (Springer-Verlag, Berlin/Göttingen/Heidelberg, 1950).

AUTHOR INDEX

SUBJECT INDEX